FURTHER MATHEMATICS

FURTHER MATHEMATICS

By

R. I. PORTER

M.B.E., M.A.

Headmaster, The Queen Elizabeth Grammar School, Penrith

LONDON

G. BELL AND SONS, LTD

1970

ISBN 0 7135 1762 X

First published 1962
Reprinted 1963, 1964, 1966, 1967
Revised, metricated, edition 1970

Printed in Great Britain by Richard Clay (The Chaucer Press), Ltd.,
Bungay, Suffolk

PREFACE TO FIRST EDITION

THE books *Elementary Analysis* and *Further Elementary Analysis* were designed to provide a complete two-year VIth Form course in Pure Mathematics for all but the outright mathematical specialist. This volume is intended to complete the two-year course for these specialists and also to extend the course to give adequate preparation for the "S" papers of the G.C.E. and similar examinations.

In choosing the subject matter, careful attention has been given to the existing or proposed future syllabuses of the different Examining Bodies for the General Certificate of Education. A great deal of thought has been given to the order of presentation of the different topics, but clearly this order is flexible and can be modified to suit different requirements and to fit in with different ideas.

As in the previous books, the aim is to introduce pupils as quickly as possible to fresh mathematical fields and to make them acquainted with new mathematical techniques. To achieve this aim and to limit the size of this book it has been necessary in many instances to dispense with formal proofs and rigid lines of approach.

Experience has proved the necessity for large numbers of examples of all types, and it will be seen that this requirement is very adequately met. Care has been taken to grade the examples in the text according to degree of difficulty. The needs of revision are catered for by a set of miscellaneous examples at the end of each chapter, together with a comprehensive set of Revision Papers, both A and S levels; a feature which has proved popular in the earlier volumes.

My thanks are due to the following examining bodies, who have kindly given permission to use questions set in their past examinations:

The Senate of the University of London: (L)
The Cambridge Local Examination Syndicate: (C)
The Oxford and Cambridge Joint Examination Board: (O.C.)
The Northern Universities Joint Matriculation Board: (N).

I am indebted to several past pupils, particularly Mr. J. D. Knowles, Mr. K. Burrell and Mr. J. B. Brelsford, for the assistance they have given in reading and checking the manuscript and the answers.

R. P.

December 1961

v

PREFACE TO REVISED EDITION

THE need for a further reprinting has given the opportunity of revising the text in order to meet the requirements of the changeover to metric and S.I. units. The number of instances where modification was necessary is small and consequently the book is essentially unchanged.

I would like to thank the users of the book who have notified me of errors; it is hoped that most of these have now been eliminated.

R. P.

March 1970

CONTENTS

CONTENTS

PAGE

CHAPTER VII

CHAPTER VIII

CHAPTER IX

CHAPTER X

CHAPTER XI

Infinite series. Expansion of a function. Algebraic and trigonometrical methods. Taylor's theorem. Maclaurin's theorem.
Expansion by differentiation or integration of a known series.
Expansion by the formation of a differential equation. Leibnitz's
theorem.

CHAPTER XII

Basic theorems of integration. Important algebraic integrals.
Integrals involving the function $\sqrt{(ax^2 + bx + c)}$. Trigonometric
integrals. Hyperbolic integrals. Reduction formulæ. General
theorems on definite integrals. The logarithmic function $\int_1^x \frac{dt}{t}$.
Infinite integrals: infinite range; infinite integrand.

CHAPTER XIII

Curves expressed in polar coordinates. Pedal equation. Arc
length and area of surface of revolution. Polar form of radius of
curvature. Radius of curvature—pedal form. Area of a closed
curve. Theorems of Pappus. Volume of revolution of a sectorial
area.

CHAPTER XIV

Rectangular Cartesian coordinates in three dimensions. Three-
dimensional loci. Fundamental results. Direction of a straight
line. Direction-cosines. Angle between two straight lines.
Direction ratios. The general equation of the first degree.
Perpendicular form of the equation of a plane. Perpendicular
from a point to a plane. Important results on the plane. The
straight line. Symmetrical form of the equations of a straight line.
Coplanar lines. Skew lines. Common perpendicular to two
skew lines. Simplified form for the equations of two skew lines.
Some properties of the tetrahedron.

CHAPTER XV

The equation of a sphere. Sphere passing through four points.
Tangent plane to a sphere. Length of tangent lines to a sphere
from a given point. Plane section of a sphere. Common points
of two spheres. Equations of a circle. Equation of a sphere
passing through a given circle. System of spheres passing through
the common points of two spheres.

CHAPTER XVI

CHAPTER I

THE TRIANGLE

Medians of a triangle. Let the medians BB', CC' of $\triangle ABC$ meet in G (Fig. 1). Then as B', C' are the mid-points of AC, AB respectively, it follows that $C'B'$ is parallel to BC and equal to half of it. Hence from the similar triangles $C'GB'$, BCG

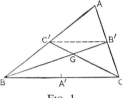

$$\frac{B'G}{GB} = \frac{C'G}{GC} = \frac{C'B'}{BC} = \frac{1}{2}.$$

I.e. the medians BB', CC' trisect each other at G.

FIG. 1.

Similarly, it can be shown that the medians AA', BB' trisect each other at G and therefore *the medians AA', BB', CC' are concurrent in G and trisect each other.*

G is called the *centroid* of $\triangle ABC$.

Analytically, if A, B, C are the points (x_1, y_1), (x_2, y_2), (x_3, y_3), by writing down the coordinates of A' and expressing the fact that G divides AA' internally in the ratio $2:1$, it follows that G is the point

$$[\tfrac{1}{3}(x_1+x_2+x_3), \tfrac{1}{3}(y_1+y_2+y_3)].$$

Ex. 1. *Show how to construct a triangle ABC given the lengths of its three medians.*

Draw median AA' and determine the point of trisection G (Fig. 2). Produce AA' to G' where $GA' = A'G'$ and mark arcs with centres G, G' and radii respectively two-thirds of each of the remaining two medians. These arcs intersect in a second vertex, B, of the required triangle and C is determined by making $A'C = BA'$.

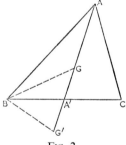

The proof depends on the fact that $BGCG'$ is a parallelogram as its diagonals bisect each other.

FIG. 2.

Apollonius' theorem. AA' is a median of $\triangle ABC$ (Fig. 3). Using the Cosine Rule with the notation of the figure,

$$c^2 = m^2 + (\tfrac{1}{2}a)^2 - 2m(\tfrac{1}{2}a) \cos(180° - \theta),$$
$$b^2 = m^2 + (\tfrac{1}{2}a)^2 - 2m(\tfrac{1}{2}a) \cos \theta.$$

Adding and using $\cos(180° - \theta) = -\cos \theta$,

$$c^2 + b^2 = 2m^2 + 2(\tfrac{1}{2}a)^2$$

i.e. $\quad \mathbf{AB^2 + AC^2 = 2AA'^2 + 2BA'^2}$—*Apollonius' median theorem.*

1

Angles between a median and the side of a triangle. Referring to Fig. 3, where $\triangle ABC$ has $B<C$, and AD is an altitude,

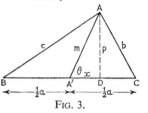

$$\cot B = \frac{BD}{AD} = \frac{\frac{1}{2}a+x}{p}; \quad \cot C = \frac{DC}{AD} = \frac{\frac{1}{2}a-x}{p}.$$

$$\therefore \cot B - \cot C = \frac{2x}{p} = 2\cot\theta$$

i.e.   **2 cot θ = cot B − cot C.**

If θ is assumed to be the acute angle between the median AA' and side BC, the more general result to cover the cases $B>C$ and $B<C$, is

Fig. 3.

$$\textbf{2 cot θ = cot B} \sim \textbf{cot C.}$$

An alternative expression can be obtained by dropping perpendiculars BX, CY to AA' (Fig. 4).

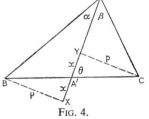

Clearly $BX = CY = p$ say,
$XA' = A'Y = x$ say.

Then

$$\cot\alpha = \frac{m+x}{p}; \quad \cot\beta = \frac{m-x}{p}, \text{ where } AA' = m.$$

$$\therefore \cot\alpha - \cot\beta = \frac{2x}{p} = 2\cot\theta.$$

Fig. 4.

Generally, **2 cot θ = cot α ∼ cot β,** when θ is taken as acute.

These angle results for a median can readily be extended to the line joining a vertex of the triangle to a given point on the opposite side.

If **BP:PC = m:n** (Fig. 5), it follows that,

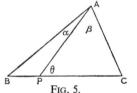

$$\textbf{(m+n) cot θ = n cot B} \sim \textbf{m cot C,}$$
$$\textbf{(m+n) cot θ = m cot α} \sim \textbf{n cot β.}$$

These results have important applications in Statics.

Fig. 5.

Ex. 2. *A uniform rod BC of length 17 cm is freely suspended from a hook A by strings AB, AC of lengths 15 cm and 8 cm. Find the inclination of the rod to the vertical.*

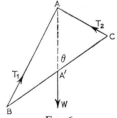

As the rod is in equilibrium under three forces W, T_1, T_2, the lines of action of these forces must be concurrent (Fig.6). It follows that A' the mid-point of BC is vertically below A and θ is the inclination of the rod to the vertical.

But $2\cot\theta = \cot B - \cot C$ and as ABC is a right-angled triangle (sides 8 cm, 15 cm, 17 cm), $\cot B = \frac{15}{8}$; $\cot C = \frac{8}{15}$.

$$\therefore 2\cot\theta = \frac{15}{8} - \frac{8}{15} = \frac{161}{120}; \cot\theta = \frac{161}{240}.$$

Using tables, $\theta = 56°\,9'$.

Fig. 6.

EXAMPLES 1a

1. Find the length of the median AA' of $\triangle ABC$, where $a = 5$ cm, $b = 12$ cm, $c = 13$ cm.

2. The sides of a triangle are of lengths 5 cm, 7 cm and 10 cm. Find the length of the shortest median.

3. Write down the coordinates of the centroid of each of the following triangles: (i) $(3, 4)$, $(2, -1)$, $(-1, 0)$; (ii) $(0, 0)$, $(a, 0)$, $(0, b)$; (iii) $(-2x, y)$, $(3x, -2y)$, $(x, 3y)$.

4. The sides of a parallelogram are of lengths 4 cm, 7 cm and one diagonal is of length 6 cm. Find the length of the other diagonal.

5. A, B are fixed points and P moves such that $AP^2 + BP^2$ is constant. Prove that the locus of P is a circle.

6. Prove that the centroid of the triangle $A'B'C'$ formed by joining the mid-points of $\triangle ABC$ is G, the centroid of $\triangle ABC$.

7. If AA', BB' are medians of $\triangle ABC$, prove that
$$AA'^2 - BB'^2 = \tfrac{3}{4}(AC^2 - BC^2).$$

8. Construct $\triangle ABC$ in which $AB = 8$ cm, $CA = 7$ cm and median $AA' = 6$ cm.

9. P is a point in the plane of rectangle $ABCD$ and lying outside the rectangle. Prove that $PA^2 + PC^2 = PB^2 + PD^2$. Is the result true if P does not lie in the plane of the rectangle?

10. Find the coordinates of the centroid of the triangle formed by the lines $y + 5x - 2 = 0$, $2y + x - 4 = 0$, $y - 4x + 7 = 0$.

11. In any quadrilateral, prove that the sum of the squares of the sides is equal to the sum of the squares of the diagonals plus four times the square of the line joining the mid-points of the diagonals.

12. The sides BC, CA, AB of $\triangle ABC$ are of lengths 10 cm, 8 cm, 5cm respectively. If X is the mid-point of the median AA', find the length BX.

13. Construct the triangle with medians of lengths 6 cm, 8·2 cm and 10·2 cm.

14. In $\triangle ABC$, P is the point on BC such that $BP:PC = m:n$. Prove that
$$nAB^2 + mAC^2 = (m+n)AP^2 + \frac{2mn}{(m+n)^2}BC^2.$$

15. Prove that a triangle can be drawn with sides equal and parallel to the medians of a given triangle ABC. Show also that the area of the triangle so formed is $\tfrac{3}{4}\triangle ABC$.

16. A uniform rod of length 13 cm is suspended freely from a fixed point by strings of lengths 12 cm and 5 cm fastened to its ends. Find the inclination of the rod to the vertical.

17. A rod AB rests in equilibrium with its ends in contact with the inside edge of a smooth vertical circular hoop. The centre of gravity of the rod is distant p from A and q from B. If 2α is the angle subtended by the rod at the centre of the hoop and θ is its inclination to the horizontal, prove that

$\tan\theta = \dfrac{q-p}{q+p}\tan\alpha$, assuming $q > p$.

Circumcentre and circumcircle. In Fig. 7, A', B', C' are the mid-points of the sides of $\triangle ABC$.

The perpendicular bisectors of CA and AB intersect at O.

As O lies on the perpendicular bisector of CA,

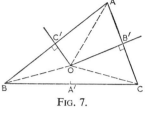

$$CO = AO.$$

Similarly, $$AO = BO.$$

$$\therefore \quad BO = CO,$$

hence O lies on the perpendicular bisector of BC, and so the perpendicular bisectors are concurrent in O.

Fig. 7.

The circle centre O, radius OA, passes through A, B and C and is called the *circumcircle* of the triangle; O is the *circumcentre*.

Radius of circumcircle. Referring to Fig. 8,

$$\angle BOC = 2A.$$

$$\therefore \quad \angle BOA' = A,$$

and as $$BA' = A'C = \tfrac{1}{2}a,$$

it follows by using the right-angled triangle BOA',

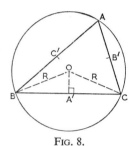

that $$2R = \frac{a}{\sin A}.$$

Similarly, $$2R = \frac{b}{\sin B} \text{ and } \frac{c}{\sin C}.$$

$$\therefore \quad \mathbf{R} = \frac{\mathbf{a}}{\mathbf{2 \sin A}} = \frac{\mathbf{b}}{\mathbf{2 \sin B}} = \frac{\mathbf{c}}{\mathbf{2 \sin C}}.$$

Fig. 8.

N.B. $OA' = R \cos A = \frac{1}{2} a \cot A$, with similar results for OB' and OC'.

Alternative expression for R.

If $$\Delta = \text{area } \triangle ABC,$$

then $$\Delta = \tfrac{1}{2}bc \sin A; \text{ i.e. } \sin A = \frac{2\Delta}{bc}.$$

$$\therefore \quad \mathbf{R} = \frac{\mathbf{a}}{\mathbf{2 \sin A}} = \frac{\mathbf{abc}}{\mathbf{4\Delta}}.$$

Ex. 3. *In $\triangle ABC$ the altitudes BE, CF intersect at H. Prove that the radius of the circle BHC is equal to the radius of the circle ABC.*

Quad. $AFHE$ is cyclic, hence $\angle EHF = 180° - A$ (Fig. 9).

$$\text{Radius circle } BHC = \frac{BC}{2 \sin \angle BHC} = \frac{a}{2 \sin(180° - A)}$$

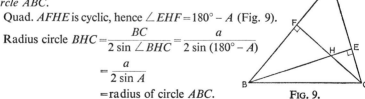

$$= \frac{a}{2 \sin A}$$

$$= \text{radius of circle } ABC.$$

Fig. 9.

Orthocentre. Through the vertices A, B, C of $\triangle ABC$ lines ZY, XZ, YX are drawn parallel respectively to sides BC, CA, AB (Fig. 10).

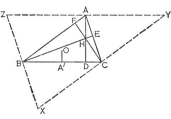

FIG. 10.

It follows that $ABCY$ is a parallelogram, and so

$$AY = BC.$$

Similarly, $ZA = BC$ and hence A is the mid-point of ZY.

If AD is an altitude of $\triangle ABC$, it is perpendicular to ZY.

∴ AD is the perpendicular bisector of ZY.

Similarly, altitudes BE, CF of $\triangle ABC$ are the perpendicular bisectors of XZ, YX respectively.

∴ AD, BE, CF are concurrent in a point H which is the circumcentre of $\triangle XYZ$.

Hence the altitudes of a triangle are concurrent. The point of concurrence H *is called the orthocentre of* $\triangle ABC$.

Important results associated with the orthocentre.

(i) As $\triangle XYZ$ is similar to $\triangle ABC$ with twice its linear dimensions, it follows that AH is twice the corresponding length $A'O$ (Fig. 10).

I.e. $$AH = 2A'O = a \cot A.$$

Similarly, $BH = 2B'O = b \cot B$; $CH = 2C'O = c \cot C$, where with the usual notation, A', B', C' are the mid-points of the sides and O is the circumcentre of $\triangle ABC$.

(ii) **If the altitude AD is produced to meet the circumcircle at P, then HD = DP** (Fig. 11).

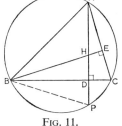

For $\quad \angle DBP = \angle PAC$ (same segment)

and $\quad \angle DBE = 90° - C = \angle PAC$.

∴ $\angle DBP = \angle DBE$

and hence $\triangle$'s DBP, DBH are congruent (2 angles and common side).

∴ $HD = DP$.

FIG. 11.

There are similar results for the altitudes from B and C.

(iii) **$OH^2 = R^2(1 - 8 \cos A \cos B \cos C)$**.   Referring to Fig. 12,

$$\angle AOC' = C$$
$$\therefore \ \angle OAB = 90° - C.$$

Also $\angle DAC = 90° - C.$
$$\therefore \ \angle OAX = A - 2(90° - C)$$
$$= A + 2C - (A + B + C) \quad \text{as} \quad A + B + C = 180°,$$
$$= C - B. \quad \text{(In the case taken } C > B.\text{)}$$

Using right-angled triangle AOX,
$$OX = R \sin(C - B)$$
and $AX = R \cos (C - B).$
But $AH = 2A'O = 2R \cos A,$
$$\therefore \ HX = R[\cos (C - B) - 2 \cos A].$$

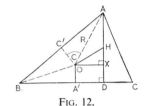

Fig. 12.

By Pythagoras,

$$OH^2 = OX^2 + HX^2 = R^2[\sin^2(C - B) + \{\cos (C - B) - 2 \cos A\}^2]$$
$$= R^2[\sin^2(C - B) + \cos^2 (C - B) - 4 \cos (C - B) \cos A + 4 \cos^2 A]$$
$$= R^2[1 - 4 \cos A\{\cos (C - B) + \cos (B + C)\}],$$
$$\text{as } \cos A - - \cos (B + C),$$
$$= R^2[1 - 8 \cos A \cos B \cos C].$$

Pedal triangle.   The triangle DEF formed by the feet of the altitudes is called the *pedal triangle* of $\triangle ABC$ (Fig. 13).
As $BCEF$ is a cyclic quadrilateral,

$$\angle AFE = C; \quad \angle AEF = B.$$

$\therefore \ \triangle$'s AFE, ABC are similar, and so

$$\frac{EF}{BC} = \frac{AE}{AB} = \frac{AB \cos A}{AB} = \cos A.$$

$$\therefore \ \mathbf{EF = a \cos A.}$$

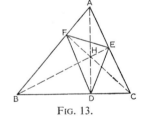

Fig. 13.

Similarly, triangles BDF and CED are each similar to $\triangle ABC$, and it follows that

$$\mathbf{FD = b \cos B; \quad DE = c \cos C.}$$

Also $\angle ADF = 90° - \angle BDF = 90° - A$
and $\angle ADE = 90° - \angle CDE = 90° - A.$

$\therefore \ \angle \mathbf{EDF = 180° - 2A}$ with similar results for $\angle DEF$ and $\angle EFD$, when $\triangle ABC$ is acute-angled as taken in Fig. 13.
It will be noted that *H is the incentre of the pedal triangle.*

The reader should repeat the previous work for the case when the triangle is obtuse-angled. It will be found that if A is obtuse,

$$EF = a \cos (180° - A), \qquad FD = b \cos B, \qquad DE = c \cos C;$$
$$\angle EDF = 2A - 180°, \qquad \angle DEF = 2B, \qquad \angle EFD = 2C.$$

Ex. 4. *If H is the orthocentre of $\triangle ABC$ obtuse-angled at A, prove that $AH . HD = BH . HE = CH . HF$* (Fig. 14).

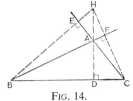

As $ADBE$ is a cyclic quadrilateral,

$HA . HD = HE . HB$ (intersecting chords).

As $ADCF$ is a cyclic quadrilateral,

$HA . HD = HF . HC$ (intersecting chords)

and hence the required result.

Fig. 14.

Ex. 5. *Given the circumcentre, the orthocentre and one vertex of a triangle, show how to determine the other two vertices.*

Suppose vertex A is given together with O and H.

Determine A', the mid-point of BC, using the fact that OA' is parallel to AH and equal to half of it (Fig. 15).

Draw a line through A' perpendicular to OA' and mark off points B, C on it, each distant OA from O.

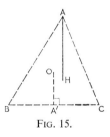

Fig. 15.

Ex. 6. *Prove that the area of the pedal triangle of $\triangle ABC$ is*

$$|2\Delta \cos A \cos B \cos C|.$$

Referring to Fig. 13, where $\triangle ABC$ is acute-angled,

$$\begin{aligned}
\text{area } \triangle DEF &= \tfrac{1}{2} DF . DE \sin \angle EDF \\
&= \tfrac{1}{2} b \cos B . c \cos C \sin (180° - 2A) \\
&= \tfrac{1}{2} bc \cos B \cos C \sin 2A = bc \sin A(\cos A \cos B \cos C) \\
&= 2\Delta \cos A \cos B \cos C.
\end{aligned}$$

When A is obtuse,

$$\text{area } \triangle DEF = -2\Delta \cos A \cos B \cos C.$$

Hence in all cases the area of the pedal triangle is numerically equal to $2\Delta \cos A \cos B \cos C$ or to $|2\Delta \cos A \cos B \cos C|$.

Nine-point circle. The circle which can be drawn through A', B', C', the mid-points of the sides of a triangle ABC, Fig. 16, will be shown to pass also through the feet of the altitudes D, E, F and through the mid-points P, Q, R of the lines joining the vertices of the triangle to the orthocentre H.

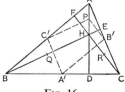

Fig. 16.

B

As $AP = PH$ and $AC' = C'B$, $C'P$ is parallel to BH.
As $BA' = A'C$ and $AC' = C'B$, $C'A'$ is parallel to AC.

∴ $\angle A'C'P = 90°$, as BH is perpendicular to AC.

Similarly, $\angle A'B'P = 90°$.

But also $\angle A'DA = 90°$ and therefore the circle on $A'P$ as diameter passes through B', C' and D.

I.e. the circle $A'B'C'$ passes through D and P.

Similarly, it can be proved that this circle passes through E, Q and also through F, R.

∴ The nine points A', B', C'; D, E, F; P, Q, R lie on a circle known as *the nine-point circle* of the $\triangle ABC$.

Centre and radius of the nine-point circle. It is clear in Fig. 17 that the perpendicular bisectors of $A'D$ and $C'F$ both pass through the mid-point of OH.

∴ *The centre N of the nine-point circle is the mid-point of the line joining the circumcentre O to the orthocentre H.*

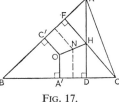

FIG. 17.

Also as $\triangle A'B'C'$ is similar to $\triangle ABC$ and has half its linear dimensions, it follows that the radius of the nine-point circle (the circumcircle of $\triangle A'B'C'$) is $\frac{1}{2}R$.

I.e. $\qquad$ **Radius of nine-point circle** $= \frac{1}{2}R = \dfrac{a}{4 \sin A}$**, etc.**

The Euler line. In Fig. 18, AA' meets OH at G, a point which will be shown to be the centroid of $\triangle ABC$.

The triangles AGH, $A'OG$ are easily proved similar, and as $AH = 2A'O$, it follows that $AG = 2GA'$ and $HG = 2GO$.

Hence G is the centroid of the triangle, and in consequence the four points O, G, N, H are collinear and $OG : ON : OH = 2 : 3 : 6$.

The line OH is called the Euler line of $\triangle ABC$.

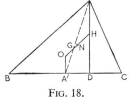

FIG. 18.

Ex. 7. *If the side BC and the circumcentre O of $\triangle ABC$ are fixed whilst A is free to move, find the locus of N, the nine-point centre.*

The radius, R, of the circumcircle is constant (it equals OB or OC).

∴ The radius of the nine-point circle $= \frac{1}{2}R =$ constant.

Hence as A', the mid-point of BC, is fixed the locus of N is the circle centre A', radius $\frac{1}{2}R$.

Ex. 8. *If O is the circumcentre of $\triangle ABC$ and AO meets BC at U, prove that the circle on AU as diameter touches the nine-point circle of $\triangle ABC$.*

The centre of the circle on AU as diameter is X, the mid-point of AU.

As $\angle ADU = 90°$, this circle passes through D, a point on the nine-point circle of $\triangle ABC$.

In order to prove the two circles touch at D it is sufficient to prove that the centre N of the nine-point circle lies on the radius XD of the circle on AU as diameter.

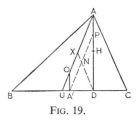

Taking P, the mid-point of AH, then AP is equal and parallel to OA' ($AH = 2OA'$).

$\therefore$ $A'P$ is parallel to UA.

Consequently as DX bisects AU it will also bisect $A'P$, and so it will pass through N, the mid-point of $A'P$, and the required result follows.

FIG. 19.

EXAMPLES 1b

1. Triangle ABC is right-angled at A. Locate: (i) the circumcentre; (ii) the orthocentre; (iii) the nine-point centre of the triangle.

2. Calculate the radius of the nine-point circle of a triangle in which one side is of length 4 cm and the opposite angle 36°.

3. Draw the pedal triangle of a triangle ABC, obtuse-angled at A, and show that its angles are $2A - 180°$, $2B$ and $2C$.

4. If BE, CF are altitudes of $\triangle ABC$, prove that the area of $\triangle AEF$ is equal to $\triangle \cos^2 A$, where $\triangle$ is the area of $\triangle ABC$.

5. If H is the orthocentre of $\triangle ABC$, prove that A, B, C are the orthocentres of the triangles BCH, CAH, ABH respectively.

6. If the base and circumcircle of a triangle are given, prove that the locus of the orthocentre is a circle equal to the circumcircle.

7. Prove that the circumcentre of $\triangle ABC$ is the orthocentre of $\triangle A'B'C'$, where A', B', C' are the mid-points of the sides of $\triangle ABC$.

8. If H is the orthocentre of $\triangle ABC$ and D the foot of the altitude from A, prove: (i) $AH = 2R \cos A = a \cot A$; (ii) $HD = 2R \cos B \cos C$.

9. H is the orthocentre and O the circumcentre of $\triangle ABC$. If AO produced and AH produced meet the circumcircle at X and Y respectively, prove: (i) $\angle BAX = \angle CAY$; (ii) $BX = CY = HC$; (iii) HX bisects BC.

10. If the pedal triangle of a given triangle is isosceles, prove that the original triangle is either isosceles or has two of its angles differing by 90°.

11. Find the radius of the nine-point circle of $\triangle PQR$ in which angle P is a right angle, $PQ = 5$ cm, $PR = 12$ cm. Identify the Euler line of this triangle.

12. If XY is the diameter of the circle ABC which is perpendicular to BC, prove that AX and AY are the bisectors of angle BAC.

13. If H is the orthocentre of $\triangle ABC$, prove that the triangles ABC, HBC have the same nine-point circle.

14. If any two of the circumcentre, centroid, nine-point centre and orthocentre coincide, prove that all four coincide and the triangle is equilateral.

15. With the usual notation, prove that H is the circumcentre of the triangle formed by joining the circumcentres of triangles HBC, HCA, HAB.

16. O is the circumcentre and H the orthocentre of $\triangle ABC$. If the circle BOC passes through H, prove that $A = 60°$.

17. Given two vertices and the nine-point centre of a triangle, show how to construct the triangle.

18. With the usual notation, if AH, BH, CH produced meet the circumcircle of $\triangle ABC$ at H_1, H_2, H_3 respectively, prove that A is the circumcentre of $\triangle HH_2H_3$ with corresponding results for B and C.

19. The internal bisector of angle A meets the circumcircle of $\triangle ABC$ at P. If M, N are the feet of the perpendiculars from P to AB, AC respectively, prove that triangles BPM, CPN are congruent and deduce that

$$AM = AN = \tfrac{1}{2}(AB + AC).$$

Incentre and excentres. As all points on a bisector of an angle are equidistant from the arms of the angle, it follows that the point of intersection, I, of the internal bisectors of angles B and C of a triangle ABC (Fig. 20), is equidistant from all three sides of the triangle.

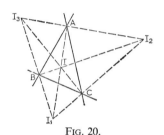

FIG. 20.

Hence I lies also on the internal bisector of angle A, i.e. the internal bisectors of the angles of a triangle are concurrent in a point I which is the centre of the circle which touches the sides of the triangle internally.

I is called the incentre and the circle is called the inscribed circle of the triangle.

In a similar way, it follows that the internal bisector of angle A and the external bisectors of angles B and C are concurrent in a point I_1.

I_1 is the centre of the circle which touches BC internally and AB, AC externally.

This circle is the escribed circle opposite A and I_1 is an excentre.

Excentres I_2, I_3 are defined similarly.

Referring to the diagram of Fig. 20, it will be noted that the excentres I_1, I_2, I_3 form a triangle whose sides pass through the vertices of the triangle ABC. Moreover, since the bisectors of an angle are at right angles, it is easily seen that *I is the orthocentre of $\triangle I_1I_2I_3$.*

Also as A, B, C are the feet of the altitudes of $\triangle I_1I_2I_3$, it follows that *the circumcircle of $\triangle ABC$ is the nine-point circle of $\triangle I_1I_2I_3$.* Hence the circumcircle of $\triangle ABC$ bisects each of the lines I_2I_3, I_3I_1, I_1I_2 and also the lines II_1, II_2, II_3.

Ex. 9. *If I is the incentre, O the circumcentre and H the orthocentre of $\triangle ABC$, prove that AI bisects angle OAH.*

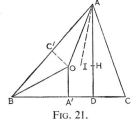

As $\qquad \angle AOB = 2C$ (angle at centre),

$\qquad\qquad \angle BAO = 90° - C$ (Fig. 21).

Also $\qquad \angle DAC = 90° - C.$

$\qquad \therefore \quad \angle BAO = \angle DAC$

and as $\qquad \angle BAI = \angle CAI,$

hence $\qquad \angle IAO = \angle IAH.$

FIG. 21.

Inscribed and escribed circles. In Fig. 22, X, Y, Z are the points of contact of the inscribed circle and the sides of $\triangle ABC$.

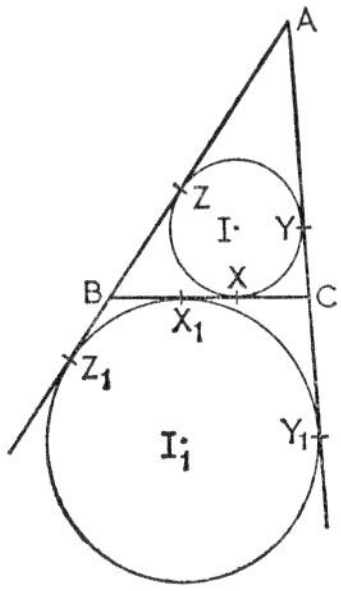

As tangents from a point to a circle are equal in length, $AY = AZ$; $BX = BZ$ and $CX = CY$.

$\qquad \therefore \quad AY + BX + CX = \frac{1}{2}$ (perimeter of $\triangle ABC$)

$\qquad\qquad\qquad\qquad = s.$

I.e. $\qquad\qquad AY + a = s.$

$\qquad\qquad \therefore \quad \mathbf{AY = AZ = s - a};$

similarly, $\qquad \mathbf{BX = BZ = s - b}; \quad \mathbf{CX = CY = s - c}.$

FIG. 22.

Now let the escribed circle opposite A touch BC at X_1 and AC, AB produced at Y_1, Z_1 respectively.

Using the equal tangents property,

$$AY_1 = AZ_1; \quad BZ_1 = BX_1 \text{ and } CY_1 = CX_1.$$
$$\therefore \text{ Perimeter } 2s = AB + BX_1 + X_1C + CA$$
$$= AZ_1 + AY_1.$$

Hence $\qquad\qquad \mathbf{AY_1 = AZ_1 = s.}$

and $\qquad\qquad \mathbf{BX_1 = AZ_1 - AB = s - c}; \quad \mathbf{CX_1 = s - b.}$

There are similar results for the other escribed circles.

Radii of the inscribed and escribed circles. If r is the radius of the inscribed circle (Fig. 23),

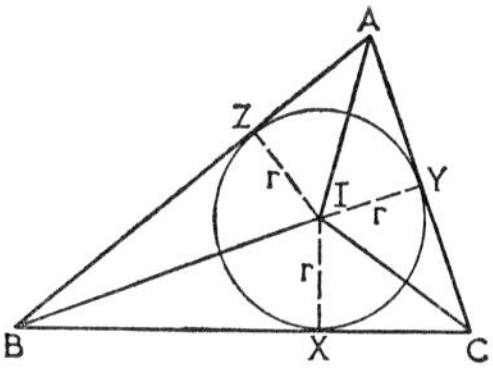

as $\qquad \triangle ABC = \triangle BIC + \triangle CIA + \triangle AIB,$

$\qquad\qquad \Delta = \frac{1}{2}ar + \frac{1}{2}br + \frac{1}{2}cr = sr.$

$\qquad\qquad \therefore \quad \mathbf{r = \dfrac{\Delta}{s}.}$

Alternatively from $\triangle AIZ$, $r = AZ \tan \frac{1}{2}A,$

i.e. $\qquad\qquad r = (s - a) \tan \frac{1}{2}A.$

FIG. 23.

Similarly, $\qquad r = (s - b) \tan \frac{1}{2}B \quad$ and $\quad (s - c) \tan \frac{1}{2}C.$

$\qquad \therefore \quad \mathbf{r = (s - a) \tan \frac{1}{2}A = (s - b) \tan \frac{1}{2}B = (s - c) \tan \frac{1}{2}C.}$

If r_1 is the radius of the escribed circle opposite A (Fig. 24),

as $\triangle ABC = \triangle CI_1A + \triangle AI_1B - \triangle BI_1C,$
$$\Delta = \tfrac{1}{2}br_1 + \tfrac{1}{2}cr_1 - \tfrac{1}{2}ar_1$$
$$= \tfrac{1}{2}r_1(b+c-a) = \tfrac{1}{2}r_1(2s-2a)$$
$$= r_1(s-a).$$

$\therefore\ \mathbf{r_1} = \dfrac{\Delta}{\mathbf{s-a}};\quad$ similarly, $\mathbf{r_2} = \dfrac{\Delta}{\mathbf{s-b}},\ \mathbf{r_3} = \dfrac{\Delta}{\mathbf{s-c}}.$

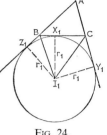

Alternatively from $\triangle AI_1Z_1,$

$$r_1 = AZ_1 \tan \tfrac{1}{2}A = s \tan \tfrac{1}{2}A.$$

FIG. 24.

I.e. $\mathbf{r_1 = s \tan \tfrac{1}{2}A};\quad$ similarly, $\mathbf{r_2 = s \tan \tfrac{1}{2}B,\ r_3 = s \tan \tfrac{1}{2}C}.$

Ex. 10. *With the usual notation, prove that* $r = 4R \sin \tfrac{1}{2}A \sin \tfrac{1}{2}B \sin \tfrac{1}{2}C.$

R.H.S. $= 2\dfrac{a}{\sin A} \sin \tfrac{1}{2}A \sin \tfrac{1}{2}B \sin \tfrac{1}{2}C$

$$= a\frac{\sin \tfrac{1}{2}B \sin \tfrac{1}{2}C}{\cos \tfrac{1}{2}A} = a\frac{\sqrt{\dfrac{(s-c)(s-a)}{ca}} \cdot \sqrt{\dfrac{(s-a)(s-b)}{ab}}}{\sqrt{\dfrac{s(s-a)}{bc}}}$$

$$= \sqrt{\frac{(s-a)(s-b)(s-c)}{s}} = \frac{\Delta}{s}$$

$$= r.$$

Ex. 11. *Prove that* $\dfrac{1}{r^2} + \dfrac{1}{r_1{}^2} + \dfrac{1}{r_2{}^2} + \dfrac{1}{r_3{}^2} = \dfrac{a^2+b^2+c^2}{\Delta^2}.$

L.H.S. $= \left(\dfrac{s}{\Delta}\right)^2 + \left(\dfrac{s-a}{\Delta}\right)^2 + \left(\dfrac{s-b}{\Delta}\right)^2 + \left(\dfrac{s-c}{\Delta}\right)^2$

$$= \frac{1}{\Delta^2}\{4s^2 - 2s(a+b+c) + a^2 + b^2 + c^2\}$$

$$= \frac{a^2+b^2+c^2}{\Delta^2}.$$

Distance between incentre and circumcentre.
Referring to Fig. 25, where PQ is the
diameter through P,

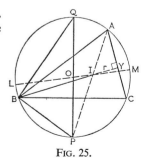

$$LI\,.\,IM = AI\,.\,IP.$$
$$\therefore\ (R+OI)(R-OI) = AI\,.\,IP$$
as $$OL = OM = R,$$
i.e. $$R^2 - OI^2 = AI\,.\,IP.$$
In $\triangle BIP,$
$$\angle IBP = \tfrac{1}{2}B + \angle CBP = \tfrac{1}{2}B + \angle CAP$$
$$= \tfrac{1}{2}B + \tfrac{1}{2}A.$$

FIG. 25.

Also $\qquad \angle BIP = \frac{1}{2}A + \frac{1}{2}B$ (exterior angle of $\triangle AIB$).

$$\therefore \ IP = BP = PQ \sin \angle BQP = 2R \sin \frac{1}{2}A.$$

In $\triangle AIY$, $\qquad AI = r \operatorname{cosec} \frac{1}{2}A.$

$$\therefore \ AI . IP = r \operatorname{cosec} \frac{1}{2}A . 2R \sin \frac{1}{2}A = 2Rr.$$

$$R^2 - OI^2 = 2Rr.$$

I.e. $\qquad\qquad \mathbf{OI^2 = R^2 - 2Rr.}$

Using similar methods, it can be proved that

$$\mathbf{OI_1{}^2 = R^2 + 2Rr_1; \quad OI_2{}^2 = R^2 + 2Rr_2; \quad OI_3{}^2 = R^2 + 2Rr_3.}$$

EXAMPLES 1c

1. Prove that $\angle BIC = 90° + \frac{1}{2}A.$

2. Show that the radius of the circumcircle of $\triangle BIC$ is $2R \sin \frac{1}{2}A.$

3. With the notation of Fig. 22, prove that $YY_1 = ZZ_1 = a.$

4. Show that: (i) $AI_1 = r_1 \operatorname{cosec} \frac{1}{2}A = s \sec \frac{1}{2}A;$ (ii) $II_1 = a \sec \frac{1}{2}A.$

5. With the usual notation, prove that the angle IAO is half the difference between the angles B and C.

6. If $\triangle ABC$ is right-angled at C, prove: (i) $2r = a + b - c$; (ii) $r_3 = s.$

7. Prove that the radius of the circumcircle of $\triangle AYZ$, where Y, Z are the points of contact of the incircle and the sides CA, AB, is $\frac{1}{2}AI.$

8. Prove that $r_1 = 4R \sin \frac{1}{2}A \cos \frac{1}{2}B \cos \frac{1}{2}C$ and write down the corresponding results for r_2, r_3.

9. In $\triangle ABC$, I is the incentre and I_1 the excentre opposite A. Prove that the circle BIC passes through I_1. What is the centre of this circle?

10. The internal bisector of $\angle A$ of $\triangle ABC$ meets the circumcircle again at P, prove that $AP = \frac{1}{2}(b + c) \sec \frac{1}{2}A.$

11. AB is a chord of a circle centre C. Prove that two excentres of $\triangle ABC$ lie on the circle.

12. In $\triangle ABC$ if $r_1 = 2r$, prove that $b + c = 3a.$

13. If H is the orthocentre of $\triangle ABC$, prove that $AH + BH + CH = 2(R + r).$

14. In $\triangle ABC$ the circle BIC passes through the circumcentre O. Prove that this circle also passes through the orthocentre of $\triangle ABC$.

15. Show that $r_1 + r_2 + r_3 - r = 4R.$

16. A', B', C' are the mid-points of the sides BC, CA, AB of $\triangle ABC$ and I, J are the incentres of triangles ABC, $A'B'C'$. Show that $AI = 2A'J.$ If G is the centroid of $\triangle ABC$, prove: (i) I, G, J are collinear; (ii) $3IG = 2IJ.$

17. In triangle ABC, $\angle A$ is obtuse. Prove that the orthocentre H is an excentre of the pedal triangle DEF.

18. In $\triangle ABC$ the line AI_1 meets the circumcircle again at P. Prove that $PB = PC = PI_1.$

19. AI, BI, CI are produced to meet the circumcircle of $\triangle ABC$ again in P, Q, R respectively. Prove that I is the orthocentre of $\triangle PQR.$

20. With the usual notation, prove that the radius of the circle II_1I_2 is equal to $2R$.

21. Given the points I, I_1, I_2, show how to construct the triangle ABC.

Concurrency and collinearity

Definition. Two segments AB, CD of the same line or of parallel lines are said to have the same or opposite *sense* or *sign* according as the directions $A \to B$, $C \to D$ are the same or opposite, e.g. in Fig. 26, AB, AC, AD, CB, BD all have the same sense, and in consequence ratios such

as $\dfrac{AB}{CB}, \dfrac{AD}{BD}$ are positive.

Fig. 26.

The segments AB, DC have opposite senses and the ratio $\dfrac{AB}{DC}$ is negative.

Ex. 12. *If P, Q divide AB internally and externally in the ratio* $5:2$, *find the ratios* $\dfrac{AP}{PB}, \dfrac{AQ}{QB}, \dfrac{BP}{AB}$.

Fig. 27.

The ratio in which P divides AB is $\dfrac{AP}{PB}$.

Hence
$$\frac{AP}{PB} = \frac{5}{2}.$$

The ratio in which Q divides AB is $\dfrac{AQ}{QB}$. The numerical value of this ratio is $\frac{5}{2}$, but as AQ and QB are of opposite senses,

$$\frac{AQ}{QB} = -\frac{5}{2}.$$

The ratio $\dfrac{BP}{AB}$ is readily seen to be $-\dfrac{2}{7}$.

N.B. When sign is taken into account it is important to note that there is only one point which divides a given line in a given ratio. In the previous example P divides AB in the ratio $5:2$ and Q in the ratio $-5:2$.

Ceva's theorem. **If points L, M, N are taken on the sides BC, CA, AB of a triangle ABC so that the lines AL, BM, CN are concurrent in some point O, then**

$$\frac{BL}{LC} \cdot \frac{CM}{MA} \cdot \frac{AN}{NB} = +1.$$

Consider the two possible cases, Fig. 28 (*a*), where O is inside the triangle, and Fig. 28 (*b*), where O is outside the triangle.

First deal with the signs of the separate ratios and their products.

In Fig. 28 (*a*) all the ratios $\dfrac{BL}{LC}, \dfrac{CM}{MA}, \dfrac{AN}{NB}$ are positive, and their product is positive.

In Fig. 28 (b) ratios $\frac{BL}{LC}$, $\frac{AN}{NB}$ are each negative and ratio $\frac{CM}{MA}$ is positive, therefore their product is once more positive.

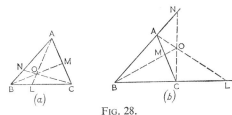

FIG. 28.

Now consider only the magnitudes of the ratios and ignore their signs. In both figures, we have

$$\frac{BL}{LC} = \frac{\text{area } \triangle BLA}{\text{area } \triangle CAL}; \quad \text{also} \quad \frac{BL}{LC} = \frac{\text{area } \triangle BLO}{\text{area } \triangle COL}.$$

$$\therefore \frac{BL}{LC} = \frac{\triangle BLA - \triangle BLO}{\triangle CAL - \triangle COL} = \frac{\triangle BOA}{\triangle COA} \text{ numerically.}$$

Similarly, $\frac{CM}{MA} = \frac{\triangle COB}{\triangle AOB}$; $\frac{AN}{NB} = \frac{\triangle AOC}{\triangle BOC}$ numerically.

But $\qquad \frac{\triangle BOA}{\triangle COA} \cdot \frac{\triangle COB}{\triangle AOB} \cdot \frac{\triangle AOC}{\triangle BOC} = 1.$

Combining the sign and magnitude results,

$$\frac{BL}{LC} \cdot \frac{CM}{MA} \cdot \frac{AN}{NB} = +1.$$

Converse of Ceva's theorem. If the points L, M, N on the sides BC, CA, AB of a triangle ABC are such that

$$\frac{BL}{LC} \cdot \frac{CM}{MA} \cdot \frac{AN}{NB} = +1,$$

then the lines AL, BM, CN are concurrent.

For let AL, BM intersect in O and suppose CO meets AB at a point N' different from N.

By Ceva's theorem, $\qquad \frac{BL}{LC} \cdot \frac{CM}{MA} \cdot \frac{AN'}{N'B} = +1.$

Using this result and that given, it follows that

$$\frac{AN'}{N'B} = \frac{AN}{NB}$$

and in consequence N' must coincide with N, as when sign is taken into account, there is only one point dividing a line in a given ratio.

This converse theorem has important applications to the solutions of problems requiring the concurrence of three lines.

Ex. 13. *The incircle of $\triangle ABC$ touches BC, CA, AB at X, Y, Z respectively. Prove that AX, BY, CZ are concurrent.*

As $AY = AZ$; $BZ = BX$; $CX = CY$ (equal tangents),

$$\frac{BX}{XC} \cdot \frac{CY}{YA} \cdot \frac{AZ}{ZB} = 1 \text{ numerically.}$$

Also all three ratios are positive, so the product is positive and the required result follows by the converse of Ceva's theorem.

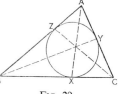

FIG. 29.

Ex. 14. *A circle cuts the sides of $\triangle ABC$ internally, BC at P_1, P_2; CA at Q_1, Q_2; AB at R_2, R_1. If AP_1, BQ_1, CR_1 are concurrent, prove that AP_2, BQ_2, CR_2 are also concurrent.*

We have

$$\left(\frac{BP_1}{P_1C} \cdot \frac{CQ_1}{Q_1A} \cdot \frac{AR_1}{R_1B}\right)\left(\frac{BP_2}{P_2C} \cdot \frac{CQ_2}{Q_2A} \cdot \frac{AR_2}{R_2B}\right)$$

$$= \frac{BP_1 . BP_2}{R_1B . R_2B} \cdot \frac{CQ_1 . CQ_2}{P_1C . P_2C} \cdot \frac{AR_1 . AR_2}{Q_1A . Q_2A}$$

$$= 1 \text{ numerically,}$$

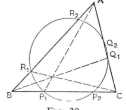

FIG. 30.

as $BP_1 . BP_2 = R_1B . R_2B$, etc. (intersecting chords theorem).

But
$$\frac{BP_1}{P_1C} \cdot \frac{CQ_1}{Q_1A} \cdot \frac{AR_1}{R_1B} = +1 \text{ (Ceva's theorem)}$$

and as each of the ratios $\dfrac{BP_2}{P_2C}$, $\dfrac{CQ_2}{Q_2A}$, $\dfrac{AR_2}{R_2B}$ is positive, it follows that their product is $+1$.

Hence by the converse of Ceva's theorem, AP_2, BQ_2, CR_2 are concurrent.

Menelaus's theorem. If a transversal LMN meets the sides BC, CA, AB of a triangle ABC at L, M, N respectively, then

$$\frac{BL}{LC} \cdot \frac{CM}{MA} \cdot \frac{AN}{NB} = -1.$$

The transversal will either cut one side externally, Fig. 31 (*a*), or all three sides externally, Fig. 31 (*b*).

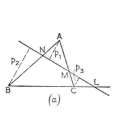

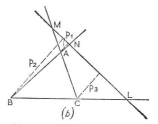

FIG. 31.

In Fig. 31 (a) the ratios $\dfrac{CM}{MA}, \dfrac{AN}{NB}$ are positive and $\dfrac{BL}{LC}$ is negative.

In Fig. 31 (b) all the ratios $\dfrac{BL}{LC}, \dfrac{CM}{MA}, \dfrac{AN}{NB}$ are negative.

∴ In both cases the product of the three ratios is negative.

Let p_1, p_2, p_3 be the lengths of the perpendiculars drawn from A, B, C respectively to the transversal LMN.

Then in both cases, by similar triangles,

$$\frac{BL}{LC} = \frac{p_2}{p_3}; \quad \frac{CM}{MA} = \frac{p_3}{p_1}; \quad \frac{AN}{NB} = \frac{p_1}{p_2} \text{ (numerically)}.$$

But

$$\frac{p_2}{p_3} \cdot \frac{p_3}{p_1} \cdot \frac{p_1}{p_2} = 1.$$

Combining the sign and magnitude results,

$$\frac{\mathbf{BL}}{\mathbf{LC}} \cdot \frac{\mathbf{CM}}{\mathbf{MA}} \cdot \frac{\mathbf{AN}}{\mathbf{NB}} = -1.$$

Converse of Menelaus's theorem. If points L, M, N on the sides BC, CA, AB of a triangle ABC are such that

$$\frac{\mathbf{BL}}{\mathbf{LC}} \cdot \frac{\mathbf{CM}}{\mathbf{MA}} \cdot \frac{\mathbf{AN}}{\mathbf{NB}} = -1,$$

then L, M, N are collinear.

For suppose the line LM meets AB at N'.

Then we have the two results

$$\frac{BL}{LC} \cdot \frac{CM}{MA} \cdot \frac{AN'}{N'B} = -1 \text{ (Menelaus's theorem)}$$

and

$$\frac{BL}{LC} \cdot \frac{CM}{MA} \cdot \frac{AN}{NB} = -1 \text{ (given)}.$$

$$\therefore \frac{AN'}{N'B} = \frac{AN}{NB}$$

and hence N' and N coincide and L, M, N are collinear.

This converse theorem has important applications to the solutions of problems involving the proof of the collinearity of three points.

Ex. 15. *Prove that the points in which the external bisectors of the angles of a triangle meet the opposite sides are collinear.*

Let the external bisectors of the angles A, B, C of $\triangle ABC$ meet the opposite sides in X, Y, Z (Fig. 32).

Then by the bisector of an angle theorem,

$$\frac{BX}{XC} = -\frac{BA}{AC}; \quad \frac{CY}{YA} = -\frac{BC}{BA}; \quad \frac{AZ}{ZB} = -\frac{AC}{BC}.$$

Hence $\dfrac{BX}{XC} \cdot \dfrac{CY}{YA} \cdot \dfrac{AZ}{ZB} = -1$ and the re-

quired result follows.

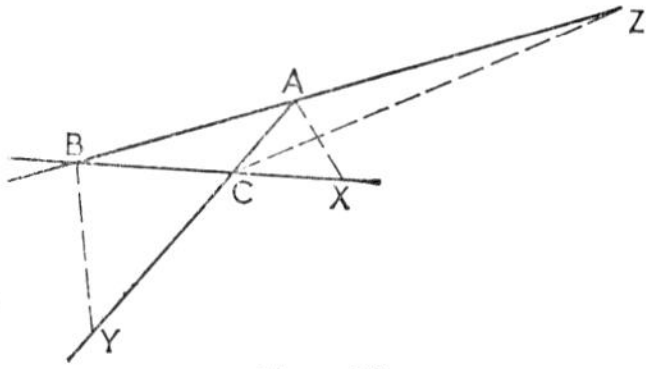

FIG. 32.

Ex. 16. *A transversal cuts the sides AB, BC, CD, DA of a quadrilateral ABCD at P, Q, R, S respectively. Prove that*

$$\frac{AP}{PB} \cdot \frac{BQ}{QC} \cdot \frac{CR}{RD} \cdot \frac{DS}{SA} = +1.$$

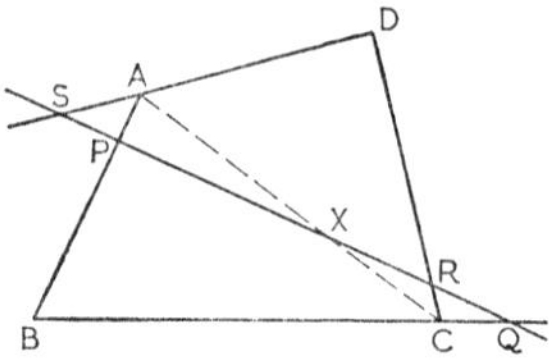

Join *AC* (Fig. 33).

Then in $\triangle ABC$, by Menelaus's theorem,

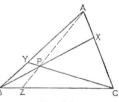

FIG. 33.

$$\frac{AP}{PB} \cdot \frac{BQ}{QC} \cdot \frac{CX}{XA} = -1.$$

Similarly in $\triangle ACD$,

$$\frac{CR}{RD} \cdot \frac{DS}{SA} \cdot \frac{AX}{XC} = -1.$$

Multiplying these two results and noting that $\dfrac{CX}{XA} \cdot \dfrac{AX}{XC} = 1$,

we have

$$\frac{AP}{PB} \cdot \frac{BQ}{QC} \cdot \frac{CR}{RD} \cdot \frac{DS}{SA} = +1.$$

Many examples are solved by the combined use of Ceva's and Menelaus's theorems as illustrated below.

Ex. 17. *Points X, Y are taken on the sides CA, AB of $\triangle ABC$. If BX, CY meet at P and $AX : XC = BY : YA = 1 : 2$, find the value of the ratio BP : PX.*

Let *AP* meet *BC* at *Z* (Fig. 34).

By Ceva's theorem, in $\triangle ABC$

$$\frac{BZ}{ZC} \cdot \frac{CX}{XA} \cdot \frac{AY}{YB} = 1.$$

$$\therefore \frac{BZ}{ZC} \cdot \frac{2}{1} \cdot \frac{2}{1} = 1; \quad \frac{BZ}{ZC} = \frac{1}{4}.$$

Now applying Menelaus's theorem to $\triangle XBC$ with transversal *ZPA*,

FIG. 34.

$$\frac{BZ}{ZC} \cdot \frac{CA}{AX} \cdot \frac{XP}{PB} = -1.$$

But $\dfrac{BZ}{ZC} = \dfrac{1}{4}; \quad \dfrac{CA}{AX} = -\dfrac{3}{1}; \quad \therefore \dfrac{XP}{PB} = \dfrac{4}{3}.$

I.e. $BP : PX = 3 : 4.$

EXAMPLES 1d

1. Use the converse of Ceva's theorem to prove: (i) the medians, (ii) the internal angle bisectors of a triangle are concurrent.

2. If *AD* is an altitude of $\triangle ABC$, prove that $BD : DC = \cot B : \cot C$ and write down similar results for the other altitudes. Deduce that the altitudes of a triangle are concurrent.

3. Points M, N are taken on the sides CA, AB of $\triangle ABC$ such that $CM : MA = 1 : 3$ and $AN : NB = 1 : 2$. If NM produced meets BC produced in L, find the ratio $BL : CL$.

4. ABC is a triangle; L divides BC externally in the ratio $5 : 2$ and M divides CA externally in the ratio $4 : 3$. If AL, BM intersect at O, find the ratio in which CO divides AB.

5. In $\triangle ABC$, $BC = 2CA$; the internal bisector of angle C meets AB at X and AA' is a median. If $A'X$ meets CA produced at Z, prove that A is the mid-point of CZ. If also AA', CX intersect at O and BO cuts CA at Y, prove that Y is a point of trisection of CA.

6. Prove that the lines joining the vertices of a triangle to the points of contact of an escribed circle are concurrent.

7. Points E, F on the sides CA, AB of $\triangle ABC$ are such that FE is parallel to BC; BE, CF intersect at X. Prove that AX is a median of $\triangle ABC$.

8. The external bisector of angle A of $\triangle ABC$ meets BC produced at L, and the internal bisector of angle B meets CA at M. If LM meets AB at R, prove that CR bisects angle C.

9. Lines concurrent in the point O are drawn through the vertices A, B, C of a triangle ABC and meet the opposite sides at D, E, F respectively. Given that $2BD = 3DC$, $CE = 3EA$, find the ratios $AO : OD$ and $CO : OF$.

10. In a trapezium $ABCD$, AB is parallel to CD. If AD and BC produced intersect at X and the diagonals intersect at Y, prove that XY bisects AB.

11. In $\triangle ABC$, A' is the mid-point of BC and P is any point on AA'. If BP meets CA at S and CP meets AB at T, prove that TS is parallel to BC. Hence, given a triangle ABC and a line parallel to BC, construct the median AA' using only a straight-edge and a pencil.

12. If P is any point inside a triangle ABC, prove that the external bisectors of angles BPC, CPA, APB meet BC, CA, AB respectively in three collinear points.

13. The altitudes of a triangle ABC are AD, BE, CF. The perpendiculars from A, B, C to EF, FD, DE respectively meet BC, CA, AB at X, Y, Z. Prove that $BX : XC = \sin \angle BAX : \sin \angle XAC = \cos C : \cos B$.

Using similar results for $CY : YA$ and $AZ : ZB$, deduce that the lines AX, BY, CZ are concurrent.

14. AD is an altitude of a triangle ABC right-angled at A. Prove that $BD : DC = AB^2 : AC^2$ by expressing the ratio of the areas of triangles ABD, ACD in two ways. If $AB : AC = 3 : 4$ and the median BB' cuts AD at X, find the ratio $AX : XD$.

15. G is the centroid of $\triangle ABC$ and AG is produced to P such that $GP = AG$. Parallels through P to BC, CA, AB meet CA, AB, BC at L, M, N respectively. Prove that L, M, N are collinear.

16. The incircle of triangle ABC touches BC, CA, AB at X, Y, Z. If YZ is produced to meet BC produced at L, prove that $BX : XC = BL : CL$.

17. $ABCD$ is a quadrilateral. Prove that the line joining the mid-points of the opposite sides AB, CD divides the other two sides in the same ratio.

18. Points D, E, F on the sides BC, CA, AB of a triangle ABC are such that AD, BE, CF are concurrent. If EF meets BC at K, prove that $BD : DC = BK : CK$.

19. The tangents to the circumcircle of $\triangle ABC$ at A, B, C meet the opposite sides at P, Q, R respectively. Prove: (i) $BP : CP = AB^2 : AC^2$; (ii) P, Q, R are collinear.

20. A transversal meets the sides BC, CA, AB of a triangle ABC at P, Q, R respectively. Points P', Q', R' are taken on BC, CA, AB so that $BP = P'C$, $CQ = Q'A$, $AR = R'B$. Prove that P', Q', R' are collinear.

21. A', B', C' are the mid-points of the sides BC, CA, AB of a triangle. AP, BQ, CR are concurrent lines through A, B, C which meet the opposite sides BC, CA, AB at P, Q, R respectively. If $C'Q$ meets BC at X, $A'R$ meets CA at Y and $B'P$ meets AB at Z, prove: (i) $BX : CX = AQ : QC$; (ii) X, Y, Z are collinear.

22. $ABCD$ is a quadrilateral and X, Y, Z are any points on BC, AD, AB respectively. YZ meets BD at R; RX meets DC at S; ZX meets AC at Q. Prove that Y, Q, S are collinear.

23. P is any point in the plane of $\triangle ABC$. Through the mid-points A', B', C' of BC, CA, AB lines are drawn parallel to PA, PB, PC respectively. Prove that these lines are concurrent.

24. P is any point inside a triangle ABC. The lines AP, BP, CP meet BC, CA, AB at L, M, N respectively. MN, NL, LM meet BC, CA, AB at X, Y, Z respectively. Prove that X, Y, Z are collinear.

Simson's line. If P is any point on the circumcircle of a triangle ABC and if L, M, N are the feet of the perpendiculars from P to BC, CA, AB respectively, then L, M, N are collinear.

Referring to Fig. 35,

as $\qquad \angle PMA = \angle PNA = 90°$,

quad. $PMAN$ is cyclic.

$\therefore \ \angle PNM = \angle PAM$
$\qquad\qquad = \angle PBL$, since $PACB$ is cyclic.

But quad. $PBLN$ is cyclic,

so $\qquad\qquad \angle PBL + \angle PNL = 180°$
$\qquad \therefore \ \angle PNM + \angle PNL = 180°$,

and hence LNM is a straight line.

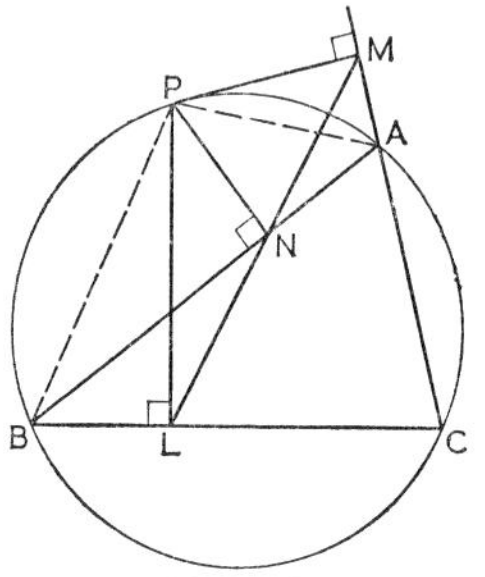

Fig. 35.

The line LMN is called the *Simson line* or *pedal line* of P with respect to the triangle ABC.

Converse theorem. If P is a point in the plane of a triangle ABC such that the feet of the perpendiculars from P to the sides of the triangle are collinear, then P lies on the circumcircle of triangle ABC.

For consider Fig. 35 with the circumcircle assumed omitted and LMN being given as a straight line.

As before $\qquad \angle PNM = \angle PAM$,
also $\qquad\qquad \angle PNM = \angle PBL$, since quad. $PBLN$ is cyclic.
$\qquad \therefore \ \angle PAM = \angle PBL$,

and so the points P, A, B, C are concyclic.

Ex. 18. *Prove that the circumcircles of the four triangles formed by four intersecting straight lines have a common point.*

The four triangles formed by the four straight lines *ABE*, *BCF*, *DCE*, *ADF* are triangles *ABF*, *AED*, *BEC*, *CFD* (Fig. 36.)

Consider the circles *ABF*, *AED* which have *A* as one common point; let the second common point be *P*.

As *P* lies on the circle *ABF*, the feet of the perpendiculars *X*, *Y*, *Z* from *P* to the sides of △*ABF* are collinear (Simson line).

Also as *P* lies on the circle *AED*, the feet of the perpendiculars *X*, *W*, *Z* from *P* to the sides of △*AED* are collinear (Simson line).

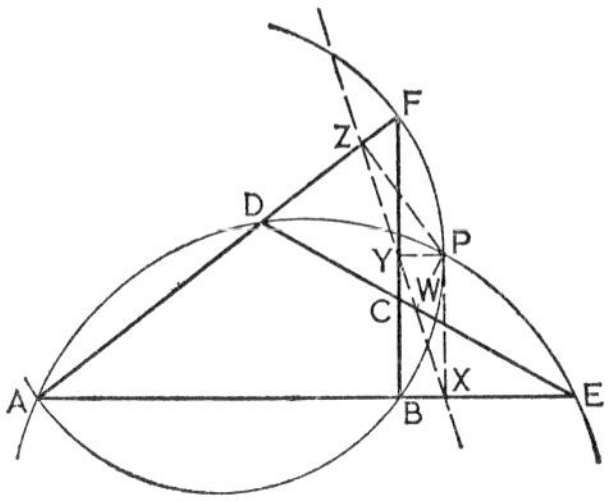

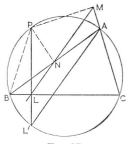

FIG. 36.

Hence the four points *X*, *Y*, *Z*, *W* are collinear.

∴ By the converse of the Simson line theorem, as *X*, *W*, *Y* are collinear, *P* lies on the circle *BEC* and as *Y*, *Z*, *W* are collinear, *P* lies also on the circle *CFD*.

Direction of a Simson line. In Fig. 37, *LNM* is the Simson line of *P* with respect to a triangle *ABC*.

The perpendicular *PL* is produced to meet the circumcircle of △*ABC* again at *L'*.

Then $\angle ABP = \angle AL'P$ (same segment)

and $\angle ABP = \angle PLN$ (same segment as quad. *BLNP* is cyclic).

∴ $\angle AL'P = \angle PLN$,

and hence *L'A* is parallel to *LNM*.

Thus the Simson line of P is parallel to the line joining vertex A to the point where the perpendicular from P to side BC meets the circumcircle again.

FIG. 37.

If M' and N' are defined in a manner similar to L', it follows also that the Simson line of P is parallel to each of the lines AL', BM', CN'.

Ex. 19. *If AD, an altitude of △ABC, is produced to meet the circumcircle again at K, prove that the pedal line of K with respect to the triangle is parallel to the tangent at A to the circumcircle.*

Using the result just proved, the pedal or Simson line of *K* is parallel to the line joining *A* to the point where the perpendicular from *K* to side *BC* meets the circumcircle again. As *KD* is this perpendicular, the required point is *A* itself. So the pedal line of *K* is parallel to the line joining two coincident points at *A* on the circumcircle—i.e. the tangent at *A*.

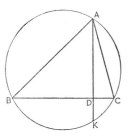

FIG. 38.

Ex. 20. *P, Q are any two points on the circumcircle of a triangle ABC. If O is the circumcentre, prove that one of the angles between the Simson lines of P and Q is equal to $\frac{1}{2}\angle POQ$.*

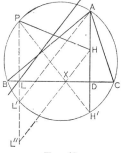

In Fig. 39, PLL' and QUU' are both drawn perpendicular to BC.

∴ The Simson lines of P and Q are respectively parallel to $L'A$ and $U'A$, and consequently $\angle L'AU'$ is one of the angles between the Simson lines.

But, by symmetry, the arcs cut off by parallel chords of a circle are equal, and as chords PL', QU' are parallel,

arc PQ = arc $L'U'$.

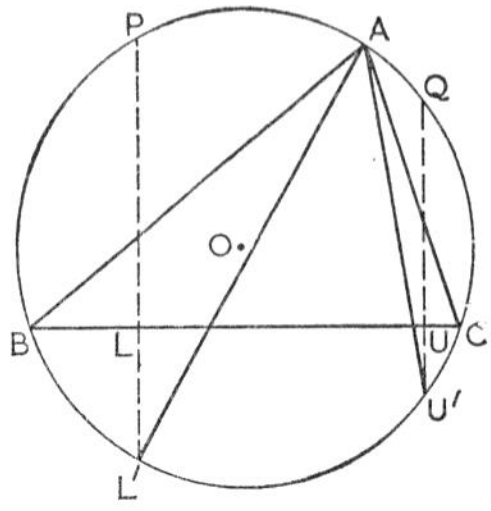

Fig. 39.

∴ As equal arcs subtend equal angles at the circumference,

$$\angle L'AU' = \angle PBQ = \frac{1}{2}\angle POQ,$$

and hence the required result.

The Simson line and the orthocentre

To prove that the Simson or pedal line of a point P bisects the line joining P to the orthocentre H of triangle ABC.

In Fig. 40 the altitude AD produced meets the circumcircle again at H' and PH' meets BC at X; HX produced meets PLL' at L''.

As $HD = DH'$, it easily follows that $\triangle HXH'$ is isosceles.

Noting that PL'' and HH' are parallel, it follows further that $\triangle PXL''$ is also isosceles.

I.e. $PL = LL''$.

Fig. 40.

Also $\angle AH'P = \angle AL'P$ (same arc),

and $\angle AH'P = \angle L''PH' = \angle HL''P$.

∴ $\angle AL'P = \angle HL''P$,

and hence $L''H$ is parallel to $L'A$ and so to the Simson line of P.

As L is the mid-point of PL'', it follows that the Simson line of P (i.e. the line through L parallel to $L''H$) bisects PH.

EXAMPLES 1e

1. What are the Simson lines with respect to a triangle ABC of the vertices A, B, C?

2. If triangle ABC is right-angled at A, identify the pedal lines of B and C with respect to the triangle.

3. Points P, Q on the circle ABC are such that PQ is perpendicular to BC. Prove that an angle between the Simson lines of P and Q with respect to the triangle ABC is equal to $\angle PAQ$.

4. Given a triangle ABC, show how to find a point P on its circumcircle such that its pedal line with respect to the triangle is parallel to the diameter of the circumcircle through B.

5. The pedal line of P with respect to $\triangle ABC$ is parallel to the diameter of the circumcircle through A. Prove that PA is parallel to BC.

6. If PQ is a diameter of the circumcircle of a triangle ABC, prove that the Simson lines of P and Q with respect to the triangle are perpendicular.

7. If AD, an altitude of $\triangle ABC$, is produced to meet the circumcircle again at P, prove that the Simson line of P makes an angle with AC equal to angle B of the triangle.

8. If I is the incentre of $\triangle ABC$ and AI produced meets the circumcircle at X, prove that the Simson line of X with respect to the triangle is perpendicular to AX.

9. P is a point in the plane of a given triangle ABC such that the feet of the perpendiculars from P to the sides of the triangle are collinear and such that P lies on the median through A. Find the position of P.

10. The triangle ABC is right-angled at A. The pedal line of a point P on the circumcircle meets AP at Q. Prove that AP is perpendicular to the diameter through Q.

11. ABC is an obtuse angle and P lies on the minor arc AB of circle ABC such that AP is perpendicular to BC. If M, N are the feet of the perpendiculars from P to CA, AB respectively, prove that the triangles AMN, ABC are similar.

12. Show how to find the position of a point P which has a pedal line with respect to a given triangle parallel to a given line.

13. If PQ is a chord of the circumcircle of $\triangle ABC$ which is parallel to BC, prove that the Simson line of P with respect to the triangle is perpendicular to AQ.

14. L, M, N are the feet of the perpendiculars from a point P on the circumcircle of the triangle ABC to the sides BC, CA, AB respectively. Prove that the triangles PLN, PAC are similar. If P is the mid-point of minor arc AC, prove that $LM:LN=AB:AC$.

15. The perpendiculars from a point P on the circumcircle of triangle ABC to the sides BC, CA, AB meet the circumcircle again in L', M', N' respectively. Prove: (i) $M'N'=BC$; (ii) triangles ABC, $L'M'N'$ are congruent.

16. The altitude AD of triangle ABC is produced to meet the circumcircle at X. The line joining X to any other point on the circumcircle meets BC at U. Prove that the join of U to the orthocentre of the triangle is parallel to the pedal line of P.

17. $ABCD$ is a cyclic quadrilateral with AB parallel to CD. If P is any point on the circumcircle of the quadrilateral, prove that the feet of the perpendiculars from P to AC, AD, BC, BD are concyclic.

18. The pedal line of a point P with respect to $\triangle ABC$ meets BC at L and the altitude AD at K. If H is the orthocentre of the triangle, prove that PK is parallel to LH.

C

19. The altitudes AD, BE, CF of $\triangle ABC$ meet the circumcircle of the triangle again at D', E', F'. Prove that the pedal line of A with respect to $\triangle D'E'F'$ is parallel to BC.

20. Triangle ABC is obtuse-angled at C; P is any point on the minor arc CA of the circumcircle of the triangle. The perpendiculars from P to the sides meet BC produced, CA, AB at L, M, N respectively. Prove that triangles PLM, PAB and triangles PMN, PBC are similar. If $LM = MN$, prove that $PA : PC = AB : BC$.

21. H is the orthocentre of an acute-angled triangle ABC. If P is any point on the circle BCH, prove that the Simson line of P with respect to triangle BCH bisects AP.

MISCELLANEOUS EXAMPLES

1. If in the triangles ABC, DEF the angles A and D are equal and BC is greater than EF, prove that the radius of the circumcircle of triangle ABC is greater than the radius of the circumcircle of triangle DEF.

2. In triangle ABC the perpendicular bisector of BC meets CA at P and AB at Q. Prove that $OP \cdot OQ = OA^2$, where O is the circumcentre of $\triangle ABC$.

3. If H is the orthocentre of the triangle ABC, prove that

$$AH^2 + BC^2 = BH^2 + CA^2 = CH^2 + AB^2.$$

4. A point D is taken on the median AA' of a triangle ABC; BD meets CA at X and CD meets AB at Y. Prove that XY is parallel to BC.

5. A, B, C, D are four points in order on a straight line such that $AB \cdot AD = AC^2$. If P is any point on the circle centre A, radius AC, prove that $PB : PD = AB : AC$.

6. A point E is taken on the diagonal AC of a parallelogram $ABCD$. If F is the second point of intersection of the circles EAB, ECD and R_1, R_2 are the radii of these circles, prove: (i) F lies on BD; (ii) $R_1 : R_2 = AF : FC$.

7. Points P, Q, R are taken on the sides BC, CA, AB respectively of a triangle ABC such that $BP : PC = CQ : QA = AR : RB = 1 : 3$. If AP, BQ, CR meet in pairs at U, V, W, prove that $VW : AP = WU : BQ = UV : CR = 8 : 13$, the elements of the ratios being in the same straight lines.

8. H is the orthocentre and O the circumcentre of the triangle ABC. If A' is the mid-point of BC and HA' produced meets the circumcircle at P, prove that $HA' = A'P$ and that PB is perpendicular to AB.

9. ABC is a triangle, right-angled at B. If the incircle of the triangle touches AC at Y, prove that $2AY \cdot YC = AB \cdot BC$.

10. Prove that an external common tangent to two circles divides the line of centres externally in the ratio of the radii. Hence show that the points of intersection of the three pairs of external common tangents to three circles taken two at a time are collinear.

11. $ABCD$ is a quadrilateral. Show how to find a point on the circumcircle of the triangle ABC whose pedal line with respect to triangle ABC is perpendicular to CD.

12. I_1, I_2, I_3 are the centres of the escribed circles of triangle ABC opposite to A, B, C respectively. Prove that the perpendiculars from I_1, I_2, I_3 to BC, CA, AB respectively are concurrent.

13. If I is the incentre of triangle ABC and I_1, I_2, I_3 the excentres opposite A, B, C respectively, prove:

(i) $r \sin \angle AIB = c \sin \frac{1}{2}A \sin \frac{1}{2}B$;   (ii) $II_1 = 4R \sin \frac{1}{2}A = a \sec \frac{1}{2}A$;
(iii) $I_2I_3 = 4R \cos \frac{1}{2}A$.

14. The internal and external bisectors of the angle A of triangle ABC cut BC at X, Y respectively. Prove: (i) $bc(b+c) = bBX^2 + cCX^2 + (b+c)AX^2$; (ii) $bc = AX^2 + BX \cdot CX$; (iii) $bc(c-b) = bBY^2 - cCY^2 + (b-c)AY^2$.

15. If H is the orthocentre of triangle ABC and the circle BCH touches CA and AB, prove that triangle ABC is equilateral.

16. P is a point on the circle ABC. If the perpendicular from A to the Simson line of P with respect to triangle ABC meets the circumcircle again at Q, prove that PQ is parallel to BC.

17. AD, BE, CF are the altitudes of triangle ABC. Prove that the area of triangle DEF equals $2\Delta \cos A \cos B \cos C$, where Δ is the area of triangle ABC.

18. If X is a point on the diagonal AC of a parallelogram $ABCD$, prove that parallels to BX, DX drawn through C, A respectively, intersect on BD produced.

19. If O is the circumcentre and G the centroid of triangle ABC, prove that $OG^2 = R^2 - \frac{1}{9}(a^2 + b^2 + c^2)$.

20. Triangle ABC is right-angled at A; AD is an altitude and P, Q are the incentres of triangles ABD, ACD respectively. Prove that triangles PDQ, ABC are similar.

21. If H is the orthocentre of a triangle ABC, prove that the radii of the circumcircles of the triangles ABC, HCA are equal. If O, S are the centres of these circles, prove that OS and AC bisect each other at right angles.

22. The side CB of a square $ABCD$ is produced to P so that $BP = 2CB$; M is the mid-point of AD. If AC, BM intersect at X and PX meets AB at Q, find the ratio $AQ:QB$.

23. P, Q, R are the mid-points of EF, FD, DE, the sides of the pedal triangle of a triangle ABC. Prove that AP, BQ, CR are concurrent.

24. The inscribed circle of a triangle ABC touches the sides at X, Y, Z. Prove that, with the usual notation, the area of triangle $XYZ = r\Delta/2R$.

25. The triangle ABC is equilateral and A' is the image of A in BC. If P is any point on the circle centre A', radius $A'C$, prove that $PA^2 = PB^2 + PC^2$.

26. PQ is a chord of the circumcircle of the triangle ABC parallel to AB. Prove that the Simson lines of P and Q with respect to the triangle intersect on the altitude CF.

27. Prove that the only point P in the plane of a triangle ABC such that $PA^2 + BC^2 = PB^2 + CA^2 = PC^2 + AB^2$, is the orthocentre of the triangle.

28. The internal bisector of angle A of a triangle ABC meets BC at P. The circle which passes through A and touches BC at P cuts CA at X and AB at Y. Prove that XY is parallel to BC.

29. Show how to construct a triangle given: (i) the lengths of two sides and of the median which bisects the third side; (ii) the nine-point centre, the orthocentre and one vertex.

30. $ABCD$ is a cyclic quadrilateral; H, K are the orthocentres of the triangles ABC, ABD. Prove that A, B, H, K are concyclic.

31. I is the incentre of a triangle ABC. The incircle touches the sides BC, CA, AB at X, Y, Z respectively. If XI, YI, ZI meet YZ, ZX, XY respectively at L, M, N, prove that AL, BM, CN are concurrent.

32. A circle touches the side BC of a triangle ABC at its mid-point A' and cuts CA at P, P' and AB at Q, Q'. If PQ, $P'Q'$ meet BC at R, R', prove by using the theorem of Menelaus or otherwise, that $BR : CR = CR' : BR'$.

33. If I, I_1, I_2, I_3 are the incentre and excentres of a triangle ABC, prove that the circumcircles of triangles II_2I_3, $I_1I_2I_3$ are equal.

34. With the usual notation for a triangle ABC, prove that

$$IH^2 = 2r^2 - 4R^2 \cos A \cos B \cos C.$$

35. $ABCD$ is a trapezium with AB parallel to DC; the diagonals AC, BD meet at E and CB meets DA at X. A line through E parallel to AB meets AD at F and BC at G. Prove that AG, BF, EX are concurrent.

36. The points P, Q are at the ends of a diameter of the circle ABC. Prove that the Simson lines of P and Q with respect to the triangle ABC intersect at right angles on the nine-point circle of the triangle.

37. $ABCD$ is a quadrilateral and P, Q, R are points on BC, AD, AB respectively. RQ meets BD at X; XP meets DC at Y; RP meets AC at Z. Prove that Q, Z, Y are collinear.

38. A transversal LMN of triangle ABC meets the sides AB, AC internally at L, M respectively and the side BC produced at N. If BM, CL intersect at X and AX meets BC at Y, prove that Y, N divide BC internally and externally in the same ratio.

39. For the four triangles formed by four intersecting straight lines prove: (i) the circumcircles of the four triangles have a common point; (ii) this common point has a common Simson line with respect to each of the four triangles; (iii) the orthocentres of the four triangles are collinear.

40. ABC is a given triangle. Find a point P in its plane for which $PA^2 + PB^2 + PC^2$ has a minimum value.

41. If three equal circles have a common point A, prove that A is the orthocentre of the triangle formed by the other three points of intersection.

42. I is the incentre of a triangle ABC and I_2, I_3 are the excentres opposite B, C respectively. Perpendiculars HX, HY are dropped from the orthocentre H to the lines AI, I_2I_3. Prove that XY bisects BC.

CHAPTER II

ALGEBRAIC METHODS

Basic identities. The following results are important:

I.
$$(x+a)(x+b) \equiv x^2 + x(a+b) + ab.$$
$$(x+a)(x+b)(x+c) \equiv x^3 + x^2(a+b+c) + x(bc+ca+ab) + abc.$$
$$(x+a)(x+b) \ldots \textbf{n factors} \equiv x^n + x^{n-1}\sum a + x^{n-2}\sum ab + \ldots + abc\ldots\ldots$$

II.
$$(a+b)(a-b) \equiv a^2 - b^2.$$
$$(a+b)^2 \equiv a^2 + b^2 + 2ab.$$
$$(a+b+c)^2 \equiv a^2 + b^2 + c^2 + 2(bc+ca+ab).$$
$$(a+b+c+ \ldots \textbf{n terms})^2 \equiv \sum a^2 + 2\sum ab.$$

Ex. 1. *Expand* $(a-2b-c)^2$.

$$\begin{aligned}
(a-2b-c)^2 &= a^2 + (-2b)^2 + (-c)^2 + 2\{(-2b)(-c) + (-c)(a) + (a)(-2b)\} \\
&= a^2 + 4b^2 + c^2 + 4bc - 2ca - 4ab.
\end{aligned}$$

Ex. 2. *Prove that*
$$(a^2 + b^2 - 2ab)(a^2 + b^2 + 2ab)(a^4 + b^4 + 2a^2b^2) = a^8 + b^8 - 2a^4b^4.$$

As $(a^2 + b^2 - 2ab)(a^2 + b^2 + 2ab) = (a^2 + b^2)^2 - (2ab)^2$
$$= a^4 + b^4 - 2a^2b^2,$$
$$\begin{aligned}
\text{L.H.S.} &= (a^4 + b^4 - 2a^2b^2)(a^4 + b^4 + 2a^2b^2) \\
&= (a^4 + b^4)^2 - (2a^2b^2)^2 \\
&= a^8 + b^8 - 2a^4b^4.
\end{aligned}$$

Ex. 3. *Find the sum of the products, taken two at a time, of the first n natural numbers.*

We have $\left(\sum n\right)^2 = \sum n^2 + 2\{\text{sum of products taken two at a time}\}.$

I.e. sum of products $= \frac{1}{2}\left\{\left(\sum n\right)^2 - \sum n^2\right\}$
$$\begin{aligned}
&= \frac{1}{2}\{\tfrac{1}{4}n^2(n+1)^2 - \tfrac{1}{6}n(n+1)(2n+1)\} \\
&= \tfrac{1}{24}n(n+1)\{3n(n+1) - 2(2n+1)\} \\
&= \tfrac{1}{24}n(n+1)(n-1)(3n+2).
\end{aligned}$$

III.
$$(a+b)^3 \equiv a^3 + b^3 + 3(a^2b + b^2a).$$
$$(a+b+c)^3 \equiv a^3 + b^3 + c^3 + 3\{a^2(b+c) + b^2(c+a) + c^2(a+b)\} + 6abc.$$
$$(a+b+c+ \ldots \textbf{n terms})^3 \equiv \sum a^3 + 3\sum a^2b + 6\sum abc.$$

Ex. 4. *Simplify* $8a^3 + (b - c)^3 + (c - b - 2a)^3$.

Write $(c - b - 2a)^3$ as $- [2a + (b - c)]^3$.

$$\begin{aligned}
\text{Expression} &= 8a^3 + (b - c)^3 - [8a^3 + (b - c)^3 + 12a^2(b - c) + 6a(b - c)^2] \\
&= - 12a^2(b - c) - 6a(b - c)^2 \\
&= - 6a(b - c)(2a + b - c).
\end{aligned}$$

IV. If n is a positive integer,

$$(a + b)^n \equiv a^n + na^{n-1}\, b + \frac{n(n-1)}{2!}\, a^{n-2}\, b^2 + \; \ldots \; + b^n.$$

For the smaller values of n, the coefficients in this expansion can be found simply by using *Newton's Rule*, which is illustrated below.

Each number in the diagram is the sum of the number above it and the one immediately to the left.

	Coefficients					
$(a+b)^2$	1	2	1			
$(a+b)^3$	1	3	3	1		
$(a+b)^4$	$1 \to$	$4 \to$	$6 \to$	$4 \to$	1	
$(a+b)^5$	1	5	10	10	5	1

Ex. 5. *Expand* $(x - 2y)^5$.

The coefficients are 1, 5, 10, 10, 5, 1.

$$\begin{aligned}
\therefore \; (x - 2y)^5 &= 1x^5 + 5x^4(- 2y) + 10x^3(- 2y)^2 + 10x^2(- 2y)^3 + 5x(- 2y)^4 \\
&\qquad\qquad\qquad\qquad\qquad\qquad\qquad\qquad\qquad\qquad + 1(- 2y)^5 \\
&= x^5 - 10x^4y + 40x^3y^2 - 80x^2y^3 + 80xy^4 - 32y^5.
\end{aligned}$$

Important factors.   The following results should be known:

I. $a^2 - b^2 = (a - b)(a + b).$

II. $a^3 + b^3 = (a + b)(a^2 - ab + b^2).$

                 $a^3 - b^3 = (a - b)(a^2 + ab + b^2).$

III. $a^3 + b^3 + c^3 - 3abc = (a + b + c)[a^2 + b^2 + c^2 - (bc + ca + ab)]$

              or $(a + b + c)\tfrac{1}{2}[(b - c)^2 + (c - a)^2 + (a - b)^2].$

$$\sum a^3 - 3\sum abc = \sum a \left[\sum a^2 - \sum ab \right].$$

IV. $a^4 - b^4 = (a - b)(a + b)(a^2 + b^2).$

$$\begin{aligned}
a^4 + b^4 &= (a^2 + b^2)^2 - 2a^2b^2 \\
&= (a^2 - \sqrt{2}ab + b^2)(a^2 + \sqrt{2}ab + b^2). \\
a^4 + a^2b^2 + b^4 &= (a^2 + b^2)^2 - a^2b^2 \\
&= (a^2 - ab + b^2)(a^2 + ab + b^2).
\end{aligned}$$

Ex. 6. *Factorise:* (*i*) $(x + 3y - 2z)^2 - 4(2x - 3y + z)^2$; (*ii*) $8(a - 2b)^3 - (2a + b)^3$.

(i) Expression

$$\begin{aligned}
&= [(x + 3y - 2z) - 2(2x - 3y + z)][(x + 3y - 2z) + 2(2x - 3y + z)] \\
&= [- 3x + 9y - 4z][5x - 3y].
\end{aligned}$$

(ii) Expression

$$= [2(a - 2b) - (2a + b)][4(a - 2b)^2 + 2(a - 2b)(2a + b) + (2a + b)^2]$$
$$= [-5b][12a^2 - 18ab + 13b^2].$$

Ex. 7. *If $a + b + c = 0$ and $a^3 + b^3 + c^3 = 0$, prove that at least one of the numbers a, b, c is zero.*

The expression $a^3 + b^3 + c^3$ is usually associated with the factorisable expression $a^3 + b^3 + c^3 - 3abc$.

We have $\qquad a^3 + b^3 + c^3 - 3abc = (a + b + c)(a^2 + b^2 + c^2 - bc - ca - ab).$

But $\qquad a^3 + b^3 + c^3 = a + b + c = 0.$

$$\therefore \ 3abc = 0.$$

Hence at least one of the numbers a, b, c is zero.

Ex. 8. *Rationalise the denominators of the fractions* (i) $\dfrac{1}{2\sqrt{3} - \sqrt{5}}$;

(ii) $\dfrac{1}{1 + \sqrt{3} - \sqrt{2}}$; (iii) $\dfrac{1}{\sqrt[3]{3} - \sqrt[3]{2}}$.

(i) $\dfrac{1}{2\sqrt{3} - \sqrt{5}} = \dfrac{2\sqrt{3} + \sqrt{5}}{(2\sqrt{3} - \sqrt{5})(2\sqrt{3} + \sqrt{5})} = \dfrac{2\sqrt{3} + \sqrt{5}}{7}.$

(ii) $\dfrac{1}{1 + \sqrt{3} - \sqrt{2}} = \dfrac{1 + \sqrt{3} + \sqrt{2}}{(1 + \sqrt{3} - \sqrt{2})(1 + \sqrt{3} + \sqrt{2})} = \dfrac{1 + \sqrt{3} + \sqrt{2}}{(1 + \sqrt{3})^2 - 2}$

$\qquad\qquad = \dfrac{1 + \sqrt{3} + \sqrt{2}}{2(1 + \sqrt{3})} = \dfrac{(1 + \sqrt{3} + \sqrt{2})(1 - \sqrt{3})}{-4}$

$\qquad\qquad = \dfrac{2 - \sqrt{2} + \sqrt{6}}{4}.$

(iii) $\dfrac{1}{\sqrt[3]{3} - \sqrt[3]{2}} = \dfrac{1}{3^{\frac{1}{3}} - 2^{\frac{1}{3}}}$

$\qquad\qquad = \dfrac{3^{\frac{2}{3}} + 3^{\frac{1}{3}}2^{\frac{1}{3}} + 2^{\frac{2}{3}}}{(3^{\frac{1}{3}} - 2^{\frac{1}{3}})(3^{\frac{2}{3}} + 3^{\frac{1}{3}}2^{\frac{1}{3}} + 2^{\frac{2}{3}})} = \dfrac{3^{\frac{2}{3}} + 6^{\frac{1}{3}} + 2^{\frac{2}{3}}}{3 - 2}$

$\qquad\qquad = 3^{\frac{2}{3}} + 6^{\frac{1}{3}} + 2^{\frac{2}{3}}.$

EXAMPLES 2a

1. Expand $(x + 1)(x + 2)(x + 3)(x + 4)$.

2. Square $a - b + 2c$.

3. Verify the identity $(2a + 3b)^2 + 2ab + (3a + 2b)^2 \equiv 13(a + b)^2$.

4. Factorise: (i) $4(a - b + c)^2 - 9(b - a - c)^2$; (ii) $(x + 2y)^3 - (2x - y)^3$;
   (iii) $(a^2 + b^2)^2 - 3a^2b^2$; (iv) $8a^3 + b^3 - 2(2a + b)$.

5. Write down the expansion of $(2 - x)^5$.

6. Simplify $(a + b + c)^2 - (b + c - a)^2 - (c + a - b)^2 - (a + b - c)^2$.

7. Expand $(x - y + 2z)^3$.

8. Simplify: (i) $(\sqrt{2} + 1)^4 - (\sqrt{2} - 1)^4$; (ii) $\dfrac{1}{(\sqrt{2} - 1)^4} - \dfrac{1}{(\sqrt{2} + 1)^4}$.

9. Show by division that $\dfrac{x^7 - 1}{x - 1} = x^6 + x^5 + x^4 + x^3 + x^2 + x + 1$.

10. Express with rational denominators:

$$\text{(i)}\ \frac{1}{\sqrt{3}-\sqrt{2}}; \quad \text{(ii)}\ \frac{1}{\sqrt{3}+\sqrt{2}-1}; \quad \text{(iii)}\ \frac{1}{\sqrt[3]{3}-1}.$$

11. Substitute $x = b + c - a$, $y = c + a - b$, $z = a + b - c$ in the following expressions and simplify the results:

$$\text{(i)}\ x^2 + y^2 + z^2; \quad \text{(ii)}\ x^2 + y^2 + z^2 + yz + zx + xy.$$

12. Prove that $x^4 + 2x^2 + 9 \equiv (x^2 + 3)^2 - 4x^2$, and hence factorise the expression.

13. Factorise $2x^2 + xy - y^2$ and $2x^2 + xy - y^2 + 9x - 6y - 5$.

14. Simplify $\left(\dfrac{1}{\sqrt{3}-\sqrt{2}}\right)^5 + \left(\dfrac{1}{\sqrt{3}+\sqrt{2}}\right)^5.$

15. Find the square roots of: (i) $x^4 - 6x^3 + 13x^2 - 12x + 4$;
(ii) $4a^4 + 4a^3b - 11a^2b^2 - 6ab^3 + 9b^4$.

16. If $x = -(y + z)$, prove that $x^3 + y^3 + z^3 = 3xyz$.

17. Simplify $\dfrac{a^3 + b^3}{a^4 + a^2b^2 + b^4}.$

18. Factorise: (i) $x^3 - 27 - 9x^2 + 27x$; (ii) $a^3 + 27 - \dfrac{b^3}{a^3} + 9b$;
(iii) $x^4 + 2x^2 + 4$.

19. Prove that $(y - z)^3 + (z - x)^3 + (x - y)^3 = 3(y - z)(z - x)(x - y)$.

20. Simplify $\dfrac{(x+a)(x+b)}{(x-y)(x-z)} + \dfrac{(y+a)(y+b)}{(y-x)(y-z)} + \dfrac{(z+a)(z+b)}{(z-x)(z-y)}.$

21. If $x > 0$ and $x - \dfrac{1}{x} = 1$, prove that $x + \dfrac{1}{x} = \sqrt{5}$ and evaluate: (i) $x^3 - \dfrac{1}{x^3}$;
(ii) $x^6 + \dfrac{1}{x^6}.$

22. Express $x^4 - 2x^3 + 7x - 4$ as a product of two quadratic factors.

23. If the function $ax^2 + 2bx + c$ can be expressed in the form

$$A(x - x_1)^2 + B(x - x_2)^2,$$

where A, B are constants, prove that $ax_1x_2 + b(x_1 + x_2) + c = 0$.

24. If $x + y + z = 2$, $x^2 + y^2 + z^2 = 4$, $x^3 + y^3 + z^3 = 5$, find the values of:
(i) $yz + zx + xy$; (ii) xyz.

25. Prove that, if $x^p = (xy)^q = (xy^2)^r$ for all values of x and y, then $2pr = q(p + r)$.

26. The sum s_n of n terms of a series is given by $s_n = \frac{1}{2}n(n + 1)(n + 2)$, write down s_{n-1} and find the nth term of the series.

27. Factorise: (i) $a^4 + 3a^2b^2 + 9b^4$; (ii) $2a^4 + a^2b^2 + ab^3 + b^4$.

28. Express $\dfrac{1}{x^4 + 1}$ as the sum of two partial fractions.

29. If $x^2 - 2y^2 - xy = 0$, prove that $\dfrac{x^3}{y^3} - \dfrac{8y^3}{x^3} = 7$.

30. If n is a positive integer, prove by long division that

$$\frac{x^n - 1}{x - 1} = x^{n-1} + x^{n-2} + \ldots + x + 1.$$

Hence simplify $\dfrac{x^7 + x^6 + \ldots + x + 1}{x^3 + x^2 + x + 1}$.

31. Factorise $a^2 + b^2 + c^2 - 2bc - 2ca - 2ab$ by expressing it in terms of $(a + b - c)^2$.

32. If a, b, c are real numbers satisfying $a + b + c = a^5 + b^5 + c^5 = 0$, prove that at least one of a, b, c is zero.

33. Given that $x + y + z = 4$, $x^2 + y^2 + z^2 = 6$, $xyz = 3$, find the value of $x^3 + y^3 + z^3$.

34. Prove that $(a^2 + b^2 + c^2)(x^2 + y^2 + z^2) - (ax + by + cz)^2$
$$\equiv (ay - bx)^2 + (bz - cy)^2 + (cx - az)^2.$$

Deduce that, if $\dfrac{x}{a} = \dfrac{y}{b} = \dfrac{z}{c}$, then $(a^2 + b^2 + c^2)(x^2 + y^2 + z^2) = (ax + by + cz)^2$.

35. If $x = a(b^3 - c^3)$, $y = b(c^3 - a^3)$, $z = c(a^3 - b^3)$, prove that

$$\frac{x^3 + y^3 + z^3}{xyz} = \frac{a^3 + b^3 + c^3}{abc}.$$

Remainder theorem. *If a polynomial $f(x)$ is divided by $(x - a)$, the remainder is $f(a)$.*

As the degree of the remainder must be less than the degree of the divisor, the remainder in this case must be a constant.

So if the quotient is $q(x)$, it follows that

$$f(x) \equiv (x - a)q(x) + r,$$

where r is a constant.

This is an identity and true for all values of x.

Let $x = a$, $\qquad\qquad f(a) = 0q(x) + r.$

I.e. $\qquad\qquad$ Remainder $= r = f(a).$

As a consequence of this theorem, it follows that if $f(a) = 0$, then $(x - a)$ is a factor of $f(x)$.

Ex. 9. *Factorise $x^5 - 1$.*

As $f(1) = 1 - 1 = 0$, $x - 1$ is a factor.

By division, the other factor is $x^4 + x^3 + x^2 + x + 1$.

$$\therefore \quad x^5 - 1 = (x - 1)(x^4 + x^3 + x^2 + x + 1).$$

Ex. 10. *Find the values of a and b if $(x^2 - x - 2)$ is a factor of*
$$2x^4 + ax^3 - 4x^2 + bx - 2.$$

Method (i). As $(x^2 - x - 2) = (x - 2)(x + 1)$, both $(x - 2)$ and $(x + 1)$ are factors of the expression.

$$\therefore \quad f(2) = 32 + 8a - 16 + 2b - 2 = 0; \quad 4a + b = -7,$$

and $\qquad\qquad f(-1) = 2 - a - 4 - b - 2 = 0; \quad a + b = -4.$

Hence $\qquad\qquad\qquad a = -1, \quad b = -3.$

Method (ii). As $x^2 - x - 2$ is one factor, it follows from the form of the given polynominal that the second factor is quadratic, with $2x^2$ and $+1$ as two of its terms.

So let $\qquad 2x^4 + ax^3 - 4x^2 + bx - 2 = (x^2 - x - 2)(2x^2 + Ax + 1)$.

Comparing coefficients of x^2, $\qquad -4 = -3 - A$; $\quad A = 1$.

$\qquad \therefore$ The given expression $\quad = (x^2 - x - 2)(2x^2 + x + 1)$,

and hence $\qquad\qquad\qquad\qquad a = -1, \quad b = -3$.

Remainder when a polynomial f(x) is divided by $(x-a)^2$. The remainder will be a linear function of x which can be written in the form $A(x-a) + B$, where A and B are constants.

So if the quotient is $q(x)$,

$$f(x) \equiv (x-a)^2 q(x) + A(x-a) + B.$$

Let $x = a$. $\qquad f(a) = B$.

Also $\qquad f'(x) \equiv 2(x-a)q(x) + (x-a)^2 q'(x) + A$.

Let $x = a$. $\qquad f'(a) = A$.

Hence the remainder when the polynomial $f(x)$ is divided by $(x-a)^2$ is

$$f'(a)(x-a) + f(a).$$

It follows that $(x-a)$ is a repeated factor of $f(x)$ if $f'(a) = f(a) = 0$.

Ex. 11. *Prove that $(2x - 1)$ is a repeated factor of $4x^4 - 4x^3 + 5x^2 - 4x + 1$.*

Let $\qquad\qquad\qquad f(x) = 4x^4 - 4x^3 + 5x^2 - 4x + 1$.

$\qquad \therefore f'(x) = 16x^3 - 12x^2 + 10x - 4$.

$\qquad\qquad f(\tfrac{1}{2}) = \tfrac{1}{4} - \tfrac{1}{2} + \tfrac{5}{4} - 2 + 1 = 0$,

and $\qquad\qquad f'(\tfrac{1}{2}) = 2 - 3 + 5 - 4 = 0$.

Hence $(2x - 1)^2$ is a factor of the given expression.

Ex. 12. *Factorise $x^4 + x^3 - 7x^2 - 8x + 4$, given that it has a repeated linear factor.*

The repeated linear factor must be a factor of $f'(x)$,

i.e. of $\qquad\qquad\qquad 4x^3 + 3x^2 - 14x - 8$.

A linear factor of this expression can be found by use of the remainder theorem.

By trial, $\qquad\qquad\qquad f'(-2) = 0$.

Also $\qquad\qquad\qquad\qquad f(-2) = 0$.

$\therefore (x+2)^2$ is a factor of the given expression $f(x)$.

So if $\qquad\qquad\qquad f(x) = (x^2 + 4x + 4)q(x)$,

$q(x)$ must be a quadratic function containing the terms x^2 and $+1$.

Let $\qquad\qquad\qquad f(x) = (x^2 + 4x + 4)(x^2 + Ax + 1)$.

Equating coefficients of x^3, $\quad 1 = A + 4$; $\quad A = -3$.

Hence the factors are $\qquad (x+2)^2(x^2 - 3x + 1)$.

Factors of symmetrical expressions. A symmetrical expression in x, y, z is one which is unaltered by a cyclic interchange of letters $\overset{\curvearrowright x \curvearrowleft}{z \underset{\curvearrowleft}{} y}$.

E.g. $(y^2 - z^2)(y + z)^3 + (z^2 - x^2)(z + x)^3 + (x^2 - y^2)(x + y)^3$ is a symmetrical function of degree five in x, y, z.

Similarly, $a^3(b - c) + b^3(c - a) + c^3(a - b)$ is a symmetrical function of degree four in a, b, c.

The method of factorising symmetrical expressions is illustrated in the following examples.

Ex. 13. *Factorise* $a^4(b - c) + b^4(c - a) + c^4(a - b)$.

When $b = c$, the expression $= b^4(b - a) + b^4(a - b) = 0$.

$$\therefore \ (b - c) \text{ is a factor.}$$

As the expression is symmetrical in a, b, c, it follows that $(c - a)$, $(a - b)$ are also factors.

N.B. If putting $b = c$ did not make the expression vanish, we would have tried $b = -c$.

Continuing, as the expression is of the fifth degree and there are three linear factors, it follows that the fourth factor must be of the second degree.

Also, as the fourth factor must be symmetrical in a, b, c, it must be of the

form $$A(a^2 + b^2 + c^2) + B(bc + ca + ab),$$

where A and B are independent of a, b, c.

I.e. Expression $= (b - c)(c - a)(a - b)[A(a^2 + b^2 + c^2) + B(bc + ca + ab)]$.

To obtain the values of A, B, give a, b, c simple numerical values, avoiding those which make any one of the factors $(b - c)$, $(c - a)$, $(a - b)$ vanish.

E.g. let $a = 0$, $b = 1$, $c = 2$,

then $\qquad 2 - 16 = (-1)(2)(-1)[A(1 + 4) + B(2)]; \quad 5A + 2B = -7.$

Let $a = 0$, $b = 1$, $c = -1$,

then $\qquad -1 - 1 = (2)(-1)(-1)[A(1 + 1) + B(-1)]; \quad 4A - 2B = -2.$

Hence $\qquad\qquad\qquad A = -1, \quad B = -1.$

$\qquad$ Expression $= -(b - c)(c - a)(a - b)(a^2 + b^2 + c^2 + bc + ca + ab).$

Ex. 14. *Factorise* $(x + y + z)^3 - (y + z - x)^3 - (z + x - y)^3 - (x + y - z)^3.$

The substitutions $y = \pm z$, $x = \pm(y + z)$ do not make the expression vanish.

Trying $x = 0$, the expression $= (y + z)^3 - (y + z)^3 - (z - y)^3 - (y - z)^3 = 0.$

$\therefore \ x$ is a factor, and similarly so are y and z.

As the expression is of degree three, any additional factor must be a constant, say k.

So $\qquad (x + y + z)^3 - (y + z - x)^3 - (z + x - y)^3 - (x + y - z)^3 = kxyz.$

Let $x = y = z = 1$,

then $\qquad\qquad\qquad 27 - 1 - 1 - 1 = k; \quad k = 24.$

$\qquad\qquad \therefore \text{ Expression} = 24xyz.$

Highest common factor of two polynomials.

Ex. 15. *Find the H.C.F. of $2x^3 + 3x^2 + 3x + 1$ and $x^3 - x^2 - x - 2$.*

Dividing $2x^3 + 3x^2 + 3x + 1$ by $x^3 - x^2 - x - 2$, the quotient is 2 and the remainder is $5x^2 + 5x + 5$.

$$\therefore\ 2x^3 + 3x^2 + 3x + 1 \equiv (x^3 - x^2 - x - 2)(2) + 5(x^2 + x + 1).$$

Consequently, any common factor of the two given expressions must also be a factor of the remainder, $5(x^2 + x + 1)$.

As clearly the given expressions have not a common factor 5, it follows that the only possible common factor is $x^2 + x + 1$.

By division it is readily seen that

$$2x^3 + 3x^2 + 3x + 1 = (x^2 + x + 1)(2x + 1); \quad x^3 - x^2 - x - 2 = (x^2 + x + 1)(x - 2).$$
$$\therefore\ \text{H.C.F.} = x^2 + x + 1.$$

General procedure. Suppose $f(x)$ and $g(x)$ are polynomials with the degree of $f(x) \geqslant$ the degree of $g(x)$.

Consider the long division of $f(x)$ by $g(x)$. This division can be continued until the remainder term $r(x)$ is of a smaller degree than $g(x)$.

If the quotient is $q(x)$ we can write

$$f(x) \equiv q(x) \cdot g(x) + r(x).$$

It follows that any common factor of $f(x)$ and $g(x)$ is also a factor of $r(x)$. Consequently the H.C.F. of $f(x)$ and $g(x)$ is also the H.C.F. of the lower degree polynomials, $g(x)$ and $r(x)$. This process can be repeated until the remainder function is sufficiently simple for its factors, and consequently the possible common factor of $f(x)$ and $g(x)$, to be readily discernible.

Ex. 16. *Find the H.C.F. of $2x^4 + x^3 + x^2 + x - 1$ and $x^4 - x^3 + 2x^2 - x + 1$.*

Dividing the first polynomial by the second, the quotient is 2 and the remainder, $3x^3 - 3x^2 + 3x - 3$.

The factor 3 in the remainder can be ignored, and the problem reduces to that of finding the H.C.F. of $x^4 - x^3 + 2x^2 - x + 1$ and $x^3 - x^2 + x - 1$.

Dividing, the quotient is x and the remainder, $x^2 + 1$.

Hence the only possible common factor of the original polynomials is $x^2 + 1$, and by division this is verified to be the H.C.F.

EXAMPLES 2b

1. Find the remainder when $4x^5 + 2x^4 + 11x^2 + x - 6$ is divided by $x + 3$.

2. Prove that $(x - 2)$ is a factor of $2x^3 - 5x^2 + 5x - 6$ and find the other factor.

3. Prove that $(x^2 - 4)$ is a factor of $x^4 - 3x^3 - 6x^2 + 12x + 8$ and completely factorise the expression.

4. If $(2x - 1)$ is a factor of $4x^4 - ax^2 + 5x - 2$, find the value of a.

5. Show that $(a - b)$ is a factor of $a^5 - b^5$ and write down the other factor.

6. The remainder when $x^5 - ax^3 + 2$ is divided by $x+1$ is 4. Find the value of a.

7. Find the H.C.F. of $x^3 - 2x^2 + x - 2$ and $x^2 - x - 2$.

8. Factorise: (i) $2x^3 - 5x^2 - x + 6$; (ii) $a^2(b-c) + b^2(c-a) + c^2(a-b)$.

9. If $x^2 - x - 6$ is a factor of $x^4 + ax^3 - 9x^2 + bx - 6$, find the values of a and b and complete the factorisation.

10. Find the H.C.F.s of:

    (i) $2x^2 + xy - y^2$ and $2x^3 - 7x^2y + 5xy^2 - y^3$;
    (ii) $2x^3 - 5x^2 - 4x + 3$ and $x^3 - 4x^2 + 4x - 3$.

11. Prove that $(y-z)^3 + (z-x)^3 + (x-y)^3 = 3(y-z)(z-x)(x-y)$.

12. For what values of c is $(x-c)$ a factor of
$$3x^3 + (c+3)x^2 - (4c^2 + c - 7)x - 4?$$

13. By first determining a factor by trial, factorise the following expressions:

    (i) $2x^3 + 11x^2 + 10x - 8$; (ii) $x^4 - 4x + 3$; (iii) $2a^3 + 5a^2b + 3ab^2 + 2b^3$.

14. Show that $(x+1)$ is a repeated factor of $x^4 + x^3 + 2x^2 + 5x + 3$ and find the other factor.

15. Find the H.C.F. of $x^4 - x^3 - 2x^2 + x + 1$ and $x^3 - 3x^2 + x + 2$.

16. Factorise: (i) $bc(b-c) + ca(c-a) + ab(a-b)$;
           (ii) $a(b^2 - c^2) + b(c^2 - a^2) + c(a^2 - b^2)$;
           (iii) $a(b-c)^3 + b(c-a)^3 + c(a-b)^3$.

17. When $x^4 + ax^3 + bx + c$ is divided by $(x+1)$, $(x+3)$, $(x-2)$ the remainders are 5, -31, 44 respectively. Find the values of a, b and c.

18. If $(x-a)^2$ is a factor of $x^3 + px + q$, prove that $4p^3 + 27q^2 = 0$.

19. By writing $x^p = X$, show that, when n is odd, $x^p - 1$ is a factor of $x^{np} - 1$. Hence factorise $x^9 - 1$.

20. Factorise: (i) $(x^2 - yz)(y+z) + (y^2 - zx)(z+x) + (z^2 - xy)(x+y)$;
           (ii) $a(b-c)^2 + b(c-a)^2 + c(a-b)^2 + 9abc$;
           (iii) $(b-c)^5 + (c-a)^5 + (a-b)^5$.

21. Find the H.C.F. of $x^4 + 2x^3 + 2x - 1$ and $2x^4 + x^3 + x^2 + x - 1$.

22. If a polynomial $f(x)$ is divided by $(x-a)(x-b)$, show that the remainder can be expressed in the form $\dfrac{1}{a-b}[f(a)(x-b) - f(b)(x-a)]$.

23. Given that $x^2 + 2x - 1$ is a factor of $x^6 + x^5 + ax^4 + 5x^3 + bx^2 - 4x + 2$, find the values of a and b and completely factorise the expression.

24. Factorise: (i) $(bc + ca + ab)^3 - b^3c^3 - c^3a^3 - a^3b^3$;
           (ii) $(a+b+c)^5 - (b+c-a)^5 - (c+a-b)^5 - (a+b-c)^5$.

25. Factorise $4x^4 + 9x^2 - 11x + 3$, given that there is a repeated linear factor.

26. Find the factors of $(x^3 + y^3)(x-y) + (y^3 + z^3)(y-z) + (z^3 + x^3)(z-x)$.

Ratio and proportion. Equal fractions

Definition. The pairs of numbers a_1b_1, a_2b_2, a_3b_3, ... a_nb_n, are said to be in proportion if $\dfrac{a_1}{b_1} = \dfrac{a_2}{b_2} = \dfrac{a_3}{b_3} = \ldots = \dfrac{a_n}{b_n}$.

Basic result. If $\dfrac{a_1}{b_1} = \dfrac{a_2}{b_2} = \dfrac{a_3}{b_3} = \ldots = \dfrac{a_n}{b_n}$, *then each of the fractions is equal to* $\dfrac{l_1a_1 + l_2a_2 + l_3a_3 + \ldots + l_na_n}{l_1b_1 + l_2b_2 + l_3b_3 + \ldots + l_nb_n}$, *where* l_1, l_2, ... l_n *are constants such that* $l_1b_1 + l_2b_2 + l_3b_3 + \ldots + l_nb_n \neq 0$.

This result is readily proved by putting each of the original fractions equal to k, and substituting $a_1 = kb_1$, $a_2 = kb_2$, ... $a_n = kb_n$ into the numerator of the compound fraction. This substitution method is useful in dealing with problems on equal fractions.

Ex. 17. *If* $\dfrac{2x + y + z}{6} = \dfrac{x - y + 2z}{3} = \dfrac{x + 2y - z}{2}$, *prove that each fraction is zero.*

Each fraction $= \dfrac{(2x + y + z) - (x - y + 2z) - (x + 2y - z)}{6 \quad - \quad 3 \quad - \quad 2} = 0$.

Ex. 18. *If* $\dfrac{x}{b - c} = \dfrac{y}{c - a} = \dfrac{z}{a - b}$, *prove that* $x + y + z = 0$.

Writing each fraction $= k$; $x = k(b - c)$, $y = k(c - a)$, $z = k(a - b)$.
Hence $\qquad\qquad\qquad x + y + z = 0$.

Ex. 19. *Solve the equations*

$$\frac{x}{1} = \frac{x + y}{3} = \frac{x - y + z}{2}, \quad x^2 + y^2 + z^2 + x + 2y + 4z - 6 = 0.$$

Let $\qquad\qquad \dfrac{x}{1} = \dfrac{x + y}{3} = \dfrac{x - y + z}{2} = k$.

Then $\quad x = k$; $\quad x + y = 3k$, $\quad y = 2k$; $\quad x - y + z = 2k$, $\quad z = 3k$.
Substituting into the quadratic equation,

$$k^2 + 4k^2 + 9k^2 + k + 4k + 12k - 6 = 0,$$
$$14k^2 + 17k - 6 = 0,$$
$$(7k - 2)(2k + 3) = 0; \quad k = \tfrac{2}{7}, \ -\tfrac{3}{2}.$$
$$\therefore \ x = \tfrac{2}{7}, \quad y = \tfrac{4}{7}, \quad z = \tfrac{6}{7};$$

or $\qquad\qquad\qquad x = -\tfrac{3}{2}, \ y = -3, \ z = -\tfrac{9}{2}.$

EXAMPLES 2c

1. If $\dfrac{a}{b} = \dfrac{c}{d}$, prove that $\dfrac{a - c}{b - d} = \dfrac{a + c}{b + d}$.

2. Given that $\dfrac{a}{b} = \dfrac{b}{c} = \dfrac{c}{d}$, prove that $c = \dfrac{5ad - dc}{5b - d}$.

3. If $\dfrac{p}{q} = \dfrac{r}{s}$, simplify $\sqrt{\dfrac{p^2 + r^2}{q^2 + s^2}}$.

4. If $\dfrac{b-c}{p} = \dfrac{c-a}{q} = \dfrac{a-b}{r}$, show that $p+q+r=0$.

5. Solve the equations $\dfrac{x+y}{1} = \dfrac{x-y}{2} = \dfrac{x-2y+z}{3}$, $2x+y+z=4$.

6. If $\dfrac{x}{2} = \dfrac{y}{3} = \dfrac{z}{4}$, evaluate $\dfrac{3xyz}{x^3+y^3+z^3}$.

7. Solve the equations $\dfrac{x}{a} = \dfrac{y}{b} = \dfrac{z}{c} = \dfrac{ax+by+cz+2}{a^2+b^2+c^2+3}$.

8. If $\dfrac{x-y}{x+z} = \dfrac{y^2}{z^2}$ and $y+z \neq 0$, express z in terms of x, y.

9. Show that, if $\dfrac{x-y+2z}{3} = \dfrac{y-x}{2}$, then $5x-5y+4z=0$.

10. If $\dfrac{x}{y} = \dfrac{y}{z}$, prove that $\dfrac{(x+y+z)^2}{x^2+y^2+z^2} = \dfrac{x+y+z}{x-y+z}$.

11. Solve the equations: (i) $\dfrac{x-2}{1} = \dfrac{y-1}{2} = \dfrac{z+1}{3}$; $4x-y-z=1$;

(ii) $\dfrac{x}{1} = \dfrac{y-x}{2} = \dfrac{x+y+z}{6}$; $3x^2+2y^2+z^2=1$.

12. Given that $\dfrac{x+y-z}{2} = \dfrac{2x-y+z}{4} = \dfrac{-x+y+2z}{3}$, evaluate $\dfrac{x^2+y^2+z^2}{yz+zx+xy}$.

13. If $\dfrac{a}{b} = \dfrac{c}{d} = \dfrac{e}{f}$, prove that $\sqrt{\dfrac{a^2+c^2+e^2}{b^2+d^2+f^2}} = \sqrt[3]{\dfrac{ace}{bdf}}$.

14. If $\dfrac{\log x}{a} = \dfrac{\log y}{b} = \dfrac{\log z}{c} = \log u$, prove that $xy/z^2 = u^{a+b-2c}$.

15. Solve the equations $\dfrac{x-a}{l} = \dfrac{y-b}{m} = \dfrac{z-c}{n}$; $ax+by+cz = a^2+b^2+c^2$.

16. If $\dfrac{y+z-x}{q-r} = \dfrac{z+x-y}{r-p} = \dfrac{x+y-z}{p-q}$, prove that $\dfrac{x}{q-r} = \dfrac{y}{r-p} = \dfrac{z}{p-q}$.

Quadratic and rational quadratic functions.

Ex. 20. *Discuss the signs of the functions*

(i) $4x^2-7x-2$; (ii) $-13+10x-2x^2$

for real values of x.

(i) This function factorises,

$$4x^2-7x-2 = (4x+1)(x-2).$$

When $x < -\frac{1}{4}$, both factors are negative and the function is positive.
When $-\frac{1}{4} < x < 2$, the factors are of opposite signs and the function is negative.
When $x > 2$, both factors are positive and the function is positive.

(ii) This function does not factorise.

Write $-13 + 10x - 2x^2 = -2[x^2 - 5x + \frac{13}{2}]$
$$= -2[(x - \tfrac{5}{2})^2 - \tfrac{25}{4} + \tfrac{13}{2}] = -2[(x - \tfrac{5}{2})^2 + \tfrac{1}{4}].$$

As the term within the bracket is positive for all real values of x, the function is always negative. It will be noted that the maximum value of the function occurs when $x = \frac{5}{2}$ and is equal to $-\frac{1}{2}$.

General case.

$$ax^2 + bx + c = a\left[x^2 + \frac{b}{a}x + \frac{c}{a}\right]$$
$$= a\left[\left(x + \frac{b}{2a}\right)^2 - \frac{b^2}{4a^2} + \frac{c}{a}\right] = a\left[\left(x + \frac{b}{2a}\right)^2 + \frac{4ac - b^2}{4a^2}\right].$$

As the least value of $\left(x + \dfrac{b}{2a}\right)^2$ is zero, the term within the bracket will be of a constant sign if $4ac - b^2 \geqslant 0$, i.e. if $b^2 \leqslant 4ac$. When this condition is satisfied the function takes the sign of a.

$\therefore$ *The necessary and sufficient conditions for $ax^2 + bx + c$ to be positive for all real values of x are:* (i) $b^2 \leqslant 4ac$, (ii) $a > 0$.

Functions of more than one variable. The methods of dealing with quadratic functions of more than one variable are illustrated in the following examples.

Ex. 21. *Prove that the function $2x^2 - 8xy + 9y^2 + 4x - 10y + 4$ is positive for all real values of x and y and determine its minimum value.*

First obtain a perfect square which includes all the terms containing one variable, say x.

$$\text{Function} = 2\{[x^2 - 4xy + 2x] + \tfrac{9}{2}y^2 - 5y + 2\}$$
$$= 2\{[(x - 2y + 1)^2 - 4y^2 + 4y - 1] + \tfrac{9}{2}y^2 - 5y + 2\}$$
$$= 2\{(x - 2y + 1)^2 + \tfrac{1}{2}[y^2 - 2y + 2]\}$$
$$= 2\{(x - 2y + 1)^2 + \tfrac{1}{2}[(y - 1)^2 + 1]\}, \text{ completing the square}$$
$$\text{for the } y \text{ terms,}$$
$$= 2\{(x - 2y + 1)^2 + \tfrac{1}{2}(y - 1)^2 + \tfrac{1}{2}\}.$$

Hence the function is positive for all real values of x and y. It has a minimum value of 1 when $x - 2y + 1 = y - 1 = 0$, i.e. when $x = y = 1$.

Ex. 22. *If x and y are real and $x^2 - 2xy - 2y^2 + 6x - y + 11 = 0$, find the possible ranges of values of x and y.*

To determine the possible values of y, treat the equation as a quadratic in x.

$$x^2 - 2x(y - 3) - 2y^2 - y + 11 = 0.$$

As x is real, $\qquad\qquad b^2 \geqslant 4ac,$
$$\therefore \quad 4(y - 3)^2 \geqslant 4(-2y^2 - y + 11),$$
$$3y^2 - 5y - 2 \geqslant 0,$$
$$(3y + 1)(y - 2) \geqslant 0.$$

$\therefore$ y can take all real values apart from those between $-\frac{1}{3}$ and 2.

Now treat the equation as a quadratic in y.

$$-2y^2 - y(2x+1) + x^2 + 6x + 11 = 0.$$

As y is real, $\qquad (2x+1)^2 \geqslant 4(-2)(x^2 + 6x + 11),$

$$12x^2 + 52x + 89 \geqslant 0.$$

But as $4ac > b^2$ and $a > 0$, this function is positive for all values of x. Hence x can take all real values.

Ex. 23. *Discuss the sign of the function $4yz + 2xy - 3x^2 - y^2 - 7z^2$.*

Proceeding as in Ex. 21 and noting that it will be simpler to deal with the y terms first,

$$\begin{aligned} \text{function} &= -\{[y^2 - 2xy - 4yz] + 3x^2 + 7z^2\} \\ &= -\{(y - x - 2z)^2 + 2x^2 - 4zx + 3z^2\} \\ &= -\{(y - x - 2z)^2 + 2[(x - z)^2 + \tfrac{1}{2}z^2]\}. \end{aligned}$$

So the function is negative for all real values of x, y, z.

Rational quadratic functions. A rational quadratic function is of the form $\dfrac{a_1 x^2 + b_1 x + c_1}{a_2 x^2 + b_2 x + c_2}$. The possible values of such a function can be discussed by equating it to y and then treating the result as a quadratic equation in x.

Ex. 24. *Find the possible range of values of $\dfrac{x^2 + 2x + 3}{x^2 + 3x + 2}$ if x is real.*

Let $\qquad\qquad\qquad y = \dfrac{x^2 + 2x + 3}{x^2 + 3x + 2}.$

$$\therefore\ x^2(y-1) + x(3y-2) + 2y - 3 = 0.$$

As x is real, $\qquad\qquad (3y-2)^2 \geqslant 4(y-1)(2y-3),$

i.e. $\qquad\qquad\qquad\qquad y^2 + 8y - 8 \geqslant 0.$

Hence $\qquad\qquad\qquad\quad (y+4)^2 \geqslant 24$

$$|y+4| \geqslant 2\sqrt{6}.$$

So $\qquad\qquad\qquad -4 - 2\sqrt{6} \geqslant y \geqslant -4 + 2\sqrt{6},$

i.e. the given function can take all values with the exception of those between $-4 - 2\sqrt{6}$ and $-4 + 2\sqrt{6}$.

Ex. 25. *Find the maximum and minimum values of $\dfrac{(x-1)^2}{x^2 + x + 1}$ and sketch the graph of the function.*

Let $\qquad\qquad\qquad\qquad y = \dfrac{(x-1)^2}{x^2 + x + 1}.$

$$\therefore\ x^2(y-1) + x(y+2) + y - 1 = 0.$$

As x is real, $\qquad\qquad (y+2)^2 \geqslant 4(y-1)(y-1),$

$$0 \geqslant 3y^2 - 12y$$

i.e. $\qquad\qquad\qquad\qquad 0 \geqslant 3y(y-4).$

$$\therefore\ y \text{ must be } \geqslant 0 \text{ or } \leqslant 4.$$

Hence the maximum and minimum values of the function are 4, 0 respectively.

D

Substituting these values for y, we find $x = -1$, 1 respectively and consequently the turning-points on the graph are

$$\text{maximum } (-1, 4); \quad \text{minimum } (1, 0).$$

Further information to assist in sketching the graph:

(i) The graph only exists for $0 \leqslant y \leqslant 4$.

(ii) From (i), or because $x^2 + x + 1 \neq 0$ for real values of x, there are no asymptotes parallel to Oy.

(iii) For numerically large values of x, the function which can be written

as $\dfrac{1 - \dfrac{2}{x} + \dfrac{1}{x^2}}{1 + \dfrac{1}{x} + \dfrac{1}{x^2}}$ clearly tends to a value 1. So $y = 1$ is an asymptote.

Substituting $y = 1$, gives $x = 0$ as the only finite solution; hence the graph cuts its asymptote only at the point $(0, 1)$.

(iv) When $y = 0$, $(x - 1)^2 = 0$. Hence the graph touches the x-axis at $(1, 0)$ and meets it at no other point.

This is sufficient information to obtain the sketch graph in Fig. 41.

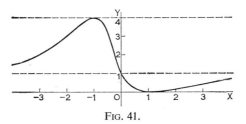

FIG. 41.

Ex. 26. *Find the range of values of λ for which the function $\dfrac{x^2 + 2\lambda x}{x^2 - 2x + \lambda}$ can take all values for real values of x.*

Let
$$y = \frac{x^2 + 2\lambda x}{x^2 - 2x + \lambda}.$$

$$x^2(y - 1) - 2x(y + \lambda) + \lambda y = 0.$$

As x is real,
$$4(y + \lambda)^2 \geqslant 4(y - 1)\lambda y$$
$$y^2(1 - \lambda) + 3\lambda y + \lambda^2 \geqslant 0.$$

This inequality is satisfied when the quadratic function $y^2(1 - \lambda) + 3\lambda y + \lambda^2$ is positive.

The required conditions are: (i) $1 - \lambda > 0$,

                               (ii) $4\lambda^2(1 - \lambda) \geqslant (3\lambda)^2$.

Condition (ii) reduces to $-\lambda^2(4\lambda + 5) \geqslant 0$,

from which $\lambda \leqslant -\frac{5}{4}$.

Condition (i) is satisfied when $\lambda < 1$.

Both conditions are satisfied, and the original function can take all values, when $\lambda \leqslant -\frac{5}{4}$.

EXAMPLES 2d

1. Show that the function $6x - 10 - x^2$ is negative for real values of x.

2. For what ranges of values of x are the following functions negative:
(i) $2x^2 + 5x - 12$;   (ii) $20 + 11x - 3x^2$?

3. Prove that the function $4x^2 - 12xy + 10y^2$ is positive if x and y are real.

4. Find the value of λ, other than zero, for which
$$(3x - 2y)^2 + \lambda(x - y)(x - 2y)$$
is a perfect square.

5. Find the maximum value of the function $6 + 3x - x^2$ and sketch its graph.

6. Obtain the minimum value of $x^2 + 2xy + 2y^2 + 2x - 6y + 5$.

7. If x is real, show that the function $\dfrac{x - 1}{(x + 1)(x - 2)}$ is capable of taking all values.   Sketch its graph.

8. Prove that the function $\dfrac{x}{x^2 + 1}$ can only take values between $-\frac{1}{2}$ and $\frac{1}{2}$ and illustrate with a rough graph.

9. Determine the sign of the function $2x^2 - 2xy + 2y^2 + 2x - 4y + 7$ for real values of the variables.

10. If x, y are real, and $x^2 + 4xy + 2y^2 - 8x - 12y + 15 = 0$, find the ranges of possible values of: (i) x; (ii) y.

11. Find the maximum and minimum values of the function $\dfrac{x^2 - x + 1}{x^2 + x + 1}$ and sketch the graph of the function.

12. Prove that the roots of the equation $x^2 + 2(\lambda + 2)x + 8\lambda = 0$ are real for all values of λ.

13. Show that the function $6xy + 6x + 6y - 3x^2 - 6y^2 - 16$ is negative.   For what values of x and y is it a maximum?

14. Prove that the function $\dfrac{x^2 + 34x - 71}{x^2 + 2x - 7}$ has a maximum value of 5 and a minimum value of 9.   Explain the apparent paradox by drawing a rough graph.

15. Find the possible range of values of the function $\dfrac{4x^2 - 2x + 1}{4x^2 + 2x + 1}$ for real values of x.

16. Find the range of values of λ for which the function $\dfrac{x - \lambda}{x^2 - 2x + \lambda}$ is capable of taking all values between $-\infty$ and $+\infty$.

17. Prove that the function $x^2 + 7y^2 + 20z^2 + 8yz - 2zx + 4xy$ is never negative for real values of x, y, z.

18. Show that, if x and λ are real, then $\dfrac{(x - \lambda)^2}{x^2 + 2x + 5}$ has a minimum value of zero and a maximum value of $\frac{1}{4}(\lambda^2 + 2\lambda + 5)$.

19. If x, y are real, prove that $2x^2 + 4xy + 3y^2 - 8x - 10y + 10 \geqslant 1$.

20. Prove that, as x varies from $-\infty$ to $+\infty$, the function $\dfrac{(x-2)^2}{x-3}$ assumes twice over all values except those in a particular interval. Find this interval and draw the graph of the function.

21. If $y^2 = \dfrac{2x}{x^2+1}$, show that y can only take values between ± 1, assuming x is real. Show also that if $y^2 = \dfrac{2x}{x^2-1}$, y can take all values. Illustrate graphically.

22. For what values of λ is the function $x^2 + 2y^2 + 2xy - 2x - 6y + \lambda \geqslant 1$ for real values of x and y?

23. If x and a are real, prove that $0 \leqslant \dfrac{(x+a)^2}{x^2+x+1} \leqslant \frac{4}{3}(a^2 - a + 1)$.

24. Prove that the function $x^2 + 2xy + y^2(a^2+1) - 2ax - 6ay + 2a^2$ is always positive if $a > 2$.

25. Prove that, for all real values of x and λ, the function $\dfrac{x+\lambda}{x^2+bx+c}$ lies between fixed limits if $b^2 < 4c$.

Partial fractions. Special methods. The basic methods of expressing an algebraic fraction as a sum of partial fractions have been dealt with in the previous volume. Two useful methods of simplification will be illustrated here.

Case I. Linear factor in denominator. Consider the algebraic fraction $\dfrac{f(x)}{g(x)}$, where the degree of $f(x)$ is less than that of $g(x)$, and suppose $g(x)$ has a non-repeated factor $(x-a)$.

We can write
$$g(x) \equiv q(x) \cdot (x-a)$$
and
$$\frac{f(x)}{g(x)} \equiv \frac{A}{x-a} + \frac{p(x)}{q(x)},$$
where $p(x)$ is a polynomial of degree one less than $q(x)$ and A is a constant.

$$\therefore f(x) \equiv Aq(x) + (x-a)p(x).$$

Putting $x = a$, $\qquad f(a) = Aq(a); \quad A = \dfrac{f(a)}{q(a)}.$

Hence the partial fraction corresponding to the factor $(x-a)$ in the denominator is $\dfrac{f(a)}{q(a)(x-a)}$.

This useful result can be expressed as follows:

The partial fraction corresponding to a factor $(x-a)$ in the denominator is $A/(x-a)$, where A is the result of putting $x=a$ in every part of the original fraction except $(x-a)$ itself.

Ex. 27. *Express in partial fractions:* (i) $\dfrac{2x-4}{x(x-1)(x-3)}$; (ii) $\dfrac{x-c}{(x-a)(x-b)}$.

(i) $\dfrac{2x-4}{x(x-1)(x-3)} = \dfrac{(-4)}{(-1)(-3)}\dfrac{1}{x} + \dfrac{(-2)}{(1)(-2)}\dfrac{1}{x-1} + \dfrac{2}{(3)(2)}\dfrac{1}{x-3}$

$$= -\frac{4}{3x} + \frac{1}{x-1} + \frac{1}{3(x-3)}.$$

(ii) $\dfrac{x-c}{(x-a)(x-b)} = \dfrac{a-c}{a-b}\dfrac{1}{x-a} + \dfrac{b-c}{b-a}\dfrac{1}{x-b}.$

Ex. 28. *Express* $\dfrac{1}{x(x+1)\ldots(x+n)}$ *in partial fractions.*

The partial fraction corresponding to the factor x

$$= \frac{1}{x}\cdot\frac{1}{1.2\ldots n} = \frac{1}{x}\frac{1}{n!}.$$

The partial fraction corresponding to the factor $x+1$

$$= \frac{1}{x+1}\cdot\frac{1}{(-1)1.2\ldots n-1} = -\frac{1}{x+1}\frac{1}{(n-1)!1!}.$$

The partial fraction corresponding to the factor $x+2$

$$= \frac{1}{x+2}\cdot\frac{1}{(-1)(-2)1.2\ldots n-2} = \frac{1}{x+2}\frac{1}{(n-2)!2!}.$$

Similarly, the partial fraction corresponding to the factor $x+r$

$$= \frac{(-1)^r}{x+r}\frac{1}{(n-r)!r!}.$$

Hence,

$$\frac{1}{x(x+1)\ldots(x+n)} = \frac{1}{x}\frac{1}{n!} - \frac{1}{x+1}\frac{1}{(n-1)!1!} + \frac{1}{x+2}\frac{1}{(n-2)!2!}$$

$$+ \cdots \frac{(-1)^r}{x+r}\frac{1}{(n-r)!r!} + \cdots \frac{(-1)^n}{x+n}\frac{1}{n!}.$$

Case II. Repeated linear factor in denominator. An elementary treatment of this case has already been given, but it is laborious when the linear factor is repeated more than two or three times. A simpler method is illustrated in the following examples.

Ex. 29. *Express in partial fractions:* (i) $\dfrac{2x+1}{x^5(x+1)}$; (ii) $\dfrac{x^2+x+1}{(x-1)^4(x+2)}$.

(i) Divide $1+2x$ by $1+x$, giving the quotient as a set of terms in *ascending* powers of x up to the term in x^4.

Then $\dfrac{2x+1}{x+1}=1+x-x^2+x^3-x^4+\dfrac{x^5}{x+1}$.

Hence $\dfrac{2x+1}{x^5(x+1)}=\dfrac{1}{x^5}+\dfrac{1}{x^4}-\dfrac{1}{x^3}+\dfrac{1}{x^2}-\dfrac{1}{x}+\dfrac{1}{x+1}$.

(ii) Writing $x-1=y$, the fraction becomes

$$\frac{y^2+3y+3}{y^4(y+3)}.$$

By dividing $3+3y+y^2$ by $3+y$ in ascending powers of y and taking the quotient as far as the term in y^3, it follows that

$$\frac{y^2+3y+3}{y+3}=1+\tfrac{2}{3}y+\tfrac{1}{9}y^2-\tfrac{1}{27}y^3+\frac{\frac{1}{27}y^4}{y+3}.$$

Dividing by y^4 and replacing y by $x-1$,

$$\frac{x^2+x+1}{(x-1)^4(x+2)}=\frac{1}{(x-1)^4}+\frac{2}{3(x-1)^3}+\frac{1}{9(x-1)^2}-\frac{1}{27(x-1)}+\frac{1}{27(x+2)}.$$

$$
\begin{array}{l}
\quad\quad 1+x-x^2+x^3-x^4 \\
1+x\,)\,\overline{1+2x} \\
\quad\underline{1+x} \\
\quad\quad x \\
\quad\quad \underline{x+x^2} \\
\quad\quad -x^2 \\
\quad\quad \underline{-x^2-x^3} \\
\quad\quad\quad x^3 \\
\quad\quad\quad \underline{x^3+x^4} \\
\quad\quad\quad -x^4 \\
\quad\quad\quad \underline{-x^4-x^5} \\
\text{Remainder} \to x^5
\end{array}
$$

EXAMPLES 2e (*Miscellaneous partial fractions*)

Express the following functions in partial fractions:

1. $\dfrac{x^2}{(x+1)(x+2)(x+3)}$.

2. $\dfrac{3x-2}{x(x-1)(2x-1)}$.

3. $\dfrac{x}{(x+1)^2(x^2+2)}$.

4. $\dfrac{x}{(x+1)(x+2)(x+3)(x+4)}$.

5. $\dfrac{1+x}{(x+2)^3(x-1)}$.

6. $\dfrac{x+2}{x^4(x+1)}$.

7. $\dfrac{2x}{x^3-1}$.

8. $\dfrac{x^5}{(x-1)^4}$.

9. $\dfrac{x^2+x-1}{x^4+x^2+1}$.

10. $\dfrac{8x(x-2)(x-4)}{(x-1)(x-3)(x-5)(x-7)}$.

11. $\dfrac{x^3}{(x+2)^5}$.

12. $\dfrac{x^2-1}{x^3+x^2+x+1}$.

13. $\dfrac{12}{x(x-2)^5}$.

14. $\dfrac{x^3}{(x-1)^4(x^2+2)}$.

15. $\dfrac{2x+1}{x^4+x^3+x+1}$.

16. $\dfrac{x-2}{x^6(x^2+1)}$.

17. Express $\dfrac{x(2x^2 - x + 3)}{(x^2 + 1)^2}$ as the sum of two partial fractions of the forms $\dfrac{Ax + B}{(x^2 + 1)^2}$ and $\dfrac{Cx + D}{x^2 + 1}$.

18. Prove that, if n is a positive integer, $\dfrac{1}{(2 - x)(x - 1)^n} = \dfrac{1}{2 - x} + \sum_1^n \dfrac{1}{(x - 1)^r}$.

19. Express $\dfrac{x^4}{x^6 - 1}$ as the sum of four partial fractions.

20. If $f(x)$ is of lower degree than $F(x)$ and $F(x) = (x - a_1)(x - a_2) \ldots (x - a_n)$, prove that $\dfrac{f(x)}{F(x)} = \dfrac{f(a_1)}{F'(a_1)} \dfrac{1}{x - a_1} + \dfrac{f(a_2)}{F'(a_2)} \dfrac{1}{x - a_2} + \ldots + \dfrac{f(a_n)}{F'(a_n)} \dfrac{1}{x - a_n}$.

Miscellaneous equations

I. Irrational equations of the form $\sqrt{(ax + b)} + \sqrt{(cx + d)} = \sqrt{(px + q)}$. The solution of this type of equation usually involves a repeated squaring process, and care must be taken to ensure that the resulting roots are checked in the original equation as additional roots are introduced by squaring.

Ex. 30. *Solve the equation* $\sqrt{(2x + 3)} - \sqrt{(x + 1)} = \sqrt{(x - 2)}$.

Squaring both sides, $2x + 3 + x + 1 - 2\sqrt{\{(2x + 3)(x + 1)\}} = x - 2$.
Isolating the irrational term, $\qquad 2x + 6 = 2\sqrt{\{(2x + 3)(x + 1)\}}$.
Dividing by 2 and squaring, $x^2 + 6x + 9 = (2x + 3)(x + 1)$
$$\therefore \quad 0 = x^2 - x - 6$$
$$x = 3, \ -2.$$

On substitution, $x = 3$ is seen to be a root of the original equation. Substituting $x = -2$ leads to square-roots of negative numbers, and hence $x = -2$ is not a solution.

Ex. 31. *Solve the equation* $\sqrt{\{3(x - 2)(x - 3)\}} - \sqrt{\{(x - 2)(x - 5)\}} = x - 2$.
The factor $\sqrt{(x - 2)}$ can be removed after noting the solution $x = 2$.
Then $\qquad \sqrt{\{3(x - 3)\}} - \sqrt{(x - 5)} = \sqrt{(x - 2)}. \quad \ldots \ldots \quad$ (i)
Proceeding as before,
$$3(x - 3) + (x - 5) - 2\sqrt{\{3(x - 3)(x - 5)\}} = x - 2,$$
$$3x - 12 = 2\sqrt{\{3(x - 3)(x - 5)\}}$$
$$(3x - 12)^2 = 4(3x^2 - 24x + 45)$$
$$3x^2 - 24x + 36 = 0$$
$$x = 2, \ 6.$$

On substitution it is found that $x = 2$ is not a solution of equation (i), but it has already been seen to be a solution of the original equation. The value $x = 6$ is also a solution.
$$\therefore \ \text{Solutions are } x = 2, \ 6.$$

II. Reciprocal equations. There are two classes of reciprocal equations, in which

> (i) the coefficients of terms equidistant from the ends are equal,

e.g. $$x^4 - 2x^3 + 3x^2 - 2x + 1 = 0;$$

> (ii) the coefficients of terms equidistant from the ends are equal in magnitude but opposite in sign,

e.g. $$x^5 + 3x^4 - 2x^3 + 2x^2 - 3x - 1 = 0.$$

Method of solution. If the degree of the equation is *odd*, $x = -1$ is a root in case (i) and $x = 1$ is a root in case (ii). The corresponding factors should be divided out and in the resulting equation of even degree, say $2m$, divide throughout by x^m and group the terms in pairs $x^m \pm \dfrac{1}{x^m}$, $x^{m-1} \pm \dfrac{1}{x^{m-1}}$, etc. Then let $x \pm \dfrac{1}{x} = X$ and solve for X.

The method for equations of *even* degree is included in that above.

Even degree equations which are partly class (i) and partly class (ii) can sometimes be solved in a similar manner (see Ex. 33).

Ex. 32. *Solve the equation* $x^5 - x^4 - 8x^3 - 8x^2 - x + 1 = 0.$

This is a reciprocal equation of type (i) and of odd degree.
By substitution it is seen that one root is $x = -1$.
Dividing out the factor $x + 1$, the equation becomes

$$x^4 - 2x^3 - 6x^2 - 2x + 1 = 0.$$

Dividing by x^2 and rearranging,

$$\left(x^2 + \frac{1}{x^2}\right) - 2\left(x + \frac{1}{x}\right) - 6 = 0.$$

Let $\quad x + \dfrac{1}{x} = X,\quad$ then $\quad x^2 + \dfrac{1}{x^2} + 2 = X^2\quad$ or $\quad x^2 + \dfrac{1}{x^2} = X^2 - 2.$

$$\therefore\ X^2 - 2X - 8 = 0$$
$$X = 4,\ -2.$$

$$\therefore\ x + \frac{1}{x} = 4; \qquad\qquad\qquad x + \frac{1}{x} = -2;$$
$$x^2 - 4x + 1 = 0 \qquad\qquad\qquad x^2 + 2x + 1 = 0$$
$$x = 2 \pm \sqrt{3}. \qquad\qquad\qquad x = -1,\ -1.$$

The roots of the equation are $-1,\ -1,\ -1,\ 2 \pm \sqrt{3}.$

Ex. 33. *Solve the equation* $2x^4 - x^3 - 7x^2 + x + 2 = 0.$

This is not strictly a reciprocal equation, but it can be solved by a similar method.

Dividing by x^2 and rearranging,

$$2\left(x^2 + \frac{1}{x^2}\right) - \left(x - \frac{1}{x}\right) - 7 = 0.$$

Let $x - \dfrac{1}{x} = X$; then $x^2 + \dfrac{1}{x^2} = X^2 + 2$.

$$\therefore 2(X^2 + 2) - X - 7 = 0$$
$$2X^2 - X - 3 = 0$$
$$X = \tfrac{3}{2}, \ -1.$$

Replacing X by $x - \dfrac{1}{x}$ and solving the resulting quadratic equations, we have

$$x = 2, \ -\tfrac{1}{2}, \tfrac{1}{2}(-1 \pm \sqrt{5}).$$

III. Miscellaneous polynomial equations. It will be sufficient here to consider only those equations where one or more roots can readily be obtained by trial or where there is a given relationship between some of the roots.

Ex. 34. *Solve the equation $x^3 - 6x^2 + 5x + 6 = 0$.*

If there is a simple root it will be a factor of 6.
By trial, $x = 2$ is a root.

But $\qquad x^3 - 6x^2 + 5x + 6 = (x - 2)(x^2 - 4x - 3)$.

As the roots of $x^2 - 4x - 3 = 0$ are $x = 2 \pm \sqrt{7}$, the solutions of the given equation are $x = 2, 2 \pm \sqrt{7}$.

Ex. 35. *Solve the equation $2x^4 + 8x^3 - 9x^2 - 19x - 6 = 0$, given that the product of two of its roots is 2.*

As the product of two roots is 2, the quadratic factor which yields these two roots when equated to zero must be of the form $x^2 + ax + 2$.

Let $\qquad 2x^4 + 8x^3 - 9x^2 - 19x - 6 = (x^2 + ax + 2)(\text{2nd quadratic factor})$.

Clearly in the second quadratic factor, two terms are $2x^2$ and -3.

$$\therefore \text{ Expression} = (x^2 + ax + 2)(2x^2 + bx - 3).$$

Equating coefficients of x^3, $\qquad 8 = 2a + b$.
Equating coefficients of x, $\quad -19 = -3a + 2b$.
$$\therefore a = 5, \ b = -2.$$

The equation is $\qquad (x^2 + 5x + 2)(2x^2 - 2x - 3) = 0$,
hence $\qquad x = \tfrac{1}{2}(-5 \pm \sqrt{17}), \tfrac{1}{2}(1 \pm \sqrt{7})$.

EXAMPLES 2f

Solve the following equations:

1. $\sqrt{x} + \sqrt{(x - 3)} = \sqrt{(x + 5)}$.
2. $2\sqrt{(x - 1)} = x - 4$.
3. $x^3 + x^2 - 9x - 9 = 0$.
4. $2x^3 - 3x^2 - 11x + 6 = 0$.
5. $3\sqrt{(2x + 1)} - 4\sqrt{(x - 3)} = \sqrt{(6x + 1)}$.
6. $x^4 - x^3 - 4x^2 - x + 1 = 0$.
7. $x^4 + 3x^3 - 2x^2 - 3x + 1 = 0$.
8. $\sqrt{(2 - x)} + \sqrt{(-1 - x)} = 3$.
9. $\sqrt{\{2x(x - 1)\}} - \sqrt{\{x(x - 8)\}} = x$.
10. $2x^5 + x^4 - 7x^3 - 7x^2 + x + 2 = 0$.
11. $(x - 1)^3 - 8x^3 = 0$.
12. $(x + 2)^4 - 16(x - 1)^4 = 0$.

13. Solve the equation $x^4 + x^3 - 16x^2 - 4x + 48 = 0$, given that the product of two roots is 6.

14. Solve the equation $x^2 + 3x + 3 = \sqrt{(2x^2 + 6x + 5)}$, by using the substitution $y = x^2 + 3x + 3$.

15. Solve the equation $2x^4 - 3x^3 - 15x^2 + 10x + 24 = 0$, given that the sum of two roots is unity.

16. Solve: (i) $(x - 2c)(x - 2b) = (a + b - c)(a - b + c)$;

(ii) $x^3 + y^3 = 26$, $x^2y + xy^2 = -6$.

17. Solve: (i) $\sqrt{(2x - 5)} + \sqrt{(6x - 9)} = x - 1$;

(ii) $\sqrt{(1 - x + x^2)} + \sqrt{(1 + x + x^2)} = 3$.

18. Find real solutions of the equation $x^4 + (x - 1)^4 = 1$.

19. Solve the equation $x^4 - 2x^3 - 16x^2 - 8x + 16 = 0$, by using the substitution $x = 2t$.

20. Find the values of a and b if $x^2 - x - 2$ is a factor of

$$f(x) \equiv x^6 + 4x^5 - ax^3 - 13x^2 - bx - 12$$

and solve the equation $f(x) = 0$.

21. Solve the simultaneous equations, $yz = 2(y + z) + 6$, $zx = 2(z + x) + 2$, $xy = 2(x + y) + 11$.

MISCELLANEOUS EXAMPLES

1. Simplify $(a + b - c)^2 + (b + c - a)^2 + (a + c - b)^2$.

2. Factorise: (i) $(a - 1)^3 - 8 + (a + 1)^3 + 6(a^2 - 1)$;

(ii) $x^2 - y^2 - 2z^2 + zx + 3yz$.

3. If $\dfrac{x}{y} = \dfrac{y}{z}$, simplify $\dfrac{(x + y + z)^2}{x^2 + y^2 + z^2}$.

4. Prove that the expression $2x^2 - 6xy + 5y^2 + 2x - 8y + 14$ is positive for all real values of x and y.

5. Find for real values of x: (i) the sign of the function $2x^2 - 13x + 15$; (ii) the possible values of the function $\dfrac{4x^2 - 2x + 1}{4x^2 + 2x + 1}$.

6. If $y = f(x)$, where $f(x) = \dfrac{ax + b}{cx - a}$, prove that $x = f(y)$.

7. Express in partial fractions: (i) $\dfrac{2x - 5}{(x - 2)(3x - 1)(2x + 5)}$;

(ii) $\dfrac{x^4}{(x + 1)^4(x^2 + 1)}$.

8. Factorise: (i) $x(y - z)^3 + y(z - x)^3 + z(x - y)^3$;

(ii) $x^2(y - z)^3 + y^2(z - x)^3 + z^2(x - y)^3$.

9. Express $x^2 + \dfrac{1}{x^2}$, $x^3 + \dfrac{1}{x^3}$, $x^4 + \dfrac{1}{x^4}$, each in terms of X, where $X = x + \dfrac{1}{x}$.

10. Solve the equations: (i) $9x^4 - 24x^3 - 2x^2 - 24x + 9 = 0$;

(ii) $5y^2 - 7x^2 = 17$, $5xy - 6x^2 = 6$.

11. (i) Find the sign of the expression $2x - 5 - 4x^2$ for real values of x.

(ii) If x is real, prove that $\dfrac{3}{5} \leqslant \dfrac{2x^2 + x + 2}{2x^2 - x + 2} \leqslant \dfrac{5}{3}$.

12. Prove that the roots of the equation $(b^2 - 4ac)x^2 + 4(a + c)x - 4 = 0$ are real if a, b, c are real and find the condition that they are equal.

13. Solve the equation $x^5 - 4x^4 + 7x^2 - 2 = 0$, given that the product of two roots is 2.

14. Express with rational denominators: (i) $\dfrac{1}{2 + \sqrt{3}}$; (ii) $\dfrac{1}{2 + \sqrt{3} - \sqrt{5}}$;

(iii) $\dfrac{1}{1 + \sqrt{x} - \sqrt{y}}$, where x, y are positive integers.

15. If x, y are real, prove that $x^2 - 4xy + 5y^2 + 2x - 8y + 5 \geqslant 0$. For what values of x, y is the function a minimum?

16. (i) Factorise $4a^4 + 3a^2b^2 + b^4$.

(ii) If $x^4 - 48x + 28 \equiv (x^2 + ax + 2)(x^2 + 4x + b)$, find the values of a and b.

17. Express $\dfrac{x^3}{(x - 1)^3(x + 2)}$ as a sum of four partial fractions and find the coefficient of x^n in the expansion of the function in a series of ascending powers of x.

18. If $f(n) = 3n^5 + 7n$, prove that $f(n + 1) - f(n)$ is a multiple of 5.

19. Solve: (i) $x^3 - x^2 - 5x + 2 = 0$;

(ii) $\sqrt{(4x - 2)} + \sqrt{(x + 1)} - \sqrt{(7 - 5x)} = 0$.

20. A rational integral function of x, $\phi(x)$, is divided by $x^2 - a^2$. Prove that the remainder is $\dfrac{\phi(a) - \phi(-a)}{2a}x + \dfrac{\phi(a) + \phi(-a)}{2}$.

21. Find the range of values of λ for which the expression

$$x^2 - 4x + 2 + \lambda(x - 4)^2$$

is positive for all real values of x.

22. If $\dfrac{x}{a + b} = \dfrac{y}{1 - a} = \dfrac{z}{b + 1}$ and $a + b \neq 0$, express x in terms of y and z.

23. If $x > 0$, prove that: (i) $x + \dfrac{1}{x} \geqslant 2$; (ii) $x^r + x^{2n-r} \geqslant 2x^n$.

24. Resolve $\dfrac{1}{(2 - x)(x - 1)^n}$ into partial fractions.

25. Find the values of λ for which the function $x^2 + 8xy - 5y^2 - \lambda(x^2 + y^2)$ can be expressed as a perfect square. If $x^2 + y^2 = 1$, prove that

$$-7 \leqslant x^2 + 8xy - 5y^2 \leqslant 3.$$

26. Solve the equations:

(i) $\sqrt{(x - 6)} + \sqrt{(x - 1)} = \sqrt{(3x - 5)}$;

(ii) $\sqrt{(6 - x)} + \sqrt{(1 - x)} = \sqrt{(5 - 3x)}$.

27. Factorise $(b^2 + c^2)(b - c)^3 + (c^2 + a^2)(c - a)^3 + (a^2 + b^2)(a - b)^3$.

28. Prove that, if x is a real variable and a, b, c are real constants, the function $\dfrac{x + a}{x^2 + bx + c^2}$ lies between two fixed values if $a^2 + c^2 > ab$ and $b^2 < 4c^2$.

29. If $\dfrac{x}{x^2 + 2yz} = \dfrac{y}{y^2 + 2zx} = \dfrac{z}{z^2 + 2xy}$, prove that each fraction is equal to $\dfrac{1}{x + y + z}$.

30. Find the least positive values of:

(i) $x + \dfrac{12}{x}$;   (ii) $x^2 + 2ax + 2(a^2 + ab + b^2)$.

31. If x, y are real and $16x^2 + 8xy + 9y^2 - 64y = 0$, prove that $0 \leqslant y \leqslant 8$, $-4 \leqslant x \leqslant 2$.

32. Factorise:

(i) $a^3 + b^3 + c^3 + a(a - b)(c - a) + b(b - c)(a - b) + c(c - a)(b - c) + 5abc$;

(ii) $4(x - 2)(x - 3)(x - 6)(x - 9) - 5x^2$.   [Hint: let $(x - 3)(x - 6) = y$.]

33. Solve the equation $\dfrac{x^2}{x + 2} + \dfrac{2(x + 2)}{x^2} = 3$.

34. Use the result, $\cos 3\theta = 4 \cos^3 \theta - 3 \cos \theta$, to solve completely the equation $8x^3 - 6x = 1$.

35. Given that $y = f(x) \equiv (ax + b)/(x + c)$, where a, b, c are constants, what is the condition that $x = f(y)$? If this condition is satisfied, find the values x_1, x_2, of x for which $f(x) = x$. Show further that, if $x_1 + x_2 = 2x_0$, then for any value of x, $4(x - x_0)(y - x_0) = (x_2 - x_1)^2$.

36. Given that $y^2 = \dfrac{5x^2 - 4x + 8}{x^2 + 1}$, determine the limitations on the values of y if x is real.

37. If $ax^3 + bx + c$, where a, c do not equal zero, has a factor of the form $x^2 + px + 1$, prove that $a^2 - c^2 = ab$. In this case, prove that the functions $ax^3 + bx + c$ and $cx^3 + bx^2 + a$ have a common quadratic factor.

38. If a, b, c are real and a lies between the limits $-(b + c)$ and $(b - c)$, prove that the function $\dfrac{ax^2 - bx + c}{cx^2 - bx + a}$ is capable of all real values.

39. (i) Prove that the expression $x^2 + 2xy + 4y^2 + 2x - 10y + 15$ has a minimum value of 2.

(ii) Find the values of λ for which the function
$$8x^2 + 6xy - 5y^2 + 4x + 2\lambda y - 4 = 0$$
can be expressed as the product of two linear factors.

40. Show that if a polynomial $f(x)$ leaves a remainder of the form $px+q$ when divided by $(x-a)(x-b)(x-c)$, where a, b, c are distinct, then

$$(b-c)f(a)+(c-a)f(b)+(a-b)f(c)=0.$$

41. By representing the equations $y-2x=0, x+y=3, 2y-x=5$ graphically, or otherwise, prove that if $y-2x>0$, $x+y>3$ and $2y-x<5$, then $\frac{1}{3}<x<\frac{5}{3}$, $2<y<\frac{10}{3}$.

42. Find all functions $f(x)$ of the form $f(x)=\dfrac{a+bx}{b+x}$, for which $f(2)=2f(5)$ and $f(0)+3f(-2)=0$.

43. Find a polynomial $f(x)$ of degree five, such that $f(x)-1$ is divisible by $(x-1)^3$ and $f(x)$ itself is divisible by x^3.

44. Find the H.C.F. of $x^5-x^4+4x^3-2x^2+2x+1$ and $x^4+3x^3+x^2+4$.

45. If x, y, z are not all equal and $\dfrac{xy+1}{y}=\dfrac{yz+1}{z}=\dfrac{zx+1}{x}=k$, prove that $x^2y^2z^2=1$ and $k^2=1$.

CHAPTER III

DETERMINANTS. LINEAR EQUATIONS

Notation and definitions. The expression $a_1b_2 - a_2b_1$ derived from the four terms, or elements, $a_1\,b_1$; $a_2\,b_2$ is denoted by the symbol $\begin{vmatrix} a_1 & b_1 \\ a_2 & b_2 \end{vmatrix}$.

This symbol $\begin{vmatrix} a_1 & b_1 \\ a_2 & b_2 \end{vmatrix}$ is called *a determinant*. Having two rows $a_1\,b_1$, $a_2\,b_2$ and two columns $a_1\,a_2$, $b_1\,b_2$, it is a *determinant of the second order*. Extending this definition, the expression

$$a_1(b_2c_3 - b_3c_2) - b_1(a_2c_3 - a_3c_2) + c_1(a_2b_3 - a_3b_2)$$

derived from the nine elements $a_1\,b_1\,c_1$; $a_2\,b_2\,c_2$; $a_3\,b_3\,c_3$ is denoted by the symbol $\begin{vmatrix} a_1 & b_1 & c_1 \\ a_2 & b_2 & c_2 \\ a_3 & b_3 & c_3 \end{vmatrix}$. This is *a determinant of the third order*, having three rows and three columns.

From the definition, it follows that

$$\begin{vmatrix} a_1 & b_1 & c_1 \\ a_2 & b_2 & c_2 \\ a_3 & b_3 & c_3 \end{vmatrix} = a_1 \begin{vmatrix} b_2 & c_2 \\ b_3 & c_3 \end{vmatrix} - b_1 \begin{vmatrix} a_2 & c_2 \\ a_3 & c_3 \end{vmatrix} + c_1 \begin{vmatrix} a_2 & b_2 \\ a_3 & b_3 \end{vmatrix},$$

the elements of the top row being taken in order from left to right with alternate plus and minus signs and multiplied by the second-order determinants which remain when the row and column through the element are deleted.

The determinants $\begin{vmatrix} b_2 & c_2 \\ b_3 & c_3 \end{vmatrix}$, $\begin{vmatrix} a_2 & c_2 \\ a_3 & c_3 \end{vmatrix}$, $\begin{vmatrix} a_2 & b_2 \\ a_3 & b_3 \end{vmatrix}$ are called *the minors* of a_1, b_1, c_1 respectively and will be denoted by $\bar{A}_1, \bar{B}_1, \bar{C}_1$.

Clearly the definition can be extended to determinants of any order. A determinant of order n will consist of n^2 elements arranged in n rows and n columns, and will be expressible in terms of n determinants of order $n-1$.

For convenience, the symbol Δ is often used to denote a determinant.

Ex. 1. *Evaluate* (i) $\begin{vmatrix} 3 & 4 \\ 1 & 2 \end{vmatrix}$; (ii) $\begin{vmatrix} 2 & 0 & -1 \\ 4 & -3 & 2 \\ 0 & 2 & 3 \end{vmatrix}$.

(i) $\Delta = (3 \times 2) - (4 \times 1) = 2$.

(ii) $\Delta = 2 \begin{vmatrix} -3 & 2 \\ 2 & 3 \end{vmatrix} - 0 \begin{vmatrix} 4 & 2 \\ 0 & 3 \end{vmatrix} + (-1) \begin{vmatrix} 4 & -3 \\ 0 & 2 \end{vmatrix}$

$= 2(-9 - 4) - 0 - (8 - 0) = -34$.

Ex. 2. *Prove that* $\begin{vmatrix} a & h & g \\ h & b & f \\ g & f & c \end{vmatrix} = abc + 2fgh - af^2 - bg^2 - ch^2.$

$\Delta = a(bc - f^2) - h(hc - fg) + g(fh - bg),$
$= abc + 2fgh - af^2 - bg^2 - ch^2.$

Ex. 3. *Expand the determinant* $\begin{vmatrix} x & 1 & 1 & 1 \\ 1 & x & 0 & 0 \\ 1 & 0 & x & 0 \\ 1 & 0 & 0 & x \end{vmatrix}.$

$\Delta = x \begin{vmatrix} x & 0 & 0 \\ 0 & x & 0 \\ 0 & 0 & x \end{vmatrix} - 1 \begin{vmatrix} 1 & 0 & 0 \\ 1 & x & 0 \\ 1 & 0 & x \end{vmatrix} + 1 \begin{vmatrix} 1 & x & 0 \\ 1 & 0 & 0 \\ 1 & 0 & x \end{vmatrix} - 1 \begin{vmatrix} 1 & x & 0 \\ 1 & 0 & x \\ 1 & 0 & 0 \end{vmatrix}$

$= x[x^3] - [x^2] + [1 \cdot 0 - x \cdot x] - [1 \cdot 0 - x(-x)]$
$= x^4 - 3x^2.$

EXAMPLES 3a

Evaluate the following determinants:

1. $\begin{vmatrix} 3 & 2 \\ 1 & 4 \end{vmatrix}.$　　**2.** $\begin{vmatrix} 2 & 3 \\ 0 & -1 \end{vmatrix}.$　　**3.** $\begin{vmatrix} 7 & -3 \\ -2 & 6 \end{vmatrix}.$

4. $\begin{vmatrix} 0 & 2 \\ -3 & 0 \end{vmatrix}.$　　**5.** $\begin{vmatrix} 1 & 1 & 1 \\ 2 & 2 & 2 \\ 3 & 3 & 3 \end{vmatrix}.$　　**6.** $\begin{vmatrix} 2 & 0 & 1 \\ 0 & 3 & -1 \\ 4 & 2 & 0 \end{vmatrix}.$

7. $\begin{vmatrix} 0 & 0 & 3 \\ 1 & 1 & 1 \\ -2 & -1 & 4 \end{vmatrix}.$　　**8.** $\begin{vmatrix} 2 & 0 & 0 \\ 0 & 2 & 0 \\ 0 & 0 & 2 \end{vmatrix}.$　　**9.** $\begin{vmatrix} 1 & 1 & 1 & 1 \\ 1 & -1 & 1 & -1 \\ -1 & 1 & -1 & 1 \\ -1 & -1 & 1 & 1 \end{vmatrix}.$

10. $\begin{vmatrix} 2 & 0 & 0 & 0 \\ 6 & 1 & -1 & 0 \\ 4 & 2 & 0 & 2 \\ 4 & 0 & 3 & 1 \end{vmatrix}.$　　**11.** $\begin{vmatrix} 1 & 0 & 0 & 1 \\ -1 & 2 & 0 & 1 \\ 0 & -3 & 1 & 1 \\ 0 & 0 & -1 & -2 \end{vmatrix}.$　　**12.** $\begin{vmatrix} 1 & -1 & 1 & -1 \\ -1 & 1 & -1 & 1 \\ 2 & 0 & -2 & 3 \\ 0 & -3 & 2 & 1 \end{vmatrix}.$

Expand the following determinants:

13. $\begin{vmatrix} a & -b \\ b & -a \end{vmatrix}.$　**14.** $\begin{vmatrix} x & y \\ 2x & -3y \end{vmatrix}.$　　**15.** $\begin{vmatrix} a+b & b \\ a-b & a \end{vmatrix}.$　**16.** $\begin{vmatrix} x-2y & x+2y \\ x+y & x-y \end{vmatrix}.$

17. $\begin{vmatrix} 0 & b & a \\ a & b & 0 \\ b & 0 & a \end{vmatrix}.$　**18.** $\begin{vmatrix} 1 & -y & z \\ x & 1 & -z \\ -x & y & 1 \end{vmatrix}.$　**19.** $\begin{vmatrix} a^2 & a & 1 \\ a & a^2 & 1 \\ 1 & a & a^2 \end{vmatrix}.$　**20.** $\begin{vmatrix} 1 & 1 & 1 \\ a & b & c \\ 1+a & 1+b & 1+c \end{vmatrix}.$

21. $\begin{vmatrix} 1 & 1 & 1 & 1 \\ 1 & x & 1 & 1 \\ 1 & 1 & x & 1 \\ 1 & 1 & 1 & x \end{vmatrix}.$　　**22.** $\begin{vmatrix} a & 0 & b & 0 \\ 0 & a & 0 & b \\ b & 0 & a & 0 \\ 0 & b & 0 & a \end{vmatrix}.$　　**23.** $\begin{vmatrix} 1 & 1 & 1 & 1 \\ a & b & a & a \\ a & a & b & a \\ a & a & a & b \end{vmatrix}.$

24. Verify that $\begin{vmatrix} 1+x & 1+y & 1+z \\ 1 & 2 & 3 \\ 3 & 2 & 1 \end{vmatrix} = \begin{vmatrix} 1 & 1 & 1 \\ 1 & 2 & 3 \\ 3 & 2 & 1 \end{vmatrix} + \begin{vmatrix} x & y & z \\ 1 & 2 & 3 \\ 3 & 2 & 1 \end{vmatrix}.$

25. Verify that $\begin{vmatrix} a & 2 & 1 \\ a & 3 & 2 \\ a & 1 & 4 \end{vmatrix} = a \begin{vmatrix} 1 & 2 & 1 \\ 1 & 3 & 2 \\ 1 & 1 & 4 \end{vmatrix}$.

26. Prove that $\begin{vmatrix} a & -b & 2c \\ a & -b & 2c \\ x & y & z \end{vmatrix} = 0$.

27. Prove that $\begin{vmatrix} a & b & 0 & c \\ b & c & 0 & -a \\ c & -a & 0 & b \\ 1 & 1 & 0 & 1 \end{vmatrix} = 0$.

28. Verify that $\begin{vmatrix} a+x & b & c \\ b+x & c & a \\ c+x & a & b \end{vmatrix} = \begin{vmatrix} a & b & c \\ b & c & a \\ c & a & b \end{vmatrix} + x \begin{vmatrix} 1 & b & c \\ 1 & c & a \\ 1 & a & b \end{vmatrix}$.

Laws of determinants. The following laws which will be proved true for third order determinants are in fact true for determinants of any order.

Law 1. *If any two parallel sets of elements, rows or columns, are interchanged, the sign of Δ is changed.*

For take

$$\Delta = \begin{vmatrix} a_1 & b_1 & c_1 \\ a_2 & b_2 & c_2 \\ a_3 & b_3 & c_3 \end{vmatrix} = a_1(b_2c_3 - b_3c_2) - b_1(a_2c_3 - a_3c_2) + c_1(a_2b_3 - a_3b_2).$$

Interchanging the first two rows,

$$\begin{vmatrix} a_2 & b_2 & c_2 \\ a_1 & b_1 & c_1 \\ a_3 & b_3 & c_3 \end{vmatrix} = a_2(b_1c_3 - b_3c_2) - b_2(a_1c_3 - a_3c_1) + c_2(a_1b_3 - a_3b_1)$$

$$= -a_1(b_2c_3 - b_3c_2) + b_1(a_2c_3 - a_3c_2) - c_1(a_2b_3 - a_3b_2)$$
$$= -\Delta.$$

A similar result will be obtained if two columns are interchanged.

Law II. *If any two parallel sets of elements are identical, then $\Delta = 0$.*

This important result follows immediately from Law 1, for if the identical sets are interchanged, the sign of Δ must also be changed. As however the new determinant is identical with Δ, it follows that $\Delta = 0$.

E.g. $\begin{vmatrix} b+c & a & a \\ c+a & b & b \\ a+b & c & c \end{vmatrix} = 0$.

Law III. The value of Δ is unchanged if all the rows are written as columns in the same order, or vice versa.

Take Δ as in Law 1. Writing the rows as columns,

$$\Delta' = \begin{vmatrix} a_1 & a_2 & a_3 \\ b_1 & b_2 & b_3 \\ c_1 & c_2 & c_3 \end{vmatrix} = a_1(b_2c_3 - b_3c_2) - a_2(b_1c_3 - b_3c_1) + a_3(b_1c_2 - b_2c_1)$$

$$= a_1(b_2c_3 - b_3c_2) - b_1(a_2c_3 - a_3c_2) + c_1(a_2b_3 - a_3b_2)$$
$$= \Delta.$$

Law IV. If every element of one row or column is multiplied, or divided, by the same factor k, then Δ is multiplied, or divided, by that factor k.

Taking Δ as before, consider the first column multiplied by k. Then

$$\begin{vmatrix} ka_1 & b_1 & c_1 \\ ka_2 & b_2 & c_2 \\ ka_3 & b_3 & c_3 \end{vmatrix} = ka_1(b_2c_3 - b_3c_2) - b_1(ka_2c_3 - ka_3c_2) + c_1(ka_2b_3 - ka_3b_2)$$

$$= k\{a_1(b_2c_3 - b_3c_2) - b_1(a_2c_3 - a_3c_2) + c_1(a_2b_3 - a_3b_2)\}$$
$$= k\Delta.$$

Alternatively, this law can be stated in the form,

if each element of a row or column of Δ has a common factor k, then k is a factor of Δ.

E.g.
$$\begin{vmatrix} x & x^2 & x^3 \\ x^2 & x & x^2 \\ x^3 & x^2 & x \end{vmatrix} = x \begin{vmatrix} 1 & x^2 & x^3 \\ x & x & x^2 \\ x^2 & x^2 & x \end{vmatrix} = x^2 \begin{vmatrix} 1 & x & x^3 \\ x & 1 & x^2 \\ x^2 & x & x \end{vmatrix} = x^3 \begin{vmatrix} 1 & x & x^2 \\ x & 1 & x \\ x^2 & x & 1 \end{vmatrix}.$$

Law V. If every element in a row or column can be resolved into the sum, or difference, of two others, then Δ can be expressed as the sum, or difference, of two determinants.

For let

$$\Delta = \begin{vmatrix} a_1 + a_1' & b_1 + b_1' & c_1 + c_1' \\ a_2 & b_2 & c_2 \\ a_3 & b_3 & c_3 \end{vmatrix} = (a_1 + a_1') \begin{vmatrix} b_2 & c_2 \\ b_3 & c_3 \end{vmatrix} - (b_1 + b_1') \begin{vmatrix} a_2 & c_2 \\ a_3 & c_3 \end{vmatrix} + (c_1 + c_1') \begin{vmatrix} a_2 & b_2 \\ a_3 & b_3 \end{vmatrix}$$

$$= a_1 \begin{vmatrix} b_2 & c_2 \\ b_3 & c_3 \end{vmatrix} - b_1 \begin{vmatrix} a_2 & c_2 \\ a_3 & c_3 \end{vmatrix} + c_1 \begin{vmatrix} a_2 & b_2 \\ a_3 & b_3 \end{vmatrix} + a_1' \begin{vmatrix} b_2 & c_2 \\ b_3 & c_3 \end{vmatrix} - b_1' \begin{vmatrix} a_2 & c_2 \\ a_3 & c_3 \end{vmatrix} + c_1' \begin{vmatrix} a_2 & b_2 \\ a_3 & b_3 \end{vmatrix}$$

i.e. $\Delta = \begin{vmatrix} a_1 & b_1 & c_1 \\ a_2 & b_2 & c_2 \\ a_3 & b_3 & c_3 \end{vmatrix} + \begin{vmatrix} a_1' & b_1' & c_1' \\ a_2 & b_2 & c_2 \\ a_3 & b_3 & c_3 \end{vmatrix}.$

E

This result can be extended to the case where the elements of a row or column are expressible as a sum or difference of three or more terms.

E.g.
$$\Delta = \begin{vmatrix} 1-x+x^2 & x & x^2 \\ 1-y+y^2 & y & y^2 \\ 1-z+z^2 & z & z^2 \end{vmatrix} = \begin{vmatrix} 1 & x & x^2 \\ 1 & y & y^2 \\ 1 & z & z^2 \end{vmatrix} - \begin{vmatrix} x & x & x^2 \\ y & y & y^2 \\ z & z & z^2 \end{vmatrix} + \begin{vmatrix} x^2 & x & x^2 \\ y^2 & y & y^2 \\ z^2 & z & z^2 \end{vmatrix}$$

$$= \begin{vmatrix} 1 & x & x^2 \\ 1 & y & y^2 \\ 1 & z & z^2 \end{vmatrix}, \text{ the last two determinants}$$

vanishing as they each have two identical columns.

Law VI. Δ *is unchanged in value when to the elements of any row (column) are added, or subtracted, any constant multiples of the elements of one or more other rows (columns).*

For taking $\Delta = \begin{vmatrix} a_1 & b_1 & c_1 \\ a_2 & b_2 & c_2 \\ a_3 & b_3 & c_3 \end{vmatrix}$, consider the determinant Δ' obtained by

adding to the first row a constant multiple λ_2 of the second row and a constant multiple λ_3 of the third row.

$$\Delta' = \begin{vmatrix} a_1+\lambda_2 a_2+\lambda_3 a_3 & b_1+\lambda_2 b_2+\lambda_3 b_3 & c_1+\lambda_2 c_2+\lambda_3 c_3 \\ a_2 & b_2 & c_2 \\ a_3 & b_3 & c_3 \end{vmatrix}$$

$$= \Delta + \lambda_2 \begin{vmatrix} a_2 & b_2 & c_2 \\ a_2 & b_2 & c_2 \\ a_3 & b_3 & c_3 \end{vmatrix} + \lambda_3 \begin{vmatrix} a_3 & b_3 & c_3 \\ a_2 & b_2 & c_2 \\ a_3 & b_3 & c_3 \end{vmatrix}, \text{ using Law V,}$$

$$= \Delta, \text{ as the other determinants are zero by Law II.}$$

E.g.
$$\Delta = \begin{vmatrix} 1 & a & a^2 \\ 1 & b & b^2 \\ 1 & c & c^2 \end{vmatrix} = \begin{vmatrix} 1-1 & a-b & a^2-b^2 \\ 1 & b & b^2 \\ 1 & c & c^2 \end{vmatrix} = (a-b)\begin{vmatrix} 0 & 1 & a+b \\ 1 & b & b^2 \\ 1 & c & c^2 \end{vmatrix}.$$

$$= (a-b)\begin{vmatrix} 0 & 1 & a+b \\ 0 & b-c & b^2-c^2 \\ 1 & c & c^2 \end{vmatrix} = (a-b)(b-c)\begin{vmatrix} 0 & 1 & a+b \\ 0 & 1 & b+c \\ 1 & c & c \end{vmatrix}.$$

Further simplification is achieved by subtracting elements of the second row from those of the first and the ensuing determinant is readily evaluated giving

$$\Delta = (a-b)(b-c)(c-a).$$

N.B. Care must be taken not to apply two or more of these operations simultaneously to the same rows or columns.

E.g.
$$\begin{vmatrix} 1 & a & a^2 \\ 1 & b & b^2 \\ 1 & c & c^2 \end{vmatrix} \neq \begin{vmatrix} 1-1 & a-b & a^2-b^2 \\ 1-1 & b-a & b^2-a^2 \\ 1 & c & c^2 \end{vmatrix}, \text{ simultaneously subtracting elements}$$

of the second row from those of the first, and vice-versa.

Ex. 4. *Evaluate:* (i) $\begin{vmatrix} 219 & 305 \\ 108 & 152 \end{vmatrix}$; (ii) $\begin{vmatrix} 30 & 40 & 50 \\ 40 & 50 & 30 \\ 50 & 40 & 30 \end{vmatrix}$; (iii) $\begin{vmatrix} 1 & 2 & 3 & 4 \\ 2 & 3 & 4 & 5 \\ 3 & 4 & 5 & 6 \\ 4 & 5 & 6 & 7 \end{vmatrix}$.

(i) Multiply elements of the second row by 2 and subtract from the first row.

Then $\Delta = \begin{vmatrix} 3 & 1 \\ 108 & 152 \end{vmatrix} = 456 - 108 = 348.$

(ii) Remove a factor 10 from each row (or column).

Then $\Delta = 10^3 \begin{vmatrix} 3 & 4 & 5 \\ 4 & 5 & 3 \\ 5 & 4 & 3 \end{vmatrix}$; now subtract elements of the last row from those

of the first and remove the resulting factor, 2.

$$\Delta = 2000 \begin{vmatrix} -1 & 0 & 1 \\ 4 & 5 & 3 \\ 5 & 4 & 3 \end{vmatrix} = 2000\{-3 - 9\} = -24,000.$$

(iii) Subtract elements of the second row from those of the first and the elements of the third row from those of the second.

$$\Delta = \begin{vmatrix} -1 & -1 & -1 & -1 \\ -1 & -1 & -1 & -1 \\ 3 & 4 & 5 & 6 \\ 4 & 5 & 6 & 7 \end{vmatrix} = 0, \text{ by Law II.}$$

Ex. 5. *Prove that* $\begin{vmatrix} b+c & a-b & a \\ c+a & b-c & b \\ a+b & c-a & c \end{vmatrix} = 3abc - a^3 - b^3 - c^3.$

$$\Delta = \begin{vmatrix} b+c & a & a \\ c+a & b & b \\ a+b & c & c \end{vmatrix} + \begin{vmatrix} b+c & -b & a \\ c+a & -c & b \\ a+b & -a & c \end{vmatrix}, \text{ using Law V,}$$

$$= \quad 0 \quad + \begin{vmatrix} b & -b & a \\ c & -c & b \\ a & -a & c \end{vmatrix} + \begin{vmatrix} c & -b & a \\ a & -c & b \\ b & -a & c \end{vmatrix}, \text{ using Law II,}$$

$$= -\begin{vmatrix} c & b & a \\ a & c & b \\ b & a & c \end{vmatrix}, \text{ as } \begin{vmatrix} b & -b & a \\ c & -c & b \\ a & -a & c \end{vmatrix} = -\begin{vmatrix} b & b & a \\ c & c & b \\ a & a & c \end{vmatrix} = 0, \text{ by Law II,}$$

$$= 3abc - a^3 - b^3 - c^3.$$

Ex. 6. *Prove that* $\begin{vmatrix} 1+a & b & c & d \\ a & 1+b & c & d \\ a & b & 1+c & d \\ a & b & c & 1+d \end{vmatrix} = 1 + a + b + c + d.$

Add the elements of the second, third and fourth columns to those of the first and remove the factor $1 + a + b + c + d$.

$$\Delta = (1+a+b+c+d)\begin{vmatrix} 1 & b & c & d \\ 1 & 1+b & c & d \\ 1 & b & 1+c & d \\ 1 & b & c & 1+d \end{vmatrix}.$$

Now subtract elements of the second row from those of the first and similarly for the third and second rows and the fourth and third rows.

Then
$$\Delta = (1+a+b+c+d)\begin{vmatrix} 0 & -1 & 0 & 0 \\ 0 & 1 & -1 & 0 \\ 0 & 0 & 1 & -1 \\ 1 & b & c & 1+d \end{vmatrix}$$

$$= (1+a+b+c+d)\begin{vmatrix} 0 & -1 & 0 \\ 0 & 1 & -1 \\ 1 & c & 1+d \end{vmatrix} = (1+a+b+c+d)\begin{vmatrix} 0 & -1 \\ 1 & 1+d \end{vmatrix}$$

$$= 1+a+b+c+d.$$

EXAMPLES 3b

Evaluate the following determinants:

1. $\begin{vmatrix} 17 & 20 \\ 15 & 19 \end{vmatrix}.$ **2.** $\begin{vmatrix} 57 & 55 \\ 38 & 44 \end{vmatrix}.$ **3.** $\begin{vmatrix} 102 & 102 \\ 76 & 78 \end{vmatrix}.$ **4.** $\begin{vmatrix} 201 & 132 \\ 100 & 67 \end{vmatrix}.$

5. $\begin{vmatrix} 10 & 20 & 30 \\ 3 & 50 & -1 \\ 0 & 60 & 4 \end{vmatrix}.$ **6.** $\begin{vmatrix} 4 & 0 & 5 \\ 8 & 2 & 6 \\ -12 & 9 & -11 \end{vmatrix}.$ **7.** $\begin{vmatrix} 29 & 38 & 40 \\ 19 & 26 & 28 \\ 24 & 32 & 34 \end{vmatrix}.$ **8.** $\begin{vmatrix} 13 & 3 & 23 \\ 30 & 7 & 53 \\ 39 & 9 & 70 \end{vmatrix}.$

9. $\begin{vmatrix} 2 & 3 & 4 & 5 \\ 3 & 4 & 5 & 6 \\ 4 & 5 & 6 & 7 \\ 5 & 10 & 15 & 20 \end{vmatrix}.$ **10.** $\begin{vmatrix} 2 & 4 & 6 & 8 \\ 0 & 3 & 6 & 9 \\ 9 & 6 & 3 & 0 \\ -8 & -6 & -4 & -2 \end{vmatrix}.$ **11.** $\begin{vmatrix} 5 & 4 & 2 & -1 \\ 6 & 5 & 2 & 1 \\ 7 & 6 & 2 & -1 \\ 8 & 7 & 2 & 1 \end{vmatrix}.$

Expand the following determinants:

12. $\begin{vmatrix} a+b & a^2+b^2 \\ 2(a+b) & 2(a^2+b^2) \end{vmatrix}.$ **13.** $\begin{vmatrix} x-2y & x+2y \\ x+y & x-y \end{vmatrix}.$ **14.** $\begin{vmatrix} a^2-b^2 & (a-b)^2 \\ a(a+b) & b(a-b) \end{vmatrix}.$

15. $\begin{vmatrix} a^2-4b^2 & a^2-ab-2b^2 \\ a^2-b^2 & a^2-2ab+b^2 \end{vmatrix}.$ **16.** $\begin{vmatrix} a^2 & a & 1 \\ a & 1 & a^2 \\ 1 & a^2 & a \end{vmatrix}.$ **17.** $\begin{vmatrix} 2x & x^2 & x^3 \\ 2y & y^2 & y^3 \\ 2z & z^2 & z^3 \end{vmatrix}.$

18. $\begin{vmatrix} 1 & 1 & 1 \\ a & b & c \\ 1+a & 1+b & 1+c \end{vmatrix}.$ **19.** $\begin{vmatrix} 2-x & 2 & 3 \\ 2 & 5-x & 6 \\ 3 & 4 & 10-x \end{vmatrix}.$ **20.** $\begin{vmatrix} a & 0 & a & a \\ a & a & 0 & a \\ a & a & a & 0 \\ 0 & a & a & a \end{vmatrix}.$

21. $\begin{vmatrix} a^3 & a^2 & a & 1 \\ a^2 & a & 1 & a^3 \\ a & 1 & a^3 & a^2 \\ 1 & a^3 & a^2 & a \end{vmatrix}.$ **22.** $\begin{vmatrix} x+1 & x-1 & x & 1 \\ 2x+2 & x-2 & x^2 & 2 \\ 3x+3 & x-3 & x^3 & 3 \\ 4x+4 & x-4 & x^4 & 4 \end{vmatrix}.$

23. Prove that $\begin{vmatrix} a^3+b^3 & a(a^2-ab+b^2) \\ b^3-a^3 & b(a^2+ab+b^2) \end{vmatrix} = (a^2+b^2)(a^4+a^2b^2+b^4).$

24. Show that $\begin{vmatrix} a+b+c & a+b-c & a-b+c \\ b & -c & a \\ c & a & -b \end{vmatrix} = \begin{vmatrix} a & b & c \\ b & -c & a \\ c & a & -b \end{vmatrix}$.

25. Solve the equation $\begin{vmatrix} x & 2 & 3 \\ -4 & -2x & 2 \\ 2 & x & 1 \end{vmatrix} = 0$.

26. Prove: (i) $\begin{vmatrix} a & a & a & a \\ b & b & b & -b \\ c & c & -c & -c \\ d & -d & -d & -d \end{vmatrix} = 8abcd$; (ii) $\begin{vmatrix} 1 & 1 & 1 & 1 \\ 1 & x & 1 & 1 \\ 1 & 1 & x & 1 \\ 1 & 1 & 1 & x \end{vmatrix} = (x-1)^3$.

27. Evaluate: (i) $\begin{vmatrix} b+c & a & a \\ b & c+a & b \\ c & c & a+b \end{vmatrix}$; (ii) $\begin{vmatrix} a & a+b & a+2b \\ a+b & a+2b & a+3b \\ a+2b & a+3b & a+4b \end{vmatrix}$.

28. Expand $\Delta = \begin{vmatrix} x & x+6 & x+3 \\ x+5 & x & x+2 \\ x+3 & x+4 & x \end{vmatrix}$ and solve the equation $\Delta = 0$.

29. Prove that $\begin{vmatrix} x & x+1 & x+2 & x+3 \\ x+1 & x+2 & x+3 & x+4 \\ x+2 & x+3 & x+4 & x+5 \\ x+3 & x+4 & x+5 & x+6 \end{vmatrix} = 0$.

30. Express $\begin{vmatrix} a_1x_1+b_1y_1 & a_1x_2+b_1y_2 \\ a_2x_1+b_2y_1 & a_2x_2+b_2y_2 \end{vmatrix}$ as a sum of four determinants and prove that it is equal to $\begin{vmatrix} a_1 & b_1 \\ a_2 & b_2 \end{vmatrix} \times \begin{vmatrix} x_1 & y_1 \\ x_2 & y_2 \end{vmatrix}$.

Factorisation of determinants. The two principal methods of factorising a determinant are:

(i) by picking out common factors from any row or column;

(ii) by use of the remainder theorem.

These methods are illustrated in the following examples.

Ex. 7. *Factorise:* (i) $\begin{vmatrix} a^2 & b^2 \\ b^2+c^2 & c^2+a^2 \end{vmatrix}$; (ii) $\begin{vmatrix} x & y & z \\ y & x & x \\ z & z & y \end{vmatrix}$; (iii) $\begin{vmatrix} x+2 & 3 & 3 \\ 3 & x+4 & 5 \\ 3 & 5 & x+4 \end{vmatrix}$.

(i) Adding the elements of the second row to those of the first,

$$\Delta = \begin{vmatrix} a^2+b^2+c^2 & a^2+b^2+c^2 \\ b^2+c^2 & c^2+a^2 \end{vmatrix} = (a^2+b^2+c^2)\begin{vmatrix} 1 & 1 \\ b^2+c^2 & c^2+a^2 \end{vmatrix}$$
$$= (a^2+b^2+c^2)(a^2-b^2) = (a^2+b^2+c^2)(a-b)(a+b).$$

(ii) Adding the elements of the second and third rows to those of the first and removing the factor $(x+y+z)$,

$$\Delta = (x+y+z)\begin{vmatrix} 1 & 1 & 1 \\ y & x & x \\ z & z & y \end{vmatrix} = (x+y+z)\begin{vmatrix} 1 & 0 & 0 \\ y & x-y & x-y \\ z & 0 & y-z \end{vmatrix},$$

subtracting the elements of the first column successively from those of the second and the third columns.

$$\therefore \quad \Delta = (x+y+z)(x-y)(y-z).$$

(iii) Subtracting the elements of the second row from those of the third row,

$$\Delta = \begin{vmatrix} x+2 & 3 & 3 \\ 3 & x+4 & 5 \\ 0 & -(x-1) & x-1 \end{vmatrix} = (x-1)\begin{vmatrix} x+2 & 3 & 3 \\ 3 & x+4 & 5 \\ 0 & -1 & 1 \end{vmatrix}$$

$$= (x-1)[(x+2)\{x+4+5\} - 3(3) + 3(-3)]$$

$$= (x-1)[x^2+11x] = x(x-1)(x+11).$$

Ex. 8. *Factorise:* (i) $\begin{vmatrix} 1 & 1 & 1 \\ a & b & c \\ bc & ca & ab \end{vmatrix}$; (ii) $\begin{vmatrix} 1 & 1 & 1 & 1 \\ a & b & c & d \\ a^2 & b^2 & c^2 & d^2 \\ a^3 & b^3 & c^3 & d^3 \end{vmatrix}$.

(i) When $b = c$, Δ vanishes as the last two columns are identical.

$$\therefore \quad (b-c) \text{ is a factor.}$$

Similarly, $(c-a)$ and $(a-b)$ are also factors.

But each term of Δ is of degree three in a, b, c, and therefore any remaining factor must be a constant.

So let $$\Delta = k(b-c)(c-a)(a-b).$$

The value of k can be obtained by giving numerical values to a, b, c, avoiding those which make one of the factors $(b-c)$, $(c-a)$, $(a-b)$ vanish.

So take $a = 0$, $b = 1$, $c = 2$.

Then $$\Delta = \begin{vmatrix} 1 & 1 & 1 \\ 0 & 1 & 2 \\ 2 & 0 & 0 \end{vmatrix} = 4 - 2 = 2,$$

and $$k(b-c)(c-a)(a-b) = k(-1)(2)(-1) = 2k.$$

$$\therefore \quad k = 1$$

and $$\Delta = (b-c)(c-a)(a-b).$$

(ii) When $a = b$, Δ vanishes as two columns are identical.

$$\therefore \quad (a-b) \text{ is a factor.}$$

Similarly, $(a-c)$, $(a-d)$, $(b-c)$, $(b-d)$ and $(c-d)$ are factors.

As each term of Δ is of the sixth degree in a, b, c, d, the remaining factor must be a constant, say k.

Giving a, b, c, d the values $0, 1, -1, 2$,

$$\Delta = \begin{vmatrix} 1 & 1 & 1 & 1 \\ 0 & 1 & -1 & 2 \\ 0 & 1 & 1 & 4 \\ 0 & 1 & -1 & 8 \end{vmatrix} = \begin{vmatrix} 1 & -1 & 2 \\ 1 & 1 & 4 \\ 1 & -1 & 8 \end{vmatrix} = 12,$$

and $$k(a-b)(a-c)(a-d)(b-c)(b-d)(c-d) = 12k.$$

$$\therefore \quad k = 1$$

and $$\Delta = (a-b)(a-c)(a-d)(b-c)(b-d)(c-d).$$

Minors and cofactors. The *minor* of any particular element in a determinant has already been defined as the determinant obtained when the row and column through the element are suppressed.

E.g. the minor $\bar{C}_2$ of c_2 in $\begin{vmatrix} a_1 & b_1 & c_1 \\ a_2 & b_2 & c_2 \\ a_3 & b_3 & c_3 \end{vmatrix}$ is $\begin{vmatrix} a_1 & b_1 \\ a_3 & b_3 \end{vmatrix}$.

The value of any determinant can be expressed in terms of the elements of any row or column and their respective minors.

For taking
$$\Delta = \begin{vmatrix} a_1 & b_1 & c_1 \\ a_2 & b_2 & c_2 \\ a_3 & b_3 & c_3 \end{vmatrix},$$

by definition
$$\Delta = a_1\bar{A}_1 - b_1\bar{B}_1 + c_1\bar{C}_1.$$

Interchanging the first and second rows and using Law I,

$$\Delta = -\begin{vmatrix} a_2 & b_2 & c_2 \\ a_1 & b_1 & c_1 \\ a_3 & b_3 & c_3 \end{vmatrix} = -\{a_2\bar{A}_2 - b_2\bar{B}_2 + c_2\bar{C}_2\}.$$

Making a second interchange,

$$\Delta = \begin{vmatrix} a_3 & b_3 & c_3 \\ a_1 & b_1 & c_1 \\ a_2 & b_2 & c_2 \end{vmatrix} = a_3\bar{A}_3 - b_3\bar{B}_3 + c_3\bar{C}_3.$$

Since rows and columns can be interchanged, it follows that

$$\begin{aligned} \Delta &= a_1\bar{A}_1 - a_2\bar{A}_2 + a_3\bar{A}_3, \\ &= -\{b_1\bar{B}_1 - b_2\bar{B}_2 + b_3\bar{B}_3\}, \\ &= c_1\bar{C}_1 - c_2\bar{C}_2 + c_3\bar{C}_3. \end{aligned}$$

It is convenient to take up the sign changes in the coefficients of the elements and write

$$\begin{aligned} A_1 &= \bar{A}_1; & B_1 &= -\bar{B}_1; & C_1 &= \bar{C}_1; \\ A_2 &= -\bar{A}_2; & B_2 &= \bar{B}_2; & C_2 &= -\bar{C}_2; \\ A_3 &= \bar{A}_3; & B_3 &= -\bar{B}_3; & C_3 &= \bar{C}_3. \end{aligned}$$

The terms A_1, B_1, . . . are called *the cofactors* of $a_1, b_1,$ . . . Their *numerical values* are obtained by evaluating the determinants remaining when the rows and columns through their respective elements are deleted; their signs are determined by the following rule:

Rule of sign. Start at the top left-hand corner and pass by rows and columns, never diagonally, to the particular element counting $+$, $-$ alternately at each element until the particular element is reached.

Using cofactors the fundamental results for a third-order determinant are

$$\Delta = a_1 A_1 + b_1 B_1 + c_1 C_1; \qquad \Delta = a_1 A_1 + a_2 A_2 + a_3 A_3;$$
$$\cdots \cdots \cdots \cdots \qquad \cdots \cdots \cdots \cdots$$

In general, *the value of a determinant is the sum of the products of the elements of any row, or column, and their corresponding cofactors.*

Ex. 9. *For the determinant* $\begin{vmatrix} x & y & z \\ p & q & r \\ y & z & x \end{vmatrix}$ *find:* (i) *the minor of r;*

(ii) *the cofactor of q.*

(i) Minor of r, $\overline{R} = \begin{vmatrix} x & y \\ y & z \end{vmatrix} = xz - y^2.$

(ii) Cofactor of q, $Q = + \begin{vmatrix} x & z \\ y & x \end{vmatrix} = x^2 - yz.$

Ex. 10. *Find the cofactor of f in the determinant* $\begin{vmatrix} a & h & g \\ h & b & f \\ g & f & c \end{vmatrix}.$

There are two elements f, but Δ is symmetrical in f, g, h, and the same result will be obtained using either of the elements.

$$F = - \begin{vmatrix} a & h \\ g & f \end{vmatrix} = gh - af.$$

General theorems on cofactors.

I.   The sum of the products of the elements of any row, or column, and their corresponding cofactors equals Δ.

A result already proved for a third-order determinant which can similarly be proved true of any determinant.

II.   The sum of the products of the elements of any row (column) and the cofactors of the corresponding elements of another row (column) is zero.

For consider $\qquad \Delta = \begin{vmatrix} a_1 & b_1 & c_1 \\ a_2 & b_2 & c_2 \\ a_3 & b_3 & c_3 \end{vmatrix}.$

Then $\quad a_1 A_2 + b_1 B_2 + c_1 C_2 = -a_1 \begin{vmatrix} b_1 & c_1 \\ b_3 & c_3 \end{vmatrix} + b_1 \begin{vmatrix} a_1 & c_1 \\ a_3 & c_3 \end{vmatrix} - c_1 \begin{vmatrix} a_1 & b_1 \\ a_3 & b_3 \end{vmatrix}$

$$= - \begin{vmatrix} a_1 & b_1 & c_1 \\ a_1 & b_1 & c_1 \\ a_3 & b_3 & c_3 \end{vmatrix} = 0, \text{ by Law II.}$$

Similarly, for products $a_1 A_3 + b_1 B_3 + c_1 C_3$, $a_2 A_1 + b_2 B_1 + c_2 C_1$, etc. This theorem can also be extended to determinants of any order.

Ex. 11. If $\Delta = \begin{vmatrix} a & b & c \\ p & q & r \\ x & y & z \end{vmatrix}$, *evaluate:* (i) $aA + pP + xX$; (ii) $pA + qB + rC$;

(iii) $(3a + 2b + c)B + (3p + 2q + r)Q + (3x + 2y + z)Y$.

(i) Using theorem I, $aA + pP + xX = \Delta$.

(ii) Using theorem II, $pA + qB + rC = 0$.

(iii) Expression $= 3(aB + pQ + xY) + 2(bB + qQ + yY) + (cB + rQ + zY)$
$= 0 + 2\Delta + 0 = 2\Delta$.

EXAMPLES 3c

Express the following determinants as products of factors:

1. $\begin{vmatrix} a & b \\ a^2 & b^2 \end{vmatrix}$.

2. $\begin{vmatrix} 3x & x \\ 4y & 8y \end{vmatrix}$.

3. $\begin{vmatrix} a-b & a+b \\ 2a-2b & 3a+3b \end{vmatrix}$.

4. $\begin{vmatrix} a^2 - b^2 & 2(a+b)^2 \\ (a-b)^2 & a+b \end{vmatrix}$.

5. $\begin{vmatrix} x & 3y & 2z \\ 2x & y & 3z \\ 3x & 2y & z \end{vmatrix}$.

6. $\begin{vmatrix} 0 & 6b & 4c \\ 4a & 0 & 6c \\ 6a & 4b & 0 \end{vmatrix}$.

7. $\begin{vmatrix} 0 & x^2 & x^2 - y^2 \\ x-y & y & x+y \\ y-x & x & 0 \end{vmatrix}$.

8. $\begin{vmatrix} 1 & 1 & 1 \\ a & b & c \\ a^2 & b^2 & c^2 \end{vmatrix}$.

9. $\begin{vmatrix} x & x & x & x \\ y & y & y & -y \\ z & z & -z & -z \\ t & -t & -t & -t \end{vmatrix}$.

10. $\begin{vmatrix} 0 & y & 3z & 3t \\ x & 0 & 5z & 2t \\ 3x & 2y & 0 & t \\ 5x & 4y & z & 0 \end{vmatrix}$.

11. $\begin{vmatrix} 1 & 1 & -1 & 1 \\ b & c & b & b \\ c & b & c & -1 \\ -1 & -1 & 1 & c \end{vmatrix}$.

12. Find: (i) the minor, (ii) the cofactor of x in the determinant $\begin{vmatrix} 0 & 1 & 1 \\ 1 & x & 1 \\ 2 & -1 & 1 \end{vmatrix}$.

13. Expand the determinant $\begin{vmatrix} 1 & 1 & 1 \\ x+1 & x^2-1 & (x+1)^2 \\ x^2-1 & (x-1)^2 & x-1 \end{vmatrix}$.

14. Show that $a+b+c$ is a factor of the determinant $\begin{vmatrix} a & b & c \\ b & c & a \\ c & a & b \end{vmatrix}$

and find the second factor.

15. Find the cofactors of a, b, c, f, g, h in the determinant $\begin{vmatrix} a & h & g \\ h & b & f \\ g & f & c \end{vmatrix}$.

16. Prove that $\begin{vmatrix} 1 & 1 & 1 \\ a & b & c \\ a^3 & b^3 & c^3 \end{vmatrix} = (b-c)(c-a)(a-b)(a+b+c)$.

17. Find one root of each of the following equations by inspection and complete their solutions:

$$\text{(i)} \begin{vmatrix} 1-x & 1 & 1 \\ 0 & 2-x & 1 \\ 1 & 1 & 3-x \end{vmatrix} = 0; \quad \text{(ii)} \begin{vmatrix} x-2 & 1 & x \\ 3 & x & -2 \\ -1 & x-4 & x+1 \end{vmatrix} = 0;$$

$$\text{(iii)} \begin{vmatrix} 2-x & 2 & 3 \\ 2 & 5-x & 6 \\ 3 & 4 & 10-x \end{vmatrix} = 0.$$

18. Prove that $\begin{vmatrix} x & 1 & 1 & 1 \\ 1 & x & 1 & 1 \\ 1 & 1 & x & 1 \\ 1 & 1 & 1 & x \end{vmatrix} = (1-x)^3(x+3).$

19. Factorise the determinants:

$$\text{(i)} \begin{vmatrix} a & a+c & c \\ a & b & a+b \\ b+c & b & c \end{vmatrix}, \quad \text{(ii)} \begin{vmatrix} 1 & 1 & \left(\dfrac{1}{x}-\dfrac{1}{y}\right) \\ \dfrac{1}{x} & \dfrac{1}{y} & \left(\dfrac{1}{x}-\dfrac{1}{y}\right) \\ \dfrac{1}{x^2} & \dfrac{1}{y^2} & \left(\dfrac{1}{x^2}-\dfrac{1}{y^2}\right) \\ \dfrac{1}{x^3} & \dfrac{1}{y^3} & \left(\dfrac{1}{x^3}-\dfrac{1}{y^3}\right) \end{vmatrix}.$$

20. If A, B, ... are the cofactors of a, b, ... in the determinant $\Delta = \begin{vmatrix} a & b & c \\ p & q & r \\ x & y & z \end{vmatrix}$, find the values of:

(i) $(a+2p+3x)A + (b+2q+3y)B + (c+2r+3z)C$;

(ii) $(2a-b+3c)C + (2p-q+3r)R + (2x-y+3z)Z$.

21. Show that $x+y+z$ is a factor of the determinant $\begin{vmatrix} y+z & -y & 2z \\ -x & z+x & -z \\ 2x & 2y & x+y \end{vmatrix}$

and find the other factors.

22. Express $\begin{vmatrix} 1 & 1 & 1 & 1 \\ a & b & c & d \\ a^2 & b^2 & c^2 & d^2 \\ bcd & cda & dab & abc \end{vmatrix}$ as a product of linear factors.

23. If $\Delta = \begin{vmatrix} 1 & 1 & 1 \\ b+c & c+a & a+b \\ b^2+bc+c^2 & c^2+ca+a^2 & a^2+ab+b^2 \end{vmatrix}$, where a, b, c are unequal, prove by multiplying the columns by $b-c$, $c-a$, $a-b$, respectively that $\Delta = 0$.

24. Prove that $\begin{vmatrix} 1 & 1 & 1 \\ a+b & b+c & c+d \\ a^2+ab+b^2 & b^2+bc+c^2 & c^2+cd+d^2 \end{vmatrix} = (d-a)(a-c)(b-d).$

25. If $A_1, B_1 \ldots$ are the cofactors of $a_1, b_1 \ldots$ in $\Delta = \begin{vmatrix} a_1 & b_1 & c_1 \\ a_2 & b_2 & c_2 \\ a_3 & b_3 & c_3 \end{vmatrix}$,

prove that $B_2C_3 - B_3C_2 = a_1\Delta$ and write down similar expressions for $C_2A_3 - C_3A_2$, $A_2B_3 - A_3B_2$.

Deduce that $\begin{vmatrix} A_1 & B_1 & C_1 \\ A_2 & B_2 & C_2 \\ A_3 & B_3 & C_3 \end{vmatrix} = \Delta(a_1A_1 + b_1B_1 + c_1C_1) = \Delta^2.$

Linear simultaneous equations. Determinants can be used to facilitate the solution of simultaneous linear equations. The method will be illustrated for the cases of equations in two and three unknowns.

Equations in two unknowns. Consider the simultaneous equations

$$a_1x + b_1y + c_1 = 0, \qquad \ldots \quad \text{(i)}$$
$$a_2x + b_2y + c_2 = 0. \qquad \ldots \quad \text{(ii)}$$

Multiplying (i) by b_2 and (ii) by b_1 and subtracting,

$$x(a_1b_2 - a_2b_1) = b_1c_2 - b_2c_1.$$

Similarly, $\qquad -y(a_1b_2 - a_2b_1) = a_1c_2 - a_2c_1.$

$$\therefore \frac{x}{b_1c_2 - b_2c_1} = \frac{-y}{a_1c_2 - a_2c_1} = \frac{1}{a_1b_2 - a_2b_1}.$$

I.e. $\qquad \dfrac{x}{\begin{vmatrix} b_1 & c_1 \\ b_2 & c_2 \end{vmatrix}} = \dfrac{-y}{\begin{vmatrix} a_1 & c_1 \\ a_2 & c_2 \end{vmatrix}} = \dfrac{1}{\begin{vmatrix} a_1 & b_1 \\ a_2 & b_2 \end{vmatrix}}, \qquad \ldots \quad \text{(A)}$

where the signs in the numerators are alternately plus and minus and the determinants are obtained from the set of elements

$$\begin{Vmatrix} a_1 & b_1 & c_1 \\ a_2 & b_2 & c_2 \end{Vmatrix}$$

omitting in turn the first, second and third columns.

The general solution (A), which is readily memorized, is particularly useful in analytical geometry.

Ex. 12. *Find the point of intersection of the straight lines with equations* $3x - y - 2 = 0$, $x + y + 6 = 0$.

We have $\qquad \dfrac{x}{\begin{vmatrix} -1 & -2 \\ 1 & 6 \end{vmatrix}} = \dfrac{-y}{\begin{vmatrix} 3 & -2 \\ 1 & 6 \end{vmatrix}} = \dfrac{1}{\begin{vmatrix} 3 & -1 \\ 1 & 1 \end{vmatrix}}.$

I.e. $\qquad \dfrac{x}{-4} = \dfrac{-y}{20} = \dfrac{1}{4},$

$$x = -1, \qquad y = -5.$$

The point of intersection is $(-1, -5)$.

Special cases. Referring to the general solution (A), it is clear that exceptional cases arise if $\begin{vmatrix} a_1 & b_1 \\ a_2 & b_2 \end{vmatrix}$ or $a_1b_2 - a_2b_1 = 0$.

When this condition is satisfied there are two possibilities, either $\begin{vmatrix} b_1 & c_1 \\ b_2 & c_2 \end{vmatrix}$ and $\begin{vmatrix} a_1 & c_1 \\ a_2 & c_2 \end{vmatrix}$ do not vanish, in which case the equations have no finite solution and are said to be *inconsistent*, or $\begin{vmatrix} b_1 & c_1 \\ b_2 & c_2 \end{vmatrix}$ and $\begin{vmatrix} a_1 & c_1 \\ a_2 & c_2 \end{vmatrix}$ also vanish, and then the values of x and y are indeterminate and the equations are *not independent*.

It should be noted that when $\begin{vmatrix} a_1 & b_1 \\ a_2 & b_2 \end{vmatrix} = 0$, if either of the determinants $\begin{vmatrix} b_1 & c_1 \\ b_2 & c_2 \end{vmatrix}$, $\begin{vmatrix} a_1 & c_1 \\ a_2 & c_2 \end{vmatrix}$ vanishes so does the other, as in fact

$$\frac{a_1}{a_2} = \frac{b_1}{b_2} = \frac{c_1}{c_2}.$$

There is a simple geometrical explanation of these special cases, for the original equations can be represented as two straight lines and the condition

$$\begin{vmatrix} a_1 & b_1 \\ a_2 & b_2 \end{vmatrix} = a_1b_1 - a_2b_1 = 0,$$

or

$$\frac{a_1}{a_2} = \frac{b_1}{b_2},$$

is satisfied when the lines are parallel and in consequence have no finite point of intersection unless they are coincident. This latter case arises when

$$\frac{a_1}{a_2} = \frac{b_1}{b_2} = \frac{c_1}{c_2},$$

i.e. when in addition one of the determinants $\begin{vmatrix} b_1 & c_1 \\ b_2 & c_2 \end{vmatrix}$, $\begin{vmatrix} a_1 & c_1 \\ a_2 & c_2 \end{vmatrix}$ also vanishes.

Ex. 13. *Solve the equations* $(1-\lambda)x + 2y - 1 = 0$, $x + y + 4 - \lambda = 0$. *Discuss the case* $\lambda = -1$.

We have

$$\frac{x}{\begin{vmatrix} 2 & -1 \\ 1 & 4-\lambda \end{vmatrix}} = \frac{-y}{\begin{vmatrix} 1-\lambda & -1 \\ 1 & 4-\lambda \end{vmatrix}} = \frac{1}{\begin{vmatrix} 1-\lambda & 2 \\ 1 & 1 \end{vmatrix}}$$

$$\frac{x}{9-2\lambda} = \frac{-y}{\lambda^2 - 5\lambda + 5} = \frac{1}{-\lambda - 1}.$$

I.e.

$$x = \frac{2\lambda - 9}{\lambda + 1}, \qquad y = \frac{\lambda^2 - 5\lambda + 5}{\lambda + 1}.$$

When $\lambda = -1$, the solutions are infinite, and in consequence the equations are inconsistent. In fact, the equations become $x + y - \frac{1}{2} = 0$, $x + y + 5 = 0$.

Equations in three unknowns. Consider the simultaneous equations

$$a_1x+b_1y+c_1z+d_1=0, \quad \ldots \quad \text{(i)}$$
$$a_2x+b_2y+c_2z+d_2=0, \quad \ldots \quad \text{(ii)}$$
$$a_3x+b_3y+c_3z+d_3=0. \quad \ldots \quad \text{(iii)}$$

Let A_1, B_1, ... be the cofactors of a_1, b_1, ... in the determinant

$$\Delta=\begin{vmatrix} a_1 & b_1 & c_1 \\ a_2 & b_2 & c_2 \\ a_3 & b_3 & c_3 \end{vmatrix},$$

where the elements are the coefficients of x, y, z in the given equations.

Now multiply the equations (i), (ii), (iii) by A_1, A_2, A_3 respectively and add.

Then $\quad x(a_1A_1+a_2A_2+a_3A_3)+y(b_1A_1+b_2A_2+b_3A_3)$
$$+z(c_1A_1+c_2A_2+c_3A_3)+d_1A_1+d_2A_2+d_3A_3=0.$$

But $\quad a_1A_1+a_2A_2+a_3A_3=\Delta \quad$ and $\quad b_1A_1+b_2A_2+b_3A_3$
$$=c_1A_1+c_2A_2+c_3A_3=0.$$

$$\therefore \ x\Delta=-(d_1A_1+d_2A_2+d_3A_3)$$
$$=-\begin{vmatrix} d_1 & b_1 & c_1 \\ d_2 & b_2 & c_2 \\ d_3 & b_3 & c_3 \end{vmatrix} = -\begin{vmatrix} b_1 & c_1 & d_1 \\ b_2 & c_2 & d_2 \\ b_3 & c_3 & d_3 \end{vmatrix}.$$

Similarly, by multiplying the equations by B_1, B_2, B_3 respectively,

$$y\Delta=+\begin{vmatrix} a_1 & c_1 & d_1 \\ a_2 & c_2 & d_2 \\ a_3 & c_3 & d_3 \end{vmatrix}.$$

Also $\qquad\qquad z\Delta=-\begin{vmatrix} a_1 & b_1 & d_1 \\ a_2 & b_2 & d_2 \\ a_3 & b_3 & d_3 \end{vmatrix}.$

Combining these results

$$\frac{x}{\begin{vmatrix} b_1 & c_1 & d_1 \\ b_2 & c_2 & d_2 \\ b_3 & c_3 & d_3 \end{vmatrix}}=\frac{-y}{\begin{vmatrix} a_1 & c_1 & d_1 \\ a_2 & c_2 & d_2 \\ a_3 & c_3 & d_3 \end{vmatrix}}=\frac{z}{\begin{vmatrix} a_1 & b_1 & d_1 \\ a_2 & b_2 & d_2 \\ a_3 & b_3 & d_3 \end{vmatrix}}=\frac{-1}{\begin{vmatrix} a_1 & b_1 & c_1 \\ a_2 & b_2 & c_2 \\ a_3 & b_3 & c_3 \end{vmatrix}}, \quad \text{(B)}$$

where the signs in the numerators are alternately plus and minus and the determinants are obtained from the set of elements

$$\begin{Vmatrix} a_1 & b_1 & c_1 & d_1 \\ a_2 & b_2 & c_2 & d_2 \\ a_3 & b_3 & c_3 & d_3 \end{Vmatrix}$$

omitting in turn the first, second, third and fourth columns.

Ex. 14. *Solve the equations*

$$3x - y + 4z + 2 = 0, \quad x + 2y - z + 3 = 0, \quad -2x + 3y + z - 5 = 0.$$

We have

$$\frac{x}{\begin{vmatrix} -1 & 4 & 2 \\ 2 & -1 & 3 \\ 3 & 1 & -5 \end{vmatrix}} = \frac{-y}{\begin{vmatrix} 3 & 4 & 2 \\ 1 & -1 & 3 \\ -2 & 1 & -5 \end{vmatrix}} = \frac{z}{\begin{vmatrix} 3 & -1 & 2 \\ 1 & 2 & 3 \\ -2 & 3 & -5 \end{vmatrix}} = \frac{-1}{\begin{vmatrix} 3 & -1 & 4 \\ 1 & 2 & -1 \\ -2 & 3 & 1 \end{vmatrix}},$$

$$\frac{x}{84} = \frac{-y}{0} = \frac{z}{-42} = \frac{-1}{42}.$$

i.e. $\qquad\qquad\qquad x = -2, \quad y = 0, \quad z = 1.$

In dealing with linear equations in three unknowns it is often more convenient to reduce them to two equations in two unknowns and complete the solution from that stage.

Ex. 15. *Solve the equations* $x + y + z = 0$, $2x - y - 3z = 4$, $3x + 3y = 7$.

Eliminating z between the first two equations gives

$$5x + 2y = 4.$$

Solving the equations $\qquad 5x + 2y - 4 = 0$
$$3x + 3y - 7 = 0,$$

$$\frac{x}{-14 + 12} = \frac{-y}{-35 + 12} = \frac{1}{15 - 6}$$

i.e. $\qquad\qquad\qquad x = -\tfrac{2}{9}, \quad y = \tfrac{23}{9};$

from the first equation, $\qquad\qquad z = -\tfrac{7}{3}.$

Special cases. Referring to the general solution (B), it is evident that special cases arise if

$$\Delta = \begin{vmatrix} a_1 & b_1 & c_1 \\ a_2 & b_2 & c_2 \\ a_3 & b_3 & c_3 \end{vmatrix} = 0.$$

In this event either x, y, z are all infinite and the equations are *inconsistent*, or x, y, z are indeterminate of the form $\frac{0}{0}$ and the equations are not all *independent*, being equivalent to two independent equations or just one.

I. *The equations are inconsistent* if $\Delta = 0$ and none of the determinants

$$\Delta_1 = \begin{vmatrix} b_1 & c_1 & d_1 \\ b_2 & c_2 & d_2 \\ b_3 & c_3 & d_3 \end{vmatrix}, \qquad \Delta_2 = \begin{vmatrix} a_1 & c_1 & d_1 \\ a_2 & c_2 & d_2 \\ a_3 & c_3 & d_3 \end{vmatrix}, \qquad \Delta_3 = \begin{vmatrix} a_1 & b_1 & d_1 \\ a_2 & b_2 & d_2 \\ a_3 & b_3 & d_3 \end{vmatrix}, \text{ vanish.}$$

II. *The equations are not independent* if $\Delta = 0$ and also two of $\Delta_1, \Delta_2, \Delta_3 = 0$. In this event it can readily be shown that all the latter determinants vanish.

Geometrically, as will be proved in a later chapter, a linear equation in three variables represents a plane in three-dimensional space. Consequently the system of three equations represents three planes with the following possible configurations and results.

(i) The planes meet in a point; the equations have a unique finite solution.

(ii) At least two planes are parallel; the equations are inconsistent with no finite solution and $\Delta = 0$; $\Delta_1, \Delta_2, \Delta_3 \neq 0$.

(iii) The planes intersect in three parallel lines; as (ii).

(iv) The planes intersect in a common line; the equations are not independent, being equivalent to two independent equations with a line of solutions and $\Delta = \Delta_1 = \Delta_2 = \Delta_3 = 0$.

(v) The planes coincide; the equations are not independent, being equivalent to a single equation with a plane of solutions and $\Delta = \Delta_1 = \Delta_2 = \Delta_3 = 0$.

(vi) Two planes coincide and the third plane intersects them in a line; as (iv).

(vii) Two planes coincide and the third plane is parallel to them; the equations are not independent and also inconsistent. There are no finite solutions and $\Delta = \Delta_1 = \Delta_2 = \Delta_3 = 0$.

In dealing with sets of linear equations it is important to remember that the elementary method of solution is often the more convenient, especially when investigating special cases. Both this method and the determinant method will be illustrated in the following examples.

Ex. 16. *Show that the equations* $2x + 5y + 3z = 0$, $x - y + 4z = 2$, $7y - 5z + 4 = 0$ *are not independent.*

Method (i).
$$\Delta = \begin{vmatrix} 2 & 5 & 3 \\ 1 & -1 & 4 \\ 0 & 7 & -5 \end{vmatrix} = 0, \text{ on expansion,}$$

and
$$\Delta_1 = \begin{vmatrix} 5 & 3 & 0 \\ -1 & 4 & -2 \\ 7 & -5 & 4 \end{vmatrix} = 0; \quad \Delta_2 = \begin{vmatrix} 2 & 3 & 0 \\ 1 & 4 & -2 \\ 0 & -5 & 4 \end{vmatrix} = 0.$$

Hence the equations are not independent.

Method (ii). The result of eliminating x between the first two equations is the equation $7y - 5z + 4 = 0$, which is identical with the third equation.

Hence the equations are equivalent to the two equations $2x + 5y + 3z = 0$, $7y - 5z + 4 = 0$. They are satisfied by all points lying on the line determined by the two planes with these equations.

Ex. 17. *Show that the equations* $x + y + z - 1 = 0$, $2x - 3y - 2z + 4 = 0$, $3x - 2y - z + 2 = 0$ *have no finite solution.*

Method (i).
$$\Delta = \begin{vmatrix} 1 & 1 & 1 \\ 2 & -3 & -2 \\ 3 & -2 & -1 \end{vmatrix} = 0,$$

and
$$\Delta_1 = \begin{vmatrix} 1 & 1 & -1 \\ -3 & -2 & 4 \\ -2 & -1 & 2 \end{vmatrix} \neq 0.$$

$\therefore$ The equations are inconsistent and have no finite solution.

Method (ii). Eliminating x between the first equation and the other equations taken consecutively, leads to the equations

$$5y + 4z = 6,$$
$$5y + 4z = 5.$$

These equations are clearly inconsistent, and in consequence so are the original equations.

Ex. 18. *Of the equations* $x - y + z = 5$, $2x + y + 4z = 12$, $3x + 3y + 7z = 18$, $4x - y + 6z = 22$, *one is inconsistent with the other three. Find this equation and modify its constant term in order to make it consistent with the others.*

Eliminating x between the first equation and the other equations taken consecutively leads to the equations

$$3y + 2z = 2, \qquad \dots \dots \dots \text{(i)}$$
$$6y + 4z = 3, \qquad \dots \dots \dots \text{(ii)}$$
$$3y + 2z = 2. \qquad \dots \dots \dots \text{(iii)}$$

As (ii) is inconsistent with (i) and (iii), it follows that of the original equations, the third is inconsistent with the others; by changing the constant term of this equation to 19, (ii) becomes

$$6y + 4z = 4$$

i.e.
$$3y + 2z = 2,$$

and the equations are now consistent. They are in fact not independent and have a line of solutions.

Ex. 19. *Solve the equations* $2x - y + z = 0$, $3y + z = 0$, $x + y + az = b$, *where a and b are constants with $a \neq 1$. Discuss the case $a = 1$.*

We have

$$\frac{x}{\begin{vmatrix} -1 & 1 & 0 \\ 3 & 1 & 0 \\ 1 & a & -b \end{vmatrix}} = \frac{-y}{\begin{vmatrix} 2 & 1 & 0 \\ 0 & 1 & 0 \\ 1 & a & -b \end{vmatrix}} = \frac{z}{\begin{vmatrix} 2 & -1 & 0 \\ 0 & 3 & 0 \\ 1 & 1 & -b \end{vmatrix}} = \frac{-1}{\begin{vmatrix} 2 & -1 & 1 \\ 0 & 3 & 1 \\ 1 & 1 & a \end{vmatrix}}$$

i.e.
$$\frac{x}{4b} = \frac{-y}{-2b} = \frac{z}{-6b} = \frac{-1}{6a - 6}.$$

So if $a \neq 1$;
$$x = \frac{-2b}{3(a-1)}, \qquad y = \frac{-b}{3(a-1)}, \qquad z = \frac{b}{a-1}.$$

If $a = 1$ and $b \neq 0$; x, y, z are each infinite and the equations are inconsistent.

If $a = 1$ and $b = 0$; x, y, z are each indeterminate and the equations are not independent.

EXAMPLES 3d

Solve, where possible, the following systems of equations:

1. $2x - y + 3 = 0$,
$x + 2y - 1 = 0$.

2. $3x - 4y + 1 = 0$,
$x + 2y - 3 = 0$.

3. $6x + y + 3 = 0$,
$3x - 2y + 9 = 0$.

4. $x + y - 4 = 0$,
$2x + 2y - 3 = 0$.

5. $5x + 2y - 5 = 0$,
$x - y - 8 = 0$.

6. $3x - 2y - 1 = 0$,
$9x - 6y - 3 = 0$.

7. $3x - 7y - 35 = 0,$
$2x + 5y - 4 = 0.$

8. $3x - 5y + 10 = 0,$
$6x - 10y + 17 = 0.$

9. $x + 3y - 10 = 0,$
$-2x + 4y = 0.$

10. $x + y + z - 2 = 0,$
$x + 2y + 3z - 1 = 0,$
$3x - y - 5z - 1 = 0.$

11. $2x - y + z - 3 = 0,$
$x + 2y - z - 1 = 0,$
$3x + y + z - 6 = 0.$

12. $x + y - 10 = 0,$
$y + z - 3 = 0,$
$x + z + 1 = 0.$

13. $2x - y - z = 6,$
$x + 3y + 2z = 1,$
$3x - y - 5z = 1.$

14. $x + 2y - 3z = 0,$
$3x + 3y - z = 5,$
$x - 2y + 2z = 1.$

15. $x + y + z - 1 = 0,$
$2x - 3y - 2z + 4 = 0,$
$3x - 2y - z + 2 = 0.$

16. $7x + y - 2z + 9 = 0,$
$x - 2y - z + 2 = 0,$
$5x + y - z + 5 = 0.$

17. $x + 2y - z + 3 = 0,$
$2x + y + z - 1 = 0,$
$3x + 3y + 2 = 0.$

18. $2x + 4y - z + 3 = 0,$
$3x - 5y + 4z - 5 = 0,$
$5x - y + 3z + 4 = 0.$

19. $4x - y + 3z - 7 = 0,$
$2x + 3y - 2z - 4 = 0,$
$x - 4y + z = 0.$

20. $-3x + 3y + 2z - 5 = 0,$
$5x - 2y + z + 6 = 0,$
$2x + y + 3z + 1 = 0.$

21. $3x + y - 2z - 3 = 0,$
$-9x - 3y + 6z + 9 = 0,$
$6x + 2y - 4z - 6 = 0.$

22. Find the points of intersection of the following pairs of straight lines:

(i) $2y - x + 6 = 0,$
$x + 3y - 2 = 0.$

(ii) $4x - y + 1 = 0,$
$3x + 7y - 3 = 0.$

(iii) $2x + 5y = 1,$
$3x - 4y = -4.$

23. Solve the following systems of equations for the ratios $x : y : z$:

(i) $2x - y + z = 0,$
$3x + 2y - 4z = 0.$

(ii) $x - 3y + 2z = 0,$
$2x + 5y - z = 0.$

(iii) $4x - 2y + z = 0,$
$3x + 5y - 4z = 0.$

24. For what values of λ are the equations $2x - (\lambda + 2)y - 1 = 0,$ $6x - 3y - \lambda = 0$: (i) inconsistent; (ii) not independent?

25. For what values of μ are the following sets of equations consistent?

(i) $x + 3 = 0,$
$y - 2 = 0,$
$x + y + \mu = 0.$

(ii) $2x - \mu y + 3 = 0,$
$x + y - 4 = 0,$
$3y - 11 = 0.$

(iii) $4x + y - 7 = 0,$
$x - y + \mu = 0,$
$3x - \mu y - 1 = 0.$

26. When $x = 2, -1, \frac{1}{2},$ the function $ax^2 + bx + c$ takes the values 15, 9, 3 respectively. Find the value of the function when $x = 0.$

27. For what values of λ are the following systems of equations: (*a*) inconsistent; (*b*) not independent?

(i) $2x - \lambda y + 4z = 1,$
$\lambda x - y = 2,$
$x + 2y - 4z = 1.$

(ii) $\lambda x + 2y + z = 0,$
$3x - 2z = 4,$
$3x - 6\lambda y - 4z = 14.$

(iii) $3x - \lambda y = 6,$
$4y + \lambda z = 1,$
$3x + 6y + 4z = 4.$

28. Solve the equations $x + y + z = 1,$ $ax + by + cz = k,$ $a^2x + b^2y + c^2z = k^2$ if a, b, c are not zero.

29. Solve the equations $5x + 2y = 3,$ $2x + 3y - 5z = 1,$ $\lambda x - 5y + 15z = \mu.$ For what values of λ and μ are the equations: (i) inconsistent; (ii) not independent?

F

30. Prove that the equations $x + y + 2 = 0$, $y + 2z - 4 = 0$, $2x + 5y + 6z - 8 = 0$ are not independent and show that their solutions can be expressed in the form $x = 2\lambda - 6$, $y = 4 - 2\lambda$, $z = \lambda$, where λ is a parameter.

31. Solve the equations $5x + y - 2z = 0$, $13y + 3az = b$, $2x + ay + z = 1$ and discuss the special cases: (i) $a = 3$, $b \neq 5$; (ii) $a = 3$, $b = 5$.

32. One of the following equations is inconsistent with the others. Find this equation and by a modification of its constant term make it consistent:

(i) $x - y + z + 2 = 0$;   (ii) $2x + 2y + z + 7 = 0$;
(iii) $3x + 5y + z + 12 = 0$;   (iv) $4y - z + 4 = 0$.

33. Solve the equations $\lambda x + y + z = 1$, $x + \lambda y + z = \lambda$, $x + y + \lambda z = \lambda^2$. Examine the special cases: (i) $\lambda = 1$, (ii) $\lambda = -2$.

34. Solve the following systems of equations by first reducing them to equations in three unknowns:

(i) $2x + y + 2z - t = 6$, $x - z - 2t = 0$, $3y + z + t = 1$, $3z + 2t = 5$.
(ii) $x + y + z + t = x - y + z - t + 4 = 2x - 3y - z - 3t - 5$
$$= 3x - 2y + 2z + 5t + 12 = 0.$$

35. For what values of λ are the following equations consistent:
$$2x - \lambda y + 2z = 0, \quad x + y - \lambda z = 4, \quad \lambda x - y + z = 2, \quad 7x - 5y + 6z = 1?$$

36. The expression $ax^3 + bx^2 + cx + d$ takes the value zero when $x = 1$ or $-\frac{1}{2}$ and takes the value 3 when $x = -1$ or 2. Find the value of the constants a, b, c, d.

Homogeneous linear equations. Linear equations of the forms

$$a_1 x + b_1 y = 0, \quad \ldots \ldots \quad \text{(i)}$$
$$a_1 x + b_1 y + c_1 z = 0, \quad \ldots \ldots \quad \text{(ii)}$$

where the constant terms are zero, are homogeneous. Such equations are always satisfied by zero values of the variables;

e.g.   equation (i) is satisfied when $x = y = 0$,
             equation (ii) is satisfied when $x = y = z = 0$.

Consideration will be given here to the conditions necessary for sets of homogeneous linear equations to have solutions in which all the variables are not zero.

Equations in two unknowns. Consider the equation
$$a_1 x + b_1 y = 0.$$

Apart from the obvious solution $x = y = 0$, we can look for other solutions by assuming at least one of the variables is not zero, say y, and dividing the equation by this variable.

I.e. $a_1 \dfrac{x}{y} + b_1 = 0; \quad \dfrac{x}{y} = -\dfrac{b_1}{a_1}.$

Hence the equation can be solved for the ratio $x : y$.

The condition necessary for two equations $a_1x + b_1y = 0$, $a_2x + b_2y = 0$ to be satisfied simultaneously by values of x and y not both zero is readily obtained.

The required condition is $\quad -\dfrac{b_1}{a_1} = -\dfrac{b_2}{a_2},$

i.e. $\qquad\qquad\qquad a_1b_2 - a_2b_1 = 0$

or $\qquad\qquad\qquad \begin{vmatrix} a_1 & b_1 \\ a_2 & b_2 \end{vmatrix} = 0.$

It is easily shown that the converse result is also true.

Ex. 20. *Find the values of λ for which the equations $(\lambda - 1)x + 2y = 0$, $4x + (\lambda + 1)y = 0$ can be simultaneously true for non-zero values of both x and y. In each case, give the value of the ratio $x : y$ which satisfies the equations.*

The required condition is
$$\begin{vmatrix} \lambda - 1 & 2 \\ 4 & \lambda + 1 \end{vmatrix} = 0.$$

I.e. $\qquad\qquad\qquad \lambda^2 - 9 = 0; \quad \lambda = \pm 3.$

When $\lambda = 3$, the equations become $2x + 2y = 0$. $\therefore x : y = -1 : 1$.
When $\lambda = -3$, the equations become $-4x + 2y = 0$. $\therefore x : y = 1 : 2$.

Equations in three unknowns. The two equations
$$a_1x + b_1y + c_1z = 0,$$
$$a_2x + b_2y + c_2z = 0,$$

can be solved uniquely for the ratios $x : y : z$, except in the cases when

(i) $x = y = z = 0$, (ii) $\dfrac{a_1}{a_2} = \dfrac{b_1}{b_2} = \dfrac{c_1}{c_2}$, in which event the equations are identical.

For assuming $z \neq 0$ and writing $X = \dfrac{x}{z}$, $Y = \dfrac{y}{z}$, the equations become

$$a_1X + b_1Y + c_1 = 0,$$
$$a_2X + b_2Y + c_2 = 0.$$

$$\therefore \quad \frac{X}{\begin{vmatrix} b_1 & c_1 \\ b_2 & c_2 \end{vmatrix}} = \frac{-Y}{\begin{vmatrix} a_1 & c_1 \\ a_2 & c_2 \end{vmatrix}} = \frac{1}{\begin{vmatrix} a_1 & b_1 \\ a_2 & b_2 \end{vmatrix}}$$

i.e. $$\frac{x}{\begin{vmatrix} b_1 & c_1 \\ b_2 & c_2 \end{vmatrix}} = \frac{-y}{\begin{vmatrix} a_1 & c_1 \\ a_2 & c_2 \end{vmatrix}} = \frac{z}{\begin{vmatrix} a_1 & b_1 \\ a_2 & b_2 \end{vmatrix}},$$

or $$x : y : z = \begin{vmatrix} b_1 & c_1 \\ b_2 & c_2 \end{vmatrix} : -\begin{vmatrix} a_1 & c_1 \\ a_2 & c_2 \end{vmatrix} : \begin{vmatrix} a_1 & b_1 \\ a_2 & b_2 \end{vmatrix}.$$

Ex. 21. *Solve the equations* $3x + y - 4z = 0$, $2x + 3y + z = 0$ *for the ratios* $x : y : z$.

We have
$$\frac{x}{\begin{vmatrix} 1 & -4 \\ 3 & 1 \end{vmatrix}} = \frac{-y}{\begin{vmatrix} 3 & -4 \\ 2 & 1 \end{vmatrix}} = \frac{z}{\begin{vmatrix} 3 & 1 \\ 2 & 3 \end{vmatrix}},$$

or
$$x : y : z = 13 : -11 : 7.$$

If there are values of x, y, z not all zero, such that the equations $a_1x + b_1y + c_1z = 0$, $a_2x + b_2y + c_2z = 0$, $a_3x + b_3y + c_3z = 0$ *hold simultaneously,*

then
$$\begin{vmatrix} a_1 & b_1 & c_1 \\ a_2 & b_2 & c_2 \\ a_3 & b_3 & c_3 \end{vmatrix} = 0 \text{ and conversely.}$$

For assuming $z \neq 0$ and writing $X = \dfrac{x}{z}$, $Y = \dfrac{y}{z}$, the equations become

$$a_1X + b_1Y + c_1 = 0,$$
$$a_2X + b_2Y + c_2 = 0,$$
$$a_3X + b_3Y + c_3 = 0.$$

From the last two equations,

$$\frac{X}{\begin{vmatrix} b_2 & c_2 \\ b_3 & c_3 \end{vmatrix}} = \frac{-Y}{\begin{vmatrix} a_2 & c_2 \\ a_3 & c_3 \end{vmatrix}} = \frac{1}{\begin{vmatrix} a_2 & b_2 \\ a_3 & b_3 \end{vmatrix}}.$$

Substituting for X, Y in the first equation,

$$a_1 \begin{vmatrix} b_2 & c_2 \\ b_3 & c_3 \end{vmatrix} - b_1 \begin{vmatrix} a_2 & c_2 \\ a_3 & c_3 \end{vmatrix} + c_1 \begin{vmatrix} a_2 & b_2 \\ a_3 & b_3 \end{vmatrix} = 0$$

i.e.
$$\Delta = \begin{vmatrix} a_1 & b_1 & c_1 \\ a_2 & b_2 & c_2 \\ a_3 & b_3 & c_3 \end{vmatrix} = 0.$$

Conversely, if $\Delta = 0$, then
$$a_1A_1 + b_1B_1 + c_1C_1 = \Delta = 0$$
and
$$a_2A_1 + b_2B_1 + c_2C_1 = 0,$$
$$a_3A_1 + b_3B_1 + c_3C_1 = 0,$$

where A_1, B_1, C_1 are the cofactors of a_1, b_1, c_1 in Δ.

But all three of A_1, B_1, C_1 only vanish if $\dfrac{a_2}{a_3} = \dfrac{b_2}{b_3} = \dfrac{c_2}{c_3}$, in which case Δ vanishes identically.

Consequently, if $\Delta = 0$, then there exist numbers x, y, z not all zero, where $x : y : z = A_1 : B_1 : C_1$, such that the three equations

$$a_1x + b_1y + c_1z = 0, \quad a_2x + b_2y + c_2z = 0, \quad a_3x + b_3y + c_3z = 0$$

hold simultaneously.

Ex. 22. *Find the values of λ for which the equations $3x - y + z = 0$, $3x + \lambda y - 5z = 0$, $\lambda x - 3y + 4z = 0$ are consistent for non-zero values of x, y, z.*

The equations have solutions other than $x = y = z = 0$, if

$$\begin{vmatrix} 3 & -1 & 1 \\ 3 & \lambda & -5 \\ \lambda & -3 & 4 \end{vmatrix} = 0.$$

I.e.
$$-\lambda^2 + 17\lambda - 42 = 0$$
$$\lambda = 3, 14.$$

Ex. 23. *Prove that the straight lines $5x - 3y - 2 = 0$, $x - 2y - 1 = 0$, $2x + 3y + 1 = 0$ are concurrent.*

The straight lines are concurrent if there are values of x, y which satisfy the three equations simultaneously.

Consequently, making the equations homogeneous by writing $z = 1$, it is necessary to show that the equations $5x - 3y - 2z = 0$, $x - 2y - z = 0$, $2x + 3y + z = 0$ are consistent.

This is so because
$$\Delta = \begin{vmatrix} 5 & -3 & -2 \\ 1 & -2 & -1 \\ 2 & 3 & 1 \end{vmatrix} = 0.$$

Ex. 24. *Eliminate λ, μ from the equations $x = \dfrac{2\mu}{\lambda + 1}$, $y = \dfrac{\mu}{2\lambda + 1}$, $z = \dfrac{\mu}{\lambda - 1}$.*

The equations can be expressed in the form

$$x\lambda - 2\mu + x.1 = 0,$$
$$2y\lambda - \mu + y.1 = 0,$$
$$z\lambda - \mu - z.1 = 0.$$

Treating these as equations in λ, μ and 1, it follows that as they are consistent

$$\begin{vmatrix} x & -2 & x \\ 2y & -1 & y \\ z & -1 & -z \end{vmatrix} = 0,$$

or
$$-6yz + 2zx - xy = 0.$$

EXAMPLES 3e

1. Prove that the following equations are consistent: (i) $4x - 3y = 0$, $6y - 8x = 0$; (ii) $x + 3y = 0$, $-2x - 6y = 0$; (iii) $ax + by = 0$, $abx + b^2y = 0$.

2. Find the values of λ for which each of the following sets of equations are consistent for non-zero values of both x and y. In each case give the ratio of x to y.

(i) $\lambda x + 4y = 0$, (ii) $8x - \lambda y = 0$, (iii) $(\lambda - 1)x + y = 0$, (iv) $\lambda^3 x - 4y = 0$,
$\quad\ 2x - y = 0.$ $\qquad\ \lambda x - 2y = 0.$ $\qquad\quad\ 2x + \lambda y = 0.$ $\qquad\quad\ \lambda x - y = 0.$

3. Write down the result of eliminating x, y from each of the following sets of equations:

    (i) $px - qy = 0$,   (ii) $lx + my = 0$,   (iii) $ax + by = 0$,   (iv) $ax + by = x - y$,
       $qx + py = 0$. $2x + 3y = 0$. $ax - by = 0$. $ax - by = x + y$.

4. If $a^2x + b^2y = bx - ay = 0$ where $x \neq 0$ and $a + b \neq 0$, prove that $a^2 + b^2 = ab$.

5. Solve the following sets of equations for the ratios $x : y : z$:

    (i) $x + y + 2z = 0$,   (ii) $3x + 4y - 2z = 0$,   (iii) $-x + ny + qz = 0$,
       $2x - y + z = 0$. $2x - 3y + 3z = 0$. $-x + my + rz = 0$.

6. Eliminate x, y, z assumed not all zero, from each of the following systems of equations:

    (i) $ax + by + cz = 0$,   (ii) $my + nz = 0$,   (iii) $x + y + z = 0$,
       $3x - y + z = 0$, $lx + mz = 0$, $xx_1 + yy_1 + zz_1 = 0$,
       $x + 2y - z = 0$. $x + y + z = 0$. $xx_2 + yy_2 + zz_2 = 0$.

7. Prove that each of the following sets of straight lines is concurrent:

    (i) $x + 2y - 3 = 0$,   (ii) $3y - x = 0$,   (iii) $ax + by = 1$,
       $3x - y + 1 = 0$, $x + y + 5 = 0$, $bx + ay = 0$,
       $x - 5y + 7 = 0$. $2y - 2x - 5 = 0$. $(a - \lambda b)x + (b - \lambda ay) = 1$.

8. Find the values of λ for which the equations

$$\lambda x + y + 1 = 0, \quad x + (\lambda - 2)y - 2 = 0, \quad 4x + 2y - 1 = 0$$

are consistent and in each case complete the solution of the equations.

9. Eliminate x, y, z from the equations

$$ax + hy + gz = 0, \quad hx + by + fz = 0, \quad gx + fy + cz = 0.$$

10. Find the values of λ for which values of x, y, z, not all zero, can be found to satisfy simultaneously the equations in each of the following sets:

    (i) $2x + y + z = 0$,   (ii) $x + \lambda y + 2z = 0$,   (iii) $(1 - \lambda)x + y + z = 0$,
         $x + y - 2z = 0$, $\lambda x - y - z = 0$, $(2 - \lambda)y + z = 0$,
        $\lambda x + 2y - z = 0$. $9x - 2y - 2z = 0$. $x + y + (3 - \lambda)z = 0$.

11. If the four equations $x + y + z = 0$, $x - 2y - z = 0$, $ax + by + cz = 0$, $bx + cy + az = 0$ are satisfied simultaneously by non-zero values of x, y, z, determine the values of the ratios $x : y : z$ and $a : b : c$.

12. Eliminate x, y, z, assumed not all zero, from the equations:

    (i) $x + by + cz = 0$, $ax + y + cz = 0$, $ax + by + z = 0$;

    (ii) $p = \dfrac{x}{y - z}$, $q = \dfrac{y}{z - x}$, $r = \dfrac{z}{x - y}$; $(x \neq y \neq z)$.

13. Show that the result of eliminating λ, μ from the equations

$$x = \lambda x_1 + \mu x_2, \quad y = \lambda y_1 + \mu y_2, \quad z = \lambda z_1 + \mu z_2$$

can be expressed in the form $\begin{vmatrix} x & y & z \\ x_1 & y_1 & z_1 \\ x_2 & y_2 & z_2 \end{vmatrix} = 0.$

14. By writing $X = xy$, $Y = x + y$, $Z = 1$, eliminate x, y from the equations

$$a_1 xy + b_1(x + y) + c_1 = 0, \quad a_2 xy + b_2(x + y) + c_2 = 0, \quad xy - t(x + y) + t^2 = 0$$

leaving the result in a determinant form.

15. If $\quad l = \dfrac{py}{a + x}, \quad m = \dfrac{qy}{b + x}, \quad n = \dfrac{ry}{c + x}, \quad$ prove that

$$pmn(b - c) + qnl(c - a) + rlm(a - b) = 0.$$

MISCELLANEOUS EXAMPLES

1. Solve the equations

$$2x + y + 6z = 2, \quad 6x - 5y - 18z = -10, \quad 4x - 2y - 3z = -9.$$

2. Prove that $\quad \begin{vmatrix} 1 & 1 & 1 \\ bc & ca & ab \\ b^2c + bc^2 & c^2a + ca^2 & a^2b + ab^2 \end{vmatrix} = 0.$

3. If $al + bm + cn = 0$, $al' + bm' + cn' = 0$, prove that $a : b : c = \bar{X} : \bar{Y} : \bar{Z}$, where $\bar{X}$, $\bar{Y}$, $\bar{Z}$ are the minors of z, y, z in the determinant $\begin{vmatrix} x & y & z \\ l & m & n \\ l' & m' & n' \end{vmatrix}$.

4. Factorise: (i) $\begin{vmatrix} 1 & 1 & 1 \\ a & b & c \\ a^2 & b^2 & c^2 \end{vmatrix}$; (ii) $\begin{vmatrix} 1 & 1 & 1 \\ a & b & c \\ a^3 & b^3 & c^3 \end{vmatrix}$.

5. Solve the equations $\quad x - y - 3z = 0, \quad 2x + y - 3\lambda z = 0, \quad x + y - \lambda z = \lambda$ for z, y, z and give the limitations on the value of λ.

6. Solve the equations:

(i) $\begin{vmatrix} 3x - 2 & 2 & 3x \\ 4 & x + 1 & 1 \\ 2x & 1 & 2x - 1 \end{vmatrix} = 0$; (ii) $\begin{vmatrix} a & a & x \\ c & c & c \\ b & x & b \end{vmatrix} = 0.$

7. Eliminate x, y, z from the equations $a = \dfrac{x}{y - z}, \quad b = \dfrac{y}{z - x}, \quad c = \dfrac{z}{x - y}.$

8. Factorise $\Delta = \begin{vmatrix} x + 2 & 3 & 3 \\ 3 & x + 4 & 5 \\ 3 & 5 & x + 4 \end{vmatrix}$ and hence solve the equation $\Delta = 0$.

9. Solve the equations

$$x + y + z = a + b + c, \quad x - y + 2z = 2(2b - c), \quad ax - by + cz = (b - a + c)(b + a - c).$$

10. If a, b, c are unequal and $\begin{vmatrix} 1 & bc + ax & a^2 \\ 1 & ca + bx & b^2 \\ 1 & ab + cx & c^2 \end{vmatrix} = 0$, prove that $x = a + b + c$.

11. Evaluate: (i) $\begin{vmatrix} \frac{1}{2} & \frac{1}{3} & \frac{1}{4} \\ \frac{1}{3} & \frac{1}{4} & \frac{1}{5} \\ \frac{1}{4} & \frac{1}{5} & \frac{1}{6} \end{vmatrix}$; (ii) $\begin{vmatrix} a + b + 2c & a & b \\ c & b + c + 2a & b \\ c & a & c + a + 2b \end{vmatrix}.$

12. The expression $ax^3 + bx^2 + cx + d$ takes the values $1, 0, 4, -11$ when x equals $1, 2, -2, 3$ respectively. Find the value of the expression when x equals 0.

13. If $ax + by + cz = 0 = x/a + y/b + z/c$, prove that $\dfrac{x}{b+c} + \dfrac{y}{c+a} + \dfrac{z}{a+b} = 0$.

14. Prove that $\begin{vmatrix} a-b-c & 2a & 2a \\ 2b & b-c-a & 2b \\ 2c & 2c & c-a-b \end{vmatrix}$ is a perfect cube.

15. Of the four equations $x + 3y + 4z = 1$, $x + y - 2z = 0$, $2x + 3y - z = -1$, $y + 3z = 1$, one is inconsistent with the other three. Find this equation and modify its constant term to make it consistent.

16. If a, b, c are unequal and $\begin{vmatrix} a^2 + a^3 & a & 1 \\ b^2 + b^3 & b & 1 \\ c^2 + c^3 & c & 1 \end{vmatrix} = 0$, prove that $a + b + c + 1 = 0$.

17. Prove that $\begin{vmatrix} 1+x & 1 & 1 & 1 \\ 1 & 1+x & 1 & 1 \\ 1 & 1 & 1+y & 1 \\ 1 & 1 & 1 & 1+y \end{vmatrix} = xy(xy + 2x + 2y)$.

18. Evaluate the determinant $\begin{vmatrix} 1+a & b & c \\ a & 1+b & c \\ a & b & 1+c \end{vmatrix}$.

19. Solve the equation $\begin{vmatrix} 2x & x+1 & 2-x \\ x+3 & 4 & 1 \\ 3-x & 2 & -4 \end{vmatrix} = 0$.

20. Prove that
$$\begin{vmatrix} (a-x)^2 & (a-y)^2 & (a-z)^2 \\ (b-x)^2 & (b-y)^2 & (b-z)^2 \\ (c-x)^2 & (c-y)^2 & (c-z)^2 \end{vmatrix} = 2(b-c)(c-a)(a-b)(y-z)(z-x)(x-y).$$

21. Solve, if possible, the equations $x + y + kz = 4k$, $x + ky + z = -2$, $2x + y + z = -2$, in the cases: (i) k not equal to 0 or 1; (ii) $k = 0$; (iii) $k = 1$.

22. Factorise the determinant $\begin{vmatrix} a & b & c \\ b+c & c+a & a+b \\ a^3 - abc & b^3 - abc & c^3 - abc \end{vmatrix}$.

23. Prove: (i) $\begin{vmatrix} 1 & 1 & 1 & 1 \\ b & a & a & b \\ a & b & a & a \\ a & a & b & b \end{vmatrix} = (b-a)^3$;   (ii) $\begin{vmatrix} a & b & a & b \\ b & a & b & a \\ c & c & d & d \\ d & d & c & c \end{vmatrix} = 0$.

24. Solve the equations:

(i) $\begin{vmatrix} 2-x & 1 & 1 \\ 4-x & 3-x & 4-x \\ 3-x & 2 & 7-x \end{vmatrix} = 0$;   (ii) $\begin{vmatrix} x & x+2 & x-2 \\ 2x & x+3 & x-3 \\ 3x & x+4 & x+4 \end{vmatrix} = 0$.

25. Prove that if $ax + by + cz = 0$, $bx + cy + az = 0$, $cx + ay + bz = 0$ are simultaneously satisfied by non-zero values of x, y, z and if a, b, c are real, then either $a = b = c$ or $a + b + c = 0$. In the latter case prove that $x = y = z$.

26. Find the square root of the determinant

$$\begin{vmatrix} 0 & a & b & c \\ -a & 0 & d & e \\ -b & -d & 0 & f \\ -c & -e & -f & 0 \end{vmatrix}.$$

27. Prove that the two determinants

$$\begin{vmatrix} a & b & c \\ a^2 & b^2 & c^2 \\ b+c & c+a & a+b \end{vmatrix}, \quad \begin{vmatrix} 1 & 1 & 1 \\ a & b & c \\ a^3 & b^3 & c^3 \end{vmatrix}$$

have the same linear factors.

28. Prove that $\begin{vmatrix} 2bc - a^2 & a^2 & a^2 \\ b^2 & 2ca - b^2 & b^2 \\ c^2 & c^2 & 2ab - c^2 \end{vmatrix}$ is divisible by $abc(a + b + c)$ and

express the determinant as a product of real factors.

29. Find the three values of λ for which the equations $\lambda x + 9y + 6z = 0$, $x + \lambda y + 2z = 0$, $7x - y + \lambda z = 0$ can be simultaneously true for non-zero values of x, y and z. In each case give the values of the ratios $x : y : z$ which satisfy the equations.

30. If $\dfrac{a_1 + \lambda a_2}{1} = \dfrac{b_1 + \lambda b_2}{-\theta} = \dfrac{c_1 + \lambda c_2}{\theta^2}$, by equating each ratio to μ and eliminating the ratios $1 : \lambda : \mu$, show that $\begin{vmatrix} a_1 & b_1 & c_1 \\ a_2 & b_2 & c_2 \\ 1 & -\theta & \theta^2 \end{vmatrix} = 0$.

31. Find the values of a for which the equations $x + a^2 y + a = 0$, $ax + y + a^2 = 0$, $a^2 x + ay + 1 = 0$ are consistent.

32. Expand the determinant $\begin{vmatrix} x^2 + y^2 + 3 & 2x^2 + y^2 + 1 & x^2 + 3y^2 + 2 \\ y^2 + 1 & 2x^2 + 3 & x^2 + 2y^2 \\ y^2 + 2 & 2x^2 + 4 & x^2 + y^2 \end{vmatrix}$.

33. Factorise: (i) $\begin{vmatrix} a & b & c & d \\ d & a & b & c \\ c & d & a & b \\ b & c & d & a \end{vmatrix}$; (ii) $\begin{vmatrix} x^4 & a^4 & b^4 & c^4 \\ x^2 & a^2 & b^2 & c^2 \\ x & a & b & c \\ 1 & 1 & 1 & 1 \end{vmatrix}$.

34. Find the values of λ for which the equations $5x - 2y - 6z = \lambda x$, $2x - 3y - 4z = \lambda y$, $x + y = \lambda z$, may be satisfied simultaneously by values of x, y, z not all zero.

35. Prove that 3 is the only real value of λ for which the equations $-\lambda x + y + 2z = 0$, $x + \lambda y + 3z = 0$, $x + 3y + \lambda z = 0$, where x, y, z are not all zero, are consistent.

36. Expand the determinant $\begin{vmatrix} -1 & \cos\psi & \cos\phi \\ \cos\psi & -1 & \cos\theta \\ \cos\phi & \cos\theta & -1 \end{vmatrix}$ and show that its value is

$4\cos\alpha\cos(\alpha-\theta)\cos(\alpha-\phi)\cos(\alpha-\psi)$ where $\alpha=\frac{1}{2}(\theta+\phi+\psi)$.

37. Solve the equations $ax+by+cz=0$, $x+y+z=0$, $\begin{vmatrix} a & b & c \\ 1 & 1 & 1 \\ x & y & z \end{vmatrix}=d$, and

point out the special cases which arise.

38. Prove that $\begin{vmatrix} 0 & a & b & x \\ -a & 0 & c & y \\ -b & -c & 0 & z \\ p & q & r & s \end{vmatrix}=-(cx-by+az)(cp-bq+ar)$.

39. If $z=(1+a^2)x$ and z is given by the equation

$$\begin{vmatrix} z & 2a & 1-a^2 \\ 1-a^2 & z & 2a \\ 1-a^2 & 2a & z \end{vmatrix}=0,$$

and a has the value $\dfrac{1}{\sqrt{3}}$, show that the two possible values of x are $\sin\dfrac{\pi}{6}$

and $\sin\dfrac{\pi}{3}$.

40. Show that the simultaneous equations $ax+y+z=p$, $x+ay+z=q$, $x+y+az=r$, have a unique solution if a has neither of the values 1 or -2. Show also that, if $a=-2$ there is no finite solution unless p, q, r satisfy a certain condition, and then there are an infinite number of solutions. Discuss the case $a=1$.

CHAPTER IV

MORE ADVANCED ANALYTICAL GEOMETRY OF THE STRAIGHT LINE AND CIRCLE

Applications of determinants

I. *Equation of the straight line determined by the two points* $(x_1, y_1), (x_2, y_2)$.

Suppose the equation of the line is

$$lx + my + n = 0. \quad \ldots \ldots \quad \text{(i)}$$

As this equation is satisfied by the values $(x_1, y_1), (x_2, y_2)$,

$$lx_1 + my_1 + n = 0, \quad \ldots \ldots \quad \text{(ii)}$$
$$lx_2 + my_2 + n = 0. \quad \ldots \ldots \quad \text{(iii)}$$

Eliminating $l : m : n$ from the equations (i), (ii), (iii) gives the equation of the line in the form

$$\begin{vmatrix} x & y & 1 \\ x_1 & y_1 & 1 \\ x_2 & y_2 & 1 \end{vmatrix} = 0.$$

An immediate corollary of this result is that, *if the points* (x_1, y_1), $(x_2, y_2), (x_3, y_3)$ *are collinear then,*

$$\begin{vmatrix} x_1 & y_1 & 1 \\ x_2 & y_2 & 1 \\ x_3 & y_3 & 1 \end{vmatrix} = 0.$$

and conversely, if the determinant vanishes, then the points are collinear.

Ex. 1. *Find the equation of the straight line joining the points* $(-3, 4), (2, 1)$.

Required equation is
$$\begin{vmatrix} x & y & 1 \\ -3 & 4 & 1 \\ 2 & 1 & 1 \end{vmatrix} = 0$$

i.e.
$$3x + 5y - 11 = 0.$$

II. *Point of intersection of two straight lines.*

Suppose the lines have equations

$$l_1 x + m_1 y + n_1 = 0,$$
$$l_2 x + m_2 y + n_2 = 0.$$

Then solving the equations, the point of intersection is given by

$$\frac{x}{\begin{vmatrix} m_1 & n_1 \\ m_2 & n_2 \end{vmatrix}} = \frac{-y}{\begin{vmatrix} l_1 & n_1 \\ l_2 & n_2 \end{vmatrix}} = \frac{1}{\begin{vmatrix} l_1 & m_1 \\ l_2 & m_2 \end{vmatrix}}.$$

As a corollary it follows that, *if the three straight lines*

$$l_1 x + m_1 y + n_1 = 0,$$
$$l_2 x + m_2 y + n_2 = 0,$$
$$l_3 x + m_3 y + n_3 = 0,$$

are concurrent, then
$$\begin{vmatrix} l_1 & m_1 & n_1 \\ l_2 & m_2 & n_2 \\ l_3 & m_3 & n_3 \end{vmatrix} = 0, \text{ and conversely.}$$

Ex. 2. *Find the value of* λ *if the straight lines* $\lambda x - y + 1 = 0$, $2x - 3y + 2 = 0$, $x + 4y - 1 = 0$ *are concurrent.*

We have
$$\begin{vmatrix} \lambda & -1 & 1 \\ 2 & -3 & 2 \\ 1 & 4 & -1 \end{vmatrix} = 0,$$

i.e.
$$-5\lambda + 7 = 0; \quad \lambda = \tfrac{7}{5}.$$

III.   *Area of the triangle with vertices* $A(x_1, y_1)$, $B(x_2, y_2)$, $C(x_3, y_3)$.

Equation of BC is
$$\begin{vmatrix} x & y & 1 \\ x_2 & y_2 & 1 \\ x_3 & y_3 & 1 \end{vmatrix} = 0.$$

Hence, as the length of the perpendicular from (x_1, y_1) to the straight line $ax + by + c = 0$ is $\pm \dfrac{ax_1 + by_1 + c}{\sqrt{(a^2 + b^2)}}$, it follows that the length of the perpendicular from A to BC is

$$\pm \begin{vmatrix} x_1 & y_1 & 1 \\ x_2 & y_2 & 1 \\ x_3 & y_3 & 1 \end{vmatrix} \div \sqrt{\{(y_2 - y_3)^2 + (x_2 - x_3)^2\}}.$$

Also the length $BC = \sqrt{\{(y_2 - y_3)^2 + (x_2 - x_3)^2\}}$.

$\therefore$ *Area of* $\triangle ABC = \pm\tfrac{1}{2} \begin{vmatrix} x_1 & y_1 & 1 \\ x_2 & y_2 & 1 \\ x_3 & y_3 & 1 \end{vmatrix}.$

Sign of area—it is usual to treat the area as positive when the vertices are taken in counterclockwise order.

Ex. 3. *Find the numerical value of the area of the triangle with vertices* (3, 2), (−1, 4), (2, 7).

$$\text{Area} = \pm\tfrac{1}{2} \begin{vmatrix} 3 & 2 & 1 \\ -1 & 4 & 1 \\ 2 & 7 & 1 \end{vmatrix} = 9 \text{ unit}^2 \text{ numerically.}$$

EXAMPLES 4a

1. Find the equations of the straight lines determined by the following pairs of points:

(i) $(3, 4)$, $(-1, 5)$; (ii) $(2, 0)$, $(-3, 4)$;
(iii) $(-5, 1)$, $(-2, -2)$; (iv) (a, b), (b, a).

2. Prove that the following sets of points are collinear:

(i) $(1, 1)$, $(-2, -8)$, $(5, 13)$; (ii) $(-2, 3)$, $(1, 9)$, $(-5, -3)$;

(iii) (t^2, t), $(1, 0)$, $\left(\dfrac{1}{t^2}, -\dfrac{1}{t}\right)$.

3. Find the coordinates of the points of intersection of the following pairs of straight lines:

(i) $2x - y + 3 = 0$, (ii) $4x - y = 1$,
$\quad x + 3y - 1 = 0$. $\quad 2x + 3y = 5$.
(iii) $5x + 7y - 3 = 0$, (iv) $7y - 3x = 2$,
$\quad 3x + 4y + 1 = 0$. $\quad 2y + 4x = -5$.

4. Show that the following sets of straight lines are concurrent:

(i) $5x + 2y - 8 = 0$, (ii) $\quad 3x - y + 4 = 0$,
$\quad x - 5y + 2 = 0$, $\quad x + 5y - 1 = 0$,
$\quad x + 7y - 6 = 0$. $\quad 6x + 14y + 1 = 0$.
(iii) $\quad x - 6y + 2 = 0$, (iv) $\quad x + y = 0$,
$\quad 3x + 5y + 6 = 0$, $\quad x - y + 1 = 0$,
$\quad 11x + 3y + 22 = 0$. $\quad x(1 + \lambda) - y(1 - \lambda) + 1 = 0$.

5. Find the areas of the triangles determined by the following sets of points:

(i) $(0, 0)$, $(3, 2)$, $(4, 3)$. (ii) $(0, 0)$, $(-5, -3)$, $(-6, -8)$.
(iii) $(1, 2)$, $(3, 4)$, $(2, 6)$. (iv) $(-4, 5)$, $(3, -2)$, $(0, -4)$.
(v) $(-3, -2)$, $(1, 4)$, $(2, 3)$. (vi) $(2, 1)$, $(2t, 3t)$, $(t, 2t)$.

6. Find the equation of the chord joining the points $(at_1^2, 2at_1)$, $(at_2^2, 2at_2)$ on the parabola $y^2 = 4ax$.

7. Find the coordinates of the point of intersection of the tangents $t_1 y - x = at_1^2$, $t_2 y - x = at_2^2$ to the parabola $y^2 = 4ax$.

8. Find the values of λ for which the following sets of straight lines are concurrent:

(i) $\quad x - 4y + 3 = 0$, (ii) $x - \lambda y + 2 = 0$, (iii) $\quad \lambda x + y - 5 = 0$,
$\quad 2x - \lambda y + 1 = 0$, $\quad \lambda x - y + 3 = 0$, $\quad 3x - 2y - 4 = 0$,
$\quad x + 3y - 6 = 0$. $\quad x + 2y = 0$. $\quad 2\lambda x - 9y + 1 = 0$.

9. Find the equation of the chord joining the points $\left(ct_1, \dfrac{c}{t_1}\right)$, $\left(ct_2, \dfrac{c}{t_2}\right)$ on the rectangular hyperbola $xy = c^2$.

10. Show that the area of the triangle with vertices $(t, t-2)$, $(t+3, t)$, $(t+2, t+2)$ is independent of t.

11. Find the equation of the chord joining the points $(t_1{}^2, t_1{}^3)$, $(t_2{}^2, t_2{}^3)$ on the curve $y^2 = x^3$.

12. Prove that the points $(3 + 4t, 2 - 6t)$ where $t = t_1, t_2, t_3$, are collinear.

13. Show that the area enclosed by the straight lines $x = a$, $y = b$, $y = mx$ is $\dfrac{1}{2m}(b - ma)^2$.

14. Find the area of the triangle whose sides are the lines $2y + x = 0$, $3y + 2x + 4 = 0$, $2y + 3x + 9 = 0$.

15. Find the area of the convex quadrilateral whose vertices are the points $(2, -1)$, $(5, 0)$, $(4, 6)$, $(0, 3)$.

The line pair.   Consider the two straight lines
$$l_1 x + m_1 y + n_1 = 0,$$
$$l_2 x + m_2 y + n_2 = 0.$$
Then the equation
$$(l_1 x + m_1 y + n_1)(l_2 x + m_2 y + n_2) = 0$$
is satisfied by the coordinates of a point on either line and by no other values.   It therefore represents the two lines as a combined locus of the second degree in x and y.

Conversely, if a second degree expression $f(x, y)$ can be expressed as a product of two linear factors, then the equation
$$f(x, y) = 0$$
represents a line pair.

E.g. as the equation
$$x^2 - xy - 2y^2 + x + 4y - 2 = 0,$$
can be written
$$(x + y - 1)(x - 2y + 2) = 0,$$
it represents a line pair made up of the lines $x + y - 1 = 0$, $x - 2y + 2 = 0$.

Condition for the general equation of the second degree to represent a line pair.   The general equation of the second degree is
$$ax^2 + 2hxy + by^2 + 2gx + 2fy + c = 0.$$

Suppose $a \neq 0$; multiplying throughout by a and completing the square of the terms in x,
$$\text{L.H.S.} = (ax + hy + g)^2 - h^2 y^2 + aby^2 - 2hgy + 2afy + ac - g^2$$
$$= (ax + hy + g)^2 - \{y^2(h^2 - ab) + 2(hg - af)y + (g^2 - ac)\}.$$

For the equation to represent a line pair, the L.H.S. must be the product of two linear factors in x and y.   This will be true, if, and only if,
$$y^2(h^2 - ab) + 2(hg - af)y + (g^2 - ac)$$
is a perfect square.

$\therefore$ The required condition is that
$$(hg - af)^2 = (h^2 - ab)(g^2 - ac).$$

Expanding and removing the factor a,

$$abc + 2fgh - af^2 - bg^2 - ch^2 = 0,$$

i.e.
$$a(bc - f^2) - h(ch - fg) + g(fh - bg) = 0,$$

or
$$\Delta = \begin{vmatrix} a & h & g \\ h & b & f \\ g & f & c \end{vmatrix} = 0.$$

This condition is readily shown to be true also in the special cases $a = 0$, $b \neq 0$; $a = 0$, $b = 0$, $h \neq 0$.

Ex. 4. *Find the value of λ if the equation $\lambda xy + 5x + 3y + 2 = 0$ represents a line pair.*

We have
$$\Delta = \begin{vmatrix} 0 & \frac{\lambda}{2} & \frac{5}{2} \\ \frac{\lambda}{2} & 0 & \frac{3}{2} \\ \frac{5}{2} & \frac{3}{2} & 2 \end{vmatrix} = 0$$

i.e.
$$\begin{vmatrix} 0 & \lambda & 5 \\ \lambda & 0 & 3 \\ 5 & 3 & 4 \end{vmatrix} = 0$$

$$4\lambda^2 - 30\lambda = 0; \quad \lambda = 0, \tfrac{15}{2}.$$

When $\lambda = 0$, the equation represents a single straight line and so the required value of λ is $\tfrac{15}{2}$.

Ex. 5. *Show that the equation $x^2 - xy - 2y^2 - 3x + 9y - 4 = 0$ represents a line pair and find the point of intersection.*

As the separate linear equations are required, it will be simpler here to show that the second degree expression does factorise.

$$x^2 - xy - 2y^2 = (x - 2y)(x + y),$$
$$\therefore \ x^2 - xy - 2y^2 - 3x + 9y - 4 = (x - 2y + A)(x + y + B).$$

Equating coefficients of x and y,

$$A + B = -3, \qquad\qquad A - 2B = 9;$$
$$A = 1, \ B = -4.$$

So the equation can be written

$$(x - 2y + 1)(x + y - 4) = 0 \text{ — a line pair.}$$

Solving the equations
$$x - 2y + 1 = 0,$$
$$x + y - 4 = 0,$$
$$\frac{x}{7} = \frac{-y}{-5} = \frac{1}{3}.$$

$\therefore$ The point of intersection is $\left(\dfrac{7}{3}, \dfrac{5}{3}\right)$.

Line pair through the origin. Consider the homogeneous equation of the second degree

$$ax^2 + 2hxy + by^2 = 0.$$

Solving for y,
$$y = \frac{-h \pm \sqrt{(h^2 - ab)}}{b} x.$$

$\therefore$ The equation represents a pair of straight lines passing through the origin.

If $h^2 > ab$, the lines are real and different;

if $h^2 = ab$, the lines are real and coincident;

if $h^2 < ab$, the lines are imaginary and the origin is the only real point satisfying the equation.

Hence, any homogeneous equation of the second degree, that is, of the form

$$ax^2 + 2hxy + by^2 = 0,$$

represents a line pair through the origin.

Ex. 6. *If one of the lines of the line pair $3x^2 + 2hxy - 2y^2 = 0$ passes through the point $(1, 2)$, find the value of h.*

The equation is satisfied when $x = 1$, $y = 2$.

$$\therefore \quad 3 + 4h - 8 = 0; \quad h = \tfrac{5}{4}.$$

Equation of the line pair joining the origin to the points of intersection of a given straight line and a given conic. Suppose the straight line has equation
$$lx + my = 1,$$
and the conic,
$$ax^2 + 2hxy + by^2 + 2gx + 2fy + c = 0\text{—the general equation}$$
of the second degree.

Then any equation derived from these two equations will be satisfied by the coordinates of the common points of the line and the conic.

Consequently, a homogeneous equation of the second degree derived from the two equations must represent the line pair joining the origin to the points of intersection of the line and the conic.

This homogeneous equation is obtained by using the linear equation to make the quadratic equation homogeneous by multiplying the term $2gx$, $2fy$ by $(lx + my)$ and the constant term by $(lx + my)^2$.

The equation of the line pair is

$$ax^2 + 2hxy + by^2 + (2gx + 2fy)(lx + my) + c(lx + my)^2 = 0,$$

or $\quad x^2(a + 2gl + cl^2) + 2xy(h + gm + fl + clm) + y^2(b + 2fm + cm^2) = 0.$

Ex. 7. *Find the equation of the line pair joining the origin to the points of intersection of the straight line $x + y - 2 = 0$ and the circle $x^2 + y^2 = 8$.*

Writing the equation of the line in the form

$$1 = \tfrac{1}{2}(x + y),$$

the required equation is

$$x^2 + y^2 = 8[\tfrac{1}{2}(x + y)]^2$$

i.e.
$$x^2 + 4xy + y^2 = 0.$$

Ex. 8. *Find the equation of the circumcircle of the triangle formed by the line pair $ax^2 + 2hxy + by^2 = 0$ and the straight line $lx + my = 1$.*

As the circle passes through the origin O, its equation is of the form

$$x^2 + y^2 + 2gx + 2fy = 0.$$

Then the equation of the line pair OA, OB (Fig. 42) is

$$x^2 + y^2 + (2gx + 2fy)(lx + my) = 0.$$

$$x^2(1 + 2gl) + 2xy(gm + fl) + y^2(1 + 2fm) = 0.$$

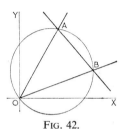

But the equation of the line pair is

$$ax^2 + 2hxy + by^2 = 0.$$

$$\therefore \quad \frac{1 + 2gl}{a} = \frac{gm + fl}{h} = \frac{1 + 2fm}{b},$$

FIG. 42.

i.e.
$$g(am - 2hl) + f(al) - h = 0,$$
$$g(mb) + f(bl - 2hm) - h = 0.$$

Solving,

$$\frac{g}{-ahl + bhl - 2h^2m} = \frac{-f}{2h^2l - ahm + bhm} = \frac{1}{(am - 2hl)(bl - 2hm) - ablm}$$

$$g = \frac{l(a - b) + 2hm}{2(am^2 - 2hlm + bl^2)}, \quad f = \frac{m(b - a) + 2hl}{2(am^2 - 2hlm + bl^2)}.$$

Hence the equation of the circumcircle is

$$(am^2 - 2hlm + bl^2)(x^2 + y^2) + x(la - lb + 2hm) + y(mb - ma + 2hl) = 0.$$

EXAMPLES 4b

1. Write down, and expand, the combined equation of each of the following line pairs:

(i) $x + y = 0$,	(ii) $2x + 3y = 0$,
$x - y = 0$.	$x - 2y = 0$.
(iii) $x - y + 1 = 0$,	(iv) $3x + 2y - 5 = 0$,
$x + y + 2 = 0$;	$2x - y + 1 = 0$.

2. Find the equations of the separate lines in each of the following line pairs:

(i) $2x^2 - xy - y^2 = 0$; (ii) $(x + 2)^2 - y^2 = 0$;
(iii) $(2x - y + 1)^2 - (y - 3)^2 = 0$; (iv) $3x^2 - 5xy - 2y^2 + x + 5y - 2 = 0$;
(v) $xy - 3x + y - 3 = 0$; (vi) $2x^2 + 2xy - 5x - 3y + 3 = 0$.

G

3. Determine which of the following equations represent line pairs:

(i) $3x^2 + xy - 4y^2 = 0$;   (ii) $4x^2 - 5y^2 = 0$;

(iii) $x^2 - y^2 + 3x - 2y + 1 = 0$;   (iv) $6x^2 + xy - y^2 - 3x + y = 0$;

(v) $x^2 - 2xy + y^2 - 3x + 4y - 2 = 0$;   (vi) $2x^2 - xy + 5x - 2y + 2 = 0$.

4. Show that the equation $2x^2 - 7xy + 3y^2 + x - 8y - 3 = 0$ represents a line pair and find the point of intersection.

5. Show that the equation $x^2 - 4xy + 4y^2 + 3x - 6y + 2 = 0$ represents a parallel pair of lines.

6. If one of the elements of the line pair $3x^2 + 2hxy - y^2 = 0$ passes through the point (2, 6), find the value of h.

7. Find the values of λ for which the following equations represent line pairs:

(i) $x^2 - y^2 + 4x + 2y + \lambda = 0$;   (ii) $2x^2 - \lambda xy + 5x - 2y + 2 = 0$;

(iii) $2x^2 - 5xy + \lambda y^2 + 6x - 4y + 4 = 0$;   (iv) $\lambda x^2 + 3xy + y^2 + 3x + y - 2 = 0$;

(v) $2x^2 - xy - 3y^2 + \lambda(x + y) = 0$;   (vi) $x^2 + 4y^2 - 4 + \lambda(xy - 2) = 0$.

8. Prove that the lines $x^2 - y^2 + x - y = 0$ are concurrent with the lines $9x^2 - y^2 + 9x - y + 2 = 0$.

9. Find the coordinates of the points of intersection of the straight line $x + y + 1 = 0$ and the line pair $2x^2 - 3xy - 2y^2 + 7x + 6y - 4 = 0$.

10. Find the equations of the line pairs joining the origin to the points of intersection of the following conics and straight lines:

(i) circle $x^2 + y^2 = 4$, straight line $x + y = 1$;

(ii) ellipse $x^2 + 8y^2 = 8$, straight line $x - 2y = 1$;

(iii) hyperbola $x^2 - 4y^2 = 4$, straight line $x - 2y - 2 = 0$;

(iv) parabola $y^2 = 4x$, straight line $x - y - 2 = 0$;

(v) circle $x^2 + y^2 - 2x + 4y + 1 = 0$, straight line $2x - y + 1 = 0$;

(vi) hyperbola $x^2 - y^2 + 8x - 1 = 0$, straight line $x - 3y + 2 = 0$.

11. Find the equation of the lines joining the origin to the points of intersection of the line pair $2x^2 + 2xy - 5x - 3y + 3 = 0$ and the straight line $x - 4y - 1 = 0$.

12. What is the condition that the equation $ax^2 + 2hxy + by^2 = 0$ should represent a line pair equally inclined to the x-axis?

13. Find the area enclosed by the lines $x^2 + 3xy + y^2 = 0$ and the line $y = 2$.

14. Prove that the equation $x^2 + 6xy + 9y^2 - 2x - 6y + 1 = 0$ represents a coincident pair of lines and that the equation $x^2 + 6xy + 9y^2 - 1 = 0$ represents a parallel pair of lines.

15. Find the equations of the three line pairs formed by the pairs of opposite sides and the diagonals of the quadrilateral with vertices $(1, -1)$, $(0, 2)$, $(-2, 1)$, $(3, 0)$.

16. The vertices of a triangle are $A(2, 0)$, $B(-3, -2)$, $C(4, 4)$; find the equations of the line pairs formed by the sides BC, CA, AB and the altitudes corresponding to them.

17. Find the equation of the common chord of the two circles
$$x^2 + y^2 - 4x - 3y + 1 = 0, \qquad x^2 + y^2 + 2x + 3y + 2 = 0$$
and hence find the equation of the line pair joining the origin to the common points of the two circles.

18. Show that the area enclosed by the line pair $ax^2 + 2hxy + by^2 = 0$ and the line $y = c$ is $\dfrac{c^2}{a}\sqrt{(h^2 - ab)}$.

19. Find the equation of the circumcircle of the triangle formed by the straight line $x - y + 1 = 0$ and the line pair $x^2 + 2xy - y^2 = 0$.

20. Write down the equation of the pair of lines joining the points of intersection of the straight line $lx + my = 1$ and the circle $x^2 + y^2 + x - 2y = 0$ to the origin. Hence find the equation of the straight line joining the points of intersection, other than the origin, of the line pair $2x^2 - 3y^2 = 0$ and the circle $x^2 + y^2 + x - 2y = 0$.

21. The line pair $x^2 + 2xy + y^2 + x + y - 2 = 0$ meets the axes of x and y at the points $A_1, A_2; B_1, B_2$ respectively. If O is the origin, obtain the values of the products $OA_1 . OA_2$ and $OB_1 . OB_2$. Deduce that the points A_1, A_2, B_1, B_2 are concyclic and find the coordinates of the centre of the circumcircle.

22. Find three values of λ for which the equation
$$\lambda(x^2 + y^2 - 25) + (3x + 4y)(x - 2y - 5) = 0$$
represents two straight lines.

23. Prove that the lines joining the origin to the points of intersection of the chord $2x + y - 4 = 0$ and the circle $x^2 + y^2 - 6x + y + 4 = 0$ are equally inclined to the coordinate axes.

Angles between two straight lines. First consider a line pair through the origin represented by the equation
$$ax^2 + 2hxy + by^2 = 0.$$

Let the gradients of the lines be m_1, m_2.
Then the equations of the separate lines are $y - m_1x = 0$, $y - m_2x = 0$.
$$\therefore \quad ax^2 + 2hxy + by^2 \equiv b(y - m_1x)(y - m_2x).$$

Comparing the coefficients of x^2 and xy,
$$a = bm_1m_2; \qquad\qquad 2h = -b(m_1 + m_2).$$

I.e.
$$m_1m_2 = \frac{a}{b}; \qquad\qquad m_1 + m_2 = -\frac{2h}{b}.$$

If θ be an angle between the lines,
$$\tan\theta = \pm \frac{m_1 - m_2}{1 + m_1m_2}.$$

But
$$(m_1 - m_2)^2 = (m_1 + m_2)^2 - 4m_1m_2 = \frac{4(h^2 - ab)}{b^2}.$$

$$\therefore \quad \tan\theta = \pm \frac{2\sqrt{(h^2 - ab)}}{a + b}.$$

Special cases. (i) *When* $h^2 = ab$, *the lines are coincident;*
(ii) *When* $a + b = 0$, *the lines are perpendicular.*

Now take the more general case of a line pair represented by the equation

$$ax^2 + 2hxy + by^2 + 2gx + 2fy + c = 0,$$

with the condition $\Delta = 0$ satisfied.

Suppose the separate lines have equations $y = m_1 x + c_1$, $y = m_2 x + c_2$, where m_1, m_2 are the gradients.

Then $ax^2 + 2hxy + by^2 + 2gx + 2fy + c \equiv b(y - m_1 x - c_1)(y - m_2 x - c_2).$

Comparing coefficients,

$$m_1 m_2 = \frac{a}{b}; \quad m_1 + m_2 = -\frac{2h}{b}.$$

As before

$$\tan\theta = \pm\frac{2\sqrt{(h^2 - ab)}}{a + b}.$$

Special cases. (i) *When* $h^2 = ab$, *the lines are parallel or coincident;*
(ii) *When* $a + b = 0$, *the lines are perpendicular.*

As the terms $ax^2 + 2hxy + by^2$ are derived from the product $b(y - m_1 x)(y - m_2 x)$, it follows that the line pair

$$ax^2 + 2hxy + by^2 + 2gx + 2fy + c = 0$$

is parallel to the line pair through the origin,

$$ax^2 + 2hxy + by^2 = 0.$$

Ex. 9. *PQ is a chord of an ellipse which subtends a right angle at the centre C. Prove that the perpendicular from the centre to the chord PQ is of constant length.*

Take the equation of the ellipse as $\dfrac{x^2}{a^2} + \dfrac{y^2}{b^2} = 1$, so that the centre C is the origin.

Let the chord PQ have equation

$$lx + my = 1.$$

Then the equation of the line pair CP, CQ is

$$\frac{x^2}{a^2} + \frac{y^2}{b^2} = (lx + my)^2$$

i.e. $x^2\left(l^2 - \dfrac{1}{a^2}\right) + 2lmxy + y^2\left(m^2 - \dfrac{1}{b^2}\right) = 0.$

As this is a perpendicular line pair

$$l^2 - \frac{1}{a^2} + m^2 - \frac{1}{b^2} = 0$$

i.e. $l^2 + m^2 = \dfrac{1}{a^2} + \dfrac{1}{b^2}.$

But the length of the perpendicular from C to PQ is $\dfrac{1}{\sqrt{(l^2+m^2)}}$, and as

$l^2+m^2=\dfrac{1}{a^2}+\dfrac{1}{b^2}=$ constant, the required result follows.

Equation of the bisectors of the angles between the lines

$$ax^2+2hxy+by^2=0.$$

If the gradients of the lines are m_1, m_2, then as before,

$$m_1m_2=\frac{a}{b}; \quad m_1+m_2=-\frac{2h}{b}.$$

The equations of the bisectors of the angles between the lines

$$y-m_1x=0, \ y-m_2x=0$$

are

$$\frac{y-m_1x}{\sqrt{(1+m_1{}^2)}}=\pm\frac{y-m_2x}{\sqrt{(1+m_2{}^2)}}$$

i.e.

$$(1+m_2{}^2)(y-m_1x)^2=(1+m_1{}^2)(y-m_2x)^2$$

$$x^2(m_1{}^2-m_2{}^2)-2xy(m_1-m_2)(1-m_1m_2)-y^2(m_1{}^2-m_2{}^2)=0.$$

As $m_1\neq m_2$, or the original lines would be coincident, this equation can be divided by m_1-m_2, giving

$$x^2(m_1+m_2)-2xy(1-m_1m_2)-y^2(m_1+m_2)=0$$

or

$$hx^2-(a-b)xy-hy^2=0.$$

Ex. 10. *Find the equation of the line pair whose angle bisectors have the equation $2x^2-5xy-2y^2=0$, and which passes through the point $(2,-1)$.*

With the notation of the general result just obtained, it follows that the required line pair has the equation

$$ax^2+2hxy+by^2=0,$$

where $h=2$ and $a-b=5$.

Also as the line pair passes through the point $(2,-1)$,

$$4a-4h+b=0.$$

Solving these equations, $a=\frac{13}{5}$, $b=-\frac{12}{5}$, $h=2$.

So the required line pair has the equation

$$13x^2+20xy-12y^2=0.$$

EXAMPLES 4c

1. Find the acute angle between each of the line pairs:

(i) $2x^2-4xy-y^2=0$; (ii) $5x^2+2xy-4y^2=0$;

(iii) $6x^2-5xy+y^2=0$; (iv) $3x^2-xy-2y^2+7x+3y+2=0$;

(v) $x^2-5xy+4y^2+3x-4=0$.

2. Determine which of the following line pairs are perpendicular:

(i) $2x^2 - xy - 2y^2 = 0$;   (ii) $x^2 + 4xy + y^2 = 0$;

(iii) $4y^2 - 7xy - 4x^2 = 0$;   (iv) $2x^2 - xy - 3y^2 + 4x + 4y = 0$;

(v) $3x^2 + 8xy - 3y^2 - 5x - 5y + 2 = 0$.

3. Find the equations of the bisectors of the angles between the line pairs:

(i) $3x^2 + 4xy + y^2 = 0$;   (ii) $5x^2 - 11xy + 2y^2 = 0$;   (iii) $7x^2 + 11xy - 6y^2 = 0$.

4. If the gradient of one of the lines $2x^2 + \lambda xy + y^2 = 0$ is twice that of the other, find the values of λ.

5. Prove that the equation $3x^2 - 8xy - 3y^2 + x + 7y - 2 = 0$ represents a perpendicular pair of lines and that the equation

$$x^2 + 4xy + 4y^2 - 4x - 8y + 3 = 0$$

represents a parallel pair of lines.

6. Find the perpendicular distance between the parallel lines

$$x^2 - 4xy + 4y^2 + 4x - 8y = 0.$$

7. Show that the lines joining the origin to the points of intersection of the straight line $2x - 3y + 4 = 0$ and the curve $x^2 + 4xy + 2y^2 + 12x + 4y = 0$ are at right angles.

8. Find the equation of the line pair, with point of intersection (1, 2), which is parallel to the line pair $x^2 - xy - 2y^2 = 0$.

9. If the equation $ax^2 - y^2 + 3x + y + b = 0$ represents a perpendicular line pair, find the values of a and b.

10. A parallelogram is formed by drawing through the origin the line pair parallel to the lines $x^2 - y^2 + 4x + 2y + 3 = 0$. Find the area of this parallelogram.

11. The straight line $x - 2y = 4$ meets the line pair

$$x^2 - xy - 2y^2 - 3x + 9y - 4 = 0$$

at the points P and Q. If O is the origin, find the tangent of the acute angle POQ.

12. Find the equation of the pair of lines intersecting at the point (2, 3) which are perpendicular to the lines $2x^2 + xy - y^2 = 0$.

13. Find the equation of the line pair which passes through the point $(1, -1)$ and has angle bisectors with the equation $2x^2 - 3xy - 2y^2 = 0$.

14. The line $lx + my = 1$ meets the ellipse $\dfrac{x^2}{a^2} + \dfrac{y^2}{b^2} = 1$ at the points P and Q. Find the condition that the lines joining P, Q to the origin are coincident and interpret the result geometrically.

15. Prove that the equation of the pair of lines through the origin which are perpendicular to the lines $ax^2 + 2hxy + by^2 = 0$ is $bx^2 - 2hxy + ay^2 = 0$.

16. Find the equation of the line pair which passes through the origin and is perpendicular to the lines $3x^2 - xy - 2y^2 + 7x + 3y + 2 = 0$.

17. The gradients of the lines $ax^2 + 2hxy + by^2 = 0$ are in the ratio $m : n$, prove that $4mnh^2 = ab(m + n)^2$.

18. Find the equation of the bisectors of the angles between the lines $2x^2 - 11xy + 5y^2 - x + 23y - 10 = 0$.

19. Find the condition that the lines joining the origin to the points of intersection of the chord $lx + my = 1$ and the circle $x^2 + y^2 + 2gx + 2fy + c = 0$ are at right angles.

20. Show that the equation of any line pair whose angle bisectors have equation $ax^2 + 2hxy - ay^2 = 0$ is of the form $(\lambda - h)x^2 + 2axy + (\lambda + h)y^2 = 0$, where λ is a parameter.

21. Show that all chords of the curve $3x^2 - y^2 - 2x + 4y = 0$ which subtend a right angle at the origin pass through the point $(1, -2)$.

22. If the equation $(ax + by)^2 + 2gx + 2fy + c = 0$ represents a line pair, prove: (i) $af = bg$; (ii) the lines are parallel. Find the perpendicular distances of the origin from the separate lines and hence determine the distance between the lines.

23. Show that the condition that the line pairs $a_1x^2 + 2h_1xy + b_1y^2 = 0$, $a_2x^2 + 2h_2xy + b_2y^2 = 0$ have a line in common is that
$$(a_1b_2 - a_2b_1)^2 = 4(h_1b_2 - h_2b_1)(h_2a_1 - h_1a_2).$$

24. Show that the equation of the lines drawn through the point (x_1, y_1) parallel to the lines $ax^2 + 2hxy + by^2 = 0$ is
$$a(x - x_1)^2 + 2h(x - x_1)(y - y_1) + b(y - y_1)^2 = 0.$$

25. The equation $ax^2 + 2hxy + by^2 + 2gx + 2fy + c = 0$ represents two straight lines; write down the transformed equation when the origin is moved to the point (α, β). Deduce that if (α, β) is the point of intersection of the lines,
$$a\alpha + h\beta + g = 0, \quad h\alpha + b\beta + f = 0.$$

26. Use the result of the previous example to determine the points of intersection of the line pairs:

(i) $2x^2 - 3xy - 2y^2 + 2x + 11y - 12 = 0$; (ii) $x^2 - 3xy - y^2 + 2x - 3y + 1 = 0$.

27. If the origin lies on one of the bisectors of the angles between the lines $x^2 + 2hxy + y^2 + 2gx + 2fy + c = 0$, prove that $g^2 = f^2$.

28. Find the equations of the diagonals of the parallelogram formed by the pairs of parallel lines
$$ax^2 + 2hxy + by^2 + 2gx + 2fy + c = 0, \quad ax^2 + 2hxy + by^2 = 0.$$

Tangents to a circle from an external point.

Let the equation of the circle be

$$x^2 + y^2 = a^2,$$

and let the given point A have coordinates (x_1, y_1).

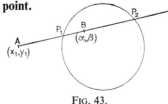

FIG. 43.

Suppose the straight line joining A to a variable point $B(\alpha, \beta)$ cuts the circle at P_1, P_2.

Now the coordinates of any point P on the line AB can be expressed as

$$\left(\frac{\lambda\alpha+x_1}{\lambda+1}, \frac{\lambda\beta+y_1}{\lambda+1}\right),$$

where $\lambda : 1$ is the ratio in which the point P divides AB.

P will lie on the circle if

$$\left(\frac{\lambda\alpha+x_1}{\lambda+1}\right)^2 + \left(\frac{\lambda\beta+y_1}{\lambda+1}\right)^2 = a^2,$$

i.e. $\lambda^2(\alpha^2+\beta^2-a^2) + 2\lambda(\alpha x_1+\beta y_1-a^2) + (x_1^2+y_1^2-a^2) = 0.$

The roots λ_1, λ_2, of this equation correspond to the points P_1, P_2.

$\therefore$ The line AB is a tangent to the circle if $\lambda_1 = \lambda_2$,

i.e. if $(\alpha x_1+\beta y_1-a^2)^2 = (\alpha^2+\beta^2-a^2)(x_1^2+y_1^2-a^2).$

This is the condition that the point (α, β) lies on one of the tangents from A to the circle and consequently the equation of the pair of tangents is

$$(\mathbf{x}\mathbf{x_1}+\mathbf{y}\mathbf{y_1}-\mathbf{a^2})^2 = (\mathbf{x^2}+\mathbf{y^2}-\mathbf{a^2})(\mathbf{x_1^2}+\mathbf{y_1^2}-\mathbf{a^2}).$$

More generally, if the circle has the equation

$$S \equiv x^2+y^2+2gx+2fy+c=0,$$

and $S_1 \equiv xx_1+yy_1+g(x+x_1)+f(y+y_1)+c,$

$$S_{11} \equiv x_1^2+y_1^2+2gx_1+2fy_1+c,$$

then the equation of the pair of tangents from (x_1, y_1) to S is

$$\mathbf{S_1^2 = SS_{11}.}$$

Ex. 11. *Find the equations of the tangents which can be drawn from the origin to the circle* $x^2+y^2-2x-6y+5=0$.

In this case, $S \equiv x^2+y^2-2x-6y+5,$

$$S_1 \equiv x0+y0-(x+0)-3(y+0)+5 = -x-3y+5,$$

$$S_{11} \equiv 5.$$

$\therefore$ The equation of the pair of tangents from $(0, 0)$ to the circle is

$$(-x-3y+5)^2 = 5(x^2+y^2-2x-6y+5)$$

i.e. $2x^2-3xy-2y^2 = 0,$

or $2x+y=0; \quad x-2y=0.$

Chord of contact of tangents from an external point to a circle. Let the equation of the circle be

$$S \equiv x^2+y^2-a^2=0,$$

and let the given point A have coordinates (x_1, y_1).

Suppose the coordinates of L, M, the points of contact of the tangents from A to the circle, are (α_1, β_1), (α_2, β_2).

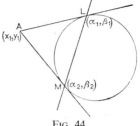

FIG. 44.

The equation of the tangent to the circle at L is

$$x\alpha_1 + y\beta_1 - a^2 = 0,$$

and as A lies on this line,

$$x_1\alpha_1 + y_1\beta_1 - a^2 = 0 \quad . \quad . \quad . \quad (i)$$

Similarly, as A lies on the tangent to the circle at M,

$$x_1\alpha_2 + y_1\beta_2 - a^2 = 0 \quad . \quad . \quad . \quad . \quad . \quad (ii)$$

Equations (i) and (ii) show that both the points (α_1, β_1), (α_2, β_2) lie on the line $x_1x + y_1y - a^2 = 0$.

Hence the equation of the chord of contact LM is

$$\mathbf{xx_1 + yy_1 - a^2 = 0.}$$

More generally, if the equation of the circle is

$$S \equiv x^2 + y^2 + 2gx + 2fy + c = 0$$

and

$$S_1 \equiv xx_1 + yy_1 + g(x + x_1) + f(y + y_1) + c,$$

then the equation of the chord of contact of tangents from (x_1, y_1) to S is

$$\mathbf{S_1 = 0.}$$

N.B. The chord of contact LM is spoken of as the *polar* of A with respect to the circle; A is the *pole* of LM.

Ex. 12. *Tangents are drawn from the points* $(0, 2)$, $(1, 3)$, $(2, 4)$ *to the circle* $x^2 + y^2 - 4x + 2y = 0$. *Prove that the three chords of contact are concurrent.*

Using the above result, the chords of contact are

$$2y - 2x + y + 2 = 0; \quad \text{i.e.} \quad -2x + 3y + 2 = 0;$$
$$x + 3y - 2(x + 1) + y + 3 = 0; \quad \text{i.e.} \quad -x + 4y + 1 = 0;$$
$$2x + 4y - 2(x + 2) + y + 4 = 0; \quad \text{i.e.} \quad 5y = 0.$$

These three lines are concurrent in the point $(1, 0)$.

EXAMPLES 4d

1. In each of the following cases find the equation of the pair of tangents which can be drawn from the given point to the given circle:

(i) $(4, 3)$, $x^2 + y^2 - 2 = 0$; (ii) $(-3, 0)$, $x^2 + y^2 = 1$;

(iii) $(-1, 2)$, $2x^2 + 2y^2 - 1 = 0$; (iv) $(0, 0)$, $x^2 + y^2 - 5x + 2y + 2 = 0$;

(v) $(0, 1)$, $x^2 + y^2 + 4y = 0$; (vi) $(-2, 1)$, $x^2 + y^2 - 4x + y = 0$;

(vii) $(-3, -4)$, $x^2 + y^2 - 4x - 2y - 5 = 0$.

2. Find: (i) the equation of each of the tangents which can be drawn from the origin to the circle $x^2 + y^2 - 4x - 4y + 4 = 0$; (ii) the equation of the chord of contact of these tangents.

3. Find the equation of the pair of tangents from the point (2, 4) to the circle $x^2 + y^2 + x - 3y = 0$ and determine the acute angle between the tangents.

4. Prove that the tangents to the circle $x^2 + y^2 + 2x - 4y + 3 = 0$ from the point (1, 2) are at right angles to each other.

5. In each of the following cases, find the equation of the chord of contact of tangents drawn from the given point to the given circle:

(i) (5, 2), $x^2 + y^2 - 2 = 0$;   (ii) $(-1, 2)$, $x^2 + y^2 = 4$;

(iii) $(-3, -4)$, $2x^2 + 2y^2 - 3 = 0$;   (iv) (0, 0), $x^2 + y^2 + 4y + 2 = 0$;

(v) (1, 1), $x^2 + y^2 + 2x + 6y + 8 = 0$;   (vi) $(-2, -4)$, $x^2 + y^2 - 6x + 1 = 0$.

6. By first obtaining the equation of the chord of contact, find the coordinates of the points of contact of tangents drawn from the point (1, 2) to the circle $x^2 + y^2 - 4x + 6y = 0$.

7. Tangents are drawn from the points $(-1, 0)$, $(0, -1)$, $(1, -2)$ to the circle $x^2 + y^2 - 2x - 2y = 0$, show that the chords of contact are concurrent.

8. The chord of contact of tangents from the point P to the circle $x^2 + y^2 + 4x - 2y - 2 = 0$ passes through the point $(-1, 0)$, find the locus of P.

9. Verify that the chord of contact of the tangents drawn from the point $P(h, k)$ to the circle $x^2 + y^2 + 2gx + 2fy + c = 0$ is perpendicular to the straight line joining the centre of the circle to P.

10. If the chord of contact of tangents from the point (g, f) to the circle $x^2 + y^2 + 2gx + 2fy + c = 0$ passes through the origin, prove that $g^2 + f^2 + c = 0$.

11. Show that, for all values of t, the chord of contact of tangents from the point $(2t, t - 4)$ to the circle $x^2 + y^2 - 4x - 6y + 1 = 0$ passes through the point (3, 1).

12. Find the condition that the tangents from the point (h, k) to the circle $x^2 + y^2 + 2gx + 2fy + c = 0$ are at right angles.

13. Find the point of intersection of the tangents drawn to the circle $x^2 + y^2 = 4$ at the extremities of the chord $y - x - 1 = 0$.

14. Tangents are drawn from the point $(2, -2)$ to the circle $x^2 + y^2 = 2$. Find: (i) the equation of the chord of contact; (ii) the equation of the circle on this chord as diameter.

15. Prove that the tangents to the circle $x^2 + y^2 = a^2$ at the extremities of the chord $lx + my = 1$ intersect at the point (a^2l, a^2m).

16. By using the properties of similar triangles, determine the point of intersection of the exterior common tangents of the two circles $(x - 2)^2 + y^2 = 1$, $(x - 4)^2 + y^2 = 4$. Hence obtain the equation of the pair of exterior common tangents.

17. Find the point of intersection of the interior common tangents of the two circles $(x+1)^2 + y^2 = 1$, $(x-4)^2 + y^2 = 4$ and hence find the equations of these tangents.

18. Find the equation of each of the exterior common tangents of the two circles $x^2 + y^2 - 3x - 4y + 4 = 0$, $x^2 + y^2 - 12x - 16y + 64 = 0$.

MISCELLANEOUS EXAMPLES

1. Find the value of a if the three lines $3x + y - 2 = 0$, $ax + 2y - 3 = 0$, $2x - y - 3 = 0$ are concurrent.

2. Show that the points $(-2, 3)$, $(1, 9)$, $(-5, -3)$ are collinear.

3. The equations of the sides of a triangle are $8x - 5y - 1 = 0$, $7x - 4y + 1 = 0$, $x - y + 1 = 0$; find: (i) the coordinates of the centroid; (ii) the area of the triangle.

4. Two equal circles of radius two units have centres at the points $(0, 1)$, $(3, 4)$; find the equations of the exterior common tangents.

5. Show that the variable line $(\lambda - 2)x + (2\lambda - 3)y - \lambda + 1 = 0$ passes through a fixed point and find the point.

6. Find the condition that the lines $ax + hy + g = 0$, $hx + by + f = 0$, $gx + fy + c = 0$ are concurrent and find the coordinates of the common point.

7. Find the values of λ for which the equation $2x^2 + 9xy + 4y^2 = \lambda x + 2y$ represents a line pair.

8. Write down the equation of the lines joining the ends of the chord $x - 2y = 2$ of the circle $x^2 + y^2 = 1$ to the origin and determine the acute angle between the lines.

9. The points (x_1, y_1), (x_2, y_2) are opposite vertices of a square, find the coordinates of the other vertices.

10. Find the equation of the line pair intersecting in the point $(-2, 1)$ and making angles of $45°$ with the line $3x + y + 5 = 0$.

11. Show that the area of the triangle with vertices $(at_1^2, 2at_1)$, $(at_2^2, 2at_2)$, $(at_1t_2, a\overline{t_1 + t_2})$ is numerically equal to $\frac{1}{2}a^2(t_1 - t_2)^3$.

12. Show that the lines joining the origin to the points of intersection of the line $2x - 3y + 4 = 0$ with the curve $x^2 + 4xy + 2y^2 + 12x + 4y = 0$ are at right angles.

13. If the equation $ax^2 + 3xy - 2y^2 - 5x + 5y + c = 0$ represents a perpendicular line pair, find the values of a and c.

14. Find the circumcentre of the triangle with sides $x + 3y = 0$, $2x + y - 10 = 0$, $x - 7y + 10 = 0$.

15. A, B are two points on the line $x - y + 1 = 0$ at distance 5 units from the origin O; find the area of triangle OAB.

16. Show that the lines $a_1x + b_1y + c_1 = 0$, $a_2x + b_2y + c_2 = 0$ meet the axes in four concyclic points if $a_1a_2 - b_1b_2 = 0$. In this case prove that the equation of the circle passing through the points is
$$a_1a_2(x^2 + y^2) + (a_1c_2 + a_2c_1)x + (b_1c_2 + b_2c_1)y + c_1c_2 = 0.$$

17. Write down the equation of the pair of tangents from the point $(3, -2)$ to the circle $x^2 + y^2 = 3$ and find the acute angle between them.

18. Prove that the perpendiculars from the points $(-8, 10)$, $(1, 2)$, $(1, 11)$ to the lines $y - 3x + 5 = 0$, $2y - x = 0$, $x + y - 15 = 0$ respectively are concurrent, and show that the same property is true of perpendiculars drawn from the vertices of the second triangle to the sides of that determined by the given points.

19. Find the equation of the chord of contact of tangents drawn from $(-1, -2)$ to the circle $x^2 + y^2 + 4x + 10y + 24 = 0$ and determine the coordinates of the points of contact.

20. Find the acute angle between the line pair $x^2 + 4xy + y^2 = 0$ and by factorisation prove that the equation $x^3 + 3x^2y - 3xy^2 - y^3 = 0$ represents three lines through the origin equally inclined to each other.

21. Find the values of λ, μ for which the equation

$$(2x + y - 4)(x + 2y - 5) + \lambda(x + 2y - 5)(x + y - 6) + \mu(x + y - 6)(2x + y - 4) = 0,$$

represents a circle. Deduce that the equation of the circumcircle of the triangle formed by the lines $x + y - 6 = 0$, $2x + y - 4 = 0$, $x + 2y - 5 = 0$ is $x^2 + y^2 - 17x - 19y + 50 = 0$.

22. Show that the circle drawn on the common chord of the curve $3x^2 + 5xy - 3y^2 + 2x + 3y = 0$ and the line $3x - 2y - 1 = 0$ as diameter passes through the origin.

23. Prove that the vertices of the quadrilateral whose sides are given by the equations $l_r x + m_r y + n_r = 0$; $r = 1, 2, 3, 4$, are concyclic if

$$(l_1 m_2 - l_2 m_1)(l_3 l_4 + m_3 m_4) + (l_3 m_4 - l_4 m_3)(l_1 l_2 + m_1 m_2) = 0.$$

24. Find the point of intersection of the tangents drawn to the circle $x^2 + y^2 - 2x + 4y + 2 = 0$ at the ends of the chord $2x - 4y = 7$.

25. Show that the two straight lines $y^2 - 2xy \sec \theta + x^2 = 0$ make an angle θ with one another.

26. Prove that the equation of the chord of the circle

$$x^2 + y^2 + 2gx + 2fy + c = 0$$

whose mid-point is (x', y') is $(x' + g)(x - x') + (y' + f)(y - y') = 0$.

27. Show that the bisectors of the angles of each of the line pairs $ax^2 + 2hxy + by^2 = 0$, $ax^2 + 2hxy + by^2 + \lambda(x^2 + y^2) = 0$ coincide. Deduce that the angle between one line of the first pair and one line of the second is equal to the angle between the other two lines.

28. The distance of the point (α, β) from each of two straight lines passing through the origin is λ; prove the equation of the pair of lines is

$$(x\beta - y\alpha)^2 = \lambda^2(x^2 + y^2).$$

29. A chord of the curve $ax^2 + by^2 = 1$ subtends a right angle at the origin, prove that it touches a fixed circle, centre the origin.

30. Find the equation of the pair of lines through the origin which are at right angles to the lines $ax^2 + 2hxy + by^2 = 0$. Deduce that the line pairs $ax^2 + 2hxy + by^2 + 2gx + 2fy + c = 0$, $bx^2 - 2hxy + ay^2 = 0$ meet in four concyclic points and find the coordinates of the centre of the circle which passes through these points.

31. By expressing in polar coordinates, or otherwise, prove that the equation $x(x^2 - 3y^2) = my(y^2 - 3x^2)$ represents three straight lines through the origin making equal angles with one another.

32. Prove that the lines joining the origin to the points of intersection other than the origin of the two curves $a_1x^2 + 2h_1xy + b_1y^2 + 2g_1x = 0$, $a_2x^2 + 2h_2xy + b_2y^2 + 2g_2x = 0$ are perpendicular if $g_2(a_1 + b_1) = g_1(a_2 + b_2)$.

33. Prove that the area of the triangle formed by the lines

$$ax^2 + 2hxy + by^2 = 0 \quad \text{and} \quad lx + my = 1$$

is $\sqrt{(h^2 - ab)}/(am^2 - 2hlm + bl^2)$.

34. Find the equation of the circumcircle of the triangle formed by the lines $2x^2 + 3xy - y^2 = 0$, $x + y = 1$.

35. Show that the product of the perpendiculars from the point (α, β) to the lines $ax^2 + 2hxy + by^2 = 0$ is equal to $(a\alpha^2 + 2h\alpha\beta + b\beta^2)/\sqrt{\{(a - b)^2 + 4h^2\}}$.

36. The line pair $y^2 - m^2x^2 = 0$ intersects the curve $ax^2 + by^2 = 1$ in the points A, B, C, D. Show that the equation $ax^2 + by^2 - 1 + \lambda(y^2 - m^2x^2) = 0$ represents a curve passing through A, B, C, D and deduce that the equation of the circle through these four points is

$$(1 + m^2)(ax^2 + by^2 - 1) + (a - b)(y^2 - m^2x^2) = 0.$$

37. If the point $(-1, -1)$ lies on one of the lines whose equation is $ax^2 + 2hxy + by^2 + 2gx + 2fy + g + f = 0$, prove that it also lies on the other.

38. Show that the condition that two of the lines represented by the equation $ax^3 + 3bx^2y + 3cxy^2 + dy^3 = 0$ may be at right angles is that $a^2 + 3ac + 3bd + d^2 = 0$.

39. Show that all chords of the curve $3x^2 - y^2 - 2x + 4y = 0$ which subtend a right angle at the origin pass through a fixed point.

40. If

$$S_1 \equiv 3x^2 + 2xy - y^2 + 5x + y + 2 = 0, \quad S_2 \equiv 4x^2 + 5xy - 6y^2 - 3x + 5y - 1 = 0,$$

show that the equations $S_1 = 0$, $S_2 = 0$ represent line pairs. Interpret the equation $S_1 + \lambda S_2 = 0$ and show that λ can be chosen so that the equation represents a circle. Deduce that the line pairs $S_1 = S_2 = 0$ intersect in concyclic points and find the equation of the circumscribing circle.

CHAPTER V

SYSTEMS OF CIRCLES

Radical axis of two circles

Definitions. The *power of a point* P with respect to a circle S, centre A, radius a, is defined as the expression $AP^2 - a^2$.

If the equation of the circle S is $x^2 + y^2 + 2gx + 2fy + c = 0$ and P is the point (α, β), then

the power of $P = AP^2 - a^2$,
$$= (\alpha + g)^2 + (\beta + f)^2 - (g^2 + f^2 - c),$$
$$= \alpha^2 + \beta^2 + 2g\alpha + 2f\beta + c. \quad \ldots \ldots \quad \text{(i)}$$

I.e. *to obtain the power of a point with respect to a circle whose equation* $f(x, y) = 0$ *is expressed with unity coefficients of* x^2 *and* y^2, *simply substitute the coordinates of the point into the expression* $f(x, y)$.

If P lies outside the circle, the expression (i) will be positive and equal to the square of the tangent from P to the circle.

If P lies within the circle, the expression (i) will be negative.

Ex. 1. *Find the power of the point* $(-1, 2)$ *with respect to the circle* $2x^2 + 2y^2 + 3x + y - 2 = 0$ *and state whether the point lies outside or inside the circle.*

Write the equation of the circle in the form
$$x^2 + y^2 + \tfrac{3}{2}x + \tfrac{1}{2}y - 1 = 0.$$
Then the power of the point $= (-1)^2 + (2)^2 + \tfrac{3}{2}(-1) + \tfrac{1}{2}(2) - 1$
$$= 3\tfrac{1}{2}.$$

As the power is positive, the point lies outside the circle.

The *radical axis* of two circles is defined as the locus of a point P which moves such that its powers with respect to the circles are equal. For all points of the locus outside the circles this is equivalent to defining the radical axis as the locus of a point from which the tangents to the two circles are equal in length.

The equation of the radical axis of two circles. Let the equations of the circles S_1, S_2 be respectively
$$x^2 + y^2 + 2g_1x + 2f_1y + c_1 = 0, \quad x^2 + y^2 + 2g_2x + 2f_2y + c_2 = 0,$$
and let the point P have coordinates (α, β).

Then P lies on the radical axis of the circles if

$$\alpha^2 + \beta^2 + 2g_1\alpha + 2f_1\beta + c_1 = \alpha^2 + \beta^2 + 2g_2\alpha + 2f_2\beta + c_2,$$

i.e. if
$$2\alpha(g_1 - g_2) + 2\beta(f_1 - f_2) + c_1 - c_2 = 0.$$

Hence the equation of the locus of P, that is of the radical axis of the circles, is

$$2x(g_1 - g_2) + 2y(f_1 - f_2) + c_1 - c_2 = 0.$$

This is a straight line perpendicular to the line of centres of the circles.

N.B. *If the equations of the circles are represented as $S_1 = 0$, $S_2 = 0$, then the radical axis is $S_1 - S_2 = 0$, it being assumed that the coefficients of x^2 and y^2 in S_1 and S_2 are unity.*

Special cases

  (i) If the two circles intersect in real points X, Y, then the equation $S_1 - S_2 = 0$ is the equation of the common chord XY.

I.e. *the radical axis of two intersecting circles is the common chord of the circles.*

  (ii) If the two circles touch at a point X, then the equation $S_1 - S_2 = 0$ is the equation of the common tangent at X.

I.e. *the radical axis of two circles which touch each other is the tangent at the common point.*

Geometrical construction of the radical axis of two non-intersecting circles. Draw any circle Σ_1 to cut the given circles at A_1, B_1; A_2, B_2 (Fig. 45).
Let A_1B_1, A_2B_2 intersect at P_1.

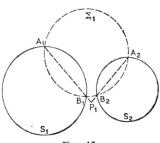

Fig. 45.

Then, as $P_1A_1 . P_1B_1 = P_1A_2 . P_1B_2$, intersecting chords of Σ_1, it follows that the square of the tangents from P_1 to the circles S_1, S_2 are equal, and consequently P_1 lies on the radical axis.

By drawing a second circle Σ_2, a second point P_2 is obtained and P_1P_2 is the radical axis.

Radical centre of three circles. The radical axes of three circles taken in pairs are concurrent in a point called the *radical centre*, except in the case where the centres of the circles are collinear, in which case the radical axes are parallel.

For representing the circles by the equations

$$S_1 = 0, \quad S_2 = 0, \quad S_3 = 0,$$

the radical axis of the circles S_2, S_3 is

$$S_2 - S_3 = 0 \quad . \quad . \quad . \quad . \quad . \quad \text{(ii)}$$

and the radical axis of the circles S_3, S_1 is

$$S_3 - S_1 = 0 \quad . \quad . \quad . \quad . \quad . \quad \text{(iii)}$$

The coordinates of the common point R of these lines will satisfy any equation derived from (ii) and (iii), i.e. the point R lies on the line $S_2 - S_1 = 0$, adding (ii) and (iii).

But $S_2 - S_1 = 0$ is the radical axis of S_1 and S_2, and hence the three radical axes of the circles taken in pairs are concurrent in R, the radical centre.

Ex. 2. *Find the coordinates of the radical centre of the three circles* $x^2 + y^2 = 2$, $x^2 + y^2 - 4x + 2y + 1 = 0$, $2x^2 + 2y^2 + 5x - 6y + 2 = 0$.

Writing the equation of the third circle in the form

$$x^2 + y^2 + \tfrac{5}{2}x - 3y + 1 = 0,$$

and referring to the circles as S_1, S_2, S_3, then the radical axes of S_1, S_2 and S_1, S_3 are respectively

$$x^2 + y^2 - 2 - (x^2 + y^2 - 4x + 2y + 1) = 0$$

and $\qquad x^2 + y^2 - 2 - (x^2 + y^2 + \tfrac{5}{2}x - 3y + 1) = 0.$

i.e. $\qquad\qquad 4x - 2y - 3 = 0,$

$$-\tfrac{5}{2}x + 3y - 3 = 0.$$

Solving these equations $x = \tfrac{15}{7}$, $y = \tfrac{39}{14}$.

∴ the radical centre of the circles is the point $(\tfrac{15}{7}, \tfrac{39}{14})$.

Simplified form for the equations of two given circles. Take the line of centres of the circles as the x-axis and their radical axis as the y-axis.

As the ordinates of the centres of the circles will be zero, the equations can be taken as

$$x^2 + y^2 + 2gx + c = 0 \quad \text{and} \quad x^2 + y^2 + 2g'x + c' = 0.$$

The radical axis of these circles has the equation

$$2x(g - g') + c - c' = 0.$$

But the radical axis is the axis of y, i.e. $x = 0$.

∴ Ignoring the special case, $g = g'$, when the circles are concentric, it follows that

$$c = c'.$$

Consequently, *the equations of the two circles can be taken as*

$$x^2+y^2+2gx+c=0, \quad x^2+y^2+2g'x+c=0.$$

These simplified equations should be used in the analytical treatment of problems involving two circles as is illustrated in the proof of the following proposition.

The difference of the powers of a point with respect to two given circles is proportional to the distance of the point from the radical axis of the circles.

The equations of the given circles can be taken as

$$S_1 \equiv x^2+y^2+2g_1x+c=0,$$
$$S_2 \equiv x^2+y^2+2g_2x+c=0.$$

Let P be the point (α, β).

Then the power of P w.r.t. $S_1 = \alpha^2 + \beta^2 + 2g_1\alpha + c$

and the power of P w.r.t. $S_2 = \alpha^2 + \beta^2 + 2g_2\alpha + c$.

∴ Difference in powers $= 2\alpha(g_1-g_2)$.

But α is the distance of P from the radical axis, $x=0$, and (g_1-g_2) is constant; hence the difference in the powers of P is proportional to the distance of P from the radical axis.

Ex. 3. *PT is a tangent from a point P on a given circle S_1, centre A, to a second circle S_2, centre B. If PM is the perpendicular from P to the radical axis, prove that $PT^2 = 2PM \cdot AB$.*

Take the equations of the circles as

$$S_1 \equiv x^2+y^2+2g_1x+c=0; \quad S_2 \equiv x^2+y^2+2g_2x+c=0.$$

Let P be the point (α, β).

Then $\qquad\qquad PT^2 = \alpha^2+\beta^2+2g_2\alpha+c$.

But as P lies on the circle S_1,

$$0 = \alpha^2+\beta^2+2g_1\alpha+c.$$

Hence $\qquad\qquad PT^2 = 2\alpha(g_2-g_1) = 2PM \cdot AB$.

EXAMPLES 5a

1. Prove from the definition that if the power of a point with respect to a circle is positive, zero or negative then the point is outside, on or inside the circle respectively.

2. Find the powers of the point $(1, -2)$ with respect to the following circles and in each case give the position of the point in relation to the circle:

(i) $x^2+y^2+8x-y+6=0$; (ii) $x^2+y^2-4x+2y=0$;
(iii) $4(x^2+y^2)-6x+2y-8=0$.

3. Prove that the point $(-2, 1)$ lies inside the circle $x^2+y^2+4x-1=0$ and outside the circle $2x^2+2y^2-2x-3y=0$.

H

4. Find the equations of the radical axes of the following pairs of circles:

(i)　　$x^2 + y^2 - 6x + 4 = 0$,　　　　　　(ii)　　　　$x^2 + y^2 = 4$,
　　$x^2 + y^2 - 2x + y - 6 = 0$;　　　　　　$2x^2 + 2y^2 - 4x = 3$;

(iii)　$x^2 + y^2 - 2x + y - 6 = 0$,
　　$3(x^2 + y^2) + x - 6y - 4 = 0$.

5. What is the radical axis of two equal non-intersecting circles with centres A, B?

6. Find the equation of the radical axis of the circles $x^2 + y^2 = 1$, $x^2 + y^2 - 6x - 4y + 9 = 0$. Draw an accurate diagram showing the circles and their radical axis.

7. Draw two non-equal, non-intersecting circles and obtain their radical axis by a geometrical method.

8. Prove that the circles $(x + 1)^2 + y^2 = 4$, $(x - 3)^2 + (y - 3)^2 = 9$ touch each other externally and find the equation of their radical axis. Show the circles and the radical axis on a diagram.

9. Find the coordinates of the radical centre of the circles

$$x^2 + y^2 + 4x + 4y + 4 = 0, \quad x^2 + y^2 - 4y + 3 = 0, \quad x^2 + y^2 - 8x - 2y - 16 = 0.$$

10. Three circles are such that each intersects the other two in real points. Prove that the three common chords are concurrent.

11. Show that the radical axis of the circles $x^2 + y^2 + 2\lambda_1 x + c = 0$, $x^2 + y^2 + 2\lambda_2 x + c = 0$ is independent of the values of the parameters λ_1, λ_2.

12. Prove that the radical axis of two unequal circles is further from the centre of the larger circle than from the centre of the smaller circle.

13. If P is a point on the radical axis of two circles, centres A, B, radii a, b, and N is the foot of the perpendicular from P to AB, prove that $AN^2 - BN^2 = a^2 - b^2$ and deduce that $AN - BN = (a^2 - b^2)/AB$.

14. A point P moves such that its power with respect to a circle S_1 is twice its power with respect to a second circle S_2. Prove that the locus of P is a circle whose centre lies on the line joining the centres of S_1 and S_2.

15. Prove that the system of circles represented by the equation $x^2 + y^2 + 2\lambda x + c = 0$, where λ is a parameter and c a constant, is such that the radical axis of every pair is the same straight line.

16. Show that the circle Σ will bisect the circumference of the circle S if the centre of the latter circle lies on the common chord. Deduce the condition that the circle $x^2 + y^2 + 2gx + 2fy + c = 0$ should bisect the circumference of the circle $x^2 + y^2 - 4 = 0$.

17. Prove that the locus of a point which moves such that the difference of the squares of the tangents from it to two given circles is constant is a straight line.

18. Find the condition that the circle $x^2 + y^2 - 2\alpha x - 2\beta y + c = 0$ should cut the circle $x^2 + y^2 - 2\alpha' x - 2\beta' y + c' = 0$ at the ends of a diameter of the latter circle.

19. P is any point on the radical axis of two non-intersecting circles S_1, S_2. Prove that the chords of contact of the tangents drawn from P to the circles intersect on the radical axis.

20. A variable circle Σ cuts two given circles S_1, S_2 at P_1, Q_1; P_2, Q_2 respectively. Prove that the locus of the point of intersection of P_1Q_1, P_2Q_2 is a fixed straight line.

21. Two fixed circles have their centres at A, B; a number of circles S are drawn so that each circle S bisects the circumference of each of the fixed circles. Prove that the centres of the circles S lie on a fixed straight line perpendicular to AB.

22. Triangle ABC is obtuse-angled at A. The altitudes AD, BE, CF intersect at the orthocentre H. Prove that $HE \cdot HB = HF \cdot HC$, and hence show that H lies on the radical axis of the circles drawn on AB and AC as diameters.

23. Prove that the radical axis of two circles bisects the common tangents of the circles. In triangle ABC, prove that the radical axis of the incircle and the escribed circle opposite A passes through the mid-point of BC.

24. A variable circle passes through two fixed points A, B and cuts a fixed circle at P, Q. Prove that PQ intersects AB at a fixed point.

Coaxal circles

A system of circles which is such that the radical axis of any pair is the same as that of any other pair is called a coaxal system.

From the definition it follows that:

(i) the centres of the circles are collinear, as the line joining each pair of centres is perpendicular to the common radical axis;

(ii) a coaxal system is determined by any two of its member circles.

Suppose two circles of a coaxal system are

$$S_1 \equiv x^2 + y^2 + 2g_1x + 2f_1y + c_1 = 0; \quad S_2 = x^2 + y^2 + 2g_2x + 2f_2y + c_2 = 0.$$

Consider the equation $S_1 + \lambda S_2 = 0$, where λ is a parameter.

Apart from the value $\lambda = -1$, when it represents the radical axis of the two given circles, the equation represents a system of circles.

Take any two circles of the system

$$S_1 + \lambda_1 S_2 = 0; \quad S_1 + \lambda_2 S_2 = 0.$$

Then the radical axis of these two circles is

$$\frac{S_1 + \lambda_1 S_2}{1 + \lambda_1} - \frac{S_1 + \lambda_2 S_2}{1 + \lambda_2} = 0,$$

care being taken to make the coefficients of x^2 and y^2 unity before subtraction.

Simplifying, $S_1(\lambda_2 - \lambda_1) - S_2(\lambda_2 - \lambda_1) = 0$

i.e. $S_1 - S_2 = 0$ as $\lambda_1 \neq \lambda_2$.

Consequently, the radical axis of any pair of circles in the given system is the same straight line, the radical axis of the original pair.

Hence the equation $S_1 + \lambda S_2 = 0$, $\lambda \neq -1$, *gives the coaxal system determined by the two circles* $S_1 = 0$, $S_2 = 0$.

Replacing the parameter λ by μ, where $\lambda = -\dfrac{\mu}{1+\mu}$, the equation $S_1 + \lambda S_2 = 0$, becomes

$$S_1 + \mu(S_1 - S_2) = 0.$$

But
$$L \equiv S_1 - S_2 = 0,$$

is the equation of the radical axis of the system and so *the equation of a coaxal system can be expressed in terms of the equations of one of the circles and the common radical axis in the form*

$$S_1 + \mu L = 0.$$

As the coefficients of x^2 and y^2 are unity, this is often the more convenient form for the equation of a coaxal system.

N.B. If the circles S_1, S_2 *intersect in real points, then the equation* $S_1 + \lambda S_2 = 0$, *represents the system of circles through the common points and consequently, in this case, this is the coaxal system determined by the two circles.*

Ex. 4. *Write down the equation of the coaxal system determined by the circles* $x^2 + y^2 = 4$, $x^2 + y^2 - 6x + 4y + 10 = 0$ *and find the equation of the circle of the system which passes through the origin.*

The equation of the coaxal system is

$$x^2 + y^2 - 6x + 4y + 10 + \lambda(x^2 + y^2 - 4) = 0.$$

This equation is satisfied by the point $(0, 0)$ if

$$10 - 4\lambda = 0; \quad \lambda = \tfrac{5}{2}.$$

∴ The equation of the circle of the system which passes through the origin is

$$2(x^2 + y^2 - 6x + 4y + 10) + 5(x^2 + y^2 - 4) = 0$$
$$7(x^2 + y^2) - 12x + 8y = 0.$$

Ex. 5. *Two circles of a coaxal system have equations* $x^2 + y^2 - x + 3y + 1 = 0$, $x^2 + y^2 + x - 2y + 1 = 0$. *Find: (i) the equation of the radical axis; (ii) the equations of the two circles of the system which touch the x-axis.*

(i) Radical axis $\qquad\qquad L \equiv S_1 - S_2 = 0$

i.e. $\qquad\qquad\qquad\qquad L \equiv 5y - 2x = 0.$

(ii) The equation of any circle of the coaxal system can be written

$$x^2 + y^2 - x + 3y + 1 + \mu(5y - 2x) = 0.$$

This circle meets the x-axis, where

$$x^2 - x(2\mu + 1) + 1 = 0.$$

Hence this circle touches the x-axis if

$$(2\mu+1)^2=4; \quad \mu=\tfrac{1}{2}, \; -\tfrac{3}{2}.$$

$\therefore$ The equations of the circles of the coaxal system which touch the x-axis are

$$2(x^2+y^2-x+3y+1)+5y-2x=0; \quad 2(x^2+y^2-x+3y+1)-3(5y-2x)=0.$$

I.e. $\qquad 2(x^2+y^2)-4x+11y+2=0; \quad 2(x^2+y^2)+4x-9y+2=0.$

Simplified form of the equation of a coaxal system of circles. Let two circles of the system have equations

$$S_1 \equiv x^2+y^2+2g_1x+2f_1y+c_1=0; \quad S_2 \equiv x^2+y^2+2g_2x+2f_2y+c_2=0.$$

Take the common radical axis as the y-axis.
Then the equation

$$2(g_1-g_2)x+2(f_1-f_2)y+c_1-c_2=0,$$

must reduce to $\qquad\qquad x=0.$

$$\therefore \quad f_1=f_2; \quad c_1=c_2.$$

Consequently, when the common radical axis is taken as the y-axis the equation of any circle of the coaxal system reduces to

$$x^2+y^2+2gx+2fy+c=0,$$

where f and c are constant in value for all circles.

The fact that f is constant shows that the centres of the circles all lie on a straight line perpendicular to the radical axis. The equation is further reduced by taking this line of centres as the x-axis; it becomes

$$x^2+y^2+2gx+c=0.$$

To stress the fact that c is constant for all the circles of the system and only g varies, the equation is usually written

$$x^2+y^2+2\lambda x+c=0,$$

where λ is a parameter.

Hence the equation of a system of coaxal circles can be expressed in the form $x^2+y^2+2\lambda x+c=0$, where λ is a parameter and c a constant.

Conversely, the equation $x^2+y^2+2\lambda x+c=0$, where λ is a parameter and c a constant, can be shown to represent a system of coaxal circles.
For take any pair of circles with $\lambda=\lambda_1, \lambda_2$.
The radical axis of this pair is

$$2x(\lambda_1-\lambda_2)=0,$$

i.e. $\qquad\qquad x=0.$

So the radical axis of each pair is the same and the system is coaxal.

Ex. 6. *Show that, in general, two circles of a coaxal system will touch a given straight line.*

Take the equation of the coaxal system as

$$x^2 + y^2 + 2\lambda x + c = 0$$

and let the given line be $lx + my + n = 0.$

The circle touches the line if the length of the perpendicular from its centre $(-\lambda, 0)$ to the line is equal to its radius $\sqrt{(\lambda^2 - c)}$,

i.e. if $\dfrac{-l\lambda + n}{\sqrt{(l^2 + m^2)}} = \sqrt{(\lambda^2 - c)}$

or, squaring and simplifying, $m^2\lambda^2 + 2ln\lambda - (n^2 + l^2c + m^2c) = 0.$

Apart from the case $m = 0$, this is a quadratic equation, and consequently, in general, there are two circles of the system touching a given line.

Types of coaxal systems. Every circle of the coaxal system

$$x^2 + y^2 + 2\lambda x + c = 0$$

cuts the radical axis, $x = 0$, where

$$y^2 + c = 0.$$

The following three cases arise according as c is less than, greater than, or equal to zero.

Case (i). *Suppose c is negative and equal to* $-k^2$. Then every circle of the system cuts the radical axis in the same two points $(0, \pm k)$. Consequently, the system consists of a series of circles passing through two fixed points A, B (Fig. 46).

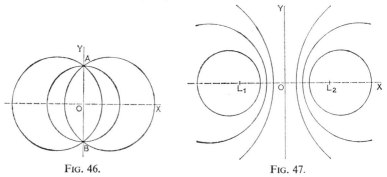

FIG. 46.   FIG. 47.

As the equation can be written in the form

$$(x + \lambda)^2 + y^2 = \lambda^2 + k^2,$$

it follows that the least circle of the system has its centre at the origin and its radius equal to k.

Case (ii). *Suppose c is positive and equal to* k^2. Then as $y^2 + k^2 = 0$ has no real solutions, no circle of the system cuts the radical axis (Fig. 47).

Writing the equation in the form,
$$(x+\lambda)^2 + y^2 = \lambda^2 - k^2$$
it follows that the radius equals $\sqrt{(\lambda^2 - k^2)}$.

Hence λ cannot lie between $-k$ and $+k$, and as λ approaches either of these values the radius tends to zero.

Consequently, there are two point circles in the system, circles with zero radius, at the points $(\pm k, 0)$. These points L_1, L_2 are called *limiting points*; it will be noted that they are reflection points in the radical axis.

N.B. In case (i), *where $c < 0$, the circles meet in real points* $(0, \pm\sqrt{-c})$ *and the limiting points* $(\pm\sqrt{c}, 0)$ *are imaginary.*

In case (ii), *where $c > 0$, the circles meet in imaginary points* $(0, \pm\sqrt{-c})$ *and the limiting points* $(\pm\sqrt{c}, 0)$ *are real.*

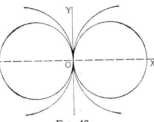
Fig. 48.

Case (iii). *Suppose $c = 0$.* Clearly in this case the common points and the limiting points all coincide at the origin.

The system consists of a series of circles touching each other at the origin. The least circle of the system is a point circle at the origin (Fig. 48).

Limiting points. As defined above, the limiting points of a coaxal system are the centres of the circles of zero radius in the system. They will be real when the circles of the system are non-intersecting. It is important to remember that the limiting points are point circles in the system; for example, if the point $(3, -4)$ is a limiting point then the circle
$$(x-3)^2 + (y+4)^2 = 0,$$
is a member of the coaxal system.

Ex. 7. *A coaxal system has limiting points* $(-1, 2)$, $(0, 3)$. *Find:* (i) *the equation of the radical axis;* (ii) *the equation of any circle of the system.*

(i) The equations of the point circles are
$$S_1 \equiv (x+1)^2 + (y-2)^2 = 0; \quad S_2 \equiv x^2 + (y-3)^2 = 0.$$
∴ The radical axis $L \equiv S_1 - S_2 = 0$, has the equation
$$x + y - 2 = 0.$$

This line is, of course, the perpendicular bisector of the line joining the limiting points.

(ii) The equation of any circle of the system can be expressed in either of the forms
$$S_1 + \lambda S_2 = 0 \quad \text{or} \quad S_1 + \mu L = 0.$$
I.e. $(x+1)^2 + (y-2)^2 + \lambda\{x^2 + (y-3)^2\} = 0$ or
$$(x+1)^2 + (y-2)^2 + \mu(x+y-2) = 0.$$

Ex. 8. *If one circle of a coaxal system, of which the origin is one limiting point, is* $x^2 + y^2 + 4x + 2y + 4 = 0$, *find:* (i) *the equation of the radical axis;* (ii) *the coordinates of the second limiting point;* (iii) *the equation of the second coaxal system formed by circles passing through the limiting points of the original system.*

(i) The equation of the point circle at the origin is

$$S_1 \equiv x^2 + y^2 = 0.$$

Also $S_2 \equiv x^2 + y^2 + 4x + 2y + 4 = 0.$

∴ The equation of the radical axis is

$$4x + 2y + 4 = 0; \quad \text{i.e. } 2x + y + 2 = 0.$$

(ii) Any circle of the coaxal system has the equation

$$x^2 + y^2 + \mu(2x + y + 2) = 0.$$

The radius of this circle is $\sqrt{(\frac{5}{4}\mu^2 - 2\mu)}$ and its centre is $(-\mu, \ -\frac{1}{2}\mu)$. So for the point circles, $\frac{5}{4}\mu^2 - 2\mu = 0$; i.e. $\mu = 0, \ \frac{8}{5}$.

The value $\mu = 0$, gives the origin.

The value $\mu = \frac{8}{5}$, gives $(-\frac{8}{5}, \ -\frac{4}{5})$ as the second limiting point.

(iii) If $\Sigma = 0$ is the equation of one circle passing through the limiting points and $M = 0$ is the equation of the line joining these points, then the equation of the second coaxal system is

$$\Sigma + \lambda M = 0,$$

where λ is a parameter.

The centre of Σ must be on the radical axis of the original system. Take as centre the point $(0, -2)$ where the radical axis meets the y-axis; as Σ passes through the origin its radius is 2.

So $\Sigma \equiv x^2 + (y + 2)^2 - 4 = 0; \quad \text{i.e. } x^2 + y^2 + 4y = 0,$

and $M \equiv x - 2y = 0.$

Hence the equation of the second coaxal system is

$$x^2 + y^2 + 4y + \lambda(x - 2y) = 0.$$

To find the limiting points of a given coaxal system geometrically. We can assume that the radical axis has been given or has been constructed. Take any point P on the radical axis and construct a tangent PT to one of the circles S of the system.

Now construct the circle, centre P, radius PT; this will cut the line of centres at the limiting points L_1, L_2.

The proof is immediate as PL_1, PL_2 are the tangents from a point P on the radical axis to the point circles L_1, L_2, and each of these tangents is equal to PT, the tangent to S.

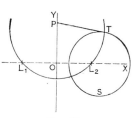

Fig. 49.

Ex. 9. *Show how to construct the two circles of a given non-intersecting coaxal system which touch a given line.*

Suppose the given line meets the radical axis at P (Fig. 50). With centre P, radius PL_1, construct a circle to cut the given line at X_1, X_2. Then X_1, X_2 are the points of contact of the required circles. The centres of these circles C_1, C_2 are obtained by drawing perpendiculars at X_1, X_2 to the given line.

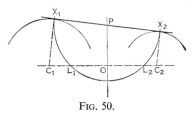

FIG. 50.

The proof follows from the fact that the length of the tangents from P to all the circles of the system is equal to PL_1 or PL_2.

EXAMPLES 5b

1. Write down two alternative forms for the equation of a circle of the coaxal system determined by each of the following pairs of circles:

(i) $x^2 + y^2 = 1$, $x^2 + y^2 - 2x = 0$;

(ii) $x^2 + y^2 = 2y$; $x^2 + y^2 - 3x - y + 1 = 0$.

(iii) $2(x^2 + y^2) - x - 2 = 0$; $x^2 + y^2 - 4y - 2 = 0$;

(iv) $x^2 + y^2 - 5x + 2y - 3 = 0$; $3x^2 + 3y^2 - 2y - 6 = 0$.

2. Find the equation of the circle of the coaxal system determined by the circles $x^2 + y^2 = 4$, $x^2 + y^2 - 6x + 2y + 5 = 0$ which passes through the point $(0, 3)$.

3. The radical axis of a coaxal system is $L = 0$, and one circle of the system is $S = 0$; write down the equation of any circle of the system in each of the following cases:

(i) $L \equiv x + y$, $S \equiv x^2 + y^2 - 6x - 2y + 2$;

(ii) $L \equiv x - 2y + 1$, $S \equiv x^2 + y^2 - 2$;

(iii) $L \equiv 2x - y - 3$, $S \equiv 2(x^2 + y^2) - 4x + 1$;

(iv) $L \equiv x$, $S \equiv ax^2 + ay^2 + 2gx + 2fy + c$.

4. The radical axis of a coaxal system is $x + 1 = 0$ and one circle of the system is $x^2 + y^2 - 5x + 2 = 0$. Find the equations of the two circles of the system which have a radius of 1.

5. Make rough sketches of the coaxal systems represented by the equations:

(i) $x^2 + y^2 + 2\lambda x - 1 = 0$; (ii) $x^2 + y^2 + 2\lambda x + 1 = 0$; (iii) $x^2 + y^2 + 2\lambda x = 0$.

6. Prove that through any point there passes one, and only one, circle of a given coaxal system.

7. Prove that the circles $x^2 + y^2 - 6x - 16 = 0$, $x^2 + y^2 - 3y - 19 = 0$, $2x^2 + 2y^2 - 18x + 3y - 29 = 0$ are coaxal and state the equation of the common radical axis.

8. Find the coordinates of the limiting points of each of the following systems of coaxal circles:

(i) $x^2 + y^2 + \lambda x + 4 = 0$; (ii) $x^2 + y^2 + \lambda y + 9 = 0$; (iii) $x^2 + y^2 + \lambda(x - 2) = 0$;
(iv) $x^2 + y^2 - 2x + 1 + 8\lambda x = 0$;   (v) $x^2 + y^2 + \lambda(x + y - 2) = 0$;
(vi) $x^2 + y^2 - 10x + 9 + \lambda(x^2 + y^2 + 8x + 9) = 0$.

9. Prove that $(1, 2)$ is one of the limiting points of the coaxal system $(x - 1)^2 + (y - 2)^2 + \lambda(x^2 + y^2 + 6x + 5) = 0$ and find the other one.

10. Find the equation of the radical axis and the coordinates of the limiting points of the coaxal system determined by the circles

$$x^2 + y^2 + 10x - 4y - 5 = 0, \quad 2x^2 + 2y^2 + 12x - 6y - 3 = 0.$$

11. Write down the general equation of the system of coaxal circles having each of the following pairs of points as limiting points: (i) $(0, 0)$, $(2, 1)$; (ii) $(0, 0)$, $(0, -4)$; (iii) $(1, 1)$, $(2, -1)$; (iii) $(2, -3)$, $(4, 0)$.

12. Draw two unequal non-intersecting circles and find by geometrical construction: (i) the radical axis; (ii) the limiting points of the system determined by the two circles.

13. The limiting points of a coaxal system are $(-2, 1)$, $(3, 3)$. Find: (i) the equation of the radical axis; (ii) the equation of the circle of the system which passes through the origin.

14. The limiting points of a coaxal system are $(1, -1)$, $(3, 0)$. Construct, on squared paper, the circles of the system which touch the line $y = 2$.

15. Prove that the radical axes of a given circle and each circle of a given coaxal system are concurrent.

16. The circle $x^2 + y^2 + 4x - 6y + 3 = 0$ is one of a coaxal system having as radical axis the line $2x - 4y + 1 = 0$. Find the coordinates of the limiting points of the system showing that one lies on the line $x + 3y - 2 = 0$. Also find the equation of the other circle of the system which touches this line.

17. Find the equation of the circle which has as diameter the common chord of the circles $x^2 + y^2 - 2x + 2y - 3 = 0$, $x^2 + y^2 - x + 7y - 1 = 0$.

18. Find the equation of the circle which has for a diameter the chord cut off on the line $x - y + 2 = 0$ by the circle $x^2 + y^2 = 4$.

19. If the line of centres of a coaxal system meets the radical axis at O and a_r is the radius of a circle of the system with centre A_r, prove that $OA_r^2 - a_r^2$ is constant.

20. Two circles, centres A, B, have radii a, b. Prove that the locus of the centre of a circle which bisects the circumferences of the two given circles is the radical axis of circles, centres A, B, radii b, a respectively.

21. Given the limiting points of a coaxal system, show how to construct the circle of the system which passes through a given point.

22. P is a point on the radical axis of the coaxal system $x^2 + y^2 + 2\lambda x + k^2 = 0$. Show that the chords of contact of tangents from P to the circles of the system are concurrent.

23. Show that the equation of the system of coaxal circles with limiting points (x_1, y_1), (x_2, y_2) can be expressed in either of the forms:

(i) $(x - x_1)^2 + (y - y_1)^2 + \lambda\{(x - x_2)^2 + (y - y_2)^2\} = 0$; or
(ii) $(x - x_1)^2 + (y - y_1)^2 + \mu\{(x_1 - x_2)(2x + x_1 + x_2) + (y_1 - y_2)(2y + y_1 + y_2)\} = 0$.

24. If the point (2, 1) is one limiting point of a coaxal system containing the circle $x^2 + y^2 + 8x - 6y - 3 = 0$, find: (i) the coordinates of the other limiting point, and (ii) the equations of the circles of the system with radius 2 units.

25. Prove that the equation of the coaxal system of circles passing through the points (x_1, y_1), (x_2, y_2) can be expressed in the form

$$(x - x_1)(x - x_2) + (y - y_1)(y - y_2) + \lambda\{(y - y_1)(x - x_2) - (y - y_2)(x - x_2)\} - 0.$$

26. The square of the tangent from a variable point P to a fixed circle is proportional to the sum of the squares of the tangents from P to two other fixed circles. If the three circles are coaxal, prove that the locus of P is a circle of the same system.

27. From a point P, the tangents PT_1, PT_2, PT_3 are drawn to each of three coaxal circles with centres A_1, A_2, A_3. Prove that

$$PT_1^2 \cdot A_2A_3 + PT_2^2 \cdot A_3A_1 + PT_3^2 \cdot A_1A_2 = 0.$$

28. If a, b, c are the radii of three coaxal circles, centres A, B, C, prove that $a^2 BC + b^2 CA + c^2 AB + BC \cdot CA \cdot AB = 0$.

29. LT is a tangent from a limiting point L to any circle, centre A, of a coaxal system. Prove that LT^2/LA is constant.

30. If $S_1 = 0$, $S_2 = 0$ are the equations of two circles which cut two given circles at ends of diameters, prove that each circle of the coaxal system $S_1 + \lambda S_2 = 0$ cuts the given circles at ends of diameters.

Orthogonal circles. If two circles, centres A, B, cut at a point X, the angle of intersection θ is the acute angle between the tangents to the two circles at that point.

Clearly this angle is also equal to the acute angle between the radii AX, BX.

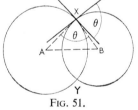

By symmetry, the angle of intersection at Y is equal to the angle of intersection at X and we can speak simply of the angle of intersection of the two circles.

Fig. 51.

Special cases. (i) If the circles touch the angle of intersection is zero; (ii) if the angle of intersection is a right angle, the circles are said *to cut orthogonally* and are called *orthogonal circles.*

Condition that two circles should cut orthogonally. Referring to the diagram in Fig. 51, when the circles cut orthogonally angle $AXB = 90°$ and hence

$$AB^2 = AX^2 + BX^2.$$

I.e. Square of distance between centres = sum of squares of radii.

If the equations of the circles are respectively

$$x^2 + y^2 + 2g_1x + 2f_1y + c_1 = 0, \quad x^2 + y^2 + 2g_2x + 2f_2y + c_2 = 0,$$

then
$$AB^2 = (g_1 - g_2)^2 + (f_1 - f_2)^2$$

and
$$AX^2 + BX^2 = (g_1^2 + f_1^2 - c_1) + (g_2^2 + f_2^2 - c_2).$$

Hence $(g_1 - g_2)^2 + (f_1 - f_2)^2 = (g_1^2 + f_1^2 - c_1) + (g_2^2 + f_2^2 - c_2)$,

i.e. $2(g_1 g_2 + f_1 f_2) = c_1 + c_2.$

The converse result is easily shown to be true.

Ex. 10. *Prove that the circle which has the points* $(0, 4)$, $(4, 2)$ *at the ends of a diameter cuts the circle* $x^2 + y^2 + 2x - 4y = 0$ *orthogonally.*

The equation of the circle on the line joining $(0, 4)$, $(4, 2)$ as diameter is

$$(x - 0)(x - 4) + (y - 4)(y - 2) = 0$$

i.e. $x^2 + y^2 - 4x - 6y + 8 = 0.$

So $g_1 = -2, \quad f_1 = -3, \quad c_1 = 8.$

Also $g_2 = 1, \quad f_2 = -2, \quad c_2 = 0.$

Hence $2(g_1 g_2 + f_1 f_2) = 8 = c_1 + c_2.$

∴ The circles cut orthogonally.

Any circle through the limiting points of a coaxal system is orthogonal to each circle of the system. The equation of any circle of the coaxal system can be taken as

$$S \equiv x^2 + y^2 + 2\lambda x + c = 0,$$

where c is a constant > 0.

The limiting points L_1, L_2 have coordinates $(\mp \sqrt{c}, 0)$.

A circle through L_1, L_2 must have its centre on the radical axis, $x = 0$, and its equation must have the form

$$\Sigma \equiv x^2 + y^2 + 2fy + k = 0.$$

As this circle Σ passes through the points $(\mp \sqrt{c}, 0)$,

$$c + k = 0; \quad k = -c.$$

So the equation of any circle through the limiting points is

$$\Sigma \equiv x^2 + y^2 + 2fy - c = 0,$$

where f is a variable parameter.

The condition $2(g_1 g_2 + f_1 f_2) = c_1 + c_2$ is clearly satisfied for the circles S and Σ and consequently they cut orthogonally.

The system of circles through the limiting points of the given coaxal system is called *the orthogonal system*. The two systems can be represented by the simplified equations:

Original coaxal system $x^2 + y^2 + 2\lambda x + c = 0$;

Orthogonal system $x^2 + y^2 + 2\mu y - c = 0$;

where λ, μ are parameters and c a positive constant.

Ex. 11. *Find the equation of the circle with centre on the y-axis and cutting each of the circles* $S_1 \equiv x^2 + y^2 + y = 0$, $S_2 \equiv x^2 + y^2 + 6x - 2y + 6 = 0$ *orthogonally.*

Method (i). The equation of the required circle Σ can be taken as

$$x^2 + y^2 + 2fy + c = 0.$$

As S_1, Σ are orthogonal, $\quad 2[\frac{1}{2}f] = c; \quad c = f.$

As S_2, Σ are orthogonal, $\quad 2[-f] = c + 6.$

$$f = c = -2,$$

and the required circle is

$$x^2 + y^2 - 4y - 2 = 0.$$

Method (ii). The required circle Σ must have its centre on the radical axis of S_1, S_2 and must pass through the limiting points of the coaxal system determined by S_1, S_2.

Radical axis of S_1, S_2 is $2x - y + 2 = 0.$

$\therefore$ Centre of Σ is the point $(0, 2)$.

As the distance of a point on the radical axis of a coaxal system from a limiting point is equal to the length of the tangent from the point to any circle of the system, it follows that the radius of Σ is equal to the length of the tangent from $(0, 2)$ to S_1.

$\therefore$ Radius of $\Sigma = \sqrt{(4+2)} = \sqrt{6}.$

Hence the equation of Σ is

$$x^2 + (y-2)^2 = 6$$

.e. $$x^2 + y^2 - 4y - 2 = 0.$$

EXAMPLES 5c

1. Prove that the following pairs of circles cut orthogonally:

(i) $x^2 + y^2 = 2$, $x^2 + y^2 - 2x + 3y + 2 = 0$;

(ii) $x^2 + y^2 - 4x + 6y - 7 = 0$, $x^2 + y^2 + 3x - 2y - 5 = 0$;

(iii) $x^2 + y^2 - 4x + 3 = 0$, $x^2 + y^2 + 5y - 3 = 0$;

(iv) $2x^2 + 2y^2 - 3x - 4y + 2 = 0$, $x^2 + y^2 - 4x + 2y = 0$.

2. Find the angle of intersection of each of the following pairs of circles:

(i) $x^2 + y^2 - 4x + 6y - 12 = 0$, $x^2 + y^2 + 2x - 2y - 23 = 0$;

(ii) $x^2 + y^2 = 3$, $x^2 + y^2 = 2x + 2y$.

3. Prove that the circles $x^2 + y^2 - 4x + 2y - 4 = 0$, $x^2 + y^2 - 10x - 6y + 30 = 0$ ouch each externally and write down the equation of the common tangent t the point of contact.

4. If the circles $x^2 + y^2 - 4 = 0$, $x^2 + y^2 + 2ax - 6y + a = 0$ cut orthogonally, nd the value of the constant a.

5. Find the equation of the circle of radius 5 which lies within the circle $^2 + y^2 + 14x + 10y = 26$ and touches it at the point $(-1, 3)$.

6. A circle passes through the origin and cuts orthogonally the circle $x^2 + y^2 + 2gx + 2fy + c = 0$, show that its centre lies on the line

$$2gx + 2fy + c = 0.$$

7. Find the equation of the circle with centre (a, b) which cuts the circle $x^2 + y^2 = r^2$ orthogonally.

8. A variable circle passes through a fixed point and cuts a given circle orthogonally; prove that the locus of its centre is a straight line.

9. Find the equation of the circle passing through the origin and the point $(-3, 2)$ and orthogonal to the circle $x^2 + y^2 - 6y + 5 = 0$.

10. Find the equation of the circle which is orthogonal to each of the circles $x^2 + y^2 - x + 2y + 1 = 0$, $x^2 + y^2 + 4x - y + 4 = 0$ and whose centre lies on the y-axis.

11. Find the equation of the orthogonal system of the coaxal system of circles with limiting points $(-1, 1)$, $(2, 2)$.

12. Find the equation of the circle which is orthogonal to each of the circles $x^2 + y^2 + 2x - 2y + 1 = 0$, $x^2 + y^2 + 4x - 4y + 3 = 0$ and whose centre lies on the line $3x - y - 2 = 0$.

13. If a circle is orthogonal to each circle of a non-intersecting coaxal system prove that it passes through the limiting points of the system.

14. Write down the general equation of a circle cutting the circle $x^2 + y^2 = r^2$ orthogonally and show that if it passes through the point (a, b) it will also pass through the point $\{r^2a/(a^2 + b^2), r^2b/(a^2 + b^2)\}$.

15. If $S_1 \equiv (x - \alpha_1)^2 + (y - \beta_1)^2 - r_1^2 = 0$ and $S_2 \equiv (x - \alpha_2)^2 + (y - \beta_2)^2 - r_2^2 = 0$ are any two circles, prove that the circles $S_1/r_1 \pm S_2/r_2 = 0$, cut orthogonally.

16. Find the condition that the circles $x^2 + y^2 + 2g_1x + 2f_1y + c_1 = 0$ $x^2 + y^2 + 2g_2x + 2f_2y + c_2 = 0$ touch each other internally.

17. Given two intersecting circles and their centres, show how a circle o given radius can be drawn so as to cut both circles orthogonally.

18. Find the equation of the circle which cuts each of the following circle orthogonally:

$$x^2 + y^2 + 4x + 6y - 5 = 0, \quad x^2 + y^2 + 8x + y - 20 = 0, \quad x^2 + y^2 + 6x + 2y - 14 = 0.$$

19. Write down the equation of the orthogonal system of the coaxa system of circles $x^2 + y^2 + \lambda x + 1 = 0$, and hence find the equations of th circles which are orthogonal to the circle $x^2 + y^2 + 10x + 1 = 0$ and whic touch the line $3x - y - 7 = 0$.

20. A circle is described on a variable chord $lx + my = 1$ of a given circl $x^2 + y^2 + 2g_1x + c = 0$ as diameter so as to cut a second given circl $x^2 + y^2 + 2g_2x + c = 0$ orthogonally. Prove that the locus of the centre of th variable circle is a circle.

The circle of Apollonius. *If A, B are two fixed points, then the locus of a point P which moves such that the ratio PA : PB is constant is, in general, a circle called the circle of Apollonius.*

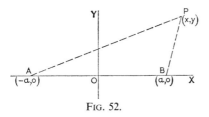

FIG. 52.

Take axes as shown in Fig. 52, O being the mid-point of AB.
Let A, B be the points $(\mp a, 0)$ and P be the point (x, y).
Take the constant ratio as λ, then

$$AP^2 = \lambda^2 BP^2.$$
$$\therefore (x+a)^2 + y^2 = \lambda^2\{(x-a)^2 + y^2\},$$

i.e. $\qquad x^2(\lambda^2 - 1) + y^2(\lambda^2 - 1) - 2ax(\lambda^2 + 1) + a^2(\lambda^2 - 1) - 0.$

Apart from the special case $\lambda = 1$, this equation represents a circle and consequently the locus of P is, in general, a circle—*the circle of Apollonius.* There is one circle corresponding to each positive value of λ.

When $\lambda = 1$, the equation becomes $x = 0$ and the locus of P is the perpendicular bisector of AB.

Centre and radius of the Apollonius circle. The above equation can be written

$$x^2 + y^2 - \frac{2a(\lambda^2 + 1)}{\lambda^2 - 1}x + a^2 = 0.$$

$\therefore$ *The centre of the Apollonius circle is the point* $\left(a\dfrac{\lambda^2 + 1}{\lambda^2 - 1}, 0\right)$.

Also $\qquad\qquad (\text{radius})^2 = a^2\left(\dfrac{\lambda^2 + 1}{\lambda^2 - 1}\right)^2 - a^2,$

$$= \frac{4a^2\lambda^2}{(\lambda^2 - 1)^2}.$$

$\therefore$ *The radius of the Apollonius circle is* $\pm\dfrac{2a\lambda}{\lambda^2 - 1}$ *or* $\pm\dfrac{\lambda AB}{\lambda^2 - 1}$.

Ex. 12. *Prove that the length of the tangent from O, the mid-point of AB, to the Apollonius circle associated with the points A, B is* $\frac{1}{2}AB$.

With axes through O as above, the equation of the Apollonius circle is

$$x^2 + y^2 - \frac{2a(\lambda^2 + 1)}{\lambda^2 - 1}x + a^2 = 0.$$

The square of the length of the tangent from O, the origin, to this circle is a^2 and hence the required result.

Ex. 13. *A, B are two fixed points; a point P moves such that AP: BP is constant. Prove that when P is moving directly towards A, angle PBA is a right angle.*

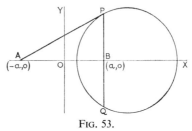

FIG. 53.

Taking axes through O, the mid-point of AB, in the usual way. The equation of the locus of P is

$$(\lambda^2 - 1)(x^2 + y^2) - 2a(\lambda^2 + 1)x + a^2(\lambda^2 - 1) = 0.$$

P is moving directly towards A when AP is a tangent to the Apollonius circle. To prove angle PBA is a right angle, it will be sufficient to prove that the chord of contact PQ passes through B.

Equation of PQ is

$$(\lambda^2 - 1)(-ax) - a(\lambda^2 + 1)(x - a) + a^2(\lambda^2 - 1) = 0$$

i.e. $\qquad -2\lambda^2 ax + 2a^2\lambda^2 = 0; \quad$ or $\quad x = a.$

Hence PQ passes through B and angle $PBA = 90°$.

Apollonius circles as a system of coaxal circles. With axes chosen as before, the equation of the Apollonius circle associated with the points A, B and the ratio λ is

$$x^2 + y^2 - \frac{2a(\lambda^2 + 1)}{\lambda^2 - 1}x + a^2 = 0. \qquad . \quad . \quad . \quad (i)$$

Taking $\lambda = \lambda_1, \lambda_2$, the radical axis of the two circles S_1, S_2 obtained is $\qquad S_1 - S_2 = 0; \quad$ i.e. $x = 0.$

$\therefore$ The equation (i) represents a set of coaxal circles with radical axis the y-axis.

As the constant term, a^2, is positive, the circles are non-intersecting and have two real limiting points, the points $(\mp a, 0)$ that is A and B.

Properties of Apollonius circles can be deduced, if necessary, from known properties of coaxal circles as, for example, the following:

(i) the length of the tangents from a point on the perpendicular bisector of AB to any Apollonius circle associated with A, B is constant and equal to the distance of the point from A or B;

(ii) there is one, and only one, Apollonius circle passing through a given point;

(iii) all circles through A, B are orthogonal to each Apollonius circle.

EXAMPLES 5d

1. If A, B are the points $(-2, 0)$, $(2, 0)$, find the equation of the locus of P which moves such that the ratio $AP:PB$ is constant and equal to λ in each of the following cases: (i) $\lambda = 2$; (ii) $\lambda = 3$; (iii) $\lambda = 1\cdot5$; (iv) $\lambda = 1$.

2. Find the centres and radii of the Apollonius circles associated with the points $(\pm1, 0)$ and the ratios 2, $\frac{5}{3}$, $\frac{1}{2}$, $\frac{3}{5}$. Illustrate by means of a diagram.

3. Show that the Apollonius circle associated with the points A, B and the ratio λ, passes through the points H, K which divide AB internally and externally in the ratio $\lambda:1$. Show further that HK is a diameter of the circle.

4. Use the result of Ex. 3 to construct accurately the locus of a point P which moves such that $PA:PB = 3:7$; A, B being 6 cm apart.

5. For any two points A, B, prove that: (i) the Apollonius circles for different ratios are non-intersecting; (ii) there is just one circle passing through a given point.

6. If $AB = 4$ cm, calculate the radius of the Apollonius circle when the ratio $PA:PB = 3:5$.

7. If A, B are the points $(\mp a, 0)$, find the equation of the Apollonius circle which passes through the point $(2a, -a)$.

8. Find the equation of the Apollonius circle associated with the points $(-3, 1)$, $(2, 0)$ in that order and the ratio $3:5$.

9. Construct the triangle ABC with $BC = 6$ cm; ratio $AB:AC = 2:1$ and the median $AA' = 4$ cm.

10. If C is the centre of the Apollonius circle S defined by the two points A, B, prove that $CA \cdot CB = r^2$, where r is the radius of S.

11. The points A, B, C have coordinates $(-2, 0)$, $(1, 0)$, $(2, 0)$. Find: (i) the equation of the locus of P which moves such that $PA:PB = 3:2$; (ii) the equation of the locus of Q which moves such that $QB:QC = 2:3$. Hence find the coordinates of the points whose distances from A, B, C are in the ratios $3:2:3$.

12. A, B, C are collinear points with $AB = 4$ cm, $BC = 2$ cm. Determine by construction the positions of a point P which is such that
$$PA:PB:PC = 3:1:2.$$

13. The tangents from A to an Apollonius circle determined by points A, B, touch the circle at T, T'. Prove that AB bisects TT' at right angles.

14. In general, show how to determine geometrically the positions of a point P whose distances from the vertices of a given triangle are in given ratios.

15. P is any point on the circle of Apollonius defined by the points A, B. Prove that the circle PAB and the Apollonius circle are orthogonal.

I

16. AB and XY are parallel lines distance b apart. A point P is taken on XY such that the ratio $PA:PB$ is a maximum. Show that the maximum value of the ratio is the positive root of the equation $bx^2 - 2ax - b = 0$, where $AB = 2a$.

17. A, B, C are collinear points with $AB = 4$ cm, $BC = 6$ cm. Show that it is not possible to find a point P such that the ratios $PA:PB:PC = \lambda:2:1$ unless $\lambda \geqslant 4$. Illustrate geometrically.

18. Two circles have centres $(-a, 0)$, $(b, 0)$ and radii a, b respectively. Find the equation of the locus of a point at which the circles subtend equal angles.

MISCELLANEOUS EXAMPLES

1. Find the equations of the two circles which touch the x-axis at the origin and also touch the line $4x - 3y + 24 = 0$.

2. Find the equations of the circles passing through the origin and making intercepts of lengths a and b on the x- and y-axes respectively.

3. Find the points of intersection of the circles $x^2 + y^2 + 4x - 2y - 5 = 0$, $x^2 + y^2 + 2x - 7 = 0$.

4. Show that the circles $x^2 + y^2 - 4x + 6y + 8 = 0$, $x^2 + y^2 - 10x - 6y + 14 = 0$ touch each other and find the equation of the common tangent at the point of contact.

5. Show that the equation $(y - x + 3)^2 + 2(x - 2)(y + 2) = 0$ represents a circle. Show on a diagram the relationships of the lines $x - 2 = 0$, $y + 2 = 0$, $y - x + 3 = 0$ to the circle.

6. Find the equation of the circle drawn on the common chord of the circles $x^2 + y^2 + 2x + 3y + 1 = 0$, $x^2 + y^2 + 4x + 3y + 2 = 0$ as diameter.

7. Find the power of the point $(3, 2)$ with respect to the circle $x^2 + y^2 + 4x + 3y - 1 = 0$, and hence find the equation of the circle, centre $(3, 2)$, which is orthogonal to the given circle.

8. Show that the point $(-2, 1)$ lies inside one of the circles
$$x^2 + y^2 + 4x - 1 = 0, \quad 2x^2 + 2y^2 - 2x - 3y = 0$$
and outside the other.

9. Find the radical axis of the circles
$$x^2 + y^2 + 4x + 3y + 4 = 0, \quad 2x^2 + 2y^2 - 4x - 3y + 5 = 0;$$
find also the coordinates of the point on this line from which the tangents to the two circles are of minimum length.

10. Find the coordinates of the two points on the x-axis from which the tangents to the circle $x^2 + y^2 - 10x - 8y + 31 = 0$ are at right angles.

11. Prove that the system of circles $x^2 + y^2 + 2\lambda x + c = 0$, where λ is a variable parameter and c a constant, is coaxal. Find the equations of the two circles of the family which touch the line $x - 2y + 2 - 0$ in the case when $c = 4$.

12. Two circles intersect at the points $(1, 0)$, $(2, -1)$ and touch the y-axis; show that they will both touch the line $y + 2 = 0$.

13. Find the equation of the radical axis and the length of the common chord of the circles $x^2 + y^2 + ax + by + c = 0$, $x^2 + y^2 + bx + ay + c = 0$.

14. Prove that from any point of the circle $4x^2 + 4y^2 - x - 18 = 0$ the length of the tangent to the circle $x^2 + y^2 + 2x = 0$ is three times the length of the tangent to the circle $x^2 + y^2 - 4 = 0$.

15. A, B are fixed points with coordinates $(\mp a, 0)$ and P moves so that $PA = nPB$, show that the locus of P is a circle. Show also, for different values of n, the circles from a coaxal system and find the coordinates of the limiting points.

16. Find the equation of the circle passing through $(3, 2)$ and cutting each of the circles $x^2 + y^2 - 7x - 3y + 12 = 0$, $x^2 + y^2 - x - 6y + 3 = 0$ orthogonally.

17. Show that the equation $x^2 + y^2 - 10x + 9 + \lambda(x^2 + y^2 + 8x + 9) = 0$ represent a system of non-intersecting coaxal circles and find the coordinates of the limiting points. Find also the equations of the circles of the system with radius $\sqrt{7}$.

18. A, B, C are collinear points with $AB = 6$ cm; $BC = 4.5$ cm; find by construction a point P which is such that $PA : PB : PC = 7 : 3 : 5$.

19. Prove that the locus of the centre of a circle which passes through a given point and cuts a given circle orthogonally is a straight line.

20. A, B, C are the points (a, b), (b, c), (c, a); show that the common chord of the circles on BC, CA as diameters has the equation
$$x(a - b) + y(b - c) + b(c - a) = 0.$$

21. Find the coordinates of the limiting points of the system of coaxal circles determined by the circles
$$x^2 + y^2 + 8x + 8y - 18 = 0, \quad 2x^2 + 2y^2 + 10x + 8y - 17 = 0;$$
find also the equation of the circle of the system whose centre lies on the line $x + 2 = 0$.

22. The limiting points of a coaxal system have coordinates $(-2, -1)$, $(1, 3)$. Find: (i) the equation of the circle of the system which passes through the origin; (ii) the equation of the circle of the system with centre on the line $2x - y + 4 = 0$.

23. Prove that, in general, there is just one circle of a coaxal system which cuts a given circle at the ends of a diameter.

24. A point P moves such that its distances from two fixed points A, B are in a constant ratio. Prove that the tangent at P to its locus passes through the centre of the circle PAB.

25. Prove that, if a, b are positive constants, the circles $x^2 + y^2 - 2ax - ab = 0$, $x^2 + y^2 + 2bx - ab = 0$, centres C, D, intersect orthogonally in real points A, B. Prove also that the equation of the circle on AB as diameter is $x^2 + y^2 = ab$; if this circle meets the line of centres CD at X, Y, show that
$$CX : DY = CA : DA.$$

26. Show that the equations of two circles can be expressed as $x^2 + y^2 + gx + c = 0$, $x^2 + y^2 + g'x + c = 0$ and that one of the circles will be within the other if gg' and c are both positive.

27. P is a variable point on a given circle of a coaxal system with limiting points L_1, L_2. Prove that the ratio $PL_1 : PL_2$ is constant.

28. The circles S_1, S_2 intersect orthogonally at P; the line of centres meets S_1 at A, B. Prove that PA, PB cut S_2 at the ends of a diameter perpendicular to AB.

29. Two concentric circles with centres at the origin have radii a, b. Find the locus of a point which moves such that the lengths of the tangents from it to the circles are in inverse ratio to the radii of the circles.

30. Show that the equations of two circles which intersect in real points can be written $x^2 + y^2 + 2\lambda_1 x - c^2 = 0$, $x^2 + y^2 + 2\lambda_2 x - c^2 = 0$. Two such circles intersect at A, B; a line through A meets one circle at P, and the parallel line through B meets the other circle at Q. Prove that the locus of the mid-point of PQ is a circle.

31. The origin is one limiting point and $x^2 + y^2 - 2ax - 2by + c = 0$ is one circle of a coaxal system; prove that the equation of the system can be written $\lambda(x^2 + y^2) - 2ax - 2by + c = 0$ and prove also that the equation of the orthogonal system is $(a + \mu b)(x^2 + y^2) - c(x + \mu y) = 0$.

32. The chords of contact of tangents drawn from a point P to two given circles meet in Q. Show that the radical axis of the circles bisects PQ. Prove also that the chord of contact of tangents from P to any circle coaxal with the given pair passes through Q.

CHAPTER VI

COMPLEX NUMBERS

Definition. If a, b are two real numbers, any number of the form
$$a+b\sqrt{-1}$$
is called a *complex number.*

Notation. It is usual to replace $\sqrt{-1}$ by the symbol i.

In general, a complex number consists of two parts, a, referred to as *the real part,* and ib, referred to as *the imaginary part.*

N.B. (i) If $b=0$, the complex number $a+ib$ is wholly real, and it follows conversely that real numbers can be thought of as special cases of complex numbers.

(ii) If $a=0$, the complex number $a+ib$ is wholly imaginary.

(iii) The complex number $a+ib$ is zero, if, and only if, $a=b=0$.

(iv) The complex numbers $a\pm ib$ are called *conjugate numbers;* if $a+ib=\alpha$, it is usual to write $a-ib=\bar{\alpha}$.

Ex. 1. *Factorise:* (*i*) x^2+1; (*ii*) $(x+a)^2+b^2$.

(i) $\qquad x^2+1 = x^2-(-1) = x^2-i^2$
$$= (x+i)(x-i).$$

(ii) $\quad (x+a)^2+b^2 = (x+a)^2-i^2b^2 = (x+a+ib)(x+a-ib).$

Ex. 2. *Solve the equation* $x^2-x+1=0$.

We have $\qquad\qquad x = \dfrac{1\pm\sqrt{(1-4)}}{2}$
$$= \tfrac{1}{2}(1\pm i\sqrt{3}).$$

Geometrical representation of complex numbers. The complex number $z(=x+iy)$ can be represented geometrically by a point P with rectangular Cartesian coordinates (x, y).

The point P corresponds uniquely to the number z and is frequently spoken of as the point z. It is sometimes convenient to represent z by the vector $\overrightarrow{OP}$ (Fig. 54).

The plane in which the complex number z is represented either by the point P (x, y), or the vector $\overrightarrow{OP}$, is called the z-plane and the diagram is called *an Argand diagram.*

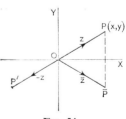

Fig. 54.

123

Special cases:

   (i) points on the x-axis correspond to wholly real numbers;

   (ii) points on the y-axis correspond to wholly imaginary numbers;

   (iii) $\bar{z}$, the conjugate of z, will be represented by $\bar{P}$, the reflection of P in the x-axis (Fig. 54);

   (iv) the number $-z$ will be represented by $P'(-x, -y)$ or the vector $\overrightarrow{OP'}$, which is equal and opposite to $\overrightarrow{OP}$.

Modulus and amplitude. If P represents the complex number $z(=x+iy)$, then the polar coordinates (r, θ) of P, where r denotes the positive value of OP and θ the angle XOP, are called respectively *the modulus* and *the amplitude* or *argument* of the complex number.

The modulus of z, OP, is written as $|z|$ and is always positive.

The amplitude of z, the angle turned through from the position OX to the position OP with the usual sign convention, is many valued; the value which satisfies the inequalities

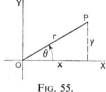

FIG. 55.

$$-\pi < \theta \leqslant \pi,$$

is called *the principal value.*

The amplitude of z is written *am z* or *amp z*, and is usually assumed to be the principal value.

As $\quad\quad\quad\quad\quad\quad x = r \cos \theta; \quad y = r \sin \theta,$

$$z = r(\cos\theta + i \sin\theta),$$

where $\quad\quad r = |z| = \sqrt{(x^2 + y^2)}; \quad \theta = am\ z = \tan^{-1} y/x.$

This is called *the modulus-amplitude or* (r, θ) *form* of the complex number.

Ex. 3. *If $z = 3 + 4i$, find $|z|$ and am z.*

$$|z| = r = \sqrt{(3^2 + 4^2)} = 5.$$
$$am\ z = \theta = \tan^{-1} \tfrac{4}{3} \ (Fig.\ 56).$$

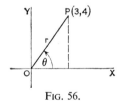

FIG. 56.

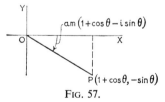

FIG. 57.

Ex. 4. *Find:* (*i*) $|1 + \cos\theta - i \sin\theta|$; (*ii*) $am(1 + \cos\theta - i \sin\theta)$, *if θ is acute.*

(i) $\quad\quad\quad |1 + \cos\theta - i \sin\theta| = OP$ (Fig. 57),

$$= \sqrt{\{(1 + \cos\theta)^2 + \sin^2\theta\}},$$
$$= \sqrt{\{2 + 2\cos\theta\}} = \sqrt{\{4\cos^2\tfrac{1}{2}\theta\}},$$
$$= 2\cos\tfrac{1}{2}\theta.$$

(ii) $\qquad am(1 + \cos\theta - i\sin\theta) = \tan^{-1}\dfrac{-\sin\theta}{1 + \cos\theta},$

$$= \tan^{-1}(-\tan\tfrac{1}{2}\theta) = -\tfrac{1}{2}\theta.$$

Fundamental processes

Equality. *The two complex numbers* $x_1 + iy_1$, $x_2 + iy_2$ *are said to be equal if, and only if,* $x_1 = x_2$; $y_1 = y_2$.

Ex. 5. *If* $S + iC = e^x(\cos x + i\sin x) + e^{-x}(\sin x + i\cos x)$, *find* S *and* C.

Equating real and imaginary parts,

$$S = e^x\cos x + e^{-x}\sin x; \quad C = e^x\sin x + e^{-x}\cos x.$$

Addition. *The sum of two complex numbers* $z_1(= x_1 + iy_1)$, $z_2(= x_2 + iy_2)$ *is defined as the complex number*

$$(x_1 + x_2) + i(y_1 + y_2).$$

Geometrically, if P_1, P_2, P_3 represent the numbers z_1, z_2, $z_1 + z_2$, then P_3 is the fourth vertex of the parallelogram determined by the points O, P_1, P_2. This result follows from the fact that the coordinates of P_1, P_2, P_3 are (x_1, y_1), (x_2, y_2), $(x_1 + x_2, y_1 + y_2)$ respectively.

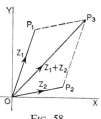

It is this parallelogram law of addition, and the similarity with vector quantities which leads to the idea of representing the complex number z_1 by the vector $\overrightarrow{OP_1}$.

FIG. 58.

Subtraction. *The difference* $(z_1 - z_2)$ *between two complex numbers* $z_1(= x_1 + iy_1)$, $z_2(= x_2 + iy_2)$ *is defined as the complex number*

$$(x_1 - x_2) + i(y_1 - y_2).$$

Writing $(z_1 - z_2)$ as $z_1 + (-z_2)$, it follows that, in the Argand diagram, the point P_4 representing the difference is the fourth vertex of the parallelogram determined by the points O, P_1, P_2' (Fig. 59).

N.B. As $\overrightarrow{P_2P_1}$ is equal and parallel to $\overrightarrow{OP_4}$, then

$$|z_1 - z_2| = \text{length } P_2P_1;$$

$$am(z_1 - z_2) = \text{angle between } \overrightarrow{OX} \text{ and } \overrightarrow{P_2P_1}.$$

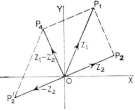

FIG. 59.

Ex. 6. *If P represents the complex number z, find the points* P_1, P_2, P_3 *which represent* (i) $2z$; (ii) $z + 2$; (iii) $2i - z$.

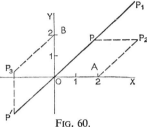

(i) P_1 is on OP produced such that $OP_1 = 2OP$.

(ii) The number 2 is represented by the point A and P_2 is the fourth vertex of the parallelogram OAP_2P.

(iii) The number $2i$ is represented by the point B and P' represents $-z$; P_3 is the fourth vertex of the parallelogram OBP_3P'.

FIG. 60.

Ex. 7. *If A represents the complex number* $a(=3 + 4i)$ *and P represents the variable complex number* $z(=x + iy)$, *find the locus of P if* $|z - a| = 1$.

$$|z - a| = \text{length } AP = 1.$$

∴ As A is the fixed point $(3, 4)$, the locus of P is the circle centre A, radius 1.

Alternatively, $\quad |z - a| = |x - 3 + i(y - 4)| = \sqrt{\{(x - 3)^2 + (y - 4)^2\}}$.
$$∴ \ (x - 3)^2 + (y - 4)^2 = 1,$$

i.e. the locus of P is a circle with centre $(3, 4)$ and radius 1.

Ex. 8. *If z is a complex number such that* $|z + (1 + i)| \leqslant 1$, *find the maximum and minimum values of* $|z|$.

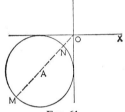

Geometrically it is easier to handle the modulus of a difference than that of a sum, so write
$$z + (1 + i) \quad \text{as} \quad z - (-1 - i).$$

We have $\quad |z - (-1 - i)| \leqslant 1$;

so if A is the point $(-1, -1)$ representing the number $(-1 - i)$, then the point P representing z must lie on or within the circle centre A, radius 1.

Now $|z|$ is a maximum when P is at its greatest distance from O.

FIG. 61.

∴ Maximum $\quad |z| = OM = OA + AM = \sqrt{2} + 1$.

Similarly, $\quad$ minimum $\quad |z| = ON = OA - AN = \sqrt{2} - 1$.

Inequalities

(i) $\quad |z_1 + z_2| \leqslant |z_1| + |z_2|$.

Geometrically (Fig. 62),

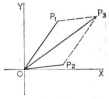

$$|z_1 + z_2| = OP_3; \quad |z_1| = OP_1; \quad |z_2| = OP_2.$$

Hence the result follows from

$$OP_3 \leqslant OP_1 + OP_2.$$

FIG. 62.

Extending this result we get
$$|z_1 + z_2 + \ldots + z_n| \leqslant |z_1| + |z_2| + \ldots + |z_n|.$$

(ii) $$|z_1 - z_2| \geqslant |z_1| - |z_2|.$$

With the notation of (i) above,

$$|z_1 - z_2| = P_2 P_1; \quad |z_1| = OP_1; \quad |z_2| = OP_2.$$

As $OP_2 + P_2 P_1 \geqslant OP_1$, the result follows. More generally,

$$|z_1 - z_2 \ldots - z_n| \geqslant |z_1| - |z_2| \ldots - |z_n|.$$

Other inequalities involving moduli can be deduced in a like manner.

EXAMPLES 6a

1. Represent the following numbers on the Argand diagram:

    (i) $2 + i$;   (ii) $-1 + 2i$;   (iii) $3i$;

    (iv) $2 - i\sqrt{3}$;   (v) $\cos \frac{1}{4}\pi + i \sin \frac{1}{4}\pi$;   (vi) $-2(\cos \frac{2}{3}\pi + i \sin \frac{2}{3}\pi)$.

2. Find the modulus and amplitude of each of the following numbers:

    (i) $3 + 4i$;   (ii) $4i$;   (iii) 3;

    (iv) $5 - 12i$;   (v) $-1 - i\sqrt{3}$;   (vi) $1 + \sin \theta + i \cos \theta$.

3. Solve the equations:

    (i) $x^2 + 4 = 0$;   (ii) $x^2 + 8x + 25 = 0$;   (iii) $x^2 - 2x \cos \theta + 1 = 0$.

4. Factorise $x^3 - 1$ and hence solve the equation $x^3 = 1$.

5. Solve the equation $x^3 + 8 = 0$.

6. Find x and y if:

    (i) $x + y + i(x - y) = 5 + 2i$;   (ii) $(x - 2y) + i(y - 2x) = -1 + i$.

7. If A, B represent the complex numbers a, b, construct the points which represent:

    (i) $a + b$;   (ii) $a - b$;   (iii) $b - a$;   (iv) $a - 2$;

    (v) $-2b$;   (vi) $2a + b$;   (vii) $a + \bar{b}$.

8. If $|z| = 2$, what is the locus of the point P which represents each of the following numbers: (i) $2z$;   (ii) $z + 1$;   (iii) $z - 2$;   (iv) $\bar{z}$?

9. If A represents the complex number $a = 1 + i$ and P represents the variable complex number $z = x + iy$, find the locus of P if: (i) $|z - a| = 3$; (ii) $|z + a| = 3$;   (iii) $am(z - a) = \frac{1}{2}\pi$;   (iv) $am(z + a) = \frac{1}{3}\pi$.

10. If $|z| < 1$, prove that $am(z + 1)$ lies between $\pm \frac{1}{2}\pi$.

11. What are the greatest and least values of $|z|$ if $|z - 7| \leqslant 3$?

12. If $|z + 2i| \leqslant 2$, find the maximum values of: (i) $|z|$;   (ii) $|z - 2|$.

13. Show that the straight line joining the points z_1, z_2 is divided in the ratio $m : n$ at the point $(mz_2 + nz_1)/(m + n)$.

14. Prove that the centroid of the triangle with vertices z_1, z_2, z_3 is $\frac{1}{3}(z_1 + z_2 + z_3)$.

15. If z_1, z_2 are complex numbers with amplitudes differing by $\frac{1}{2}\pi$, prove that $|z_1 - z_2| = |z_1 + z_2|$.

16. If $|z_1| = |z_2|$ and $am(z_1) + am(z_2) = 0$, show that z_1 and z_2 are conjugate numbers.

17. If $am(z_3 - z_1) = am(z_2 - z_1)$, prove that the points z_1, z_2, z_3 are collinear.

18. The complex numbers 0, 5, $1 + 3i$ are represented by the points O, A, B. Find the complex numbers represented by: (i) the centroid; (ii) the orthocentre of triangle OAB.

19. If A, B are the points 4, $2i$ in the Argand diagram, find the complex number represented by the circumcentre of the triangle OAB.

20. Express the roots of the equation $x^3 + 1 = 0$ in the (r, θ) form and show they will be represented by the vertices of an equilateral triangle.

Multiplication and division. *The product of the two complex numbers* $x_1 + iy_1$, $x_2 + iy_2$ *is defined by the relationship,*

$$(x_1 + iy_1) \times (x_2 + iy_2) = (x_1 x_2 - y_1 y_2) + i(x_1 y_2 + y_1 x_2).$$

This definition makes it possible to use the ordinary processes of real algebra with the symbols x_1, y_1, x_2, y_2, i; for assuming these rules apply we have,

$$(x_1 + iy_1)(x_2 + iy_2) = x_1 x_2 + i x_1 y_2 + i y_1 x_2 + i^2 y_1 y_2,$$
$$= (x_1 x_2 - y_1 y_2) + i(x_1 y_2 + y_1 x_2), \text{ as } i^2 = -1.$$

The quotient of the two complex numbers $x_1 + iy_1$, $x_2 + iy_2$ *is defined as*

$$\frac{(x_1 x_2 + y_1 y_2) + i(y_1 x_2 - x_1 y_2)}{x_2^2 + y_2^2},$$

a result which is readily deduced as follows:

$$\frac{x_1 + iy_1}{x_2 + iy_2} = \frac{(x_1 + iy_1)(x_2 - iy_2)}{(x_2 + iy_2)(x_2 - iy_2)} = \frac{(x_1 x_2 + y_1 y_2) + i(y_1 x_2 - x_1 y_2)}{x_2^2 + y_2^2}.$$

It will be noted that the process used to make the denominator wholly real is similar to that used to rationalise the denominator of an irrational surd fraction.

Ex. 9. *Express* $(2 + i)^2/(1 + i)$ *in the form* $a + ib$.

We have
$$\frac{(2 + i)^2}{1 + i} = \frac{(2 + i)^2(1 - i)}{(1 + i)(1 - i)} = \frac{(4 + 4i + i^2)(1 - i)}{2}$$
$$= \tfrac{1}{2}(7 + i).$$

Product and quotient of two complex numbers in the (r, θ) form.
Let
$$z_1 = r_1(\cos \theta_1 + i \sin \theta_1); \quad z_2 = r_2(\cos \theta_2 + i \sin \theta_2).$$

Then

$$z_1 z_2 = r_1 r_2 (\cos \theta_1 + i \sin \theta_1)(\cos \theta_2 + i \sin \theta_2),$$
$$= r_1 r_2 \{(\cos \theta_1 \cos \theta_2 - \sin \theta_1 \sin \theta_2) + i(\cos \theta_1 \sin \theta_2 + \sin \theta_1 \cos \theta_2)\},$$
$$= r_1 r_2 \{\cos (\theta_1 + \theta_2) + i \sin (\theta_1 + \theta_2)\}.$$

I.e. *the modulus of the product of two complex numbers is the product of their moduli and the amplitude of the product is the sum of their amplitudes.*

This result can be extended and, in general, we have

$$z_1 z_2 \ldots z_n = r_1 r_2 \ldots r_n \{\cos (\theta_1 + \theta_2 + \ldots + \theta_n) + i \sin (\theta_1 + \theta_2 + \ldots + \theta_n)\}.$$

N.B. Taking $z_1 = z_2 = \ldots = z_n = \cos \theta + i \sin \theta$,

$$(\cos \theta + i \sin \theta)^n = \cos n\theta + i \sin n\theta,$$

if n is a positive integer.

Taking the case of the quotient,

$$\frac{z_1}{z_2} = \frac{r_1(\cos \theta_1 + i \sin \theta_1)}{r_2(\cos \theta_2 + i \sin \theta_2)} = \frac{r_1(\cos \theta_1 + i \sin \theta_1)(\cos \theta_2 - i \sin \theta_2)}{r_2(\cos \theta_2 + i \sin \theta_2)(\cos \theta_2 - i \sin \theta_2)},$$
$$= \frac{r_1}{r_2} \frac{(\cos \theta_1 \cos \theta_2 + \sin \theta_1 \sin \theta_2) + i(\sin \theta_1 \cos \theta_2 - \cos \theta_1 \sin \theta_2)}{\cos^2 \theta_2 + \sin^2 \theta_2},$$
$$= \frac{r_1}{r_2} \{\cos (\theta_1 - \theta_2) + i \sin (\theta_1 - \theta_2)\}.$$

I.e. *the modulus of the quotient of two complex numbers is the quotient of their moduli and the amplitude of the quotient is the difference of their amplitudes.*

Geometrical representation of a product and a quotient. Let P_1, P_2 represent the complex numbers z_1, z_2 and let A be the unit point on the x-axis. Then $OA = 1$, $OP_1 = r_1$, $OP_2 = r_2$; $\angle XOP_1 = \theta_1$, $\angle XOP_2 = \theta_2$.

Referring to Fig. 63, the point P representing the product $z_1 z_2$ is obtained by making $\angle P_1 OP = \angle AOP_2 = \theta_2$ and $\angle OP_1 P = \angle OAP_2$. For $\angle XOP = \theta_1 + \theta_2$ and by similar triangles, $OP = r_1 r_2$.

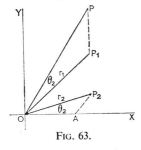

FIG. 63.

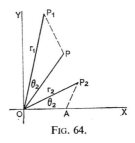

FIG. 64.

In the case of the quotient the point P representing z_1/z_2 is obtained by making $\angle POP_1 = \angle AOP_2 = \theta_2$ and $\angle OP_1 P = \angle OP_2 A$ (Fig. 64). For $\angle XOP = \theta_1 - \theta_2$ and by similar triangles, $OP = r_1/r_2$.

Ex. 10. *Simplify:*   (i) $\dfrac{1}{\cos\theta + i\sin\theta}$;   (ii) $\dfrac{(\cos\theta - i\sin\theta)^3}{\cos 2\theta + i\sin 2\theta}$.

(i) $\dfrac{1}{\cos\theta + i\sin\theta} = \dfrac{\cos\theta - i\sin\theta}{(\cos\theta + i\sin\theta)(\cos\theta - i\sin\theta)} = \cos\theta - i\sin\theta$;

or alternatively, writing $1 = \cos 0 + i\sin 0$,

$$\frac{1}{\cos\theta + i\sin\theta} = \frac{\cos 0 + i\sin 0}{\cos\theta + i\sin\theta} = \cos(0-\theta) + i\sin(0-\theta)$$
$$= \cos\theta - i\sin\theta \text{ as before.}$$

(ii) $(\cos\theta - i\sin\theta)^3 = \{\cos(-\theta) + i\sin(-\theta)\}^3 = \cos(-3\theta) + i\sin(-3\theta).$

$\therefore \dfrac{(\cos\theta - i\sin\theta)^3}{\cos 2\theta + i\sin 2\theta} = \cos(-3\theta - 2\theta) + i\sin(-3\theta - 2\theta) = \cos 5\theta - i\sin 5\theta.$

Ex. 11. *If P_1, P_2 represent the numbers z_1, z_2, show that OP_1, OP_2 are perpendicular if z_1/z_2 is wholly imaginary.*

As z_1/z_2 is wholly imaginary, its amplitude is $\pm\pi/2$.

But the angle P_2OP_1 is equal to $am(z_1/z_2)$, and hence OP_1, OP_2 are perpendicular.

EXAMPLES 6b

1. Simplify the following expressions giving each result in the form $a + ib$:

    (i) $-2i(3-i)$;   (ii) $(1+i)(1-i)$;   (iii) $(2-3i)^2$;

    (iv) $(1-i)^3$;   (v) $(2+i)/(1+i)$;   (vi) $(2+3i)/(3-4i)$;

    (vii) $(2-i)^2/(1+3i)$;   (viii) $1/(1+i)^3$.

2. Express the following in the amplitude–modulus form:

    (i) $(\cos\theta + i\sin\theta)^2$;   (ii) $\{\sqrt{2}(\cos\theta + i\sin\theta)\}^4$;

    (iii) $1/(\cos\theta - i\sin\theta)$;   (iv) $(\cos\theta - i\sin\theta)^3$;

    (v) $\dfrac{\cos\theta + i\sin\theta}{\cos\theta - i\sin\theta}$;   (vi) $\dfrac{\cos 4\theta - i\sin 4\theta}{\cos 2\theta + i\sin 2\theta}$;

    (vii) $(\cos\tfrac{1}{3}\pi - i\sin\tfrac{1}{3}\pi)^3$;   (viii) $(\sin\tfrac{1}{6}\pi + i\cos\tfrac{1}{6}\pi)^3$.

3. Simplify $\{x - (\cos\tfrac{1}{3}\pi + i\sin\tfrac{1}{3}\pi)\}\{x - (\cos\tfrac{1}{3}\pi - i\sin\tfrac{1}{3}\pi)\}$.

4. By expressing $\cos\tfrac{9}{5}\pi$, $\sin\tfrac{9}{5}\pi$ in terms of $\cos\tfrac{1}{5}\pi$, $\sin\tfrac{1}{5}\pi$, simplify the product $\{x - (\cos\tfrac{1}{5}\pi + i\sin\tfrac{1}{5}\pi)\}\{x - (\cos\tfrac{9}{5}\pi + i\sin\tfrac{9}{5}\pi)\}$.

5. Find x and y in each of the following equations:

    (i) $x - iy = \dfrac{1}{2-5i}$;   (ii) $x + iy = (1-i)^4$;   (iii) $\sqrt{(x+iy)} = 5 + 3i$.

6. If $z = \cos\theta + i\sin\theta$, find the values of:

    (i) $1/z$;   (ii) $z + 1/z$;   (iii) $z - 1/z$.

7. If $\omega = \tfrac{1}{2}(-1 + i\sqrt{3})$, show that the cubes of ω and ω^2 are each unity.

8. Simplify: (i) $(1+i\sqrt{3})^4 - (1-i\sqrt{3})^4$;   (ii) $(1+\cos\theta+i\sin\theta)^3$.

9. Given that $\sqrt{(x+iy)}=a+ib$, prove that $x=a^2-b^2$, $y=2ab$.   Hence express $\sqrt{(3+4i)}$ in the form $a+ib$.

10. If $z=2^{\frac{1}{3}}(\cos\frac{1}{3}\pi+i\sin\frac{1}{3}\pi)$, find the value of $2z+1/z^2$.

11. Prove that $|1-az|=|a||z-1/a|$.

12. Given that $|z-a||z-b|=k$, where a, b, k are real constants, prove that the point P, which represents z, moves such that the product of its distances from two fixed points is constant and equal to k.

13. If P_1, P_2, P_3 are the points z_1, z_2, z_3, show that $am(z_1-z_2)/(z_1-z_3)$ is represented numerically by the angle $P_2P_1P_3$.   Deduce the condition that P_1P_2, P_1P_3 are perpendicular.

14. If $z=x+iy$, $w=u+iv$ and $zw=1$, prove that
$$u=x/(x^2+y^2), \quad v=-y/(x^2+y^2).$$

15. If $\left|\dfrac{z-1}{z+2}\right|=k$, a constant, prove that the locus of P is a circle.

16. The complex numbers $z=x+iy$, $w=u+iv$, are connected by the relationship $(1-z)(1-w)=1$.   Express z in terms of w and prove the results:
$$x=\frac{u^2+v^2-u}{(u-1)^2+v^2}; \quad y=\frac{-v}{(u-1)^2+v^2}.$$

Geometrical properties of the Argand diagram.   In the following section, P, P_1, P_2, . . . will be taken as points in the Argand diagram representing the complex numbers z, z_1, z_2, . . .

(i) $|z_1-z_2|=length\ P_1P_2$, a result already established.

Consequently if the variable number z is such that
$$\left|\frac{z-z_1}{z-z_2}\right|=\text{constant},$$

then P moves such that the ratio $PP_1:PP_2$ is constant and its locus is a circle—a circle of Apollonius associated with the fixed points P_1, P_2.

(ii) $am(z_1-z_2)=angle\ between\ the\ vectors\ \overrightarrow{OX}\ and\ \overrightarrow{P_2P_1}\ measured\ from\ the\ former.$

This result follows directly from the fact that $\overrightarrow{P_2P_1}$ is equal and parallel to the vector representing (z_1-z_2).

Clearly, $\qquad am(z_1-z_2)-am(z_2-z_1)=+\pi$ or $-\pi$.

(iii) *am z_1/z_2 = angle between the vectors $\overrightarrow{OP_2}$ and $\overrightarrow{OP_1}$ measured from the former.*

This result follows from the fact that

$$am\ z_1/z_2 = am\ z_1 - am\ z_2,$$

where *am z_1* = the angle between $\overrightarrow{OX}$ and $\overrightarrow{OP_1}$ and *am z_2* = angle between $\overrightarrow{OX}$ and $\overrightarrow{OP_2}$.

N.B. In Fig. 65(i), *am z_1/z_2* is positive and in Fig. 65(ii), *am z_1/z_2* is negative.

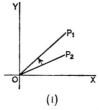 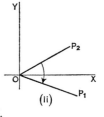

(i)   (ii)

Fig. 65.

(iv) *am $\dfrac{z - z_1}{z - z_2}$ = angle between the vectors $\overrightarrow{P_2P}$ and $\overrightarrow{P_1P}$ measured from the former.*

This result follows from (ii) and (iii) above.

In Fig. 66, *am $\dfrac{z - z_1}{z - z_2}$* = the positive angle ϕ as the direction from $\overrightarrow{P_2P}$ to $\overrightarrow{P_1P}$ is counter-clockwise.

It will be seen from the diagram that *am $\dfrac{z - z_1}{z - z_2}$* is of constant sign for all points P

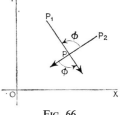

Fig. 66.

on the same side of the line P_1P_2 and of opposite signs for points on opposite sides of this line.

(v) *If am $\dfrac{z_3 - z_1}{z_3 - z_2}$ = am $\dfrac{z_4 - z_1}{z_4 - z_2}$, the points P_1, P_2, P_3, P_4 are concyclic.*

Referring to Fig. 67, the given condition is equivalent to

$$\angle P_2P_3P_1 = \angle P_2P_4P_1,$$

and hence the result.

N.B. Alternatively, the condition for four concyclic points can be expressed as

$$\frac{z_3 - z_1}{z_3 - z_2} \cdot \frac{z_4 - z_2}{z_4 - z_1}\ \text{is real.}$$

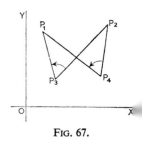

Fig. 67.

For this leads to

$$am\left\{\frac{z_3-z_1}{z_3-z_2}\cdot\frac{z_4-z_2}{z_4-z_1}\right\}=0,$$

i.e.

$$am\frac{z_3-z_1}{z_3-z_2}+am\frac{z_4-z_2}{z_4-z_1}=0,$$

or,

$$am\frac{z_3-z_1}{z_3-z_2}=-am\frac{z_4-z_2}{z_4-z_1}=am\frac{z_4-z_1}{z_4-z_2}.$$

(vi) *If $P_1P_2P_3$ is an equilateral triangle,*

$$(z_2-z_3)^2+(z_3-z_1)^2+(z_1-z_2)^2=0.$$

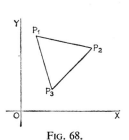

FIG. 68.

As $P_1P_2=P_1P_3$, $\left|\dfrac{z_1-z_2}{z_1-z_3}\right|=1.$

Also as $\angle P_3P_1P_2=\frac{1}{3}\pi$, $am\left(\dfrac{z_1-z_2}{z_1-z_3}\right)=\frac{1}{3}\pi.$

$$\therefore \frac{z_1-z_2}{z_1-z_3}=\cos\tfrac{1}{3}\pi+i\sin\tfrac{1}{3}\pi.$$

Similarly,

$$\frac{z_2-z_3}{z_2-z_1}=\cos\tfrac{1}{3}\pi+i\sin\tfrac{1}{3}\pi.$$

$$\therefore \frac{z_1-z_2}{z_1-z_3}=\frac{z_2-z_3}{z_2-z_1},$$
$$(z_1-z_2)(z_2-z_1)=(z_2-z_3)(z_1-z_3),$$
$$z_1^2+z_2^2+z_3^2=z_2z_3+z_3z_1+z_1z_2,$$

i.e.

$$(z_2-z_3)^2+(z_3-z_1)^2+(z_1-z_2)^2=0.$$

Transformations. If $w(=u+iv)$ is a function of $z(=x+iy)$, then the point $P(x, y)$ is transformed into the point $Q(u, v)$ and the locus of P transforms into the locus of Q.

(i) $w=z+a$, *where a is a constant complex number $\alpha+i\beta$.*

We have
$$u+iv=x+iy+\alpha+i\beta,$$
$$=(x+\alpha)+i(y+\beta).$$
$$\therefore u=x+\alpha;\quad v=y+\beta.$$

So $P(x, y)$ is transformed into $Q(x+\alpha, y+\beta)$—a simple translation.

If $f(x, y)=0$ is the locus of P, then $f(x-\alpha, y-\beta)=0$ will be the locus of Q.

Consequently, the curve $f(x, y)=0$ is unaltered by the transformation —it is merely moved distances α, β parallel to the axes.

(ii) $w = az$.

We have $u + iv = (\alpha + i\beta)(x + iy) = \alpha x - \beta y + i(\beta x + \alpha y)$.

$$\therefore \ u = \alpha x - \beta y; \quad v = \beta x + \alpha y.$$

So $P(x, y)$ is transformed into $Q(\alpha x - \beta y, \ \beta x + \alpha y)$—this is equivalent to a magnification of $\sqrt{(\alpha^2 + \beta^2)}$ and a rotation $\tan^{-1} \beta/\alpha$.

By writing

$$z = \frac{w}{a} = \frac{u + iv}{\alpha + i\beta},$$

we get

$$x = \frac{\alpha u + \beta v}{\alpha^2 + \beta^2}; \quad y = \frac{\alpha v - \beta u}{\alpha^2 + \beta^2},$$

and hence the locus $f(x, y) = 0$ becomes $f\left(\dfrac{\alpha x + \beta y}{\alpha^2 + \beta^2}, \dfrac{\alpha y - \beta x}{\alpha^2 + \beta^2} \right) = 0$.

(iii) $w = az + b$. This general linear transformation can be effected by applying transformations (i), (ii) successively. It gives magnification, rotation and translation and the nature of the locus of P is unaltered.

The method of dealing with more complicated transformations is illustrated in the following examples.

Ex. 12. *Under the transformation $w = 1/z$, show that a circle passing through the origin transforms into a straight line.*

We have

$$z = \frac{1}{w},$$

$$x + iy = \frac{1}{u + iv} = \frac{u - iv}{u^2 + v^2}.$$

I.e.

$$x = \frac{u}{u^2 + v^2}; \quad y = \frac{-v}{u^2 + v^2}.$$

The locus of P is a circle passing through the origin; its equation will be of the form

$$x^2 + y^2 + 2gx + 2fy = 0.$$

Hence $\left(\dfrac{u}{u^2 + v^2} \right)^2 + \left(\dfrac{-v}{u^2 + v^2} \right)^2 + 2g\left(\dfrac{u}{u^2 + v^2} \right) + 2f\left(\dfrac{-v}{u^2 + v^2} \right) = 0,$

or, $2gu - 2fv + 1 = 0.$

So the locus of $Q(u, v)$ is the straight line $2gu - 2fv + 1 = 0$.

Ex. 13. *If $w = z + 1/z$, show that when z describes the semicircle $|z| = k > 1$, $y \geqslant 0$, w describes part of an ellipse whose axes are the coordinate axes.*

We have $u + iv = x + iy + \dfrac{1}{x + iy},$

$$= x + iy + \frac{x - iy}{x^2 + y^2}.$$

$$\therefore \ u = x + \frac{x}{x^2 + y^2}; \quad v = y - \frac{y}{x^2 + y^2}.$$

The locus of z is $|z| = \sqrt{(x^2 + y^2)} = k,\ y \geqslant 0$,

i.e.
$$x^2 + y^2 = k^2,\ y \geqslant 0 \quad . \quad . \quad . \quad . \quad . \quad . \quad \text{(i)}$$

$$\therefore\ u = x + \frac{x}{k^2};\quad x = \frac{k^2 u}{k^2 + 1}.$$

$$v = y - \frac{y}{k^2};\quad y = \frac{k^2 v}{k^2 - 1}.$$

Substituting in equation (i),

$$\left(\frac{k^2 u}{k^2 + 1}\right)^2 + \left(\frac{k^2 v}{k^2 - 1}\right)^2 = 1.$$

As $k^2 \geqslant 1$, this is the equation of an ellipse with the coordinate axes as principal axes.

Also the condition $y \geqslant 0$ is equivalent to $v \geqslant 0$.

Hence the locus of w, the point (u, v), is the upper part of an ellipse with axes OX, OY.

EXAMPLES 6c

1. Plot the points $z_1 = 1 + 4i$, $z_2 = 2 + 3i$, $z_3 = -1 + i$ and use your diagram to find: (i) $|z_1 - z_2|$; (ii) $|z_2 - z_3|$; (iii) $|z_3 - z_1|$. Is the triangle formed by the points z_1, z_2, z_3 acute-angled, right-angled or obtuse-angled?

2. With the same three points as in Question 1, determine the signs of $am(z_1 - z_2)$, $am\dfrac{z_1 - z_2}{z_1 - z_3}$, $am\dfrac{z_3 - z_2}{z_3 - z_1}$ and indicate the angles on the diagram.

3. Show geometrically that $|z_2 - z_3| + |z_3 - z_1| \geqslant |z_1 - z_2|$. When does the equality arise?

4. If $|z - (1 + 2i)| \leqslant 1$, show the area occupied by z on the Argand diagram and find the maximum and minimum values of $|z|$. What is the value of $am(z)$ at these points?

5. The vertices of triangle $P_1 P_2 P_3$ represent the numbers z_1, z_2, z_3. Show that the triangle is right-angled at P_2 if one of the conditions

$$|z_1 - z_3|^2 = |z_3 - z_2|^2 + |z_1 - z_2|^2;\quad am\frac{z_2 - z_3}{z_2 - z_1} = \pm\tfrac{1}{2}\pi,$$

is satisfied.

6. If z, $\bar{z}$ are conjugate numbers, plot points P, $\bar{P}$ to represent them and in the same diagram represent the numbers: (i) $z + i$; (ii) $1/\bar{z}$; (iii) $-1/z$; (iv) $2\bar{z} - (1 + i)$.

7. If $z = x + iy$, $w = u + iv$ and $w = z^2$, find u, v in terms of x, y. Show that the rectangular hyperbola $xy = 1$ transforms into the straight line $v = 2$.

8. Given that $\left|\dfrac{z - 2}{z - i}\right| = 1$, show that the locus of P is a straight line bisecting a certain line at right angles. Construct the locus.

9. If $am(z_2 - z_1) = am(z_3 - z_4)$, show that $(z_2 - z_1)/(z_3 - z_4)$ is real. In this case what is true about the lines $z_1 z_2$, $z_4 z_3$?

K

10. Given that $|z| \leqslant 1$, find the greatest and least values of: (i) $|z - 2|$; (ii) $|z + 3i|$.

11. If A is the point $(2, 0)$ and P is a point on the unit circle $|z| = 1$, show on the Argand diagram an angle equal to $am(z - 2)$. Prove that $am\, z/(z - 2) = \pm\frac{1}{2}\pi$ when $am(z) = \mp\frac{1}{3}\pi$ and deduce that $z/(z - 2)$ is wholly imaginary when $z = \cos\frac{1}{3}\pi \pm i\sin\frac{1}{3}\pi$.

12. Show that the points P_1, P_2, P_3 are collinear if $(z_1 - z_3)/(z_1 - z_2)$ is real.

13. If $w = 1/z$ and the point P representing z moves along the line $x = 1$, show that the locus of Q, the point representing w, is a circle passing through the origin.

14. Find the equation of the locus of a point z which moves such that $\left|\dfrac{z - 1}{z + 2}\right| = 2$. Identify the locus.

15. If P represents the complex number z, show geometrically how to find the points which represent z^2, $1/z$, $z + 1/z$.

16. If z_1, z_2, z_3 are the vertices of an isosceles triangle right-angled at z_2, prove that $z_1^2 + 2z_2^2 + z_3^2 = 2z_2(z_1 + z_3)$.

17. If $\left|\dfrac{z - 2i}{z + i}\right| = 2$, show that the locus of z is a circle and find its centre and radius. Sketch the locus and use it to determine: (i) the maximum and minimum values of $|z|$; (ii) the range of possible values of $am(z)$.

18. When the transformation $w = (2z + 1)/z$ is applied to the circle $x^2 + y^2 - 2x + y = 0$, find the equation of the transformed figure and show that it is a straight line.

19. If $w = z^2$ and z describes the line $x = 1$, show that w describes the parabola $u = 1 - \frac{1}{4}v^2$. Trace on a figure the course of w as z moves along $x = 1$ from $-\infty$ to $+\infty$.

20. If $(z_1 - z_2)/(z_3 - z_4)$ and $(z_2 - z_3)/(z_1 - z_4)$ are each wholly imaginary, prove that P_3 is the orthocentre of triangle $P_1P_2P_4$ and deduce that $(z_1 - z_3)/(z_2 - z_4)$ is also wholly imaginary.

21. Prove that the triangles with vertices 0, $2 + 3i$, $3 + 4i$; $1 + i$, $7 - 3i$, $9 - 5i$ are equiangular.

22. If $w = (2 + z)/(2 - z)$, show that as z describes the y-axis from $-\infty$ to $+\infty$, then w describes the circle $x^2 + y^2 = 1$ in a counter-clockwise direction.

23. P, Q represent the complex numbers z, w, where $|z| = 1$ and $w = 1/(1 - z + z^2)$. Prove that OP, OQ are equally inclined to the x-axis.

Exponential functions of a complex variable. When x is real, it has been shown that

$$e^x = 1 + \frac{x}{1!} + \frac{x^2}{2!} + \frac{x^3}{3!} + \cdots,$$

the expansion being true for all values of x.

If z is a complex number, we *define* e^z by the relationship,

$$e^z = 1 + \frac{z}{1!} + \frac{z^2}{2!} + \frac{z^3}{3!} + \cdots$$

It can be shown that the infinite series on the right is convergent for all values of z, and in consequence the definition holds for all values of z. Moreover, using this definition for e^z, it can be shown that complex exponential functions obey the ordinary laws of real algebra; e.g.
$$e^{z_1} \times e^{z_2} = e^{z_1 + z_2}.$$

Exponential form of a complex number

We have
$$e^{i\theta} = 1 + \frac{i\theta}{1!} + \frac{(i\theta)^2}{2!} + \frac{(i\theta)^3}{3!} + \frac{(i\theta)^4}{4!} + \frac{(i\theta)^5}{5!} + \cdots,$$
$$= 1 - \frac{\theta^2}{2!} + \frac{\theta^4}{4!} - \cdots + i\left(\theta - \frac{\theta^3}{3!} + \frac{\theta^5}{5!} - \cdots\right),$$
$$= \cos\theta + i\sin\theta.$$

$\therefore$ **The complex number $r(\cos\theta + i\sin\theta)$ can be expressed as $re^{i\theta}$.**

Ex. 14. *Express (i) $\cos\frac{1}{3}\pi + i\sin\frac{1}{3}\pi$; (ii) -1; (iii) $2 + i$ in the exponential form.*

(i) $\cos\frac{1}{3}\pi + i\sin\frac{1}{3}\pi = e^{\frac{1}{3}i\pi}$;

(ii) $-1 = \cos\pi + i\sin\pi = e^{i\pi}$;

(iii) $2 + i = \sqrt{5}(\cos\theta + i\sin\theta)$, where $\theta = \tan^{-1}\frac{1}{2}$,
$$= \sqrt{5}e^{i\theta}.$$

Applications of the exponential form of a complex number. The use of the exponential form for a complex number leads to simple proofs of some of the results obtained previously.

E.g.
$$z_1 z_2 = r_1 e^{i\theta_1} \times r_2 e^{i\theta_2} = r_1 r_2 e^{i(\theta_1 + \theta_2)},$$

So the modulus of a product is the product of the moduli and the amplitude of a product is the sum of the amplitudes.

Such a result as $(\cos\theta + i\sin\theta)^3 = \cos 3\theta + i\sin 3\theta$ follows from the corresponding exponential result, $(e^{i\theta})^3 = e^{3i\theta}$.

Some of the most important applications of the exponential forms are in integration and the solution of linear differential equations.

Ex. 15. *Integrate: (i) $e^x \sin x$; (ii) $e^{-x}\cos 3x$.*

(i) We evaluate $\int e^x e^{ix}\,dx$ and take the imaginary part of the result.

Now
$$\int e^x e^{ix}\,dx = \int e^{x(1+i)}\,dx = \frac{1}{1+i}e^{x(1+i)},$$
$$= \frac{1-i}{2}e^x(\cos x + i\sin x), \quad \text{ignoring the arbitrary constant.}$$

$\therefore \int e^x(\cos x + i\sin x)dx = \frac{1}{2}e^x\{(\cos x + \sin x) + i(\sin x - \cos x)\}$

and equating imaginary parts,
$$\int e^x \sin x\,dx = \frac{1}{2}e^x(\sin x - \cos x).$$

(ii) We note that $\cos 3x$ is the real part of e^{3ix}.

Now
$$\int e^x e^{3ix}\,dx = \int e^{x(1+3i)}\,dx = \frac{1}{1+3i}\,e^{x(1+3i)}$$

$$= \frac{1-3i}{10}\,e^x(\cos 3x + i \sin 3x), \text{ ignoring the arbitrary}$$
$$\text{constant.}$$

Equating real parts,

$$\int e^x \cos 3x\,dx = \tfrac{1}{10}e^x\,(\cos 3x + 3 \sin 3x).$$

Ex. 16. *Show that the general solution of the equation* $\dfrac{d^2y}{dx^2} + 2\dfrac{dy}{dx} + 4y = 0$ *is*
$y = e^{-x}\{C \cos \sqrt{3}x + S \sin \sqrt{3}x\}$, *where C, S are constants.*

The function e^{mx} is a solution of the equation if

$$m^2 + 2m + 4 = 0; \quad \text{i.e. } m = -1 \pm i\sqrt{3}.$$

Hence the general solution of the equation is of the form

$$y = A\,e^{(-1+i\sqrt{3})x} + B\,e^{(-1-i\sqrt{3})x}, \text{ where } A,\,B \text{ are arbitrary constants,}$$
$$= A\,e^{-x}(\cos \sqrt{3}x + i \sin \sqrt{3}x) + B\,e^{-x}\{\cos(-\sqrt{3}x) + i \sin(-\sqrt{3}x)\},$$
$$= e^{-x}\{(A+B) \cos \sqrt{3}x + i(A-B) \sin \sqrt{3}x\},$$
$$= e^{-x}\{C \cos \sqrt{3}x + S \sin \sqrt{3}x\}.$$

EXAMPLES 6d

1. Express in the (r, θ) form: (i) $e^{i\pi}$; (ii) $e^{\frac{1}{2}i\pi}$; (iii) $e^{-\frac{1}{4}i\pi}$; (iv) $e^{1+\frac{1}{2}i\pi}$;
(v) $e^{-i\theta}$; (vi) $e^{i\omega t}$; (vii) $e^{x(1+i\sqrt{2})}$; (viii) $\frac{1}{2}(e^{i\theta} + e^{-i\theta})$.

2. Express in the exponential form:

(i) 1;   (ii) $\frac{1}{2}(i + \sqrt{3})$;   (iii) $\cos 4\theta + i \sin 4\theta$;
(iv) $\cos \theta - i \sin \theta$;   (v) $\sin \theta + i \cos \theta$;   (vi) $4 - 3i$.

3. Express each of the following functions as the real part of a complex number in the exponential form: (i) $\cos 2x$; (ii) $\cos 5x$; (iii) $\cos(A+B)$; (iv) $\cos(A-B)$; (v) $e^{ax} \cos bx$.

4. Use the result $e^{i(A+B)} = e^{iA} \cdot e^{iB}$ to obtain the expansions of $\cos(A+B)$ and $\sin(A+B)$.

5. Obtain expressions for $\cos(A-B)$ and $\sin(A-B)$ by the method of the previous example.

6. Establish the results:

$$\text{(i) } \cos \theta = \tfrac{1}{2}(e^{i\theta} + e^{-i\theta}); \quad \text{(ii) } \sin \theta = \frac{1}{2i}(e^{i\theta} - e^{-i\theta}).$$

7. Use the result $\cos 3\theta + i \sin 3\theta = (\cos \theta + i \sin \theta)^3$ to obtain expressions for: (i) $\cos 3\theta$ in terms of $\cos \theta$; (ii) $\sin 3\theta$ in terms of $\sin \theta$.

8. If $x + iy = e^{1+i\theta}$, prove that $x^2 + y^2 = e^2$.

9. Simplify $e^{(a+ib)x} + e^{(a-ib)x}$.

10. Express: (i) $\cos 2\theta$; (ii) $\sin 3\theta$; (iii) $\tan \theta$ in the exponential form.

11. Evaluate: (i) $\displaystyle\int e^x \cos x \, dx$;   (ii) $\displaystyle\int e^x \sin 2x \, dx$;

       (iii) $\displaystyle\int e^{2x} \cos \tfrac{1}{2}x \, dx$;   (iv) $\displaystyle\int e^{-x} \sin \tfrac{3}{2}x \, dx$.

12. Obtain the general solutions of the following equations:

   (i) $\dfrac{d^2y}{dx^2} + \dfrac{dy}{dx} + y = 0$;   (ii) $\dfrac{d^2y}{dx^2} - \dfrac{dy}{dx} + 2y = 0$;

   (iii) $2\dfrac{d^2y}{dx^2} + 3\dfrac{dy}{dx} + 2y = 0$;   (iv) $\dfrac{d^2x}{dt^2} + m^2x = 0$;

   (v) $\dfrac{d^2s}{dt^2} + 2k\dfrac{ds}{dt} + \mu s = 0$, where $k^2 < \mu$.

13. Write down the expansion of $e^{(1+i)x}$ as far as the term in x^4 and deduce the first four terms in the expansion of $e^x \cos x$ as a power series in x.

14. Obtain the first three terms in the expansion of $e^{-x} \sin 2x$ as a power series in x.

15. Write down the third derivative of $e^{x(2+i)}$ with respect to x and deduce the values of $\dfrac{d^3}{dx^3}(e^{2x}\cos x)$, $\dfrac{d^3}{dx^3}(e^{2x}\sin x)$.

16. Find the value of the fourth derivative of $e^{-x} \cos 4x$ with respect to x, when x takes the value zero.

MISCELLANEOUS EXAMPLES

1. Express $1/(1+z)$ in the form $a + ib$, where $z = \cos\theta + i\sin\theta$.

2. Simplify $(1 + i\sqrt{3})^6 + (1 - i\sqrt{3})^6$.

3. If $|z| \neq 1$, show graphically that $|1 - z| \geqslant |1 - |z||$.

4. The point P represents the complex number z. Show how to find the point Q which represents $1/z$. If P moves round the circle $|z| = 1$ in a clockwise direction, find the path traced out by Q.

5. Find the centre and radius of the circle $|z - 1 - i| = 2$. Determine the curves traced out by the points: (i) $z + 2$; (ii) $1/z$.

6. If $w_1 = az_1 + b$, $w_2 = az_2 + b$, $w_3 = az_3 + b$, prove that

$$am\left(\frac{w_1 - w_2}{w_1 - w_3}\right) = am\left(\frac{z_1 - z_2}{z_1 - z_3}\right).$$

Deduce that the triangle with vertices w_1, w_2, w_3 is similar to that with vertices z_1, z_2, z_3.

7. Simplify: (i) $e^{ix} + e^{-ix}$; (ii) $e^{(1+i\sqrt{2})x} + e^{(1-i\sqrt{2})x}$; (iii) $e^{i\omega t} - e^{-i\omega t}$.

8. A, B, C, D are the points in the Argand diagram representing the complex numbers α, β, γ, δ. If $ABCD$ is a parallelogram, show that $\alpha + \gamma = \beta + \delta$.

9. Find the equations of the loci of the points representing the complex number z which satisfy: (i) $|z| = 2$; (ii) $|z - 3| = 4$; (iii) $am\ z = \frac{1}{3}\pi$;

(iv) $|z - 2 - i| = 1$; (v) $am(z - 1) = \frac{1}{4}\pi$; (vi) $\left|\dfrac{z}{z - 2}\right| = 2$; (vii) $am\dfrac{z - 1}{z + 1} = \frac{1}{2}\pi$.

10. Prove that $|z_1 + z_2|^2 + |z_1 - z_2|^2 = 2|z_1|^2 + 2|z_2|^2$ and illustrate the result geometrically.

11. Express $\cos\theta$ and $\sin\theta$ in terms of $e^{i\theta}$, $e^{-i\theta}$ and deduce the results: (i) $\cos^2\theta + \sin^2\theta = 1$; (ii) $\cos^4\theta + \sin^4\theta = \frac{1}{4}(3 + \cos 4\theta)$.

12. If $z = \cos\theta + i\sin\theta$, prove that $\left(1 - \dfrac{1}{z^2}\right) / \left(1 + \dfrac{1}{z^2}\right) = i\tan\theta$.

13. Two fixed points A, B and a variable point P represent the complex numbers a, b, z respectively. What is the locus of P if: (i) $|z - a| = |b|$; (ii) $am(z - a) = am(z - b)$?

14. If $|z + 2 - i| \leqslant 1$, find: (i) the maximum value of $|z|$; (ii) the minimum value of $|z - 2i|$.

15. Find the modulus and amplitude of each of the following complex numbers: (i) $(1 + i)(1 + i\sqrt{3})$; (ii) $(1 - i)^2$; (iii) $(1 + i)^4$; (iv) $1/(1 + i)^5$; (v) $(1 + i\sqrt{3})^3$.

16. Take a point P to represent the complex number z, and in the same diagram find the points representing (i) iz; (ii) $2z - 1$; (iii) z^2; (iv) $-1/z$.

17. Evaluate $\displaystyle\int_0^{\frac{1}{2}\pi} e^{ax}\cos bx\ dx$, $\displaystyle\int_0^{\frac{1}{2}\pi} e^{ax}\sin bx\ dx$, where b is a positive even integer.

18. Prove that the points representing the complex numbers 1, -1, $a + ib$, $1/(a + ib)$ are concyclic.

19. $PQRS$ is a parallelogram and X is the point of intersection of the diagonals; if P, R, S represent the numbers $1 + 3i$, $2 + 6i$, $5 + 7i$ respectively find the numbers represented by the points Q and X.

20. If $w = z^2$, where $w = u + iv$, $z = x + iy$, prove that $u = x^2 - y^2$, $v = 2xy$. Show that when z describes the unit circle $|z| = 1$, w describes the unit circle $|w| = 1$ twice.

21. If u and v are real, find the moduli of: (i) $e^{u + iv}$; (ii) $e^{u - iv}$; (iii) $(e^u)^{iv}$.

22. Find the modulus and principal value of the amplitude of $(1 + \cos 2\theta + i\sin 2\theta)$ in each of the following cases: (i) $0 < \theta < \frac{1}{2}\pi$; (ii) $\frac{1}{2}\pi < \theta < \pi$; (iii) $-\frac{1}{2}\pi < \theta < 0$; (iv) $\frac{3}{2}\pi < \theta < 2\pi$.

23. P_1, P_2, P_3, P_4 are the points z_1, z_2, z_3, z_4 and O is the origin; show that if $z_1z_2 + z_3z_4 = 0$ and $z_1 + z_2 = 0$, then P_1, P_2, P_3, P_4 are concyclic and the triangles AOC, DOA are similar.

24. The complex number z is represented by the point P; if $(z - 1)/(z - i)$ is wholly imaginary, prove that P moves on the circle centre $(\frac{1}{2}, \frac{1}{2})$ radius $1/\sqrt{2}$.

25. P, Q are the points representing the complex numbers α, β and O is the origin. If $OP = OQ$, prove that $(\alpha - \beta)/(\alpha + \beta)$ is of the form iq, where q is real.

26. Prove that the two triangles whose vertices represent the complex numbers a_1, a_2, a_3 and b_1, b_2, b_3 respectively are directly similar if, and only if,

$$\begin{vmatrix} a_1 & b_1 & 1 \\ a_2 & b_2 & 1 \\ a_3 & b_3 & 1 \end{vmatrix} = 0.$$

27. Prove that $e^x \sin x = \dfrac{1}{2i}\{e^{(1+i)x} - e^{(1-i)x}\}$, and hence obtain the coefficient of x^n in the expansion of $e^x \sin x$ as a power series in x.

28. Prove that the relationship $w = (1 + iz)/(i + z)$ transforms the part of the real axis between $z = 1$ and $z = -1$ into a semicircle connecting $w = 1$ and $w = -1$.

29. If the points z_1, z_2, z_3 lie on a circle through the origin, prove that the points $1/z_1, 1/z_2, 1/z_3$ are collinear.

30. If $(z_1 - z_2)(z_1' - z_2') = (z_2 - z_3)(z_2' - z_3') = (z_3 - z_1)(z_3' - z_1')$, show that the triangles with vertices z_1, z_2, z_3 and z_1', z_2', z_3' are equilateral.

31. Find the modulus and amplitude of $(1 + z)/(1 - z)$ where $z = e^{i\theta}$ and θ is acute.

32. If the points A, B, C representing the complex numbers α, β, γ are the vertices of an isosceles triangle, right-angled at B, prove that

$$(\alpha - \beta)^2 + (\gamma - \beta)^2 = 0.$$

33. Solve the equation $x^3 = 1$.   Show that the complex roots are of the form ω, ω^2 and obtain their moduli and amplitudes.   If the points z_1, z_2, z_3 form an equilateral triangle taken in anti-clockwise order, prove that

$$z_1 + \omega z_2 + \omega^2 z_3 = 0.$$

34. Find the region of the Argand diagram in which z must lie if

$$\left| \frac{z - 3 + 2i}{1 - 3z - 2iz} \right| > 1.$$

35. Prove that the curves $\left| \dfrac{z-1}{z+1} \right| = \text{constant}$ and $am\left(\dfrac{z-1}{z+1} \right) = \text{constant}$ are orthogonal circles.

36. Two complex numbers z, w are connected by the relation $w = (z - 1)/(z + 1)$; the point z describes the circle $x^2 + y^2 = 1$ in a counter-clockwise direction starting from $z = 1$. Find the path traced out by the point w.

37. Find the value of $\dfrac{d^4}{dx^4}(\cos x \cosh x)$ when $x = 0$.

38. Show that the transformation $w = 4/(z + 1)^2$ transforms the circle $|z| = 1$ into the parabola $v^2 = 4(1 - u)$, where $w = u + iv$, and that the interior of the circle corresponds to the exterior of the parabola.

39. Show that with the transformation $w = z/(z - 1)$, the straight line $x = \frac{1}{2}$ is transformed into a unit circle.

40. If $w = a(z - c)/(z + c)$, where a, c are real and positive, show that the interior of the circle $|z| = c$ in the z-plane corresponds to that half of the w-plane which lies to the left of the imaginary axis.

41. If $z = e^{i\theta}$, express: (i) $1/(1 - z \cos \theta)$; (ii) $(1 - z^n)/(1 - z)$, n a positive integer, in the form $a + ib$.

CHAPTER VII

ELEMENTARY THEORY OF EQUATIONS

Polynomials and polynomial equations. Consideration will be given to elementary properties of equations of the form

$$P(x) \equiv a_0 x^n + a_1 x^{n-1} + a_2 x^{n-2} + \ldots + a_{n-1}x + a_n = 0,$$

where the coefficients $a_0, a_1, \ldots a_n$ are real.

The function $P(x)$ is called *a polynomial of degree n* and the equation is a *polynomial equation* of like degree.

E.g. $$3x^4 - 2x^2 + x - 6 = 0,$$

is a polynomial equation of degree four.

Basic theorems

(i) *Every polynomial equation of degree $\geqslant 1$ has at least one root.*

The proof of this fundamental theorem is beyond the scope of this text.

(ii) *A polynomial equation of degree n has n roots, real or complex.*

For by (i), the equation will have one root, say α_1.

$$\therefore \ P(x) \equiv (x - \alpha_1)P_1(x),$$

where $P_1(x)$ is a polynomial of degree $n-1$.

Again, the equation $P_1(x) = 0$, has a root, say α_2,

hence $$P_1(x) \equiv (x - \alpha_2)P_2(x),$$

where $P_2(x)$ is a polynomial of degree $n-2$.

Proceeding in this way, it follows that

$$P(x) \equiv a_0(x - \alpha_1)(x - \alpha_2) \ldots (x - \alpha_n).$$

$\therefore$ the equation $$P(x) = 0,$$

will have n roots $\alpha_1, \alpha_2, \ldots \alpha_n$.

Ex. 1. *Given that two of the roots of the equation $x^4 + x^3 - 5x^2 - 4x + 4 = 0$ are numerically equal but opposite in sign, solve the equation.*

Two of the four roots can be taken as $\pm a$ and the quadratic factor corresponding to them will be $x^2 - a^2$.

We can write $x^4 + x^3 - 5x^2 - 4x + 4 = (x^2 - a^2)(x^2 + bx + c).$

142

Equating coefficients of x^3, $\qquad 1 = b$;
equating coefficients of x, $\qquad -4 = -a^2b$; $\quad a^2 = 4$;
equating constant terms, $\qquad 4 = -a^2c$; $\quad c = -1$.

$$\therefore (x^2 - 4)(x^2 + x - 1) = 0,$$
$$x = \pm 2, \tfrac{1}{2}(-1 \pm \sqrt{5}).$$

(iii) *Complex roots occur in pairs.*

For suppose $x = \alpha + i\beta$, $\beta \neq 0$, is a root of $P(x) = 0$.

Let $\qquad S(x) \equiv (x - \overline{\alpha + i\beta})(x - \overline{\alpha - i\beta})$
$$\equiv x^2 - 2\alpha x + \alpha^2 + \beta^2.$$

When $P(x)$ is divided by $S(x)$ let the quotient be $Q(x)$ and the remainder $Ax + B$, where A, B are real constants.

Then $\qquad P(x) \equiv Q(x)S(x) + Ax + B.$

Putting x equal to $\alpha + i\beta$ and noting that $P(\alpha + i\beta) = 0 = S(\alpha + i\beta)$,

$$0 = A(\alpha + i\beta) + B.$$
$$\therefore A\alpha + B = 0; \quad A\beta = 0, \text{ where } \beta \neq 0.$$

Hence $\qquad\qquad A = B = 0.$

$\therefore$ $S(x)$ is a factor of $P(x)$ and consequently $x = \alpha - i\beta$ is also a root of the given equation.

N.B. From theorems (ii) and (iii), it follows that an equation of odd degree must have at least one real root.

(iv) *Irrational roots of the form* $\alpha + \sqrt{\beta}$, *where* β *is not a perfect square, occur in pairs.*

This is proved in a similar manner to (iii).

Ex. 2. *Solve the equation* $x^4 + x^3 - 8x^2 + 14x - 8 = 0$, *being given that* $1 + i$ *is one root.*

As $1 - i$ is also a root, a quadratic factor of the polynomial is

$$(x - \overline{1 + i})(x - \overline{1 - i}) \quad \text{or} \quad x^2 - 2x + 2.$$

By division, $\qquad P(x) \equiv (x^2 - 2x + 2)(x^2 + 3x - 4)$
$$\equiv (x^2 - 2x + 2)(x + 4)(x - 1).$$

Hence the roots of the equation are $1 \pm i$, 1, -4.

Zeros of a polynomial. Corresponding to the roots of the equation $P(x) = 0$ are the zeros of the function $P(x)$. In particular, real and distinct roots correspond to the points of intersection of the graph $y = P(x)$ and the axis of x. A repeated real root of the equation corresponds to a point where the graph is tangential to the axis of x.

Consequently, knowledge of the shapes of polynomial graphs will be valuable in the location of the real roots of the corresponding equations.

A feature of a polynomial graph is its continuity, and hence the following important results:

(i) if $P(a)$, $P(b)$ are of opposite signs, there is at least one zero of $P(x)$ between a and b;

(ii) if $P(a)$, $P(b)$ are of like sign, there is either no zero of $P(x)$ between a and b, or an even number of zeros.

Ex. 3. *If* $P(x) \equiv 3x^4 - 8x^3 - 6x^2 + 24x - 10,$ *obtain the signs of* $P(-\infty)$, $P(-1)$, $P(1)$, $P(2)$, $P(+\infty)$ *and deduce that the equation* $P(x) = 0$ *has four real roots.*

For numerically large values of x, the sign of $P(x)$ is determined by the sign of the term $3x^4$; the signs for other values are determined by substitution.

We have,

x	$-\infty$	-1	1	2	$+\infty$
$P(x)$	$+$	$-$	$+$	$-$	$+$

∴ the equation $P(x) = 0$ has at least one real root in each of the intervals $-\infty$ to -1, -1 to 1, 1 to 2, 2 to $+\infty$; but the equation has at the most four real roots, and so one must lie in each of these intervals.

Ex. 4. *Prove that the equation* $x^3 + 4x - 1 = 0$ *has only one real root and find the integers between which this root lies.*

In locating the roots of $P(x) = 0$, it is useful to consider the roots of $P'(x) = 0$ as these give turning-points on the corresponding graph.

In this case, $$P'(x) \equiv 3x^2 + 4.$$

Clearly there are no real solutions of the equation $P'(x) = 0$, and consequently the graph $y = P(x)$ has no turning-points. As $P(-\infty)$ is negative and $P(+\infty)$ positive, $P(x)$ increases steadily and only cuts the x-axis once.

Hence the equation has only one real root.

By trial, $$P(0) = - \text{ve}; \quad P(1) = + \text{ve},$$

and so the real root lies between 0 and 1.

Rolle's theorem. This theorem, which is helpful in locating the real roots of a polynomial equation, can be stated as follows:

If a, b are consecutive real roots of the equation $P(x) = 0$, then the equation $P'(x) = 0$ has an odd number of real roots between a and b.

This result can be justified geometrically.

Referring to Fig. 69, the graph $y = P(x)$ cuts the x-axis at points A, B corresponding to $x = a$, b. As the graph is continuous, there must be one turning-point C between A and B or an odd number of turning-points.

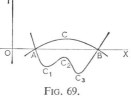

Fig. 69.

As turning-points correspond to roots of $P'(x) = 0$, the result follows.

As a corollary of this theorem and the results on the zeros of a polynomial, it follows that, *if* α, β *are consecutive real roots of* $P'(x) = 0$:

(i) *there is exactly one real root of* $P(x) = 0$ *between* α *and* β *if* $P(\alpha)$, $P(\beta)$ *are of opposite signs;*

(ii) *there is no real root of* $P(x) = 0$ *between* α *and* β *if* $P(\alpha)$, $P(\beta)$ *are of like sign.*

Ex. 5. *Show that* (i) *the equation* $x^3 - 3x + 1 = 0$ *has three real roots;* (ii) *the equation* $x^3 - 2x^2 = 1$ *has only one real-root.*

(i) $\qquad\qquad P(x) \equiv x^3 - 3x + 1; \quad P'(x) \equiv 3x^2 - 3.$

The equation $P'(x) = 0$ has real roots ± 1.

Now $\qquad\qquad P(-1) = +\text{ve}; \quad P(1) = -\text{ve}.$

So there is one root of the equation between -1 and 1.

Also $P(-\infty) = -\text{ve}$; $P(+\infty) = +\text{ve}$, and as the equation has at the most three real roots, there is also one real root in each of the intervals $-\infty$ to -1, 1 to $+\infty$.

(ii) $\qquad\qquad P(x) \equiv x^3 - 2x^2 - 1; \quad P'(x) \equiv 3x^2 - 4x.$

Here $P'(x) = 0$ has real roots 0, $\frac{4}{3}$.

Now $\qquad\qquad P(0) = -\text{ve}; \quad P(\frac{4}{3}) = -\text{ve}.$

So there is no real root between 0 and $\frac{4}{3}$.

Also $P(-\infty)$ is negative as is $P(0)$ and, as there are no turning-points between $-\infty$ and 0, it follows that there can be no real roots of $P(x) = 0$ in this interval.

As $P(\frac{4}{3})$, $P(+\infty)$ are of opposite signs and $P'(x)$ does not vanish between $\frac{4}{3}$ and $+\infty$, there is exactly one real root of $P(x) = 0$ in this interval.

Hence the equation has only one real root, which can be verified as lying between 2 and 3.

EXAMPLES 7a

1. Without solving, show that the roots of the equation $2x^2 + 5x - 4 = 0$ are real and lie one in each of the intervals -4 to -3, 0 to 1.

2. Show that the roots of the equation $\dfrac{1}{x+1} + \dfrac{1}{x-1} + \dfrac{1}{x-2} = 0$ lie between -1 and 1, 1 and 2.

3. How many roots has the equation $x^5 - x^2 + 1 = 0$? Show that at least one real root lies between -1 and 0.

4. Solve the equation $3x^3 - 7x^2 - 60x + 140 = 0$ being given that $2\sqrt{5}$ is one root.

5. Two roots of the equation $7x^3 + 9x^2 - 14x - 18 = 0$ are numerically equal but opposite in sign. Solve the equation.

6. Show that the equation $x^3 - 27x - 36 = 0$ has a real root in each of the intervals -5 to -4, -2 to -1, 5 to 6.

7. One root of the equation $2x^3 - 19x^2 + 54x - 55 = 0$ is $2 - i$, find the other roots.

8. Solve the equation $x^4 - x^3 + 3x^2 - 4x - 4 = 0$ being given that one root is $2i$.

9. Prove that $x^3 - 4x - 1 = 0$ has three real roots.

10. The product of two of the roots of $2x^4 - 10x^3 + 3x^2 + 5x - 2 = 0$ is 2. By expressing the polynomial as the product of two quadratic factors, obtain the roots of the equation.

11. If $1 + \sqrt{3}$ is a root of $x^4 - 2x^3 - x^2 - 2x - 2 = 0$, complete the solution of the equation.

12. Determine the number of real roots of the equation $x^3 - 7x + 2 = 0$.

13. Given that one root of $2x^4 + x^3 + 5x^2 + 4x - 12 = 0$ is a purely imaginary complex number, find all the roots.

14. Prove that $2x^3 + x^2 = 1$ has a real root between 0 and 1 and no other real root.

15. By considering the turning-points of the function $x^3 - 3bx + c$, show that the equation $x^3 - 3bx + c = 0$ has three real roots, or only one, according as $4b^3 - c^2$ is positive or negative.

16. One root of the equation $x^5 - 5x^4 + 12x^3 - 12x^2 + 11x - 7 = 0$ is $2 - i\sqrt{3}$; complete the solution.

17. Prove that the equation $x^3 - 3x^2 - 4x + 4 = 0$ has three real roots and find the integers between which they lie.

18. The product of two of the roots of $x^4 - 10x^3 + 24x^2 + 4x - 4 = 0$ is equal and opposite in sign to the product of the other two. Express the polynomial as a product of two quadratic factors and solve the equation.

19. If $p > q > 0$, prove that $x^3 + x^2 - px - q = 0$ has three real roots.

20. If $p \neq 0$, prove that $3x^4 + 4x^3 + p = 0$ has two or no real roots according as $p < 1$ or $p > 1$.

Conditions for two equations to have a common root. If two equations $P_1(x) = 0$, $P_2(x) = 0$ have a common root, they are both satisfied by a particular value of x.

If one of the equations can be solved the necessary condition is readily obtained by substituting the solutions obtained into the second equation.

Ex. 6. *Find the values of k for which the equations $2x^3 - x^2 + 4x + k = 0$, $x^2 - x - 2 = 0$ have a root in common.*

The equation $x^2 - x - 2 = 0$ has solutions $x = 2, -1$.

Substituting these values in turn into the second equation, we have

$$k = -20, 7.$$

Two quadratic equations. Suppose the equations

$$a_1 x^2 + b_1 x + c_1 = 0,$$
$$a_2 x^2 + b_2 x + c_2 = 0,$$

have a common root α, then

$$a_1 \alpha^2 + b_1 \alpha + c_1 = 0,$$
$$a_2 \alpha^2 + b_2 \alpha + c_2 = 0.$$

Treating these as linear equations in α^2 and α,

we have
$$\frac{\alpha^2}{b_1c_2-b_2c_1}=\frac{-\alpha}{a_1c_2-a_2c_1}=\frac{1}{a_1b_2-a_2b_1}.$$

$\therefore$ The common root, $\quad \alpha=-\dfrac{a_1c_2-a_2c_1}{a_1b_2-a_2b_1},$

and $\qquad\qquad\qquad \alpha^2=\dfrac{b_1c_2-b_2c_1}{a_1b_2-a_2b_1}.$

Eliminating α, the condition for a common root is
$$(a_1c_2-a_2c_1)^2=(a_1b_2-a_2b_1)(b_1c_2-b_2c_1).$$

Ex. 7. *If $a^2+x^2=b^2+y^2=ay-bx=1$, prove that $a^2+b^2=1$.*

Eliminating y from the last two equations, we have
$$b^2+\left(\frac{bx+1}{a}\right)^2=1,$$

i.e. $\qquad\qquad b^2x^2+2bx+a^2b^2-a^2+1=0.$

Also $\qquad\qquad\qquad x^2+a^2-1=0.$

$\therefore \dfrac{x^2}{2b(a^2-1)}=\dfrac{-x}{b^2(a^2-1)-(a^2b^2-a^2+1)}=\dfrac{1}{-2b}.$

Eliminating x, $\qquad (a^2-b^2-1)^2+4b^2(a^2-1)=0,$
$$(a^2+b^2-1)^2=0,$$
$$\therefore\ a^2+b^2=1.$$

A quadratic and a cubic equation. Suppose the equations
$$a_1x^3+b_1x^2+c_1x+d_1=0,$$
$$a_2x^2+b_2x+c_2=0,$$

have a common root $\alpha\neq 0$, then

$$a_1\alpha^3+b_1\alpha^2+c_1\alpha+d_1=0. \qquad \cdot \quad \cdot \quad \cdot \quad \cdot \quad \text{(i)}$$
$$a_2\alpha^2+b_2\alpha+c_2=0. \qquad \cdot \quad \cdot \quad \cdot \quad \cdot \quad \text{(ii)}$$

Multiplying (i) by a_2 and (ii) by $a_1\alpha$ and subtracting gives

$$\alpha^2(a_1b_2-a_2b_1)+\alpha(a_1c_2-a_2c_1)-a_2d_1=0. \quad \cdot \quad \cdot \quad \text{(iii)}$$

The common root α can now be eliminated between the two quadratic equations (ii), (iii) as shown above.

Two cubic equations. Suppose the equations
$$a_1x^3+b_1x^2+c_1x+d_1=0,$$
$$a_2x^3+b_2x^2+c_2x+d_2=0,$$

have a common root $\alpha\neq 0$, then

$$a_1\alpha^3+b_1\alpha^2+c_1\alpha+d_1=0,$$
$$a_2\alpha^3+b_2\alpha^2+c_2\alpha+d_2=0.$$

Eliminating α^3,

$$\alpha^2(a_1b_2-a_2b_1)+\alpha(a_1c_2-a_2c_1)+a_1d_2-a_2d_1=0. \qquad \text{(i)}$$

Eliminating constant terms,

$$\alpha^3(a_1d_2-a_2d_1)+\alpha^2(b_1d_2-b_2d_1)+\alpha(c_1d_2-c_2d_1)=0,$$

i.e. $\qquad \alpha^2(a_1d_2-a_2d_1)+\alpha(b_1d_2-b_2d_1)+c_1d_2-c_2d_1=0. \qquad \text{(ii)}$

The common root α can now be eliminated between the two quadratic equations (i), (ii).

Ex. 8. *If the equations $x^3+ax+b=0$, $x^4+cx+d=0$ have a root in common, show that this common root is $\{(b-c)d-a^2b\}/\{(b-c)^2+a(a^2+d)\}$.*

Let the common root be α, then

$$\alpha^3+a\alpha+b=0, \qquad \text{(i)}$$
$$\alpha^4+c\alpha+d=0. \qquad \text{(ii)}$$

Multiplying (i) by α, as $\alpha\neq0$, and eliminating α^4,

$$a\alpha^2+\alpha(b-c)-d=0. \qquad \text{(iii)}$$

Multiplying (i) by a and (iii) by α and subtracting,

$$\alpha^2(b-c)-\alpha(a^2+d)-ab=0. \qquad \text{(iv)}$$

Solving (iii) and (iv) for α^2, α,

$$\frac{\alpha^2}{-ab(b-c)-d(a^2+d)}=\frac{-\alpha}{-a^2b+d(b-c)}=\frac{1}{-a(a^2+d)-(b-c)^2}.$$

$\therefore$ Common root, $\qquad \alpha=\dfrac{d(b-c)-a^2b}{(b-c)^2+a(a^2+d)}.$

Repeated roots of a polynomial equation. Suppose the equation $P(x)=0$, where $P(x)$ is a polynomial of degree greater than two, has a root α repeated twice.

Then $P(x)$ must have a factor $(x-\alpha)^2$

and $\qquad\qquad P(x)\equiv(x-\alpha)^2Q(x).$

$\qquad \therefore\ P'(x)\equiv(x-\alpha)\{2Q(x)+(x-\alpha)Q'(x)\}.$

I.e. $x-\alpha$ is a factor of $P'(x)$, and consequently α is also a root of the equation $P'(x)=0$.

So a twice repeated root of $P(x)=0$ is also a root of $P'(x)=0$.

Extending this result,

If $P(x)=0$ has a root repeated r times then the equations $P'(x)=0$ $P''(x)=0$, . . . have the same root repeated $r-1$, $r-2$, . . . times.

Ex. 9. *Find the condition that the equation $x^4+px^3+qx^2+r=0$, $p,q,r\neq0$ has three equal roots.*

$$P(x)\equiv x^4+px^3+qx^2+r,$$
$$P'(x)\equiv 4x^3+3px^2+2qx,$$
$$P''(x)\equiv 12x^2+6px+2q.$$

The equations $P'(x)=0$, $P''(x)=0$ will have a common root, α, $\neq 0$.

$$\therefore \ 4\alpha^2 + 3p\alpha + 2q = 0,$$
$$6\alpha^2 + 3p\alpha + q = 0.$$

Solving for α^2, α,

$$\frac{\alpha^2}{-3pq} = \frac{-\alpha}{-8q} = \frac{1}{-6p}.$$

Eliminating α, $\qquad 32q = 9p^2$—the required condition.

Repeated root, $\alpha = -4q/3p$.

Solutions of equations with repeated roots. If $P(x)=0$ has two equal roots α, then $P'(x)=0$ has also a root α. The common root can be found either

(i) by solving, if possible, $P'(x)=0$ and determining the common root by trial; or

(ii) by finding the H.C.F. of $P(x)$, $P'(x)$; or

(iii) by using the fact that $P(x)=0=P'(x)$ have a root in common.

Ex. 10. *Solve the equation* $12x^3 - 4x^2 - 5x + 2 = 0$, *given that two roots are equal.*

$$P'(x) \equiv 36x^2 - 8x - 5 = (2x-1)(18x+5).$$

$\therefore$ The roots of $P'(x)=0$ are $\frac{1}{2}$, $-\frac{5}{18}$.

But $\qquad\qquad\qquad\qquad P(\frac{1}{2}) = 0$,

$\therefore$ $x = \frac{1}{2}$ is a common root of $P(x) = 0$, $P'(x) = 0$ and consequently it is a double root of the former.

By division, $\qquad 12x^3 - 4x^2 - 5x + 2 = (2x-1)^2(3x+2)$.

$\therefore$ The roots of the given equation are $\frac{1}{2}, \frac{1}{2}, -\frac{2}{3}$.

Ex. 11. *Prove that the equation* $x^3 + px + q = 0$ *has a double root if* $4p^3 + 27q^2 = 0$.

$$P(x) \equiv x^3 + px + q,$$
$$P'(x) \equiv 3x^2 + p.$$

So the equations $\qquad x^3 + px + q = 0$,
$$3x^2 + p = 0,$$

have a common root, say α.

Hence $\qquad\qquad \alpha^3 + p\alpha + q = 0, \quad . \quad . \quad . \quad . \quad . \quad$ (i)
$$3\alpha^2 + p = 0. \quad . \quad . \quad . \quad . \quad . \quad \text{(ii)}$$

Multiplying (i) by 3 and (ii) by α and subtracting,

$$2p\alpha + 3q = 0; \quad \alpha = -3q/2p.$$

Substituting in (ii), gives the condition $4p^3 + 27q^2 = 0$.

EXAMPLES 7b

1. If $a \neq b$, find the condition that the equations $x^2 + ax + b = 0$, $x^2 + bx + a = 0$ have a common root.

2. Solve the equation $12x^3 + 4x^2 - 5x - 2 = 0$ given that it has a repeated root.

3. For what values of k have the equations $2x^3 - x^2 + 3x + k = 0$, $2x^2 - x - 3 = 0$ a root in common?

4. Find the values of k for which the equation $x^3 + x^2 - 8x + k = 0$ has a repeated root and solve the equation in each case.

5. Find the condition that $p^2x^2 + qx + 1 = 0$, $q^2x^2 - px + 1 = 0$ should have a root in common.

6. Solve the equation $3x^4 + 16x^3 + 24x^2 - 16 = 0$ given that three roots are equal.

7. What is the condition that $x^2 - 3xy - 10y^2$ and $ax^2 + 2hxy + by^2$ have a common factor?

8. Solve the equation $27x^3 - 36x - 16 = 0$, given that it has two equal roots.

9. Find the condition that $8x^2 - 30x + 7 = 0$, $2x^2 + ax + b = 0$ have a common root.

10. Find the condition that the two line pairs $ax^2 + 2hxy + by^2 = 0$, $a'x^2 + 2h'xy + b'y^2 = 0$ have a common line.

11. Solve the equation $x^4 + 3x^3 + 3x^2 + 8x + 12 = 0$ given that it has two equal roots.

12. Find the condition that the equations $x^3 + ax^2 + b = 0$, $x^2 + bx + c = 0$ have a root in common.

13. The equation $2x^4 + 11x^3 + 18x^2 + 4x - 8 = 0$ has a root repeated three times; find this root and solve the equation.

14. Show that the only real value of a for which the equations $x^2 - 2x + a = 0$, $2x^2 - ax + 1 = 0$ have a common root is -3.

15. Find the condition that the equation $x^4 + ax^3 + b = 0$, $b \neq 0$, has a double root.

16. For what rational value of λ have the equations $2x^2 - 3x + \lambda = 0$, $2x^3 - 3x^2 - 3x - 5 = 0$ a common root?

17. Show that the equation $4x^4 - 4x^3 - 11x^2 + 12x - 3 = 0$ has a repeated root and complete its solution.

18. Find the condition that the equations $x^3 + px + q = 0$, $x^3 + rx + s = 0$ shall have a common root.

19. If $p, q \neq 0$, prove that the equation $x^4 + px^3 + q = 0$ cannot have a root repeated three times.

20. If the equation $x^4 + px^2 + qx + r = 0$ has a root repeated three times, show that the value of this root is $-3q/4p$.

Relations between the roots and coefficients of an equation

Cubic equation.   Let the equation

$$ax^3 + bx^2 + cx + d = 0,$$

have roots α, β, γ.

Then

$$ax^3 + bx^2 + cx + d \equiv a(x - \alpha)(x - \beta)(x - \gamma),$$
$$\equiv a\{x^3 - x^2(\alpha + \beta + \gamma) + x(\beta\gamma + \gamma\alpha + \alpha\beta) - \alpha\beta\gamma\}.$$

Comparing coefficients,

$$\left.\begin{aligned} \alpha + \beta + \gamma &= -b/a, \\ \beta\gamma + \gamma\alpha + \alpha\beta &= c/a, \\ \alpha\beta\gamma &= -d/a. \end{aligned}\right\}$$

Ex. 12. *If α, β, γ are the roots of $x^3 - 2x^2 + x - 6 = 0$, find the values of*
(i) $\alpha^2 + \beta^2 + \gamma^2$; (iii) $\alpha^3 + \beta^3 + \gamma^3$.

We have $\qquad \alpha + \beta + \gamma = 2; \ \beta\gamma + \gamma\alpha + \alpha\beta = 1; \ \alpha\beta\gamma = 6.$
$$\therefore \ \alpha^2 + \beta^2 + \gamma^2 \equiv (\alpha + \beta + \gamma)^2 - 2(\beta\gamma + \gamma\alpha + \alpha\beta)$$
$$= 4 - 2 = 2.$$

Also $\qquad \alpha^3 + \beta^3 + \gamma^3 - 3\alpha\beta\gamma \equiv (\alpha + \beta + \gamma)\{\alpha^2 + \beta^2 + \gamma^2 - \beta\gamma - \gamma\alpha - \alpha\beta\}.$
$$\therefore \ \alpha^3 + \beta^3 + \gamma^3 - 18 = 2\{2 - 1\}.$$
$$\alpha^3 + \beta^3 + \gamma^3 = 20.$$

Application to the solution of symmetrical simultaneous equations in three unknowns.   Equations of the form

$$x + y + z = a,$$
$$x^2 + y^2 + z^2 = b,$$
$$x^3 + y^3 + z^3 = c,$$

can be solved by deriving the values of $yz + zx + xy$ and xyz and noting that x, y, z are the roots of the cubic equation

$$t^3 - t^2(x + y + z) + t(yz + zx + xy) - xyz = 0.$$

This method also applies to equations which are such that the values of $x + y + z$, $yz + zx + xy$ and xyz can be obtained.

Ex. 13. *Solve the equations $x + y + z = 3$, $x^2 + y^2 + z^2 = 29$, $x^3 + y^3 + z^3 = 45$.*

We have $\qquad yz + zx + xy \equiv \frac{1}{2}\{(x + y + z)^2 - (x^2 + y^2 + z^2)\}$
$$= -10.$$

Also $\qquad x^3 + y^3 + z^3 - 3xyz \equiv (x + y + z)(x^2 + y^2 + z^2 - yz - zx - xy),$
i.e. $\qquad\qquad 3xyz = 45 - 3(29 + 10)$
$$xyz = -24.$$

$\therefore \ x$, y, z are the roots of the equation

$$t^3 - 3t^2 - 10t + 24 = 0 \quad . \quad . \quad . \quad . \quad . \quad . \quad \text{(i)}$$

L

By trial, one solution is $t = 2$ and by division

$$t^3 - 3t^2 - 10t + 24 = (t - 2)(t^2 - t - 12)$$
$$= (t - 2)(t - 4)(t + 3).$$

∴ The roots of (i) are $-3, 2, 4$, and hence x, y, z have the values $-3, 2, 4$ in any order.

Quartic equation. Let the roots of

$$ax^4 + bx^3 + cx^2 + dx + e = 0,$$

be $\alpha, \beta, \gamma, \delta$.

Then $ax^4 + bx^3 + cx^2 + dx + e \equiv a(x - \alpha)(x - \beta)(x - \gamma)(x - \delta)$
$$\equiv a\{x^4 - x^3\sum\alpha + x^2\sum\alpha\beta - x\sum\alpha\beta\gamma + \alpha\beta\gamma\delta\}.$$

where
$$\sum\alpha = \alpha + \beta + \gamma + \delta,$$
$$\sum\alpha\beta = \alpha\beta + \alpha\gamma + \alpha\delta + \beta\gamma + \beta\delta + \gamma\delta,$$
$$\sum\alpha\beta\gamma = \alpha\beta\gamma + \alpha\beta\delta + \alpha\gamma\delta + \beta\gamma\delta.$$

Comparing coefficients,

$$\left.\begin{array}{rcl}\sum\alpha &=& -b/a, \\ \sum\alpha\beta &=& c/a, \\ \sum\alpha\beta\gamma &=& -d/a, \\ \alpha\beta\gamma\delta &=& e/a. \end{array}\right\}$$

Ex. 14. *If the equation $x^4 - px^2 + qx - r = 0$ has three equal roots prove that* (i) $p^2 = 12r$; (ii) $9q^2 = 32pr$.

Let the roots be $\alpha, \alpha, \alpha, \beta$.

Then
$$3\alpha + \beta = 0; \qquad\qquad \beta = -3\alpha. \qquad . \quad . \quad \text{(i)}$$
$$\alpha^2 + \alpha^2 + \alpha\beta + \alpha^2 + \alpha\beta + \alpha\beta = -p; \qquad 3\alpha^2 + 3\alpha\beta = -p. \qquad . \quad . \quad \text{(ii)}$$
$$\alpha^3 + \alpha^2\beta + \alpha^2\beta + \alpha^2\beta = -q; \qquad \alpha^3 + 3\alpha^2\beta = -q. \qquad . \quad . \quad \text{(iii)}$$
$$\alpha^3\beta = -r; \qquad\qquad \alpha^3\beta = -r. \qquad . \quad . \quad \text{(iv)}$$

From (i), (ii), $\qquad\qquad p = 6\alpha^2;$

from (i), (iv), $\qquad\qquad r = 3\alpha^4;$

from (i), (iii), $\qquad\qquad q = 8\alpha^3.$

$$\therefore \ p^2 = 36\alpha^4 = 12r; \quad 9q^2 = 9 \cdot 64\alpha^6 = 32pr.$$

Equation of the nth degree. Let the roots of the equation

$$a_0x^n + a_1x^{n-1} + a_2x^{n-2} + \ \ldots \ + a_n = 0,$$

be $\alpha_1, \alpha_2, \alpha_3 \ldots \alpha_n$.

Then using the method as in the cases of the cubic and quartic equations it follows that

$$\sum\alpha_1 = -a_1/a_0; \quad \sum\alpha_1\alpha_2 = a_2/a_0; \quad \sum\alpha_1\alpha_2\alpha_3 = -a_3/a_0 \ \ldots;$$
$$\alpha_1\alpha_2 \ \ldots \ \alpha_n = (-1)^n a_n/a_0.$$

Sums of powers of roots of an equation. A method of relating the sums of powers of the roots of a given equation is illustrated in the following examples.

Ex. 15. *If α, β are the roots of $x^2 - 2x - 1 = 0$ and s_n represents $\alpha^n + \beta^n$, $n > 2$, prove that $s_n - 2s_{n-1} - s_{n-2} = 0$. Hence evaluate* (i) $\alpha^3 + \beta^3$; (ii) $\alpha^5 + \beta^5$.

As α is a root,
$$\alpha^2 - 2\alpha - 1 = 0.$$

Clearly $\alpha \neq 0$ and we can multiply throughout by α^{n-2} and obtain
$$\alpha^n - 2\alpha^{n-1} - \alpha^{n-2} = 0.$$

Similarly,
$$\beta^n - 2\beta^{n-1} - \beta^{n-2} = 0.$$
$$\therefore \ \alpha^n + \beta^n - 2(\alpha^{n-1} + \beta^{n-1}) - (\alpha^{n-2} + \beta^{n-2}) = 0,$$

or
$$s_n - 2s_{n-1} - s_{n-2} = 0 \quad \ldots \quad \ldots \quad \text{(i)}$$

Now
$$s_1 = \alpha + \beta = 2; \quad s_2 = \alpha^2 + \beta^2 = 6.$$

But
$$s_3 - 2s_2 - s_1 = 0,$$
$$\therefore \ s_3 = 12 + 2 = 14.$$

Also, using (i),
$$s_4 = 2s_3 + s_2 = 34;$$
$$s_5 = 2s_4 + s_3 = 82.$$
$$\alpha^3 + \beta^3 = s_3 = 14; \quad \alpha^5 + \beta^5 = s_5 = 82.$$

Ex. 16. *The roots of the equation $x^3 - px - q = 0$ are α, β, γ; prove:*

(i) $\alpha^2 + \beta^2 + \gamma^2 = 2p$;   (ii) $\alpha^3 + \beta^3 + \gamma^3 = 3q$;

(iii) $6(\alpha^5 + \beta^5 + \gamma^5) = 5(\alpha^3 + \beta^3 + \gamma^3)(\alpha^2 + \beta^2 + \gamma^2)$.

We have
$$\alpha + \beta + \gamma = 0; \quad \beta\gamma + \gamma\alpha + \alpha\beta = -p; \quad \alpha\beta\gamma = q.$$
$$\therefore \ \alpha^2 + \beta^2 + \gamma^2 \equiv (\alpha + \beta + \gamma)^2 - 2(\beta\gamma + \gamma\alpha + \alpha\beta) = 2p.$$

Substituting $x = \alpha$, β, γ successively in the given equation and adding,
$$(\alpha^3 + \beta^3 + \gamma^3) - p(\alpha + \beta + \gamma) - 3q = 0,$$
$$\therefore \ \alpha^3 + \beta^3 + \gamma^3 = 3q.$$

Also α, β, γ are roots of the equation
$$x^5 - px^3 - qx^2 = 0.$$
$$\therefore \ \alpha^5 + \beta^5 + \gamma^5 - p(\alpha^3 + \beta^3 + \gamma^3) - q(\alpha^2 + \beta^2 + \gamma^2) = 0,$$

i.e.
$$\alpha^5 + \beta^5 + \gamma^5 = 5pq$$
$$\therefore \ 6(\alpha^5 + \beta^5 + \gamma^5) = 30pq = 5(\alpha^3 + \beta^3 + \gamma^3)(\alpha^2 + \beta^2 + \gamma^2).$$

EXAMPLES 7c

1. If α, β, and γ are the roots of the equation $x^3 - 3x + 1 = 0$, find the values of: (i) $\alpha^2 + \beta^2 + \gamma^2$;   (ii) $\alpha^3 + \beta^3 + \gamma^3$;   (iii) $1/\alpha + 1/\beta + 1/\gamma$.

2. Solve the equation $x^3 - 7x^2 + 36 = 0$ given that one root is double another.

3. If α, β, γ are the roots of $x^3 = px + q$, prove that $\alpha^3 + \beta^3 + \gamma^3 = 3\alpha\beta\gamma$.

4. Solve the equation $4x^3 + 16x^2 - 19x - 76 = 0$ given that two of its roots are equal but opposite in sign.

5. If α, β are the roots of $x^2 - 3x - 1 = 0$, find the values of: (i) $\alpha^3 + \beta^3$; (ii) $\alpha^5 + \beta^5$.

6. Solve the equation $24x^3 - 14x^2 - 63x + 45 = 0$ given that one root is double another.

7. If α, β, γ, δ are the roots of $x^4 - 3x^2 - x + 2 = 0$, find the values of: (i) $\alpha^2 + \beta^2 + \gamma^2 + \delta^2$; (ii) $1/\alpha + 1/\beta + 1/\gamma + 1/\delta$.

8. With the data of the previous example, prove that $\sum \alpha^4 = 3 \sum \alpha^2 + \sum \alpha - 8$ and deduce the value of $\sum \alpha^4$.

9. Find the equation whose roots are the squares of the roots of the equation $x^3 - 4x^2 + x - 1 = 0$.

10. Solve the equation $12x^3 - 35x^2 + 33x - 10 = 0$ given that two roots are in the ratio $2 : 3$.

11. Solve the equation $8x^3 + 36x^2 + 22x - 21 = 0$ given that the roots are in arithmetical progression.

12. If α, β, γ are the roots of the equation $2x^3 - 3x^2 + 2x - 8 = 0$ calculate the values of: (i) $(\alpha + 1)(\beta + 1)(\gamma + 1)$; (ii) $(\beta + \gamma)(\gamma + \alpha)(\alpha + \beta)$.

13. If α, β, γ are the roots of the equation $x^3 + 3ax - b = 0$, prove that $(\alpha - \beta)(\alpha - \gamma) = 3(\alpha^2 + a)$.

14. Solve the equation $4x^4 + 20x^3 - 7x^2 - 32x + 15 = 0$ given that three of the roots are in the ratios $1 : 2 : -3$.

15. Solve the simultaneous equations:

(i) $x + y + z = 1$,   (ii) $x + y + z = 1$,   (iii) $x + y + z = -2$,
    $yz + zx + xy = -4$, $x^2 + y^2 + z^2 = 29$, $x^2 + y^2 + z^2 = 6$,
    $xyz = -4$. $xyz = -24$. $x^3 + y^3 + z^3 = -8$.

16. Solve the equation $2x^4 - x^3 - 7x^2 - 5x - 1 = 0$ given that one root is double another.

17. Find the sum of the fifth powers of the roots of the equation $x^3 - px - q = 0$.

18. Given that one root of the equation $x^3 + 2ax^2 - b = 0$ equals the sum of the other two, prove that $a^3 = b$.

19. If the roots of the equation $x^3 + px^2 + qx + r = 0$ are in geometrical progression, prove that $rp^3 = q^3$.

20. From the point $Q(2, 0)$ on the curve $y = x^3 - 4x^2 + 7x - 6$ a line is drawn to touch the curve at P; find the coordinates of P.

21. Solve the simultaneous equations $a^2 + b^2 + c^2 = 14$, $bc + ca + ab = -5$, $abc = 6$.

22. If α, β, γ are the roots of the equation $x^3 + ax^2 + b = 0$, find the value of $(\alpha^2 - \beta\gamma)(\beta^2 - \gamma\alpha)(\gamma^2 - \alpha\beta)$ in terms of a, b.

23. If α, β, γ are the roots of the equation $x^3 + px + q = 0$, form the equations whose roots are: (i) $\alpha + \beta$, $\beta + \gamma$, $\gamma + \alpha$; (ii) $\alpha^2 + \beta^2$, $\beta^2 + \gamma^2$, $\gamma^2 + \alpha^2$.

24. If one root of the equation $x^3 + ax + b = 0$ is twice the difference of the other two, prove that one root is $13b/3a$.

25. Solve the equation $4x^4 - 4x^3 - 21x^2 + 11x + 10 = 0$ given that its roots are in arithmetical progression.

26. If the points $(t_1, t_1{}^3)$, $(t_2, t_2{}^3)$, $(t_3, t_3{}^3)$ on the curve $y = x^3$ lie on a straight line $y = mx + c$, prove that $t_1 + t_2 + t_3 = 0$. Deduce that the tangent to the curve at the point (t, t^3) meets the curve again at the point $(-2t, -8t^3)$.

27. A point P on the curve $ay^2 = x^3$ is given parametically in the form (at^2, at^3); if the points with parameters t_1, t_2, t_3 are collinear, prove that $1/t_1 + 1/t_2 + 1/t_3 = 0$ and deduce that the tangent at the point P meets the curve again at the point $(\frac{1}{4}at^2, -\frac{1}{8}at^3)$.

Transformation of equations. It is often useful to transform a given equation into another whose roots are related in some simple way to those of the original equation. Some important cases are dealt with below.

(i) *Roots increased or decreased by a constant amount.* Suppose the roots of $P(x) = 0$ are to be increased by h.

Write $\qquad\qquad y = x + h;$ i.e. $x = y - h.$

The transformed equation is

$$P(y - h) = 0.$$

This type of transformation is frequently used to simplify a given equation by removing an assigned term from it.

Ex. 17. *Find the equation whose roots are those of $x^3 + ax^2 + bx + c = 0$ increased by h. Hence by suitable choice of h reduce the equation to the form $x^3 + px + q = 0$.*

Substituting $\qquad\qquad y = x + h;$ i.e. $x = y - h,$
$$(y - h)^3 + a(y - h)^2 + b(y - h) + c = 0,$$
$$y^3 + y^2(a - 3h) + y(3h^2 - 2ah + b) - h^3 + ah^2 - bh + c = 0.$$

Choosing $h = \frac{1}{3}a$, the equation reduces to

$$27y^3 + 9y(3b - a^2) + 2a^3 - 9ab + 27c = 0,$$

which is of the required form.

(ii) *Roots multiplied by a given quantity.* Suppose the roots of $P(x) = 0$ are to be multiplied by k.

Write $\qquad\qquad y = kx;$ i.e. $x = y/k.$

The transformed equation is
$$P(y/k) = 0.$$

Ex. 18. *Find the equation whose roots are ten times the roots of the equation $x^3 - 2x + 1 = 0$.*

Writing $\qquad\qquad y = 10x;$ $\qquad$ i.e. $x = y/10,$
$$(y/10)^3 - 2(y/10) + 1 = 0$$
$$y^3 - 200y + 1000 = 0.$$

(iii) *Reciprocal roots.* The equation whose roots are the reciprocals of the roots of $P(x)=0$ is obtained by writing

$$y=1/x; \quad \text{i.e.} \quad x=1/y.$$

Required equation is $\qquad P(1/y)=0.$

Ex. 19. *If the roots of the equation $2x^4 - 3x^3 + 4x^2 - 7 = 0$ are α, β, γ, δ, prove that $\sum 1/\alpha = 0$ and obtain the value of $\sum 1/\alpha^2$.*

The equation with roots $1/\alpha$, $1/\beta$, $1/\gamma$, $1/\delta$ is

$$2\left(\frac{1}{y}\right)^4 - 3\left(\frac{1}{y}\right)^3 + 4\left(\frac{1}{y}\right)^2 - 7 = 0,$$

i.e. $\qquad 7y^4 - 4y^2 + 3y - 2 = 0.$

$$\therefore \; \sum 1/\alpha = 0.$$

Also $\qquad \sum 1/\alpha^2 = \left(\sum 1/\alpha\right)^2 - 2\sum 1/\alpha\beta,$

$$= 0 - 2(-\tfrac{4}{7})$$

$$= \tfrac{8}{7}.$$

Miscellaneous transformations. Further examples of transformations are given in the following examples.

Ex. 20. *The roots of the equation $x^3 - ax^2 + bx - c = 0$ are α, β, γ. Form the equation whose roots are $\beta + \gamma$, $\gamma + \alpha$, $\alpha + \beta$ and show that*

$$(\beta + \gamma)(\gamma + \alpha)(\alpha + \beta) = ab - c.$$

Since $\alpha + \beta + \gamma = a$, the roots of the required equation are

$$a - \alpha, \; a - \beta, \; a - \gamma.$$

Hence we can write $\qquad y = a - x; \quad \text{i.e.} \quad x = a - y.$

Required equation is

$$(a - y)^3 - a(a - y)^2 + b(a - y) - c = 0,$$

or $\qquad y^3 - 2ay^2 + (a^2 + b)y + c - ab = 0.$

Product of roots $= (\beta + \gamma)(\gamma + \alpha)(\alpha + \beta) = ab - c.$

Ex. 21. *If α, β, γ are the roots of the equation $x^3 - 2x + 3 = 0$, form the equations whose roots are (i) α^2, β^2, γ^2; (ii) $\beta\gamma/\alpha$, $\gamma\alpha/\beta$, $\alpha\beta/\gamma$.*

(i) Write $\qquad y = x^2; \quad \text{i.e.} \quad x = \sqrt{y}.$

Required equation is $\qquad (\sqrt{y})^3 - 2\sqrt{y} + 3 = 0,$

$$\sqrt{y}(y - 2) = -3,$$

Squaring $\qquad y(y - 2)^2 = 9.$

i.e. $\qquad y^3 - 4y^2 + 4y - 9 = 0.$

(ii) As $\alpha\beta\gamma = -3$, the given roots are $-3/\alpha^2$, $-3/\beta^2$, $-3/\gamma^2$.

Write $\qquad y = -3/x^2; \quad \text{i.e.} \quad x = \sqrt{(-3/y)}.$

Required equation is

$$\{\sqrt{(-3/y)}\}^3 - 2\sqrt{(-3/y)} + 3 = 0,$$

$$\sqrt{(-3/y)}\left\{-\frac{3}{y} - 2\right\} = -3.$$

Squaring,

$$-\frac{3}{y}\left\{\frac{9}{y^2} + \frac{12}{y} + 4\right\} = 9,$$

i.e.

$$3y^3 + 4y^2 + 12y + 9 = 0.$$

EXAMPLES 7d

1. Form the equation whose roots are each one less than those of the equation $x^3 - 3x + 1 = 0$.

2. If α, β, γ are the roots of the equation $x^3 - 2x^2 = 1$, form the equations with roots: (i) 2α, 2β, 2γ;   (ii) $-\alpha$, $-\beta$, $-\gamma$;   (iii) $1/\alpha$, $1/\beta$, $1/\gamma$.

3. Form the equation whose roots are the reciprocals of the roots of the equation $x^4 - 2x^3 + x^2 - 3 = 0$; deduce that the sum of the reciprocals of the roots of the original equation is zero.

4. Form the equation whose roots exceed by 2 the roots of the equation $x^3 + 6x - 2 = 0$.

5. Find the equation whose roots are the squares of the roots of $x^4 + x^3 + 2x^2 + x + 1 = 0$.

6. If α, β, γ, δ are the roots of $2x^4 - x^3 - 3x^2 + 5x - 1 = 0$, find the value of $\sum 1/\alpha^2$.

7. If α, β, γ are the roots of $x^3 - 3x + 3 = 0$, find the equation with roots $2\alpha + \beta + \gamma$, $2\beta + \gamma + \alpha$, $2\gamma + \alpha + \beta$ and deduce the value of

$$(2\alpha + \beta + \gamma)(2\beta + \gamma + \alpha)(2\gamma + \alpha + \beta).$$

8. With the data of the previous question, form the equation with roots $\beta\gamma$, $\gamma\alpha$, $\alpha\beta$.

9. Increase the roots of the equation $x^4 + 4x^3 - 7x^2 - 22x + 24 = 0$ by 1, and hence solve the equation.

10. Given that α, β, γ are the roots of the equation $x^3 + 3bx + c = 0$, form the equation whose roots are $(\alpha - 1)^2$, $(\beta - 1)^2$, $(\gamma - 1)^2$.

11. Increase the roots of the equation $x^3 + 6x^2 + 9x + 4 = 0$ by a quantity h and by choice of h reduce the equation to the form $y^3 + py + q = 0$.

12. Apply the transformation $x = ay + b$ to the equation

$$8x^3 + 36x^2 + 40x + 12 = 0$$

and by choice of the values of a, b reduce the equation to the form $y^3 + py + q = 0$.

13. If α, β, γ, δ are the roots of $x^4 + ax^3 + b = 0$, find the equation with roots $(1 - \alpha)/\alpha$, $(1 - \beta)/\beta$, $(1 - \gamma)/\gamma$, $(1 - \delta)/\delta$.

14. If α, β, γ are the roots of $x^3 + x^2 - 3x - 4 = 0$, form the equation with roots $\alpha(\beta + \gamma)$, $\beta(\gamma + \alpha)$, $\gamma(\alpha + \beta)$.

15. With the data of the previous question, form the equation with roots $\alpha/(\beta+\gamma)$, $\beta/(\gamma+\alpha)$, $\gamma/(\alpha+\beta)$ and deduce the value of $\sum \alpha^2/(\beta+\gamma)^2$.

16. If α, β, γ, δ are the roots of $x^4 + ax^2 + bx + c = 0$, find the value of $(\alpha+\beta+\gamma)(\alpha+\beta+\delta)(\alpha+\gamma+\delta)(\beta+\gamma+\delta)$.

17. If α, β, γ are the roots of the equation $x^3 + ax^2 + b = 0$, form the equation with roots $1 - \beta\gamma$, $1 - \gamma\alpha$, $1 - \alpha\beta$.

18. If α, β, γ are the roots of the equation $x^3 + px^2 + q = 0$, prove that $(\beta+\gamma-2\alpha)(\gamma+\alpha-2\beta)(\alpha+\beta-2\gamma) = 2p^3 + 27q$.

19. If α, β, γ are the roots of $x^3 - 2x^2 + 4x - 5 = 0$, express $\gamma\alpha + \alpha\beta$ as a function of α alone, and hence form the equation with roots, $\gamma\alpha + \alpha\beta$, $\alpha\beta + \beta\gamma$, $\beta\gamma + \gamma\alpha$.

20. Prove that the roots of the equation $x^3 + (9b - 3a^2)x - 2a^3 + 9ab - 27c = 0$ are $\beta+\gamma-2\alpha$, $\gamma+\alpha-2\beta$, $\alpha+\beta-2\gamma$, where α, β, γ are the roots of $x^3 + ax^2 + bx + c = 0$.

MISCELLANEOUS EXAMPLES

1. If the roots of the equation $x^2 + 4p^3x + q^3 = 0$ are the cubes of the roots of the equation $x^2 + px + q = 0$, prove that $p^2 + q = 0$.

2. Solve the equation $2x^3 - 7x^2 - 52x - 55 = 0$, given that $3 - 2\sqrt{5}$ is one root.

3. Prove that $2x^3 - 7x^2 - 12x + 45 = 0$ has a repeated root and solve the equation.

4. If $f(x) \equiv x^4 + 3x^3 - 15x^2 - 19x + 13$ obtain the signs of $f(-\infty)$, $f(-2)$, $f(0)$, $f(1)$, $f(+\infty)$ and deduce that the equation $f(x) = 0$ has 4 real roots.

5. If $f(x)$ is a polynomial and $f(a) = f'(a) = 0$, prove that $(x - a)^2$ is a factor of $f(x)$. Solve the equation $x^4 - 4a^3x + 3a^4 = 0$.

6. If the equations $ax^2 + 3x - 1 = 0$, $2x^2 - x - 1 = 0$ have a common root, find the values of a.

7. Solve the equation $3x^3 - 7x^2 + 17x - 5 = 0$ given that one root is $1 - 2i$.

8. Prove that the equation $4x^3 - 9x^2 - 12x - 2 = 0$ has 3 real roots.

9. If p, q are the roots of the equation $x^2 + ax + b = 0$ and r, s the roots of the equation $x^2 + cx + d = 0$, find the equation with roots $pr + qs$, $ps + qr$.

10. If α, β, γ are the roots of the equation $2x^3 - x^2 + x - 2 = 0$, find the values of: (i) $\alpha^2 + \beta^2 + \gamma^2$; (ii) $\alpha^3 + \beta^3 + \gamma^3$; (iii) $\alpha^4 + \beta^4 + \gamma^4$.

11. Find the condition that the equation $x^3 + px^2 + q = 0$ has two equal roots.

12. Solve the equation $12x^3 + 16x^2 - 27x - 36 = 0$ given that the sum of two roots is zero.

13. Given that the sum of the reciprocals of two of the roots of the equation $6x^3 - 11x^2 - 22x + 12 = 0$ is equal to 5/2, solve the equation.

14. By considering maximum and minimum values of the function $f(x) \equiv 2x^4 + 8x + 7$, show that the equation $f(x) = 0$ has no real roots.

15. If α, β, γ are the roots of the equation $x^3 + px + q = 0$, form the equation with roots $\beta + \gamma - \alpha$, $\gamma + \alpha - \beta$, $\alpha + \beta - \gamma$.

16. Find the condition that the equations $x^3 + b_1 x + c_1 = 0$, $x^2 + b_2 x + c_2 = 0$ may have a common root.

17. Solve the equations $x + y + z = 0$; $\quad x^2 + y^2 + z^2 = 42$; $\quad xyz = 20$.

18. Prove that the equation $x^3 + 3x - 1 = 0$ has only one real root, and find the two integers between which this root lies.

19. Solve the equation $x^4 + 4x^3 + 5x^2 + 4x + 4 = 0$ given that two of the roots are equal.

20. For what values of λ have the equations $4x^2 + \lambda x - 3 = 0$, $3x^2 + 2x - \lambda = 0$ a common root?

21. If α, β, γ are the roots of the equation $x^3 - 3x^2 + 2x - 5 = 0$, find the value of $(\alpha + \beta)(\beta + \gamma)(\gamma + \alpha)$.

22. Solve the equation $24x^3 - 14x^2 - 63x + 45 = 0$ given that one root is double another.

23. If α, β, γ are the roots of the equation $x^3 = 3ax^2 + b$, find the values of $\sum \alpha^3$ and $\sum \alpha^5$.

24. Solve the equations:

(i) $x + y + z = 2$, $\quad x^2 + y^2 + z^2 = 14$, $\quad xyz = -6$.
(ii) $x + y + z = 18$, $\quad x^2 + y^2 + z^2 = 110$, $\quad x(y + z) = 65$.

25. Find the condition that the equations $ax^3 + bx + c = 0$, $cx^3 + bx^2 + a = 0$ may have a common root.

26. If the equation $4x^3 - ax^2 + bx + 175 = 0$ has a repeated root $x = 5$, find the values of a and b.

27. Solve the equation $x^4 + 4x^3 + 2x^2 - 8x - 8 = 0$ given that it has two equal roots.

28. If $P(x) \equiv 3x^4 - 8x^3 - 6x^2 + 24x + a$, determine the roots of the equation $P'(x) = 0$. Hence determine the range of values of a for which the equation $P(x) = 0$ has four real unequal roots.

29. Solve the equation $x^5 + x^2 - 4x + 2 = 0$ given that one root is $i\sqrt{2}$.

30. If the roots of $x^3 + ax^2 + bx + c = 0$ are in arithmetical progression, prove that $2a^3 - 9ab + 27c = 0$.

31. Solve the equations
$$x + y + z = -xyz, \quad yz + zx + xy = -1,$$
$$(1 + x^2)(1 + y^2)(1 + z^2) = 20.$$

32. Given that two of the roots of the equation
$$45x^4 - 54x^3 - 98x^2 + 150x - 75 = 0$$
are equal in numerical value but opposite in sign, complete the solution of the equation.

33. Form the cubic equation whose roots x, y, z satisfy the conditions $x+y+z=0$, $x^2+y^2+z^2=b$, $x^3+y^3+z^3=c$. Hence find a relation connecting b and c if two of x, y, z are equal.

34. The equation $x^3+px+q=0$ has roots α, β, γ; find the equation whose roots are $(\beta-\gamma)^2$, $(\gamma-\alpha)^2$, $(\alpha-\beta)^2$. Hence, or otherwise, deduce the condition for the equation $a_0x^3+3a_1x+a_2=0$ to have a pair of equal roots, in the form $a_0a_2^2+4a_1^3=0$.

35. Solve the equation $81x^4+54x^3-189x^2-66x+40=0$ given that the roots are in arithmetical progression.

36. Find the conditions for the roots α, β, γ of the equation

$$x^3-ax^2+bx-c=0$$

to be in: (i) A.P.; (ii) G.P.

If the roots are not in A.P. and if $\alpha+\lambda$, $\beta+\lambda$, $\gamma+\lambda$ are in G.P., prove that λ is given by a cubic equation.

37. If $ax^3+3bx^2+3cx+d=0$ has two equal roots, prove that they are equal to $\frac{1}{2}(bc-ad)/(ac-b^2)$.

38. Find the values of a and b such that the equations

$$x^3+ax^2+11x+6=0, \quad x^3+bx^2+14x+8=0$$

have two roots in common.

39. Prove that the equation $3x^4+4px^3+q=0$ has no real roots if $q>p^4$.

40. Factorise
$$\Delta \equiv \begin{vmatrix} 1 & 1 & 1 \\ \alpha & \beta & \gamma \\ \alpha^2 & \beta^2 & \gamma^2 \end{vmatrix}.$$

Determine the value of Δ^2 in terms of a and b if α, β, γ are the roots of the equation $x^3+ax+b=0$.

CHAPTER VIII

THE CONICS. MISCELLANEOUS PROBLEMS

Chord of contact of tangents from a point to a conic

The parabola $y^2 = 4ax.$

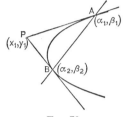

Let the points of contact of tangents from $P(x_1, y_1)$ be $A(\alpha_1, \beta_1)$, $B(\alpha_2, \beta_2)$.

Equation of tangent at A is

$$y\beta_1 = 2a(x + \alpha_1);$$

as this passes through P,

$$y_1\beta_1 = 2a(x_1 + \alpha_1) \quad . \quad . \quad . \quad . \quad . \quad \text{(i)}$$

Similarly, as the tangent at B passes through P,

$$y_1\beta_2 = 2a(x_1 + \alpha_2) \quad . \quad . \quad . \quad . \quad . \quad \text{(ii)}$$

FIG. 70.

The equations (i) and (ii) show that the line

$$y_1 y = 2a(x_1 + x)$$

passes through A and B.

Hence the equation of the chord of contact AB is

$$\mathbf{yy_1 = 2a(x + x_1).}$$

The above method applies equally well in the cases of the ellipse and hyperbola with the following results:

The ellipse $\qquad \dfrac{x^2}{a^2} + \dfrac{y^2}{b^2} = 1.$

Chord of contact of tangents from (x_1, y_1) is

$$\mathbf{\dfrac{xx_1}{a^2} + \dfrac{yy_1}{b^2} = 1.}$$

The hyperbola $\qquad \dfrac{x^2}{a^2} - \dfrac{y^2}{b^2} = 1.$

Chord of contact of tangents from (x_1, y_1) is

$$\mathbf{\dfrac{xx_1}{a^2} - \dfrac{yy_1}{b^2} = 1.}$$

N.B. The chord of contact of tangents from a point P to a conic is *the polar* of P with respect to the conic.

P is *the pole* of the chord of contact.

161

Ex. 1. *Find the equation of the chord of contact of tangents from* $(-3, 2)$ *to the hyperbola* $4x^2 - 9y^2 = 36$.

Chord of contact is $4(-3)x - 9(2)y = 36,$

i.e. $2x + 3y + 6 = 0.$

Ex. 2. *Find the coordinates of the point of intersection of tangents to the parabola* $y^2 = 4ax$ *drawn at the ends of the chord* $lx + my = 1$.

Let the point of intersection of the tangents be (x_1, y_1).
Then the chord of contact has the equation

$$yy_1 = 2a(x + x_1). \qquad \cdot \quad \cdot \quad \cdot \quad \cdot \quad \cdot \quad \text{(i)}$$

But the given equation of the chord of contact is

$$lx + my = 1. \qquad \cdot \quad \cdot \quad \cdot \quad \cdot \quad \cdot \quad \cdot \quad \text{(ii)}$$

Comparing (i) and (ii), $\dfrac{2a}{l} = \dfrac{-y_1}{m} = \dfrac{2ax_1}{-1}.$

$$\therefore \ x_1 = -1/l; \quad y_1 = -2am/l.$$

Parallel chords of a conic

The parabola $y^2 = 4ax.$

Let the equation of the system of parallel chords be

$$y = mx + \lambda,$$

where m is constant and λ a parameter.

Then the ordinates y_1, y_2 of the ends of a chord of the system are the roots of the equation

$$y^2 = 4a\left(\frac{y - \lambda}{m}\right)$$

or, $my^2 - 4ay + 4a\lambda = 0.$

Hence the ordinate of the mid-point of the chord

$$= \tfrac{1}{2}(y_1 + y_2) = 2a/m = \text{constant}.$$

$\therefore$ The locus of the mid-points of the system of parallel chords is the diameter

$$\mathbf{y = 2a/m.}$$

The ellipse $\dfrac{x^2}{a^2} + \dfrac{y^2}{b^2} = 1.$

With the equation of the system of parallel chords as before, it follows that the x-coordinates, x_1, x_2, of the ends of a chord are the roots of the equation

$$\frac{x^2}{a^2} + \frac{(mx + \lambda)^2}{b^2} = 1.$$

Hence the coordinates of the mid-point of the chord are

$$X = \tfrac{1}{2}(x_1 + x_2) = -ma^2\lambda/(a^2m^2 + b^2);$$
$$Y = mX + \lambda \quad = b^2\lambda/(a^2m^2 + b^2).$$
$$\therefore \frac{X}{Y} = -\frac{ma^2}{b^2},$$

i.e. the locus of the mid-points of the system of parallel chords is the diameter

$$y = -\frac{b^2}{a^2m}x.$$

The hyperbola $\qquad\qquad \dfrac{x^2}{a^2} - \dfrac{y^2}{b^2} = 1.$

Following the method used in the case of the ellipse, the locus of the mid-points of a system of parallel chords is found to be the diameter

$$y = \frac{b^2}{a^2m}x.$$

Equation of a chord with a given mid-point

The parabola $\qquad\qquad y^2 = 4ax.$

Let the mid-point of the chord be (x', y').

Then if m is the gradient of the chord,

$$y' = \frac{2a}{m}; \quad \text{i.e. } m = \frac{2a}{y'}.$$

$\therefore$ Equation of the chord is

$$y - y' = \frac{2a}{y'}(x - x')$$

i.e. $\qquad\qquad y'(y - y') = 2a(x - x').$

The ellipse $\qquad\qquad \dfrac{x^2}{a^2} + \dfrac{y^2}{b^2} = 1.$

Let the mid-point of the chord be (x', y').

Then if m is the gradient of the chord,

$$y' = -\frac{b^2}{a^2m}x'; \quad \text{i.e. } m = -\frac{b^2x'}{a^2y'}.$$

$\therefore$ Equation of the chord is

$$y - y' = -\frac{b^2x'}{a^2y'}(x - x')$$

.e. $\qquad\qquad \dfrac{x'(x - x')}{a^2} + \dfrac{y'(y - y')}{b^2} = 0.$

The hyperbola $\dfrac{x^2}{a^2} - \dfrac{y^2}{b^2} = 1.$

As before, the equation of the chord with mid-point (x', y') is

$$\frac{\mathbf{x'(x - x')}}{\mathbf{a^2}} - \frac{\mathbf{y'(y - y')}}{\mathbf{b^2}} = \mathbf{0}.$$

Ex. 3. *Find the coordinates of the point of intersection of tangents to the ellipse $b^2x^2 + a^2y^2 = a^2b^2$ at the ends of the chord with mid-point (α, β).*

Equation of the chord is

$$b^2\alpha(x - \alpha) + a^2\beta(y - \beta) = 0. \qquad \ldots \ldots \quad \text{(i)}$$

Let the point of intersection of the tangents at the ends of the chord be (h, k).

Then the equation of the chord of contact is

$$b^2hx + a^2ky = a^2b^2. \qquad \ldots \ldots \ldots \quad \text{(ii)}$$

As (i) and (ii) represent the same line,

$$\frac{b^2h}{b^2\alpha} = \frac{a^2k}{a^2\beta} = \frac{a^2b^2}{b^2\alpha^2 + a^2\beta^2}.$$

Hence, $h = \dfrac{a^2b^2\alpha}{b^2\alpha^2 + a^2\beta^2}; \quad k = \dfrac{a^2b^2\beta}{b^2\alpha^2 + a^2\beta^2}.$

Ex. 4. *Find the locus of the mid-points of chords of the hyperbola $x^2 - 4y^2 = 1$ which pass through the point $(1, 2)$.*

Let the mid-point of a chord be (x', y').

Then the equation of the chord is

$$x'(x - x') - 4y'(y - y') = 0.$$

As the chord passes through the point $(1, 2)$,

$$x'(1 - x') - 4y'(2 - y') = 0.$$

Hence the locus of the mid-point is the curve

$$x^2 - 4y^2 - x + 8y = 0.$$

EXAMPLES 8a

In each of the examples 1–6, obtain the equation of the chord of contact of tangents drawn from the point stated to the given conic:

1. $(-1, 0)$; $y^2 = 2x$.   2. $(3, 4)$; $x^2 + 4y^2 = 4$.
3. $(-1, 1)$; $x^2 - 2y^2 = 2$.   4. $(-2, 4)$; $y^2 = 8x$.
5. $(2, 5)$; $2x^2 + 4y^2 = 3$.   6. $(-3, 1)$; $3x^2 - y^2 = 1$.

7. Show that the equation of the chord of contact of tangents to the ellipse $b^2x^2 + a^2y^2 = a^2b^2$ from the point (a, b) is $bx + ay = ab$.

8. Find the equation of the chord of contact of tangents drawn from a point $(-a, \beta)$ on the directrix to the parabola $y^2 = 4ax$. Prove that the chord of contact passes through the focus.

In each of the examples 9–14, find the coordinates of the point of intersection of tangents drawn to the given conic at the ends of the chord stated:

9. $y^2 = 4x$; $y - x + 1 = 0$.

10. $\dfrac{x^2}{9} + \dfrac{y^2}{4} - 1$; $x + 2y - 2$.

11. $2x^2 - 3y^2 = 6$; $y - 2x = 1$.

12. $x^2 - y^2 = 4$; $3x - 2y = 2$.

13. $x^2 + 2y^2 = 1$; $3x + 2y = 1$.

14. $x^2 + 8y = 0$; $y + x + 2 = 0$.

15. Find the coordinates of the point of intersection of tangents drawn to the hyperbola $x^2 - 2y^2 = 4$ at the ends of the chord whose mid-point is $(-3, 1)$.

16. Find the locus of the mid-points of chords of the ellipse $x^2 + 4y^2 = 1$ which pass through the point $(1, 1)$.

17. Prove that the locus of the mid-points of the system of parallel chords $y = mx + \lambda$ of the rectangular hyperbola $xy = c^2$ is the diameter $y + mx = 0$.

18. Prove that the equation of the chord of the rectangular hyperbola $xy = c^2$ with mid-point (x', y') is $x'(y - y') + y'(x - x') = 0$.

19. Tangents are drawn from a point P to an ellipse, centre C. If the chord of contact is AB, show that CP bisects AB.

20. If the chord of contact of a variable point P with respect to a parabola passes through a fixed point, prove that the locus of P is a straight line.

21. Prove that the locus of the mid-points of chords of the rectangular hyperbola $xy = c^2$ which pass through a fixed point is a rectangular hyperbola.

22. Prove that the chord of contact of tangents drawn from any point on the line $y - 2x - 1 = 0$ to the hyperbola $x^2 - 2y^2 = 4$ pass through a fixed point and find the coordinates of this point.

Normals to a conic

The parabola $\qquad\qquad y^2 = 4ax.$

The equation of the normal at the point $(at^2, 2at)$ is
$$y + tx = 2at + at^3.$$

If this normal passes through a given point (x_1, y_1), on substitution of these coordinates we get
$$at^3 + (2a - x_1)t - y_1 = 0. \qquad \ldots \quad \ldots \quad \text{(i)}$$

This is a cubic equation in t whose roots t_1, t_2, t_3 are the parameters of the feet of the normals from (x_1, y_1) to the parabola.

So, in general, three normals can be drawn from a given point to a parabola.

Also as $\qquad\qquad t_1 + t_2 + t_3 = 0,$

the sum of the parameters of the feet of the three normals is zero and conversely, if the sum of the parameters of three points on a parabola is zero, the normals at these points are concurrent.

Ex. 5. *Prove that the normals at the ends of a system of parallel chords of a parabola intersect on a fixed normal to the parabola.*

As the locus of the mid-points of a system of parallel chords of a parabola is a line parallel to the axis, the sum of the ordinates of the ends of each chord is constant.

So if the parameters of the ends of a chord are t_1, t_2,

$$2at_1 + 2at_2 = \text{constant}; \quad \text{i.e. } t_1 + t_2 = \text{constant}.$$

If the normals at the points t_1, t_2 meet at P and the parameter of the foot of the third normal through P is t_3,

$$t_1 + t_2 + t_3 = 0.$$

Hence
$$t_3 = \text{constant},$$

and therefore P lies on a fixed normal.

The ellipse
$$\frac{x^2}{a^2} + \frac{y^2}{b^2} = 1.$$

The equation of the normal at the point $(a \cos \phi, b \sin \phi)$ is

$$\frac{ax}{\cos \phi} - \frac{by}{\sin \phi} = a^2 - b^2.$$

This normal passes through a given point (x_1, y_1) if

$$\frac{ax_1}{\cos \phi} - \frac{by_1}{\sin \phi} = a^2 - b^2.$$

Writing $\tan \frac{1}{2}\phi = t$; then $\sin \phi = \dfrac{2t}{1+t^2}$, $\cos \phi = \dfrac{1-t^2}{1+t^2}$,

and
$$\frac{ax_1(1+t^2)}{1-t^2} - \frac{by_1(1+t^2)}{2t} = a^2 - b^2.$$

I.e. $by_1 t^4 + 2(ax_1 + a^2 - b^2)t^3 + 2(ax_1 - a^2 + b^2)t - by_1 = 0.$.   (ii)

This is a quartic equation whose roots t_1, t_2, t_3, t_4 are the parameters of the feet of the normals which can be drawn from the point (x_1, y_1) to the ellipse.

Hence, in general, four normals can be drawn from a given point to an ellipse.

From equation (ii) $t_1 t_2 t_3 t_4 = -1$,

and $\sum t_1 t_2 = 0.$

But $\tan \frac{1}{2}(\phi_1 + \phi_2 + \phi_3 + \phi_4) = \dfrac{\sum t_1 - \sum t_1 t_2 t_3}{1 - \sum t_1 t_2 + t_1 t_2 t_3 t_4}$

and $1 - \sum t_1 t_2 + t_1 t_2 t_3 t_4 = 0.$

$\therefore \quad \frac{1}{2}(\phi_1 + \phi_2 + \phi_3 + \phi_4) = $ an odd multiple of $\frac{1}{2}\pi$.

I.e. *if the normals at four points $(a \cos \phi_r, b \sin \phi_r)$, $r = 1, 2, 3, 4$, on an ellipse are concurrent, then $\phi_1 + \phi_2 + \phi_3 + \phi_4 = $ an odd multiple of π.*

Ex. 6. *Show that the feet of the four normals drawn from a given point to an ellipse lie on a rectangular hyperbola.*

The normal at the point $P(a \cos \phi, b \sin \phi)$ passes through the given point (x_1, y_1) if

$$\frac{ax_1}{\cos \phi} - \frac{by_1}{\sin \phi} = a^2 - b^2 \qquad \ldots \ldots \quad \text{(i)}$$

If the coordinates of P are written as (x, y),

$$\cos \phi = \frac{x}{a}; \quad \sin \phi = \frac{y}{b}.$$

Substituting in (i),
$$\frac{a^2 x_1}{x} - \frac{b^2 y_1}{y} = a^2 - b^2,$$

i.e.
$$(a^2 - b^2)xy + b^2 y_1 x - a^2 x_1 y = 0.$$

This, the equation of the locus of P, represents a rectangular hyperbola as it can be expressed in the form $k(x - \alpha)(y - \beta) = \text{constant}$.

The hyperbola
$$\frac{x^2}{a^2} - \frac{y^2}{b^2} = 1.$$

The equation of the normal at the point $(a \sec \phi, b \tan \phi)$ is

$$\frac{ax}{\sec \phi} + \frac{by}{\tan \phi} = a^2 + b^2.$$

This normal passes through a given point (x_1, y_1) if

$$\frac{ax_1}{\sec \phi} + \frac{by_1}{\tan \phi} = a^2 + b^2.$$

Writing $\tan \tfrac{1}{2}\phi = t$; then

$$\sec \phi = \frac{1 + t^2}{1 - t^2}, \quad \tan \phi = \frac{2t}{1 - t^2},$$

and
$$\frac{ax_1(1 - t^2)}{1 + t^2} + \frac{by_1(1 - t^2)}{2t} = a^2 + b^2.$$

I.e.
$$by_1 t^4 + 2(ax_1 + a^2 + b^2)t^3 + 2(a^2 + b^2 - ax_1)t - by_1 = 0.$$

Hence, as this is a quartic equation in t, in general four normals can be drawn from a given point to a hyperbola.

In a similar manner to the ellipse, it follows that *if the normals at the four points $(a \sec \phi_r, b \tan \phi_r)$, $r = 1, 2, 3, 4$, on a hyperbola are concurrent,*

then
$$\phi_1 + \phi_2 + \phi_3 + \phi_4 = an \ odd \ multiple \ of \ \pi.$$

M

The rectangular hyperbola $xy = c^2$.

The equation of the normal at the point $(ct, c/t)$ is

$$t^3x - ty = c(t^4 - 1).$$

This normal passes through a given point (x_1, y_1) if

$$t^3x_1 - ty_1 = c(t^4 - 1),$$

i.e.

$$ct^4 - x_1t^3 + y_1t - c = 0.$$

The roots t_1, t_2, t_3, t_4 of this equation are the parameters of the feet of the perpendiculars from the point (x_1, y_1) to the rectangular hyperbola.

From the equation,

$$\sum t_1t_2 = 0; \quad t_1t_2t_3t_4 = -1.$$

Ex. 7. *From any point P on the normal at a given point A of a rectangular hyperbola the other three normals to the curve are drawn. Show that the locus of the centroid of the triangle formed by their feet is the diameter parallel to the normal at A.*

Let the curve be $xy = c^2$; A the point $(cT, c/T)$; P the point (x_1, y_1). Then the feet of the four normals from P are the roots of

$$ct^4 - x_1t^3 + y_1t - c = 0. \qquad \ldots \ldots \ldots \text{ (i)}$$

One root is T; let the other roots be t_1, t_2, t_3.
The centroid of the triangle $t_1t_2t_3$ has coordinates

$$\bar{x} = \tfrac{1}{3}c(t_1 + t_2 + t_3); \quad \bar{y} = \tfrac{1}{3}c(1/t_1 + 1/t_2 + 1/t_3) = \tfrac{1}{3}c\,\frac{t_2t_3 + t_3t_1 + t_1t_2}{t_1t_2t_3}.$$

But from (i),
$$t_1t_2t_3T = -1; \quad \text{i.e. } t_1t_2t_3 = -1/T;$$

and $t_2t_3 + t_3t_1 + t_1t_2 + T(t_1 + t_2 + t_3) = 0$; i.e. $t_2t_3 + t_3t_1 + t_1t_2 = -T(t_1 + t_2 + t_3)$.

$$\therefore \ \bar{y} = \tfrac{1}{3}cT^2(t_1 + t_2 + t_3) = T^2\bar{x}.$$

I.e. the locus of the centroid is the diameter $y = T^2x$, which is parallel to the normal at A.

EXAMPLES 8b

1. Find the condition that the normal at the point $(t, 1/t)$ of the rectangular hyperbola $xy = 1$ passes through the origin.

2. The normal at the point $(2 \cos \phi, \sin \phi)$ of the ellipse $x^2 + 4y^2 = 4$ passes through the point $(0, -1)$. Prove that $t^4 - 6t^3 + 6t - 1 = 0$, where $t = \tan \tfrac{1}{2}\phi$ and deduce the coordinates of the points on the ellipse at which the normals pass through the point $(0, -1)$.

3. Write down the equation of the normal to the parabola $y^2 = 4x$ at the point $(t^2, 2t)$ and deduce that only one real normal passes through the point $(2, 1)$. Also find the length of the perpendicular from this point to the curve.

4. The normal at the point $(\sec \phi, \tan \phi)$ on the hyperbola $x^2 - y^2 = 1$ passes through the point $(-3, 2)$, prove that $t^4 - t^3 + 5t - 1 = 0$, where $t = \tan \tfrac{1}{2}\phi$. Deduce that, if ϕ_1, ϕ_2, ϕ_3, ϕ_4 are the feet of the four normals through $(-3, 2)$, then

$$\tan \tfrac{1}{2}\phi_1 + \tan \tfrac{1}{2}\phi_2 + \tan \tfrac{1}{2}\phi_3 + \tan \tfrac{1}{2}\phi_4 = 1,$$
$$\tan \tfrac{1}{2}\phi_1 \tan \tfrac{1}{2}\phi_2 \tan \tfrac{1}{2}\phi_3 \tan \tfrac{1}{2}\phi_4 = -1.$$

5. Find the equation of the only real normal of the parabola $y^2 = 8x$ which passes through the point $(1, -5)$.

6. Four normals are drawn to the rectangular hyperbola $xy = 4$ from a point on the line $x = 2$; if the feet of the normals have parameters t_1, t_2, t_3, t_4 establish the results: (i) $\sum t_1 = 1$; (ii) $\sum t_1 t_2 = 0$; (iii) $t_1 t_2 t_3 t_4 = -1$.

7. Find the equations of the three normals which can be drawn from the point $(9, 6)$ to the parabola $y^2 = 4x$.

8. Find the equation of the normal to the hyperbola $b^2 x^2 - a^2 y^2 = a^2 b^2$ at the point $[\frac{1}{2}a(t + 1/t), \frac{1}{2}b(t - 1/t)]$ and deduce that in general four normals pass through a given point.

9. If the normal to the parabola $y^2 = 4ax$ at the point $P(ap^2, 2ap)$ cuts the curve again at the point Q and the lines joining P, Q to the vertex are perpendicular, prove that $p^2 = 2$.

10. Prove that the sum of the parameters of the feet of the four perpendiculars from a point on the y-axis to the rectangular hyperbola $x = ct$, $y = c/t$ is zero.

11. Four normals are drawn to the ellipse $x^2/a^2 + y^2/b^2 = 1$ from a point on the line $ax + a^2 - b^2 = 0$; if the eccentric angles of the feet of the normals are ϕ_1, ϕ_2, ϕ_3, ϕ_4, prove that $\sum \tan \frac{1}{2}\phi_1 = 0$.

12. Show that two of the three normals from the point $(5a, 2a)$ to the parabola $y^2 = 4ax$ coincide.

13. Prove that the normal to the rectangular hyperbola $xy = c^2$ at the point $P(ct, c/t)$ meets the curve again at a point Q with coordinates $(-c/t^3, ct^3)$. If P is not on the axis of the curve, deduce that it is nearer the origin than Q.

14. If the feet of the normals to the parabola $y^2 = 4ax$ from the point $(3a, 0)$ on its axis are A, B and the vertex O, find the equation of the chord AB.

15. Find the coordinates of the feet of the normals which can be drawn from the point $(9a, 6a)$ to the parabola $y^2 = 4ax$.

16. Taking the coordinates of a point on the hyperbola $x^2/a^2 - y^2/b^2 = 1$ as $[\frac{1}{2}a(t + 1/t), \frac{1}{2}b(t - 1/t)]$, prove that the parameters t_1, t_2, t_3, t_4 of the feet of the normals from a point on the line $ax + by = 0$ to the hyperbola are connected by the relationships $\sum t_1 = 0$; $\sum t_1 t_2 = 0$, $t_1 t_2 t_3 t_4 = -1$.

17. If P_1, P_2, P_3, P_4 are the feet of the four normals from a point P to the rectangular hyperbola $xy = c^2$ and O is the origin, prove that $OP^2 = \sum OP_1^2$.

18. P, Q are the points parameters t_1, t_2 on the parabola $y^2 = 4ax$. If the normals at P, Q meet at a point on the parabola, show that $t_1 t_2 = 2$.

19. Prove that the equation of the normal to the hyperbola $x^2/a^2 - y^2/b^2 = 1$ at (x', y') is $a^2 x/x' + b^2 y/y' = a^2 + b^2$. Deduce that the feet of the four normals which can be drawn from a given point lie on a rectangular hyperbola.

20. Normals to the parabola $y^2 = 4ax$ from the point $(3a, a)$ meet the curve at points with abscissae x_1, x_2, x_3; show that $x_1 + x_2 + x_3 = 2a$.

21. Show that the feet of the four normals to the ellipse $x^2/a^2 + y^2/b^2 = 1$ from the point P lie on a rectangular hyperbola which passes through P and the centre of the ellipse and has asymptotes parallel to the axes of the ellipse.

22. Prove that three real normals cannot be drawn from a point $(h, 0)$ on the axis of the parabola $y^2 = 4ax$ to the curve unless $h > 2a$. Find the area of the triangle whose vertices are the feet of the three normals from the point $(3a, 0)$.

Concyclic points on a conic. The following worked examples illustrate the methods of procedure in dealing with problems involving concyclic points on a conic.

Ex. 8. *A circle cuts a parabola at points A, B, C, D; the tangents to the parabola at A, B meet at T and those at C, D meet at V. Show that TV is bisected by the axis of the parabola.*

Take the equation of the parabola as $y^2 = 4ax$ and let the equation of the circle be

$$x^2 + y^2 + 2gx + 2fy + c = 0.$$

Any point $(at^2, 2at)$ on the parabola lies on the circle if

$$a^2t^4 + 4a^2t^2 + 2gat^2 + 4fat + c = 0,$$

i.e. $\qquad\qquad a^2t^4 + 2a(2a + g)t^2 + 4fat + c = 0. \qquad \ldots \quad \text{(i)}$

The roots t_1, t_2, t_3, t_4 of this equation are the parameters of A, B, C, D.

But the ordinates of the points of intersection T, V of the tangents to the parabola at A, B and at C, D are respectively $a(t_1 + t_2)$ and $a(t_3 + t_4)$.

From (i), $\qquad t_1 + t_2 + t_3 + t_4 = 0$; i.e. $t_1 + t_2 = -(t_3 + t_4)$.

$\therefore$ The ordinates of T and V are equal in numerical value and opposite in sign, and it follows that the axis, $y = 0$, bisects TV.

Ex. 9. *The ellipse $x^2/a^2 + y^2/b^2 = 1$ is cut in four points A, B, C, D by the concentric circle $x^2 + y^2 = r^2$, $b < r < a$. Prove that A, B, C, D are the ends of two diameters of the ellipse equally inclined to the axes.*

The equation $\qquad\qquad \dfrac{x^2}{a^2} + \dfrac{y^2}{b^2} = \dfrac{x^2 + y^2}{r^2}$

derived from the equations of the ellipse and the circle, is satisfied by the coordinates of points common to the two curves.

Also the equation, being homogeneous in x, y, represents a line pair through the origin.

Hence A, B, C, D lie on a line pair through the origin—i.e. on a pair of diameters of the ellipse or the circle.

Also as the equation can be written $y^2\left(\dfrac{1}{b^2} - \dfrac{1}{r^2}\right) = x^2\left(\dfrac{1}{r^2} - \dfrac{1}{a^2}\right)$, it is of the form $By = \pm Ax$, and in consequence represents a line pair equally inclined to the axes.

Ex. 10. *P, Q, R, S are concyclic points on a rectangular hyperbola. If PQ is a diameter of the curve, prove that the chords PR, PS are perpendicular.*

Take the rectangular hyperbola as $xy = c^2$ and the parameter of the points P, Q, R, S as $t_1, -t_1, t_2, t_3$.

Suppose the circle $PQRS$ has the equation

$$x^2 + y^2 + 2gx + 2fy + k = 0. \qquad \ldots \quad \ldots \quad \text{(i)}$$

The parameters of P, Q, R, S are the roots of the equation obtained by substituting $x = ct$, $y = c/t$ in equation (i).

i.e. the roots of $\qquad c^2t^2 + \dfrac{c^2}{t^2} + 2gct + 2f\dfrac{c}{t} + k = 0$,

or $\qquad\qquad c^2t^4 + 2gct^3 + kt^2 + 2fct + c^2 = 0$.

$\therefore$ Product of roots $= -t_1{}^2t_2t_3 = 1$. . . . . (ii)

Now the gradients of chords PR, PS are $-1/t_1t_2$, $-1/t_1t_3$ respectively, hence by (ii), the chords are perpendicular.

EXAMPLES 8c

1. Prove that the point (t^2, t) lies on the circle $x^2 + y^2 - 10x + 1 = 0$ if $t^4 - 9t^2 + 1 = 0$. Deduce that the circle meets the parabola $y^2 = x$ in four real points which are such that the pair of chords defined by them are either perpendicular to the axis of the parabola or equally inclined to it.

2. Find the equation whose roots are the parameters t_1, t_2, t_3, t_4 of the common points of the rectangular hyperbola $x = t$, $y = 1/t$ and the circle $x^2 + y^2 - 2x + 2y + 1 = 0$. Deduce the values of: (i) $\sum t_1$; (ii) $\sum t_1t_2$; (iii) $\sum t_1t_2t_3$; (iv) $t_1t_2t_3t_4$.

3. Taking the parametric coordinates of a point on the ellipse $x^2/a^2 + y^2/b^2 = 1$ as $[a(1-t^2)/(1+t^2), \; 2bt/(1+t^2)]$, find the equation whose roots are the parameters t_1, t_2, t_3, t_4 of the points of intersection of the ellipse and the circle $x^2 + y^2 = a^2 - b^2$.

4. The points $A(ct_1, c/t_1)$, $B(ct_2, c/t_2)$, $C(ct_3, c/t_3)$ lie on the rectangular hyperbola $xy = c^2$. Find the coordinates of the point L in which the circumcircle of triangle ABC cuts the hyperbola again.

5. Prove that, if the four points $\left[\dfrac{1}{2}a\left(t + \dfrac{1}{t}\right), \; \dfrac{1}{2}b\left(t - \dfrac{1}{t}\right)\right]$, $t = t_1, t_2, t_3, t_4$, on the hyperbola $x^2/a^2 - y^2/b^2 = 1$ are concyclic, then $t_1t_2t_3t_4 = 1$.

6. The four concyclic points A, B, C, D on the parabola $y^2 = 4ax$ have the coordinates $(at^2, 2at)$, $t = t_1, t_2, t_3, t_4$. Prove that: (i) $t_1 + t_2 = -(t_3 + t_4)$; (ii) the line joining the mid-points of chords AB, CD is bisected by the axis of the parabola.

7. Taking the coordinates of any point on the ellipse $x^2/a^2 + y^2/b^2 = 1$ as $[a(1-t^2)/(1+t^2), \; 2bt/(1+t^2)]$ show that if the points with parameters t_1, t_2, t_3, t_4 are concyclic, then $\sum t_1 = \sum t_1t_2t_3$.

8. The rectangular hyperbola $xy = c^2$ is cut by a circle in four points with parameters t_1, t_2, t_3, t_4; prove that $t_1t_2t_3t_4 = 1$. If the centre of the circle lies on the asymptote $x = 0$, prove also that $\sum t_1 = 0$.

9. Show that the coordinates of any point on the hyperbola $x^2/a^2 - y^2/b^2 = 1$ can be taken as $[a(1+t^2)/(1-t^2), \; 2bt/(1-t^2)]$. Show also that if the points with parameters t_1, t_2, t_3, t_4 are concyclic, then $\sum t_1 + \sum t_1t_2t_3 = 0$.

10. Four points P, Q, R, S on a parabola are concyclic; if PQ is a focal chord and PR is normal to the curve at P, prove that the axis divides QS in the ratio $1 : 3$.

11. A hyperbola is cut by a concentric circle in four points; prove that these points are the ends of diameters equally inclined to the axes of the hyperbola.

12. A circle touches a parabola at P and meets the curve again at Q and R. Show that the axis bisects the line joining P to the mid-point of the chord QR.

13. A circle cuts a rectangular hyperbola in the points P, Q, R, S. Perpendiculars PP', QQ' are drawn to one asymptote and perpendiculars RR', SS' to the other. Prove that PP' . $QQ' = RR'$. SS'.

14. Two given points A, B lie on the same branch of a rectangular hyperbola, prove that two circles can be drawn through A and B to touch the rectangular hyperbola at points P, Q which are at the ends of a diameter of the curve.

General equation of a conic. Geometrically the conics are the curves of intersection of a variable plane and a double cone; they have five different forms:

the line pair; the circle; the ellipse; the hyperbola; the parabola.

Each of these conics has the property that it is met in two points, real or imaginary, by a straight line, and consequently its equation must be of the second degree.

Hence the most general equation of a conic is

$$ax^2 + 2hxy + by^2 + 2gx + 2fy + c = 0.$$

This equation represents the different conics according to the following conditions:

(i) if $a = b$ and $h = 0$, the conic is a *circle*;

(ii) if $h^2 < ab$, the conic is an *ellipse* with the exception of the special case (i);

(iii) if $h^2 > ab$, the conic is, in general, *a hyperbola except* when
$\Delta = \begin{vmatrix} a & h & g \\ h & b & f \\ g & f & c \end{vmatrix} = 0$, when it is a *line pair*.

(iv) if $a + b = 0$, and in consequence $h^2 > ab$, the conic is *a rectangular hyperbola* or *a perpendicular line pair*—the latter requiring the extra condition $\Delta = 0$.

(v) if $h^2 = ab$, the conic is, in general, *a parabola*.

Ex. 11. *Identify the following conics:*

$\quad$ (i) $2x^2 + 4xy + 3y^2 - 1 = 0;$ $\qquad$ (ii) $x^2 - y^2 + 2x - 4y + 1 = 0.$
$\quad$ (iii) $9x^2 + 6xy + y^2 + 2x - 3 = 0;$ $\qquad$ (iv) $4x^2 + 4y^2 - 7x - 8y - 2 = 0.$

(i) in this case $h^2 < ab$; $\therefore$ an ellipse.
(ii) in this case $a + b = 0$; $\therefore$ a rectangular hyperbola ($\Delta \neq 0$).
(iii) in this case $h^2 = ab$; $\therefore$ a parabola.
(iv) in this case $a = b$; $h = 0$; $\therefore$ a circle.

Systems of conics. Consider the equation

$$S + \lambda S' = 0,$$

where $S = 0$, $S' = 0$ are the equations of two conics and λ is a parameter.

As S, S' will be of the second degree, so will $S + \lambda S'$, hence the equation represents a conic for all values of λ. Moreover, the coordinates of a point common to $S = 0$ and $S' = 0$ will satisfy the equation.

Hence the equation $S + \lambda S' = 0$ represents a system of conics passing through the points of intersection of the conics $S = 0$, $S' = 0$.

Ex. 12. *Write down the equation of the system of conics passing through the points of intersection of the ellipse $4x^2 + 9y^2 = 36$ and the circle $x^2 + y^2 = 6$. Find the equation of the conic of the system which passes through the point $(0, -1)$.*

Equation of the system of conics is

$$4x^2 + 9y^2 - 36 + \lambda(x^2 + y^2 - 6) = 0.$$

This equation is satisfied by the point $(0, -1)$ if

$$9 - 36 + \lambda(-5) = 0,$$

i.e. $$\lambda = -\tfrac{27}{5}.$$

Hence the required conic has the equation

$$7x^2 - 18y^2 + 18 = 0 \text{ — a hyperbola.}$$

System of conics passing through four given points. Let the four given points be A, B, C, D.

Then the line pairs BC, AD; CA, BD; AB, CD are members of the system of conics passing through the four points.

Taking the first two pairs and writing the separate equations of the lines BC, AD, CA, BD as $L_1 = 0$, $L_2 = 0$, $L_3 = 0$, $L_4 = 0$ respectively, it follows that the equation of the required system can be expressed in the form

$$L_1 L_2 + \lambda L_3 L_4 = 0.$$

Ex. 13. *Find the equation of the system of conics determined by the points $A(1, 0)$, $B(1, -1)$, $C(0, 2)$, $D(2, 2)$.*

The equations of AB, CD; BC, AD are respectively

$$x - 1 = 0, \; y - 2 = 0; \quad y + 3x - 2 = 0, \; y - 2x + 2 = 0.$$

∴ The equation of the system can be written

$$(y + 3x - 2)(y - 2x + 2) + \lambda(x - 1)(y - 2) = 0.$$

Ex. 14. *Prove that all conics passing through the vertices of a triangle ABC and its orthocentre H are rectangular hyperbolae.*

Simplify the problem by choosing *AB* and the altitude through *C* as coordinate axes (Fig. 71).

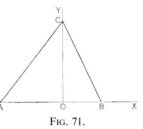

Let *A*, *B*, *C* have coordinates $(a, 0)$ $(b, 0)$, $(0, c)$ respectively.

Then the equations of *AB*, *CH*; *BC*, *AH* are

$$y = 0, \ x = 0; \quad cx + by - bc = 0, \ bx - cy - ab = 0.$$

Hence the equation of the system of conics through *A*, *B*, *C*, *H* is

Fig. 71.

$$(cx + by - bc)(bx - cy - ab) + \lambda xy = 0.$$

As the coefficients of x^2 and y^2 are equal and opposite, the equation represents a rectangular hyperbola, except of course when it gives the line pairs *BC*, *AH*; *CA*, *BH*; *AB*, *CH*.

Special cases of the system $S + \lambda S' = 0$. Special cases arise when one or both of the conics $S = 0$, $S' = 0$ degenerate into line pairs. In these cases the separate lines will be expressed by equations $L = 0$, $M = 0$, $N = 0$, etc.

(i) *The equation $S + \lambda LM = 0$.*

(a) This equation represents a system of conics passing through the common points *A*, *B*, *C*, *D* of the conic *S* and the lines *L* and *M* (Fig. 72).

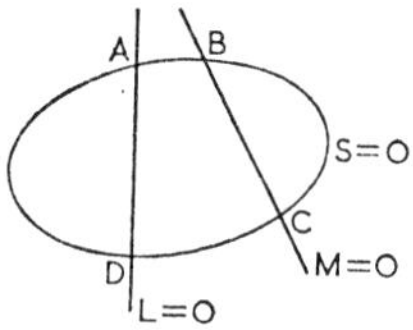

(b) If the lines *L*, *M* intersect at a point *A* on the conic *S*—i.e. points *A* and *B* coincide, then the equation represents a system of conics touching *S* at *A* and passing through *C* and *D*.

Fig. 72.

(c) If the line *L* touches *S* at *A*—i.e. points *A* and *D* coincide, then the equation represents a system of conics touching *S* at *A* and passing through *B* and *C*.

(d) If both *L* and *M* are tangents to *S* at *A*, *B* respectively, the equation represents a system of conics touching *S* at *A* and *B* —a case of *double contact*.

(e) If *L* is a tangent to *S* at *A* and *M* also passes through *A* (Fig. 73), three of the points of intersection of the conic and the line pair coincide in *A* and the equation represents a system of conics passing through *C* and having *three-point contact* with *S* at *A*.

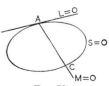

Fig. 73.

(ii) The equation $S + \lambda L^2 = 0$.

Here we can imagine the line $M = 0$ of the previous case to have coincided with the line $L = 0$ and the four points of intersection have become two coincident pairs of points at A and D (Fig. 74).

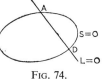

FIG. 74.

Hence the equation (ii) represents a system of conics touching S at the ends of the chord AD—a case of double contact and equivalent to (i) (*d*) above.

Further special cases arise when S itself is a line pair. For example, *if* $L = 0$, $M = 0$, $N = 0$ *are straight lines*, the equation

$$LM + \lambda N^2 = 0,$$

represents a system of conics touching L and M at their points of intersection A, B with N (Fig. 75).

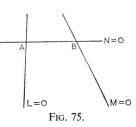

FIG. 75.

Ex. 15. *Identify the system of conics represented by the equation*

$$x^2/a^2 + y^2/b^2 - 1 + \lambda(x - a)(y - b) = 0.$$

The lines $x - a = 0$, $y - b = 0$ are tangents to the ellipse $x^2/a^2 + y^2/b^2 = 1$ at the ends $A(a, 0)$, $B(0, b)$ of the principal axes.

∴ The equation $x^2/a^2 + y^2/b^2 - 1 + \lambda(x - a)(y - b) = 0$,

represents a system of conics touching the ellipse at A and B.

Ex. 16. *Find the equation of the rectangular hyperbola which touches the parabola* $y^2 = 4x$ *at the ends of the chord* $3x + y = 6$.

The equation of the system of conics touching the parabola $y^2 - 4x = 0$ at the ends of the chord $3x + y - 6 = 0$ is

$$y^2 - 4x + \lambda(3x + y - 6)^2 = 0.$$

This equation represents a rectangular hyperbola if

$$1 + 9\lambda + \lambda = 0; \quad \text{i.e. } \lambda = -\tfrac{1}{10}.$$

∴ The equation of the rectangular hyperbola in the system is

$$y^2 - 4x - \tfrac{1}{10}(3x + y - 6)^2 = 0$$

or
$$9x^2 + 6xy - 9y^2 + 4x - 12y + 36 = 0.$$

EXAMPLES 8d

1. Identify the following conics:

(i) $3x^2 + xy + y^2 = 1$;
(ii) $2x^2 - xy - y^2 = 0$;
(iii) $xy - 2x - y = 0$;
(iv) $x^2 - xy - y^2 - 2 = 0$;
(v) $(x + y)^2 - 2x + y = 0$;
(vi) $x^2 + 2xy - y^2 - x + y + 1 = 0$;
(vii) $3x^2 + 2xy + 4y^2 - 10x - 18y + 28 = 0$;
(viii) $x^2 - 4xy + 4y^2 - 24x - 2y = 0$.

2. Find the values of λ for which the equation
$$2x^2 + y^2 - 1 + \lambda(y - 2x)(y + x) = 0$$
represents: (i) a rectangular hyperbola; (ii) a parabola.

3. Prove that for all values of the parameter μ the equation
$$(ax + by - 1)(bx - ay + 1) + \mu(x - y)(x + y) = 0$$
represents a rectangular hyperbola.

4. Find the equation of the conic which passes through the points of intersection of the conics $x^2 + 2y^2 = 1$, $2xy = 1$ and also through the point $(3, 1)$. Identify the conic.

5. Find the equation of the conic which passes through the points of intersection of the circle $x^2 + y^2 - 4x + 2y + 1 = 0$ and the lines $y + 1 = 0$, $y + 3 = 0$ and also through the origin.

6. Identify the following systems of conics:

(i) $x^2 + y^2 - 1 + \lambda(xy - 1) = 0$;
(ii) $x^2/4 + y^2/2 - 1 + \lambda(x^2 + y^2 - 3) = 0$;
(iii) $y^2 - 8x + \lambda(x + y - 1)(2y - x) = 0$;
(iv) $x^2 - y^2 - 1 + \lambda(x^2/8 + y^2/2 - 1) = 0$;
(v) $(x - y + 1)(x + y - 1) + \lambda xy = 0$;
(vi) $4x^2 + 9y^2 - 36 + \lambda(9x^2 + 4y^2 - 36) = 0$.

7. Find the equation of the rectangular hyperbola passing through the common points of the parabola $y^2 - 2x = 0$ and the circle $x^2 + y^2 - 8x + 7 = 0$.

8. Eliminate t between the equations $x = t^2 + a_1 t + b_1$, $y = t^2 + a_2 t + b_2$ and deduce that they are the parametric equations of a parabola.

9. Find the equation of the system of conics which pass through the points $(0, 0)$, $(0, 2)$, $(1, 3)$, $(3, 0)$, and hence find the equation of the conic which passes through these four points and the point $(-1, -1)$.

10. Find the equation of the conic which passes through the five points $(-1, 0)$, $(0, 1)$, $(2, 2)$, $(2, 0)$, $(3, 3)$. What is the nature of the conic?

11. Show that the system of conics $x^2/a^2 + y^2/b^2 - 1 + \lambda xy = 0$, pass through the ends of the principal axes of the ellipse $x^2/a^2 + y^2/b^2 = 1$.

12. Find the equation and nature of the conic which passes through the four points of intersection of the circle $x^2 + y^2 - 4x - 4y - 2 = 0$ and the coordinate axes and also passes through the centre of the circle.

13. Show that the equations of the two parabolas which pass through the common points of the circle $x^2 + y^2 = 4$ and the line pair $(x-1)(y-1) = 0$ are $x^2 + 2xy + y^2 - 2x - 2y - 2 = 0$ and $x^2 - 2xy + y^2 + 2x + 2y - 6 = 0$.

14. Find the equation of the rectangular hyperbola which passes through the common points of the ellipse $x^2 + 4y^2 = 16$ and the circle $x^2 + y^2 = 8$.

15. Show that for all values of λ except zero the equation

$$x^2 + y^2 - a^2 + \lambda(x-a)(y-a) = 0$$

represents a conic touching the circle $x^2 + y^2 = a^2$ at the points $(a, 0)$, $(0, a)$. For what values of λ is the conic a parabola?

16. Find the finite values of λ for which the conic

$$16x^2 - y^2 - 96x + 24y + \lambda(y^2 - 16x) = 0,$$

represents: (i) a rectangular hyperbola; (ii) a parabola; (iii) a line pair.

17. Find the equation of the conic which touches the ellipse $x^2/a^2 + y^2/b^2 = 1$ at the ends of the chord $x + y = b$ and also passes through the origin.

18. Identify the following systems of conics:
      (i) $(x+y-1)(2x-y+3) + \lambda(x-1)(y-2) = 0$;
      (ii) $x^2 + y^2 - 4 + \lambda(x-y)(x+y+1) = 0$;
      (iii) $xy - 1 + \lambda(x+y-2)^2 = 0$;
      (iv) $(x-y)(x+y) + \lambda(x-2)^2 = 0$.

19. Find the equation of the conic which has three-point contact with the circle $x^2 + y^2 - 4x + 3y = 0$ at the point $(2, 1)$ and which meets the circle again at the origin and also passes through the point $(1, -1)$.

20. Find the equation of the system of conics which touch the circle $x^2 + y^2 = 2a^2$ at the point (a, a) and meet it again at the ends of the chord $x + y - a = 0$. Find also the equation of the rectangular hyperbola in the system.

21. Show that all conics passing through the vertices and orthocentre of the triangle formed by the lines $y + x - 1 = 0$, $x + 1 = 0$, $2y - x = 0$ are rectangular hyperbolae.

22. Prove that the equation $5(y^2 - 4ax) + (x - 2y - a)(x + 2y + 3a) = 0$ represents a circle which meets the parabola $y^2 = 4ax$ at the ends of a focal chord and find where it meets the curve again.

23. Prove that the equation $(1 + t^2)(y^2 - 4ax) + (x - ty + at^2)(x + ty + 3a) = 0$ represents a circle which touches the parabola $y^2 = 4ax$ at the point $(at^2, 2at)$ and passes through its focus.

24. Find the coordinates of the foci of the conic $x^2/(a^2 - \lambda) + y^2/(b^2 - \lambda) = 1$, $a > b$, and deduce that the system of conics represented by the equation have common foci. Prove that in general two conics of the system pass through a given point.

MISCELLANEOUS EXAMPLES

1. Find the equation of the chord of the ellipse $4x^2 + 9y^2 = 36$ with mid-point $(-1, 1)$.

2. Find the coordinates of the point of intersection of the tangents to the parabola $y^2 = 8x$ at the ends of the chord $y - 2x + 2 = 0$.

3. Find the locus of the mid-points of chords of the rectangular hyperbola $xy = 4$ which pass through the point $(2, 3)$.

4. Prove that the locus of the mid-points of chords of a parabola which pass through a fixed point is a parabola.

5. A tangent to the conic $x^2 - y^2 = 9$ cuts the circle $x^2 + y^2 = 9$ at L, M; find the locus of the mid-point of LM.

6. The perpendicular bisector of a chord of the ellipse $b^2x^2 + a^2y^2 = a^2b^2$ passes through the point $(-a, b)$. Find the locus of the mid-point of the chord.

7. If the normal at P meets the curve $xy = c^2$ again at Q, prove that $c^2PQ = OP^3$, where O is the centre.

8. P, Q are points on the parabola $y^2 = 4ax$ such that PQ subtends a right angle at the vertex. Prove that PQ meets the axis of the parabola at a fixed point.

9. Chords of an ellipse are drawn through a fixed point P; show that their mid-points lie on an ellipse whose centre bisects the line joining P to the centre of the given ellipse.

10. P is a point on a rectangular hyperbola and a chord VW subtends a right angle at P. Prove that VW is parallel to the normal at P.

11. Chord PQ is normal at P to the parabola $y^2 = 4ax$. If P is the point $(at^2, 2at)$, find the coordinates of the point of intersection of the tangents at P and Q and deduce the locus of this point as P varies.

12. Show that the equation $xy + 2x - y - 6 = 0$ represents a rectangular hyperbola and find the equations of its axes.

13. Prove that the locus of the mid-points of focal chords of a parabola having latus rectum of length $2l$ is a parabola with latus rectum of length l.

14. The extremities of any diameter of an ellipse are L, L' and M is any other point on the curve. Prove that the product of the gradients of the chords LM, $L'M$ is constant.

15. A normal to the hyperbola $x^2/a^2 - y^2/b^2 = 1$ meets the axes in M and N. Find the locus of the mid-point of MN.

16. P, Q, R are points on the parabola $y^2 = 4ax$ such that PR, QR are normal to the curve at P, Q respectively. Show that the centroid of the triangle PQR lies on the axis of the parabola.

17. Find the locus of the mid-points of chords of the hyperbola $x^2/a^2 - y^2/b^2 = 1$ which pass through the fixed point (h, k).

18. Write down the equation of the chord of the parabola $y^2 = 4ax$ which has mid-point (α, β). Hence deduce that the locus of the mid-points of focal chords of the parabola is the parabola $y^2 = 2a(x - a)$.

19. The chords AB, CD of an ellipse are equally inclined to the axes, prove that the same is true of the chords AC, BD.

20. The normal to a hyperbola at a point P meets the transverse axis produced at N. From N a perpendicular is drawn to an asymptote, meeting it at L; show that LP is parallel to the conjugate axis.

21. Show that the feet of the three normals that can be drawn from any point to a parabola lie on a circle which passes through the vertex of the parabola.

22. Find the equation of the locus of the mid-points of chords of the ellipse $x^2/a^2 + y^2/b^2 = 1$ which are drawn from the positive end of the minor axis.

23. P, Q are variable points on the rectangular hyperbola $xy = c^2$ such that the tangent at P passes through the foot of the ordinate at Q. Show that the locus of the mid-point of the chord PQ is a rectangular hyperbola with the same asymptotes as the given curve.

24. If two of the normals from the point $P\,(x_1, y_1)$ to the parabola $y^2 = 4ax$ are perpendicular to each other, prove that: (i) P lies on the curve $y^2 - ax + 3a^2 = 0$; (ii) the foot of the third normal through P has coordinates $(x_1 - 3a, -2y_1)$.

25. Prove that the chords of contact of tangents drawn from a point to an ellipse and its auxiliary circle meet on a fixed straight line.

26. Show that the chords joining the feet of the four perpendiculars from a point to a rectangular hyperbola are perpendicular to each other.

27. Prove that a circle cuts the parabola $y^2 = 4ax$ in four points, the sum of whose ordinates is zero.

28. The point P on a hyperbola, with focus S, is such that the tangent at P, the latus rectum through S and one asymptote are concurrent. Prove that SP is parallel to the other asymptote.

29. Prove that if the normals at the ends P, Q of a focal chord of an ellipse meet at R, then the line through R parallel to the major axis bisects PQ.

30. If the points of contact of tangents from the point $(2a, k)$ to the parabola $y^2 = 4ax$ are P, Q, prove that the perpendicular bisector of PQ cuts the axis of the parabola at the point $(k^2/2a, 0)$.

31. The normals to a rectangular hyperbola at four points H, P_1, P_2, P_3 on it are concurrent; parallels through H to the normals at P_1, P_2, P_3 cut the curve again at Q_1, Q_2, Q_3. Prove that H is the orthocentre of the triangle $Q_1Q_2Q_3$.

32. If two normals to a parabola intersect on a fixed line, prove that the locus of the points of intersection of the corresponding tangents is a hyperbola.

33. Find the equation of the conic which touches the ellipse $x^2/a^2 + y^2/b^2 = 1$ at the points $(a, 0)$, $(0, -b)$ and passes through the point (a, b).

34. Find the equation of the conic through the points $(2, 3)$, $(3, 2)$, $(3, 1)$, $(1, 3)$, $(1, 2)$ and show that the conic is an ellipse.

35. Tangents are drawn from any point on the rectangular hyperbola $x^2 - y^2 = a^2 - b^2$ to the ellipse $b^2x^2 + a^2y^2 = a^2b^2$. Prove that these tangents are equally inclined to the asymptotes of the hyperbola.

36. If the normals at points A, B, D, E on an ellipse are concurrent, show that DE and the diameter which bisects AB are equally inclined to the major axis of the ellipse.

37. Identify the system of conics $(2x - y + 1)(x + 2y - 1) + \lambda x^2 = 0$ and determine the values of λ which correspond to: (i) a perpendicular line pair; (ii) a parabola.

38. A, B, C, D are the points $(at^2, 2at)$, $t = t_1, t_2, t_3, t_4$, on the parabola $y^2 = 4ax$. Find the equation of the line pair AB, CD and hence write down the equation of the system of conics passing through A, B, C, D. Show that the conic of this system which passes through the point of intersection of the tangents to the parabola at A and B also passes through the intersection of the tangents at C and D.

39. The line $lx + my = 1$ meets the line pair $ax^2 + 2hxy + by^2 = 0$ at P and Q; find the equation of the rectangular hyperbola which touches the line pair at P and Q.

40. A rectangular hyperbola passes through a fixed point P and has double contact with the conic $ax^2 + by^2 = 1$. Prove that the chord of contact touches a fixed circle whose centre is P.

CHAPTER IX

DE MOIVRE'S THEOREM AND SIMPLE APPLICATIONS

De Moivre's theorem. **For all values of n, the value, or one of the values in the case where n is fractional, of $(\cos \theta + i \sin \theta)^n$, is**

$$\cos n\theta + i \sin n\theta.$$

(i) Let n be a *positive integer*, then using the result

$$(\cos \theta_1 + i \sin \theta_1)(\cos \theta_2 + i \sin \theta_2) = \cos (\theta_1 + \theta_2) + i \sin (\theta_1 + \theta_2),$$

it follows that

$$(\cos \theta + i \sin \theta)^2 = \cos 2\theta + i \sin 2\theta;$$
$$(\cos \theta + i \sin \theta)^3 = (\cos \theta + i \sin \theta)(\cos 2\theta + i \sin 2\theta),$$
$$= \cos 3\theta + i \sin 3\theta.$$

Continuing this process, when n is a positive integer,

$$(\cos \theta + i \sin \theta)^n = \cos n\theta + i \sin n\theta.$$

(ii) Let n be a *negative integer* equal to $-m$; where m is a positive integer.

Then

$$(\cos \theta + i \sin \theta)^n = (\cos \theta + i \sin \theta)^{-m} = \frac{1}{(\cos \theta + i \sin \theta)^m}$$

$$= \frac{\cos 0 + i \sin 0}{\cos m\theta + i \sin m\theta}, \quad \text{from (i) above,}$$

$$= \cos (-m\theta) + i \sin (-m\theta) = \cos n\theta + i \sin n\theta.$$

(iii) Let n be a *fraction* equal to p/q, where p, q are integers and q is positive.

In this case, $(\cos \theta + i \sin \theta)^n$ has not a unique value; we prove that *one* of its values is $\cos n\theta + i \sin n\theta$.

We have

$$\left(\cos \frac{p\theta}{q} + i \sin \frac{p\theta}{q}\right)^q = \cos p\theta + i \sin p\theta, \quad \text{from (i),}$$

$$= (\cos \theta + i \sin \theta)^p, \quad \text{from (i), (ii).}$$

i.e. $\cos \dfrac{p\theta}{q} + i \sin \dfrac{p\theta}{q}$ is *one* of the qth roots of $(\cos \theta + i \sin \theta)^p$.

$\therefore$ $\cos \dfrac{p\theta}{q} + i \sin \dfrac{p\theta}{q}$ is one value of $(\cos \theta + i \sin \theta)^{p/q}$ and the theorem is proved.

Ex. 1. *If* $z = \cos\theta + i\sin\theta$, *find the values of* $z^n + z^{-n}$ *and* $z^n - z^{-n}$, *where* n *is a positive integer.*

$$z^n = \cos n\theta + i\sin n\theta; \quad z^{-n} = \cos(-n\theta) + i\sin(-n\theta)$$
$$= \cos n\theta - i\sin n\theta.$$
$$\therefore \; z^n + z^{-n} = 2\cos n\theta; \quad z^n - z^{-n} = 2i\sin n\theta.$$

Ex. 2. *If* $z + 1/z = 1$, *find the value of* $z^5 + 1/z^5$.

As θ exists such that $2\cos\theta = 1$, in fact $\theta = \frac{1}{3}\pi$ is one value, we can take

$$z = \cos\theta + i\sin\theta,$$

giving $z + 1/z = 2\cos\theta = 1$, when $\theta = \frac{1}{3}\pi$.

Hence $z^5 + 1/z^5 = 2\cos 5\theta = 2\cos\dfrac{5\pi}{3} = 1.$

Ex. 3. *Simplify* $(\sqrt{3} + i)^n + (\sqrt{3} - i)^n$, *where* n *is an integer.*

$$\sqrt{3} + i = 2(\cos\theta + i\sin\theta), \text{ where } \tan\theta = \frac{1}{\sqrt{3}}; \; \theta = \frac{1}{6}\pi.$$

I.e. $\sqrt{3} + i = 2(\cos\frac{1}{6}\pi + i\sin\frac{1}{6}\pi).$

Similarly, $\sqrt{3} - i = 2\{\cos(-\frac{1}{6}\pi) + i\sin(-\frac{1}{6}\pi)\}.$

$$\therefore \; (\sqrt{3} + i)^n + (\sqrt{3} - i)^n = 2^n\{\cos\tfrac{1}{6}n\pi + i\sin\tfrac{1}{6}n\pi + \cos(-\tfrac{1}{6}n\pi)$$
$$+ i\sin(-\tfrac{1}{6}n\pi)\}$$
$$= 2^n \cdot 2\cos\tfrac{1}{6}n\pi = 2^{n+1}\cos\tfrac{1}{6}n\pi.$$

Values of $(\cos\theta + i\sin\theta)^{1/q}$, where q is a positive integer. It has been shown that one value of $(\cos\theta + i\sin\theta)^{1/q}$ is $\cos\dfrac{1}{q}\theta + i\sin\dfrac{1}{q}\theta$; other values are obtained by writing

$$\cos\theta + i\sin\theta = \cos(2r\pi + \theta) + i\sin(2r\pi + \theta),$$

where r is integral.

Then as one value of $\{\cos(2r\pi + \theta) + i\sin(2r\pi + \theta)\}^{1/q}$ is

$$\cos\frac{1}{q}(2r\pi + \theta) + i\sin\frac{1}{q}(2r\pi + \theta),$$

it follows by taking $r = 0, 1, 2, \ldots$, that each of the following is a value of $(\cos\theta + i\sin\theta)^{1/q}$:

$$\cos\frac{1}{q}\theta + i\sin\frac{1}{q}\theta; \quad \cos\frac{1}{q}(2\pi + \theta) + i\sin\frac{1}{q}(2\pi + \theta);$$
$$\cos\frac{1}{q}(4\pi + \theta) + i\sin\frac{1}{q}(4\pi + \theta), \; \ldots$$

The values obtained are different when r is equal to $0, 1, 2, \ldots q-1$ but for higher values of r the previous values of $(\cos\theta + i\sin\theta)^{1/q}$ are repeated.

Hence the q different values of $(\cos\theta + i\sin\theta)^{1/q}$ *are given by the expression*

$$\cos\frac{1}{q}(2r\pi + \theta) + i\sin\frac{1}{q}(2r\pi + \theta),$$

where r is taken as $0, 1, 2, \ldots q-1$.

Ex. 4. *Find the values of* (i) $(\cos\frac{1}{3}\pi + i\sin\frac{1}{3}\pi)^{\frac{1}{3}}$; (ii) $(1+i)^{-\frac{1}{4}}$; (iii) *the cube roots of* $-i$.

(i) $(\cos\frac{1}{3}\pi + i\sin\frac{1}{3}\pi)$

$$= \cos\frac{1}{3}(2r\pi + \frac{1}{3}\pi) + i\sin\frac{1}{3}(2r\pi + \frac{1}{3}\pi), \text{ with } r = 0, 1, 2,$$

$$= \cos\frac{1}{9}\pi + i\sin\frac{1}{9}\pi, \ \cos\frac{7}{9}\pi + i\sin\frac{7}{9}\pi, \ \cos\frac{13}{9}\pi + i\sin\frac{13}{9}\pi,$$

$$= \cos\frac{1}{9}\pi + i\sin\frac{1}{9}\pi, \ \cos\frac{7}{9}\pi + i\sin\frac{7}{9}\pi, \ \cos\frac{5}{9}\pi - i\sin\frac{5}{9}\pi.$$

(ii) $\quad (1+i)^{-\frac{1}{4}} = \dfrac{1}{(1+i)^{\frac{1}{4}}}.$

But $\quad 1+i = \sqrt{2}(\cos\frac{1}{4}\pi + i\sin\frac{1}{4}\pi).$

$\quad (i+i)^{\frac{1}{4}} = 2^{\frac{1}{8}}\{\cos\frac{1}{4}(2r\pi + \frac{1}{4}\pi) + i\sin\frac{1}{4}(2r\pi + \frac{1}{4}\pi)\}, \text{ with } r = 0, 1, 2, 3.$

Hence $\quad (1+i)^{-\frac{1}{4}} = 2^{-\frac{1}{8}}\{\cos\frac{1}{4}(2r\pi + \frac{1}{4}\pi) - i\sin\frac{1}{4}(2r\pi + \frac{1}{4}\pi)\},$

$$\text{with } r = 0, 1, 2, 3.$$

(iii) $\quad -i = \cos(-\frac{1}{2}\pi) + i\sin(-\frac{1}{2}\pi).$

$\quad \therefore \ (-i)^{\frac{1}{3}} = \cos\frac{1}{3}(2r\pi - \frac{1}{2}\pi) + i\sin\frac{1}{3}(2r\pi - \frac{1}{2}\pi), \text{ with } r = 0, 1, 2,$

$$= \cos(-\frac{1}{6}\pi) + i\sin(-\frac{1}{6}\pi), \ \cos\frac{1}{2}\pi + i\sin\frac{1}{2}\pi,$$

$$\cos\frac{7}{6}\pi + i\sin\frac{7}{6}\pi,$$

$$= \frac{1}{2}(\sqrt{3} - i), \ i, \ -\frac{1}{2}(\sqrt{3} + i).$$

EXAMPLES 9a

1. Simplify the following expressions:

(i) $(\cos\theta + i\sin\theta)^5$; (ii) $(\cos\frac{1}{3}\pi + i\sin\frac{1}{3}\pi)^6$; (iii) $(\cos\theta + i\sin\theta)^{-3}$;

(iv) $(\cos\theta - i\sin\theta)^{-4}$; (v) $(\sin\theta + i\cos\theta)^8$;

(vi) $(\cos3\theta + i\sin3\theta)(\cos\theta - i\sin\theta)^{-2}$; (vii) $(\sin2\theta - i\cos2\theta)^{-3}$.

2. Simplify:

(i) $(1+i)^6$; (ii) $(1-i)^7$; (iii) $(1-i\sqrt{3})^8$; (iv) $(\sqrt{3}+i)^{-4}$;

(v) $(\sqrt{3}+i)^{10} - (\sqrt{3}-i)^{10}$; (vi) $(\sqrt{3}-i)^{-10} - (\sqrt{3}+i)^{-10}$.

3. Express $\left(\dfrac{2+i}{1-i}\right)^6$ in the (r, θ) form.

4. If $z = \cos\theta + i\sin\theta$, find the values of: (i) z^{-1}; (ii) $z+z^{-1}$; (iii) $z^2 + z^{-2}$; (iv) $z^3 - z^{-3}$; (v) $z^5 + z^{-5}$; (vi) $z^4 + z^2 + 1 + z^{-2} + z^{-4}$; (vii) $(z^5 - z^{-5})/(z - z^{-1})$.

5. Prove that $(\sin x + i\cos x)^n = \cos n(\frac{1}{2}\pi - x) + i\sin n(\frac{1}{2}\pi - x)$ when n is an integer.

6. Simplify $(1 + i\sqrt{3})^n + (1 - i\sqrt{3})^n$, where n is integral.

7. Express $(1+3i)^n(1+i)^{-n}$, where n is integral, in the (r, θ) form.

N

8. Find the square roots of: (i) $\cos 2\theta + i \sin 2\theta$; (ii) $4(\cos \theta + i \sin \theta)$; (iii) $\cos 4\theta - i \sin 4\theta$; (iv) $\sin \theta + i \cos \theta$; (v) $\cos \frac{1}{2}\pi + i \sin \frac{1}{2}\pi$; (vi) $4i$; (vii) $1 + i$; (viii) $2(1 + i\sqrt{3})$; (ix) $-i$.

9. Find the cube roots of: (i) $\cos 3\theta + i \sin 3\theta$; (ii) $\cos 6\theta + i \sin 6\theta$; (iii) $8(\cos \theta + i \sin \theta)$; (iv) $\sin \theta - i \cos \theta$; (v) $\cos \frac{3}{2}\pi + i \sin \frac{3}{2}\pi$; (vi) -1; (vii) $8i$; (viii) $1 - i$.

10. Obtain all the values of: (i) $1^{\frac{1}{4}}$; (ii) $i^{\frac{1}{3}}$; (iii) $(-4)^{\frac{1}{2}}$; (iv) $(-1)^{\frac{1}{4}}$; (v) $32^{\frac{1}{5}}$; (vi) $(-1)^{\frac{1}{6}}$; (vii) $(1 + i)^{\frac{1}{3}}$; (viii) $(\sqrt{3} + i)^{\frac{2}{3}}$.

11. Represent on the Argand diagram: (i) the cube roots of 1; (ii) the fourth roots of 81; (iii) the square roots of i.

12. Obtain the values of: (i) $\sqrt{\dfrac{1}{1+i}}$; (ii) $\sqrt[3]{\dfrac{1+i}{1-i}}$.

13. Find the product of the four values of $(\cos \frac{1}{3}\pi + i \sin \frac{1}{3}\pi)^{\frac{3}{4}}$.

14. Find the values of: (i) $(-i)^{\frac{1}{4}}$; (ii) $(1 - i)^{-\frac{1}{3}}$.

15. If $z + \dfrac{1}{z} = 1$, find the values of: (i) $z^3 + \dfrac{1}{z^3}$; (ii) $z^4 + \dfrac{1}{z^4}$; (iii) $z^7 + \dfrac{1}{z^7}$.

16. If $\left(z - \dfrac{1}{z}\right)^2 = -3$, find the values of: (i) $z^2 - \dfrac{1}{z^2}$; (ii) $z^3 + \dfrac{1}{z^3}$; (iii) $z^6 + \dfrac{1}{z^6}$.

17. Solve the equations: (i) $x^3 + 1 = 0$; (ii) $x^4 + 16i = 0$.

Binomial equations

Type (i). $x^n - a^n = 0$, *where n is a positive integer and a is real.*

We have $\qquad x^n = a^n = a^n(\cos 2r\pi + i \sin 2r\pi)$.

$$\therefore\ x = a\left(\cos \frac{2r\pi}{n} + i \sin \frac{2r\pi}{n}\right),\ \text{with } r = 0, 1, 2, \ldots n-1.$$

Geometrical representation of the roots. The numbers

$$a\left(\cos \frac{2r\pi}{n} + i \sin \frac{2r\pi}{n}\right)$$

with $r = 0, 1, 2, \ldots n-1$, are represented by the vertices $A_1, A_2, \ldots A_n$ of a regular n-sided polygon inscribed in a circle, centre O, radius a, with the vertex A_1 on the x-axis (Fig. 76).

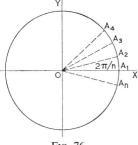

Fig. 76.

Special case a = 1. $\qquad x^n - 1 = 0$,

$$x = \cos \frac{2r\pi}{n} + i \sin \frac{2r\pi}{n},\ \text{with } r = 0, 1, 2, \ldots n-1,$$

$$= 1, \cos \frac{2}{n}\pi + i \sin \frac{2}{n}\pi, \cos \frac{4}{n}\pi + i \sin \frac{4}{n}\pi, \ldots,$$

$$\cos \frac{2}{n}(n-1)\pi + i \sin \frac{2}{n}(n-1)\pi.$$

Writing $\quad \alpha = \cos \dfrac{2}{n}\pi + i\sin \dfrac{2}{n}\pi,$

then $\quad \alpha^2 = \left(\cos \dfrac{2}{n}\pi + i\sin \dfrac{2}{n}\pi\right)^2 = \cos \dfrac{4}{n}\pi + i\sin \dfrac{4}{n}\pi,$

$\quad\quad\quad \alpha^3 = \left(\cos \dfrac{2}{n}\pi + i\sin \dfrac{2}{n}\pi\right)^3 = \cos \dfrac{6}{n}\pi + i\sin \dfrac{6}{n}\pi,$

. . . .

$\alpha^{n-1} = \left(\cos \dfrac{2}{n}\pi + i\sin \dfrac{2}{n}\pi\right)^{n-1} = \cos \dfrac{2}{n}(n-1)\pi + i\sin \dfrac{2}{n}(n-1)\pi.$

∴ The roots of the equation $x^n - 1 = 0$, are

$$1, \alpha, \alpha^2, \alpha^3, \ldots \alpha^{n-1},$$

where $\quad\quad\quad\quad\quad \alpha = \cos \dfrac{2}{n}\pi + i\sin \dfrac{2}{n}\pi.$

More generally, it can be verified that the roots are

$$1, \omega, \omega^2, \omega^3, \ldots \omega^{n-1},$$

where $\omega = \cos \dfrac{2r\pi}{n} + i\sin \dfrac{2r\pi}{n}$ for any one of the values

$$r = 1, 2, \ldots n-1.$$

Type (ii). $\quad x^n + a^n = 0$, *where n is a positive integer and a is real.*

Following the method used in type (i),

$$x = a\left\{\cos \dfrac{\pi}{n}(2r+1) + i\sin \dfrac{\pi}{n}(2r+1)\right\}, \text{ with } r = 0, 1, 2, \ldots (n-1).$$

Geometrically the roots are represented by the vertices of a regular n-sided polygon $A_1, A_2, \ldots A_n$ inscribed in a circle, centre O, radius a, with the vertex A_1 such that angle $XOA_1 = \pi/n$.

Type (iii). $\quad (x-p)^n = a^n(x-q)^n$, *where n is a positive integer and p, q are real.*

As $x \neq q$, by writing $(x-p)/(x-q)$ as X, this equation reduces to type (i),

so $\quad\quad \dfrac{x-p}{x-q} = a\left(\cos \dfrac{2r\pi}{n} + i\sin \dfrac{2r\pi}{n}\right),$ with $n = 0, 1, 2, \ldots n-1.$

Hence values of x can be determined.

Type (*iv*). *The general complex binomial equation,* $(z-z_1)^n = z_0{}^n$, *where n is a positive integer and z_1, z_0 are given complex numbers.*

Suppose $z_0 = a(\cos \alpha + i \sin \alpha)$ and $z_1 = x_1 + iy_1$.
Then

$$(z-z_1)^n = a^n(\cos n\alpha + i \sin n\alpha) = a^n\{\cos (2r\pi + n\alpha) + i \sin (2r\pi + n\alpha)\}.$$

$$\therefore \quad z - z_1 = a \left\{ \cos \frac{1}{n}(2r\pi + n\alpha) + i \sin \frac{1}{n}(2r\pi + n\alpha) \right\},$$

with $r = 0, 1, 2, \ldots n-1$.

I.e. $\quad z = z_1 + a \left\{ \cos \left(\alpha + \frac{2r\pi}{n} \right) + i \sin \left(\alpha + \frac{2r\pi}{n} \right) \right\}.$

Geometrically these values of z will be represented by the vertices of a n-sided polygon inscribed in a circle, centre $C(x_1, y_1)$, radius a.

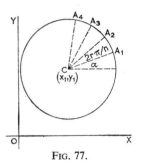

FIG. 77.

with the vertex A, displaced an angle α from the line through the centre parallel to the x-axis.

Ex. 5. *Solve* (*i*) $x^5 + 1 = 0$; (*ii*) $(x-1)^4 = 16x^4$; (*iii*) $x^5 + x^3 - x^2 - 1 = 0.$

(i) $\qquad\qquad x^5 = -1 = \cos (2r\pi + \pi) + i \sin (2r\pi + \pi).$

$x = \cos \tfrac{1}{5}(2r+1)\pi + i \sin \tfrac{1}{5}(2r+1)\pi$, with $r = 0, 1, 2, 3, 4,$

$= \cos \tfrac{1}{5}\pi + i \sin \tfrac{1}{5}\pi, \ \cos \tfrac{3}{5}\pi + i \sin \tfrac{3}{5}\pi, \ \cos \pi + i \sin \pi,$

$\cos \tfrac{7}{5}\pi + i \sin \tfrac{7}{5}\pi, \ \cos \tfrac{9}{5}\pi + i \sin \tfrac{9}{5}\pi.$

But $\cos \tfrac{7}{5}\pi + i \sin \tfrac{7}{5}\pi = \cos \tfrac{3}{5}\pi - i \sin \tfrac{3}{5}\pi; \ \cos \tfrac{9}{5}\pi + i \sin \tfrac{9}{5}\pi = \cos \tfrac{1}{5}\pi - i \sin \tfrac{1}{5}\pi.$

$\therefore \ x = -1, \ \cos \tfrac{1}{5}\pi \pm i \sin \tfrac{1}{5}\pi, \ \cos \tfrac{3}{5}\pi \pm i \sin \tfrac{3}{5}\pi.$

(ii) $\qquad (x-1)^4 = 16x^4 = 2^4 x^4(\cos 2r\pi + i \sin 2r\pi).$

$x - 1 = 2x(\cos 2r\pi/4 + i \sin 2r\pi/4)$, with $r = 0, 1, 2, 3.$

$\therefore \ x - 1 = 2x; \quad x = -1.$

$x - 1 = 2ix; \quad x = 1/(1-2i) = \tfrac{1}{5}(1+2i).$

$x - 1 = -2x; \quad x = \tfrac{1}{3}.$

$x - 1 = -2ix; \quad x = 1/(1+2i) = \tfrac{1}{5}(1-2i).$

I.e. $\qquad x = -1, \ \tfrac{1}{3}, \ \tfrac{1}{5}(1 \pm 2i).$

(iii) $$x^5 + x^3 - x^2 - 1 = (x^3 - 1)(x^2 + 1).$$

So the given equation is equivalent to the equations

$$x^3 - 1 = 0; \quad x^2 + 1 = 0,$$

which give the solutions

$$x = 1, \tfrac{1}{2}(-1 \pm i\sqrt{3}), \pm i.$$

Factors. Functions of the forms $x^n \pm 1$, $x^n \pm a^n$, $x^{2n} - 2x^n \cos n\theta + 1$, where n is a positive integer, can be expressed as products of real factors by first solving the corresponding equations and then combining pairs of linear complex factors.

(i) $x^n - 1$, where n is a positive integer

When $x^n = 1 = \cos 2r\pi + i \sin 2r\pi$,

$$x = 1, \cos 2\pi/n + i \sin 2\pi/n, \cos 4\pi/n + i \sin 4\pi/n, \ldots$$
$$\cos 2(n-1)\pi/n + i \sin 2(n-1)\pi/n.$$

The last root, $\cos 2(n-1)\pi/n + i \sin 2(n-1)\pi/n = \cos 2\pi/n - i \sin 2\pi/n$, and is closely related to the first complex root.

Similarly, the second from the last root is equal to $\cos 4\pi/n - i \sin 4\pi/n$ and so on.

∴ *When n is even*, there will be $\tfrac{1}{2}(n-2)$ pairs of complex roots together with the root 1 and the root $\cos n\pi/n + i \sin n\pi/n$, that is, -1.

When n is odd, there will be $\tfrac{1}{2}(n-1)$ pairs of complex roots together with the root 1.

Now a pair of corresponding complex roots such as

$$\cos 2\pi/n \pm i \sin 2\pi/n,$$

lead to factors

$$\{x - (\cos 2\pi/n + i \sin 2\pi/n)\}\{x - (\cos 2\pi/n - i \sin 2\pi/n)\};$$

i.e. to the quadratic factor $x^2 - 2x \cos 2\pi/n + 1$.

Hence, *when n is even and >2*,

$$x^n - 1 = (x-1)(x+1)(x^2 - 2x \cos 2\pi/n + 1)(x^2 - 2x \cos 4\pi/n + 1) \ldots$$
$$(x^2 - 2x \cos (n-2)\pi/n + 1),$$

and, *when n is odd and >1*,

$$x^n - 1 = (x-1)(x^2 - 2x \cos 2\pi/n + 1)(x^2 - 2x \cos 4\pi/n + 1) \ldots$$
$$(x^2 - 2x \cos (n-1)\pi/n + 1).$$

(ii) $x^n + 1$, where n is a positive integer

In this case, the factors are obtained by solving the equation

$$x^n = -1 = \cos (2r+1)\pi + i \sin (2r+1)\pi,$$

and proceeding as in (i) above with the following results:

When n is even and >2,

$$x^n + 1 = (x^2 - 2x \cos \pi/n + 1)(x^2 - 2x \cos 3\pi/n + 1) \ldots$$
$$(x^2 - 2x \cos (n-1)\pi/n + 1);$$

When n is odd and >1,

$$x^n + 1 = (x+1)(x^2 - 2x \cos \pi/n + 1)(x^2 - 2x \cos 3\pi/n + 1) \ldots$$
$$(x^2 - 2x \cos (n-2)\pi/n + 1).$$

(iii) $x^{2n} - 2x^n \cos n\theta + 1$, where n is a positive integer

If $x^{2n} - 2x^n \cos n\theta + 1 = 0,$

$$x^n = \frac{2 \cos n\theta \pm \sqrt{(4 \cos^2 n\theta - 4)}}{2} = \cos n\theta \pm i \sin n\theta.$$

I.e. $\quad x^n = \cos (2r\pi + n\theta) \pm i \sin (2r\pi + n\theta),$
$$x = \cos (\theta + 2r\pi/n) \pm i \sin (\theta + 2r\pi/n), \ n = 0, 1, 2, \ldots \ (n-1).$$

So $\quad x = \cos \theta \pm i \sin \theta, \cos (\theta + 2\pi/n) \pm i \sin (\theta + 2\pi/n), \ldots$

The pair of roots $\cos \theta \pm i \sin \theta$ gives rise to the quadratic factor

$$x^2 - 2x \cos \theta + 1,$$

and similarly for the other pairs.

Hence

$$x^{2n} - 2x^n \cos n\theta + 1 = (x^2 - 2x \cos \theta + 1)\{x^2 - 2x \cos (\theta + 2\pi/n) + 1\}$$
$$\ldots \{x^2 - 2x \cos (\theta + (2n-2)\pi/n) + 1\}.$$

Ex. 6. *Express in real factors (i) $x^7 - 1$; (ii) $x^6 - x^3 + 1$.*

(i) If $\quad x^7 = 1,$
$$x = \cos \tfrac{2}{7}r\pi + i \sin \tfrac{2}{7}r\pi, \text{ with } r = 0, 1, 2, \ldots 6.$$
$$= 1, \cos \tfrac{2}{7}\pi \pm i \sin \tfrac{2}{7}\pi, \cos \tfrac{4}{7}\pi \pm i \sin \tfrac{4}{7}\pi, \cos \tfrac{6}{7}\pi \pm i \sin \tfrac{6}{7}\pi.$$

But $\quad \{x - (\cos \tfrac{2}{7}\pi + i \sin \tfrac{2}{7}\pi)\}\{x - (\cos \tfrac{2}{7}\pi - i \sin \tfrac{2}{7}\pi)\}$
$$= x^2 - 2x \cos \tfrac{2}{7}\pi + 1, \text{ etc.}$$
$$\therefore \ x^7 - 1 = (x - 1)(x^2 - 2x \cos \tfrac{2}{7}\pi + 1)(x^2 - 2x \cos \tfrac{4}{7}\pi + 1)$$
$$(x^2 - 2x \cos \tfrac{6}{7}\pi + 1).$$

(ii) If $\quad x^6 - x^3 + 1 = 0,$
$$x^3 = \tfrac{1}{2}(1 \pm i\sqrt{3}) = \cos \tfrac{1}{3}\pi \pm i \sin \tfrac{1}{3}\pi.$$
$$\therefore \ x = \cos \tfrac{1}{3}(2r\pi + \tfrac{1}{3}\pi) \pm i \sin \tfrac{1}{3}(2r\pi + \tfrac{1}{3}\pi), \ r = 0, 1, 2,$$
$$= \cos \tfrac{1}{9}\pi \pm i \sin \tfrac{1}{9}\pi, \cos \tfrac{7}{9}\pi \pm i \sin \tfrac{7}{9}\pi, \cos \tfrac{13}{9}\pi \pm i \sin \tfrac{13}{9}\pi.$$

Hence $\quad x^6 - x^3 + 1 = (x^2 - 2x \cos \tfrac{1}{9}\pi + 1)(x^2 - 2x \cos \tfrac{7}{9}\pi + 1)$
$$(x^2 - 2x \cos \tfrac{13}{9}\pi + 1).$$

EXAMPLES 9b

1. Solve the following equations: (i) $x^4 - 1 = 0$; (ii) $x^7 + 1 = 0$; (iii) $8x^3 + 27 = 0$; (iv) $(x - 1)^3 = 8$; (v) $x^7 + x^4 + x^3 + 1 = 0$.

2. Express in real factors: (i) $x^3 + 1$; (ii) $x^4 + 1$; (iii) $x^5 - 1$; (iv) $x^6 + 1$; (v) $32x^5 + 1$; (vi) $x^5 + x^4 + x^3 + x^2 + x + 1$.

3. Solve the equation $(z - 1)^6 = 64$ and show that the roots can be represented by the vertices of a regular hexagon in the Argand diagram.

4. Find the common roots of the equations $x^{12} - 1 = 0$, $x^4 + x^2 + 1 = 0$.

5. Solve the equations: (i) $(x + 1)^3 = 8(x - 1)^3$; (ii) $(x + 1)^4 = (x - 1)^4$.

6. Factorise: (i) $x^6 + x^3 + 1$; (ii) $x^6 - 2x^3 \cos 3\theta + 1$.

7. Solve the equation $x^8 = 1$ and show that one root is $\alpha = \cos \frac{1}{4}\pi + i \sin \frac{1}{4}\pi$. Prove that the roots can be expressed as $1, \alpha, \alpha^2, \ldots \alpha^7$ and represent them on the Argand diagram. Prove also that $1 + \alpha + \alpha^2 + \ldots + \alpha^7 = 0$.

8. Show that the cube roots of unity can be written $1, \omega, \omega^2$ and prove that: (i) $1 + \omega + \omega^2 = 0$; (ii) $\omega^3 = 1$; (iii) $\omega^4 = \omega$; (iv) $\omega^5 = \omega^2$.

9. Express each of the following fractions as the sum of two partial fractions: (i) $\dfrac{1}{x^2 + 1}$; (ii) $\dfrac{1}{x^2 - 2x \cos \theta + 1}$; (iii) $\dfrac{1}{x^4 - x^2 + 1}$.

10. Find the solutions of the equation $(x + 1)^6 = x^6$.

11. Express in real factors: (i) $x^8 + x^4 + 1$; (ii) $x^{12} + x^6 + 1$.

12. Show that the roots of the equation $(z - i)^3 = i^3$ can be represented by the vertices of an equilateral triangle.

13. Solve the equations: (i) $x^5 + (x - i)^5 = 0$; (ii) $(z - \overline{1 + i})^4 = (1 - i)^4$.

14. Prove that the n values of $1^{\frac{1}{n}}$ form a G.P.

15. Show that

$$x^n + x^{-n} - 2 \cos n\theta = \{x + x^{-1} - 2 \cos \theta\}\{x + x^{-1} - 2 \cos (\theta + 2\pi/n)\} \ldots$$
$$\{x + x^{-1} - 2 \cos (\theta + \overline{2n - 2}\,\pi/n)\}.$$

16. $P_1 P_2 \ldots P_n$ is a regular polygon of n sides inscribed in a circle, centre O, radius r; P is a point on OP_1, such that $OP = x$. Write down expressions for $PP_1^2, PP_2^2, \ldots PP_n^2$ by using the cosine rule and deduce that

$$PP_1^2 . PP_2^2 \ldots PP_n^2 = (x^n - r^n)^2.$$

17. Write down the factors of $x^{2n} - 2x^n \cos n\theta + 1$ and by the substitutions $x = 1$, $\theta = 2\phi$, prove the result,

$$\sin n\phi = 2^{n-1} \sin \phi \sin (\phi + \pi/n) \sin (\phi + 2\pi/n) \ldots \sin (\phi + \overline{n - 1}\,\pi/n).$$

18. Use the result of the previous question to express the quotient $\sin n\phi / \sin \phi$ in a factorised form and by letting $\phi \longrightarrow 0$ deduce the result

$$2^{n-1} \sin \pi/n \sin 2\pi/n \sin 3\pi/n \ldots \sin \overline{n - 1}\,\pi/n = n.$$

Expressions for $\cos^n \theta$, $\sin^n \theta$ in terms of multiple angles

Let $z = \cos\theta + i\sin\theta$, then $z^{-1} = \cos\theta - i\sin\theta$.

$$\therefore\ 2\cos\theta = z + z^{-1}; \quad 2i\sin\theta = z - z^{-1}. \qquad \text{. . . (i)}$$

Also $z^n = \cos n\theta + i\sin n\theta$ and $z^{-n} = \cos n\theta - i\sin n\theta$.

$$\therefore\ 2\cos n\theta = z^n + z^{-n}; \quad 2i\sin n\theta = z^n - z^{-n}. \qquad \text{. . (ii)}$$

The results (i) and (ii) enable the expression of functions of the forms $\cos^n\theta$, $\sin^n\theta$, $\cos^p\theta$, $\sin^q\theta$, where n, p, q are positive integers, in terms of the cosines and sines of multiple angles as illustrated in the following worked examples.

Ex. 7. *Express $\cos^6\theta$ in terms of multiple angles.*

Writing $\qquad\qquad z = \cos\theta + i\sin\theta,$

then $\qquad\qquad 2\cos\theta = z + \dfrac{1}{z}.$

$$\therefore\ 2^6\cos^6\theta = \left(z + \frac{1}{z}\right)^6$$

$$= z^6 + 6z^4 + 15z^2 + 20 + \frac{15}{z^2} + \frac{6}{z^4} + \frac{1}{z^6}$$

$$= \left(z^6 + \frac{1}{z^6}\right) + 6\left(z^4 + \frac{1}{z^4}\right) + 15\left(z^2 + \frac{1}{z^2}\right) + 20$$

$$= 2\cos 6\theta + 12\cos 4\theta + 30\cos 2\theta + 20.$$

I.e. $\qquad\qquad \cos^6\theta = \tfrac{1}{32}(\cos 6\theta + 6\cos 4\theta + 15\cos 2\theta + 10).$

Ex. 8. *Express $\sin^6\theta\cos^2\theta$ in terms of multiple angles and hence evaluate*
$$\int_0^{\frac{1}{2}\pi} \sin^6\theta\cos^2\theta\,d\theta.$$

As before,

$$(2i\sin\theta)^6(2\cos\theta)^2 = \left(z - \frac{1}{z}\right)^6\left(z + \frac{1}{z}\right)^2 = \left(z^2 - \frac{1}{z^2}\right)^2\left(z - \frac{1}{z}\right)^4$$

$$= \left(z^4 - 2 + \frac{1}{z^4}\right)\left(z^4 - 4z^2 + 6 - \frac{4}{z^2} + \frac{1}{z^4}\right)$$

$$= \left(z^8 + \frac{1}{z^8}\right) - 4\left(z^6 + \frac{1}{z^6}\right) + 4\left(z^4 + \frac{1}{z^4}\right) + 4\left(z^2 + \frac{1}{z^2}\right) - 10$$

$$= 2\cos 8\theta - 8\cos 6\theta + 8\cos 4\theta + 8\cos 2\theta - 10.$$

I.e. $\qquad \sin^6\theta\cos^2\theta = \tfrac{1}{128}(-\cos 8\theta + 4\cos 6\theta - 4\cos 4\theta - 4\cos 2\theta + 5).$

$$\therefore\ \int_0^{\frac{1}{2}\pi}\sin^6\theta\cos^2\theta\,d\theta = \tfrac{1}{128}\left[-\tfrac{1}{8}\sin 8\theta + \tfrac{4}{6}\sin 6\theta - \sin 4\theta - 2\sin 2\theta + 5\theta\right]_0^{\frac{1}{2}\pi}$$

$$= \tfrac{5}{256}\pi.$$

Ex. 9. *If $z = \cos\theta + i\sin\theta$, express (i) $\dfrac{1}{1 - z\cos\theta}$; (ii) $\dfrac{1 - z^n}{1 - z}$ in the form*
$a + ib$.

In dealing with fractional functions of z where $z = \cos\theta + i\sin\theta$, the denominator $f(z)$ should be expressed as a real function by multiplying by $f\left(\dfrac{1}{z}\right)$ and using the results $z + z^{-1} = 2\cos\theta$, $z^2 + z^{-2} = 2\cos 2\theta$, etc.

(i)
$$\frac{1}{1 - z\cos\theta} = \frac{1 - \dfrac{\cos\theta}{z}}{(1 - z\cos\theta)\left(1 - \dfrac{\cos\theta}{z}\right)}$$

$$= \frac{1 - \cos\theta(\cos\theta - i\sin\theta)}{1 - \cos\theta\left(z + \dfrac{1}{z}\right) + \cos^2\theta}, \quad \text{as } \frac{1}{z} = \cos\theta - i\sin\theta,$$

$$= \frac{1 - \cos^2\theta + i\sin\theta\cos\theta}{1 - 2\cos^2\theta + \cos^2\theta}$$

$$= \frac{\sin^2\theta + i\sin\theta\cos\theta}{\sin^2\theta}$$

$$= 1 + i\cot\theta.$$

(ii)
$$\frac{1 - z^n}{1 - z} = \frac{(1 - z^n)\left(1 - \dfrac{1}{z}\right)}{(1 - z)\left(1 - \dfrac{1}{z}\right)}$$

$$= \frac{1 - \dfrac{1}{z} + z^{n-1} - z^n}{1 - \left(z + \dfrac{1}{z}\right) + 1}$$

$$= \frac{1 - (\cos\theta - i\sin\theta) + \cos\overline{n-1}\,\theta + i\sin\overline{n-1}\,\theta - (\cos n\theta + i\sin n\theta)}{2 - 2\cos\theta}$$

$$= \frac{1 - \cos\theta + \cos\overline{n-1}\,\theta - \cos n\theta + i(\sin\theta + \sin\overline{n-1}\,\theta - \sin n\theta)}{2 - 2\cos\theta}.$$

Expansions of $\cos n\theta$, $\sin n\theta$, $\tan n\theta$, where n is a positive integer.
Expansions of $\cos n\theta$, $\sin n\theta$ and hence also of $\tan n\theta$ in terms of powers of the corresponding ratios are obtained by direct application of De Moivre's theorem.

For $$\cos n\theta + i\sin n\theta = (c + is)^n,$$

where $c = \cos\theta$, $s = \sin\theta$,

$$= c^n + {}_nC_1 c^{n-1}(is) + {}_nC_2 c^{n-2}(is)^2 + \ldots + {}_nC_r c^{n-r}(is)^r + \ldots + (is)^n,$$

$$= c^n - {}_nC_2 c^{n-2}s^2 + {}_nC_4 c^{n-4}s^4 - \ldots$$
$$+ is({}_nC_1 c^{n-1} - {}_nC_3 c^{n-3}s^2 + {}_nC_5 c^{n-5}s^4 - \ldots).$$

$$\therefore \; \cos n\theta = c^n - {}_nC_2 c^{n-2}s^2 + {}_nC_4 c^{n-4}s^4 - \ldots,$$
$$\sin n\theta = s({}_nC_1 c^{n-1} - {}_nC_3 c^{n-3}s^2 + {}_nC_5 c^{n-5}s^4 - \ldots).$$

$$\tan n\theta = \frac{\sin n\theta}{\cos n\theta},$$

$$= \frac{s(_nC_1c^{n-1} - {}_nC_3c^{n-3}s^2 + {}_nC_5c^{n-5}s^4 - \ldots)}{c^n - {}_nC_2c^{n-2}s^2 + {}_nC_4c^{n-4}s^4 - \ldots}.$$

Dividing numerator and denominator by c^n and writing $\tan\theta = s/c = t$, we have

$$\boldsymbol{\tan n\theta} = \frac{_n\mathbf{C_1}\mathbf{t} - {}_n\mathbf{C_3}\mathbf{t^3} + {}_n\mathbf{C_5}\mathbf{t^5} - \ldots}{1 - {}_n\mathbf{C_2}\mathbf{t^2} + {}_n\mathbf{C_4}\mathbf{t^4} - \ldots}.$$

Ex. 10. *Express:* (*i*) $\cos 5\theta$ *in terms of* $\cos\theta$; (*ii*) $\tan 6\theta$ *in terms of* $\tan\theta$.

(i) Substituting $n = 5$ in the expression for $\cos n\theta$,

$$\cos 5\theta = c^5 - {}_5C_2c^3s^2 + {}_5C_4cs^4$$
$$= c^5 - 10c^3(1 - c^2) + 5c(1 - c^2)^2$$
$$= 16c^5 - 20c^3 + 5c.$$

I.e. $\cos 5\theta = 16\cos^5\theta - 20\cos^3\theta + 5\cos\theta.$

(ii) Substituting $n = 6$ in the expression for $\tan n\theta$,

$$\tan 6\theta = \frac{6t - 20t^3 + 6t^5}{1 - 15t^2 + 15t^4 - t^6},$$

where $t = \tan\theta$.

Ex. 11. *Obtain the equation in* $\tan\theta$ *whose roots are* $\tan\frac{1}{5}\pi$, $\tan\frac{2}{5}\pi$, $\tan\frac{3}{5}\pi$, $\tan\frac{4}{5}\pi$ *and hence obtain the equation with roots* $\tan^2\frac{1}{5}\pi$, $\tan^2\frac{2}{5}\pi$. *Deduce that:*
(*i*) $\tan^2\frac{1}{5}\pi + \tan^2\frac{2}{5}\pi = 10$;   (*ii*) $\tan\frac{1}{5}\pi \tan\frac{2}{5}\pi = \sqrt{5}$.

If θ denotes one of the angles $\frac{1}{5}\pi$, $\frac{2}{5}\pi$, $\frac{3}{5}\pi$, $\frac{4}{5}\pi$,

$$\tan 5\theta = 0.$$

But $\tan 5\theta = \dfrac{5t - 10t^3 + t^5}{1 - 10t^2 + 5t^4}$,   where $t = \tan\theta$.

$$\therefore \; 5t - 10t^3 + t^5 = 0$$
$$t(5 - 10t^2 + t^4) = 0.$$

The root $t = 0$, corresponds to $\theta = 0$ or π.

∴ The roots of the equation

$$t^4 - 10t^2 + 5 = 0 \qquad \ldots \quad \ldots \quad \ldots \quad (i)$$

are $\tan\frac{1}{5}\pi$, $\tan\frac{2}{5}\pi$, $\tan\frac{3}{5}\pi$, $\tan\frac{4}{5}\pi$.

As $\tan\frac{4}{5}\pi = -\tan\frac{1}{5}\pi$ and $\tan\frac{3}{5}\pi = -\tan\frac{2}{5}\pi$, the roots of (i) are

$$\pm\tan\tfrac{1}{5}\pi, \; \pm\tan\tfrac{2}{5}\pi.$$

Hence, writing $t^2 = T$, the equation

$$T^2 - 10T + 5 = 0,$$

has roots $\tan^2\frac{1}{5}\pi$, $\tan^2\frac{2}{5}\pi$.

$$\therefore \; \tan^2\tfrac{1}{5}\pi + \tan^2\tfrac{2}{5}\pi = 10;$$
$$\tan^2\tfrac{1}{5}\pi \tan^2\tfrac{2}{5}\pi = 5,$$

and as $\tan\frac{1}{5}\pi$, $\tan\frac{2}{5}\pi$ are both positive,

$$\tan\tfrac{1}{5}\pi \tan\tfrac{2}{5}\pi = \sqrt{5}.$$

EXAMPLES 9c

1. If $z = \cos\theta + i\sin\theta$, find the values of the following expressions:

(i) $z^2 + \dfrac{1}{z^2}$;   (ii) $z - \dfrac{1}{z}$;   (iii) $z^6 + \dfrac{1}{z^6}$;   (iv) $z^4 - \dfrac{1}{z^4}$;

(v) $z^2 + 2z + \dfrac{1}{z^2} + \dfrac{2}{z}$;   (vi) $z^3 - \dfrac{2}{z} + 1 + 2z + \dfrac{1}{z^3}$;

(vii) $(1 + 2z)\left(1 + \dfrac{2}{z}\right)$;   (viii) $(1 + z\sin\theta)\left(1 + \dfrac{\sin\theta}{z}\right)$.

2. If $z = \cos\theta + i\sin\theta$, express the following in terms of z:

(i) $2\cos 4\theta$;   (ii) $2i\sin 5\theta$;   (iii) $\cos 7\theta$;

(iv) $\cos^2\theta$;   (v) $\sin^4\theta$;   (vi) $\sin^4\theta\cos^4\theta$.

3. Express in terms of cosines or sines of multiple angles: (i) $\cos^3\theta$; (ii) $\sin^4\theta$;   (iii) $\sin^5\theta$;   (iv) $\cos^7\theta$;   (v) $\sin^3\theta\cos\theta$;   (vi) $\cos^4\theta\sin^3\theta$.

4. Prove that $2^6\sin^5\theta\cos^2\theta = \sin 7\theta - 3\sin 5\theta + \sin 3\theta + 5\sin\theta$.

5. Express the following in terms of $\cos\theta$: (i) $\cos 4\theta$;   (ii) $\sin 4\theta/\sin\theta$; (iii) $\cos 6\theta$;   (iv) $\sin 6\theta/\sin\theta$.

6. Express the following in terms of $\sin\theta$: (i) $\sin 3\theta$;   (ii) $\cos 4\theta$; (iii) $\sin 5\theta$;   (iv) $\cos 5\theta/\cos\theta$.

7. Express in terms of $\tan\theta$: (i) $\tan 3\theta$;   (ii) $\tan 4\theta$;   (iii) $\tan 7\theta$.

8. When $\theta = 0$, $\frac{1}{3}\pi$, $\frac{2}{3}\pi$, verify that $\tan 3\theta = 0$. By expressing $\tan 3\theta$ in terms of $\tan\theta$, show that the equation $t^2 - 3 = 0$ has roots $\tan\frac{1}{3}\pi$, $\tan\frac{2}{3}\pi$ and deduce the values of these ratios.

9. Prove that $\cos 5\theta + 5\cos\theta = 2\cos\theta(8\cos^4\theta - 5\cos 2\theta)$.

10. If $z = e^{-i\theta}$, show that $(1 + z)/(1 - z) = i\cot\frac{1}{2}\theta$.

11. Evaluate: (i) $\displaystyle\int_0^{\frac{1}{2}\pi}\cos^6\theta\, d\theta$;   (ii) $\displaystyle\int_0^{\pi}\cos^4\theta\sin^6\theta\, d\theta$.

12. Verify that $\cos 4\theta = -\cos 3\theta$ when $\theta = \frac{1}{7}\pi$, $\frac{3}{7}\pi$, $\frac{5}{7}\pi$, π. If $c = \cos\theta$, prove that the roots of the equation $8c^4 + 4c^3 - 8c^2 - 3c + 1 = 0$ are $\cos\frac{1}{7}\pi$, $\cos\frac{3}{7}\pi$, $\cos\frac{5}{7}\pi$, -1 and deduce that $\cos\frac{1}{7}\pi + \cos\frac{3}{7}\pi + \cos\frac{5}{7}\pi = \frac{1}{2}$.

13. When $\theta = 0$, $\frac{2}{7}\pi$, $\frac{4}{7}\pi$, $\frac{6}{7}\pi$ verify that $\cos 4\theta = \cos 3\theta$ and prove that $\cos\frac{2}{7}\pi$, $\cos\frac{4}{7}\pi$, $\cos\frac{6}{7}\pi$ are the roots of the equation $8x^3 + 4x^2 - 4x - 1 = 0$.

14. Express $\sin 5\theta$ in terms of $\sin\theta$, and hence prove that $\sin\frac{1}{5}\pi$, $\sin\frac{2}{5}\pi$, $\sin\frac{6}{5}\pi$, $\sin\frac{7}{5}\pi$ are the roots of the equation $16s^4 - 20s^2 + 5 = 0$. Deduce that $\sin^2\frac{1}{5}\pi$, $\sin^2\frac{2}{5}\pi$ are the roots of the equation $16x^2 - 20x + 5 = 0$.

15. Express the following functions in the form $a + ib$, z being written for $\cos\theta + i\sin\theta$:

(i) $\dfrac{1}{1 + z^2}$;   (ii) $\dfrac{1}{1 + z\cos\theta}$;   (iii) $\left(z + \dfrac{1}{z}\right)^3$;   (iv) $\dfrac{(1 + z)(1 + z^4)}{1 - 2z}$;

(v) $\dfrac{1}{1 - xz}$;   (vi) $(1 + z)^n$;   (vii) $\dfrac{1 - z^n\cos^n\theta}{1 - z\cos\theta}$;   (viii) $\dfrac{1 - x^n z^n}{1 - xz}$.

16. By expressing $\cos 5\theta$ in terms of $\cos \theta$, prove that

$$16(x - \cos \tfrac{2}{5}\pi)(x - \cos \tfrac{4}{5}\pi)(x - \cos \tfrac{6}{5}\pi)(x - \cos \tfrac{8}{5}\pi)$$
$$= 16x^4 + 16x^3 - 4x^2 - 4x + 1.$$

17. By expressing the equation $\cos 6\theta = -\cos 5\theta$ in terms of $\cos \theta$, prove that $\cos \tfrac{1}{11}\pi + \cos \tfrac{3}{11}\pi + \cos \tfrac{5}{11}\pi + \cos \tfrac{7}{11}\pi + \cos \tfrac{9}{11}\pi = \tfrac{1}{2}$.

18. Show that the equation with roots $\tan^2 \tfrac{1}{7}\pi$, $\tan^2 \tfrac{3}{7}\pi$, $\tan^2 \tfrac{5}{7}\pi$ is $x^3 - 21x^2 + 35x - 7 = 0$ and deduce the values of:

(i) $\tan^2 \tfrac{1}{7}\pi + \tan^2 \tfrac{3}{7}\pi + \tan^2 \tfrac{5}{7}\pi$;   (ii) $\sec^2 \tfrac{1}{7}\pi + \sec^2 \tfrac{3}{7}\pi + \sec^2 \tfrac{5}{7}\pi$.

MISCELLANEOUS EXAMPLES

1. Evaluate $(\sqrt{3}+i)^8 + (\sqrt{3}-i)^8$.

2. Find the values of $(-i)^{\frac{1}{3}}$.

3. Express $\dfrac{1}{1 + \cos\theta + i\sin\theta}$ in the form $a + ib$.

4. Express in real factors: (i) $x^7 + 1$; (ii) $x^6 - \sqrt{3}x^3 + 1$.

5. Find the principal values of $am\,(4 + 3i)^{\frac{1}{4}}$.

6. Represent on the Argand diagram the roots of the equation $z^5 + 1 = 0$.

7. Use De Moivre's theorem to obtain the expansions of $\cos 8\theta$ and $\sin 8\theta$ in terms of $\cos \theta$ and $\sin \theta$.

8. Find the three cube roots of $1 + i\sqrt{3}$, each correct to two decimal places.

9. Express $1/(1 + x^2)$ as a sum of two partial fractions, and hence find the fourth derivative of the function.

10. If $z = \cos\theta + i\sin\theta$, prove that $\dfrac{1 - 1/z^2}{1 + 1/z^2} = i\tan\theta$.

11. Find the roots of the equation $x^8 - 4x^4 + 16 = 0$ and represent them on the Argand diagram.

12. Prove that $\sin 7\theta/\sin\theta = 8\cos^3 2\theta + 4\cos^2 2\theta - 4\cos 2\theta - 1$.

13. Find the principal values of $am\left(\dfrac{2+i}{2-i}\right)^{\frac{5}{3}}$.

14. If $\alpha = \cos \tfrac{2}{7}\pi + i\sin \tfrac{2}{7}\pi$, represent the points α, α^2, α^3, α^4, α^5, α^6, α^7 on the Argand diagram and show that they are the vertices of a regular polygon.

15. Find the square roots of $(1 + z)/(1 - z)$, where $z = e^{i\theta}$, and show that the principal values of their amplitudes differ numerically by $\tfrac{1}{2}\pi$.

16. Find the four fourth roots of $4 - 2i$ in the form $a + ib$, where a, b are each correct to two decimal places.

17. Solve the equation $x^{12} - x^6 + 1 = 0$ by treating it as a quadratic in x^6.

18. Prove that $\sin 7\theta = 7\sin\theta - 56\sin^3\theta + 112\sin^5\theta - 64\sin^7\theta$ and deduce that $\sin^2 \tfrac{1}{7}\pi + \sin^2 \tfrac{2}{7}\pi + \sin^2 \tfrac{3}{7}\pi = \tfrac{7}{4}$.

19. Express $1/(x^2 - 2ax\cos\theta + a^2)$ in partial fractions and find the coefficient of x^n in the expansion of the function in ascending powers of x.

20. Solve the equation $z^4 = \sqrt{3} - i$.

21. If $x + \dfrac{1}{x} = 2\cos\theta$, prove that $x^n + \dfrac{1}{x^n} = 2\cos n\theta$, when n is integral.

22. Find the modulus of $z(z-i)/(1+iz)$ when $|z| = 1$.

23. Show that $\cos^5\theta\,\sin^4\theta$ can be expressed in the form

$$a_1\cos\theta + a_3\cos 3\theta + a_5\cos 5\theta + a_7\cos 7\theta + a_9\cos 9\theta,$$

and show by integration or otherwise, that $a_1 - \tfrac{1}{3}a_3 + \tfrac{1}{5}a_5 - \tfrac{1}{7}a_7 + \tfrac{1}{9}a_9 = \tfrac{8}{315}$.

24. Prove that all the roots of the equation $(z+2)^n = z^n$ have their real parts equal to -1.

25. Find the values of θ which satisfy the equation $\tan 4\theta = 1$. Hence show that the roots of the equation $t^4 + 4t^3 - 6t^2 - 4t + 1 = 0$ are $\tan\tfrac{1}{16}r\pi$, where $r = 1, 5, 9, 13$.

26. Factorise $x^{14} + x^7 + 1$.

27. Find the seven 7th roots of unity and prove that the sum of their nth powers always vanishes unless n is a multiple of 7.

28. Show that the equation $32z^5 = (z+1)^5$ has four complex roots, two in each of the second and third quadrants. Show that all the roots lie on a circle.

29. If n is a positive integer, prove that $(1+i)^n + (1-i)^n = 2^{\frac{1}{2}n+1}\cos\tfrac{1}{4}n\pi$.

30. Expand $\cot 7\theta$ in terms of $\cot\theta$ and by means of the equation $\cot 7\theta = 0$, prove that the roots of the equation $x^6 - 21x^4 + 35x^2 - 7 = 0$ are $\cot\tfrac{1}{14}r\pi$, $r = 1, 3, 5, 9, 11, 13$. Deduce that $\cot^2\tfrac{1}{14}\pi\,\cot^2\tfrac{3}{14}\pi\,\cot^2\tfrac{5}{14}\pi = 7$.

31. Solve the equation $z^n = (z+i)^n$ and represent the roots geometrically.

32. If the point z moves on the circle $|z| = 1$, find the locus of the point $(2z - 1)$ and sketch the locus of the point $+\sqrt{(2z-1)}$.

33. A regular polygon of n sides is inscribed in a circle of radius x and centre O. P is a point within the circle on the radius to one of the vertices of the polygon and such that $OP = a$. Prove that the product of the squares of the distances of P from the vertices of the polygon is $(x^n - a^n)^2$.

34. Prove that $\cos\tfrac{2}{7}\pi$, $\cos\tfrac{4}{7}\pi$, $\cos\tfrac{6}{7}\pi$ are the roots of the equation $8x^3 + 4x^2 - 4x - 1 = 0$ and show that $\sin\tfrac{1}{7}\pi\,\sin\tfrac{2}{7}\pi\,\sin\tfrac{3}{7}\pi = \tfrac{1}{8}\sqrt{7}$.

35. If $2\cos\theta = x + \dfrac{1}{x}$ and $2\cos\phi = y + \dfrac{1}{y}$, prove that one of the values of

$x^m y^n + \dfrac{1}{x^m y^n}$ is $2\cos(m\theta + n\phi)$.

36. A regular polygon of n sides is inscribed in a circle centre O, radius r; P is any point within the circle with $OP = a$. Prove that the sum of the squares of the distances of P from the vertices of the polygon is $n(a^2 + r^2)$.

37. If $a + b + c = 0$, prove that $a^3 + b^3 + c^3 = 3abc$.
By writing $a = \cos\alpha + i\sin\alpha$, $b = \cos\beta + i\sin\beta$, $c = \cos\gamma + i\sin\gamma$, prove that, if $\sin\alpha + \sin\beta + \sin\gamma = \cos\alpha + \cos\beta + \cos\gamma = 0$, then

$$\cos 3\alpha + \cos 3\beta + \cos 3\gamma = 3\cos(\alpha + \beta + \gamma);$$
$$\sin 3\alpha + \sin 3\beta + \sin 3\gamma = 3\sin(\alpha + \beta + \gamma).$$

CHAPTER X

FINITE SERIES.   MATHEMATICAL INDUCTION

Finite series.   Let s_n be the sum to n terms of the series whose rth term is u_r.

Then $$s_n = \sum_1^n u_r = u_1 + u_2 + \ldots + u_r + \ldots + u_n.$$

Now suppose that u_r can be expressed in the form $f(r) - f(r-1)$, where $f(r)$ is some function of r.

So
$$u_n = f(n) - f(n-1)$$
$$u_{n-1} = f(n-1) - f(n-2)$$
$$u_{n-2} = f(n-2) - f(n-3)$$
$$\cdot \quad \cdot \quad \cdot \quad \cdot \quad \cdot \quad \cdot$$
$$\cdot \quad \cdot \quad \cdot \quad \cdot \quad \cdot \quad \cdot$$
$$u_2 = f(2) - f(1)$$
$$u_1 = f(1) - f(0).$$

Adding, $$s_n = f(n) - f(0).$$

Hence s_n can be determined if it is possible to express the general term u_r as a difference of a function of r and the same function of $r-1$. This *difference method* is the basis of the methods of summation of many types of finite series.

Series related to the arithmetic series

(i) $u_r = r(r+1)(r+2) \ldots (r+p)$.

E.g. $$u_r = r(r+1)(r+2),$$

i.e. the series $1 . 2 . 3 + 2 . 3 . 4 + \ldots + n(n+1)(n+2)$.

Take $$f(r) = r(r+1)(r+2)(r+3), \quad \textit{adding the next term to } u_r$$

then $$f(r) - f(r-1) = r(r+1)(r+2)[\overline{r+3} - \overline{r-1}] = 4u_r.$$
$$\therefore \; u_r = \tfrac{1}{4}\{f(r) - f(r-1)\},$$

and $$s_n = \tfrac{1}{4}\{f(n) - f(0)\}$$
$$= \tfrac{1}{4}n(n+1)(n+2)(n+3).$$

Generally, if $$u_r = r(r+1)(r+2) \ldots (r+p),$$
$$s_n = \frac{1}{p+2} n(n+1)(n+2) \ldots (n+p+1).$$

(ii) $u_r = (a + \overline{r-1}\, d)(a + rd)\ \ldots\ (a + \overline{r+p}\, d).$

E.g. $\qquad\qquad\qquad u_r = (2r+1)(2r+3)(2r+5),$

i.e. $\qquad$ the series $3 . 5 . 7 + 5 . 7 . 9 + \ \ldots\ + (2n+1)(2n+3)(2n+5).$

Take $\qquad\qquad f(r) = (2r+1)(2r+3)(2r+5)(2r+7),$

$\qquad\qquad\qquad\qquad\qquad$ *adding the next term to* u_r,

then $\quad f(r) - f(r-1) = (2r+1)(2r+3)(2r+5)[\overline{2r+7} - \overline{2r-1}] = 8u_r.$

I.e. $\qquad\qquad u_r = \tfrac{1}{8}\{f(r) - f(r-1)\},$

and $\qquad\qquad s_n = \tfrac{1}{8}\{f(n) - f(0)\}$

$\qquad\qquad\qquad = \tfrac{1}{8}\{(2n+1)(2n+3)(2n+5)(2n+7) - 1 . 3 . 5 . 7\}$

$\qquad\qquad\qquad = \tfrac{1}{8}\{(2n+1)(2n+3)(2n+5)(2n+7) - 105\}.$

N.B. The first factors in successive terms must be part of the *same* A.P. as must be the separate factors in each term.

If this is not so, the procedure is as illustrated in the following worked examples.

Ex. 1. *Find the sum to n terms of the series*

$$1 . 2 . 4 + 2 . 3 . 5 + \ \ldots\ n(n+1)(n+3).$$

Here $\qquad\qquad u_r = r(r+1)(r+3)$

$\qquad\qquad\qquad = r(r+1)(r+2) + r(r+1) = v_r + w_r.$

$$\therefore\ \sum_1^n u_r = \sum_1^n v_r + \sum_1^n w_r,$$

$$= \tfrac{1}{4}n(n+1)(n+2)(n+3) + \tfrac{1}{3}n(n+1)(n+2)$$

$$= \tfrac{1}{12}n(n+1)(n+2)(3n+13).$$

Ex. 2. *Evaluate* $\displaystyle\sum_1^n (r+1)(r+3)(r+5).$

Here the first factors of each term are in A.P. with common difference 1 and the separate factors in each term are in A.P. with common difference 2.

Write $\qquad u_r \equiv (r+1)(r+2)(r+3) + A(r+1)(r+2) + B(r+1) + C.$

By equating coefficients we have,

$$A = 3;\quad B = 3;\quad C = 0.$$

I.e. $\quad u_r = (r+1)(r+2)(r+3) + 3(r+1)(r+2) + 3(r+1),$

$\qquad = v_r + 3w_r + 3x_r.$

$$s_n = \sum_1^n v_r + 3\sum_1^n w_r + 3\sum_1^n x_r,$$

$$= \tfrac{1}{4}\{(n+1)(n+2)(n+3)(n+4) - 24\} + \tfrac{3}{3}\{(n+1)(n+2)(n+3) - 6\}$$

$$\qquad\qquad\qquad\qquad\qquad\qquad + \tfrac{3}{2}\{(n+1)(n+2) - 2\}$$

$$= \tfrac{1}{4}(n+1)(n+2)(n+5)(n+6) - 15.$$

(iii) $$u_r = \frac{1}{(a+\overline{r-1}d)(a+rd) \ldots (a+\overline{r+p}d)}.$$

The terms of this series are the reciprocals of those in case (ii).

E.g. $$u_r = \frac{1}{(2r+1)(2r+3)(2r+5)}.$$

In this case, take

$$f(r) = \frac{1}{(2r+3)(2r+5)}, \text{ removing the first factor,}$$

then $$f(r) - f(r-1) = \frac{1}{(2r+3)(2r+5)} - \frac{1}{(2r+1)(2r+3)}$$

$$= \frac{-4}{(2r+1)(2r+3)(2r+5)} = -4u_r.$$

$$\therefore u_r = -\tfrac{1}{4}\{f(r) - f(r-1)\},$$

and $$s_n = -\tfrac{1}{4}\{f(n) - f(0)\}$$

$$= \frac{1}{4}\left\{\frac{1}{15} - \frac{1}{(2n+3)(2n+5)}\right\}.$$

As in the previous case, the method used here can be extended to apply in examples where u_r is not exactly of the standard form above.

Ex. 3. *Sum to n terms each of the following series:*

(i) $\dfrac{1}{3 \cdot 5} + \dfrac{1}{5 \cdot 7} + \dfrac{1}{7 \cdot 9} + \ldots;$ (ii) $\dfrac{1}{2 \cdot 3 \cdot 4} + \dfrac{2}{3 \cdot 4 \cdot 5} + \dfrac{3}{4 \cdot 5 \cdot 6} + \ldots$

(i) $$u_r = \frac{1}{(2r+1)(2r+3)}.$$

Take $$f(r) = \frac{1}{2r+3},$$

then $$f(r) - f(r-1) = \frac{1}{2r+3} - \frac{1}{2r+1} = -2u_r.$$

$$\therefore u_r = -\tfrac{1}{2}\{f(r) - f(r-1)\},$$

and $$s_n = -\tfrac{1}{2}\{f(n) - f(0)\} = \frac{1}{2}\left\{\frac{1}{3} - \frac{1}{2n+3}\right\}.$$

(ii) $$u_r = \frac{r}{(r+1)(r+2)(r+3)} = \frac{(r+1)-1}{(r+1)(r+2)(r+3)}$$

$$= \frac{1}{(r+2)(r+3)} - \frac{1}{(r+1)(r+2)(r+3)}$$

$$= v_r - w_r.$$

Following the standard method,

$$\sum_1^n v_r = \frac{1}{3} - \frac{1}{n+3}; \qquad \sum_1^n w_r = \frac{1}{2}\left\{\frac{1}{6} - \frac{1}{(n+2)(n+3)}\right\}.$$

$$\therefore \; s_n = \sum_1^n v_r + \sum_1^n w_r$$

$$= \frac{1}{4} - \frac{2n+3}{2(n+2)(n+3)}.$$

EXAMPLES 10 a

In each of the questions 1–12, write down the rth term of the given series and deduce its sum to n terms.

1. $1.2 + 2.3 + 3.4 + \ldots$

2. $3.4 + 4.5 + 5.6 + \ldots$

3. $2.5 + 5.8 + 8.11 + \ldots$

4. $1.6 + 6.11 + 11.16 + \ldots$

5. $\dfrac{1}{1.2} + \dfrac{1}{2.3} + \dfrac{1}{3.4} + \ldots$

6. $\dfrac{1}{3.5} + \dfrac{1}{5.7} + \dfrac{1}{7.9} + \ldots$

7. $1.2.3 + 2.3.4 + 3.4.5 + \ldots$

8. $1.4.7 + 4.7.10 + 7.10.13 + \ldots$

9. $\dfrac{1}{1.2.3} + \dfrac{1}{2.3.4} + \dfrac{1}{3.4.5} + \ldots$

10. $\dfrac{1}{3.5.7} + \dfrac{1}{5.7.9} + \dfrac{1}{7.9.11} + \ldots$

11. $2.3.4.5 + 3.4.5.6 + 4.5.6.7 + \ldots$

12. $\dfrac{1}{1.3.5.7} + \dfrac{1}{3.5.7.9} + \dfrac{1}{5.7.9.11} + \ldots$

13. Use known results for $\sum_1^n r$, $\sum_1^n r^2$, $\sum_1^n r^3$ to sum each of the following series to n terms:

    (i) $u_r = 2r^3 - r + 1$;   (ii) $u_r = r^2(r+2)$;   (iii) $u_r = (r+2)(r+3)(2r-1)$.

14. Sum to n terms the series:

    (i) $1.4 + 2.7 + 3.10 + \ldots$;   (ii) $1^2.5 + 2^2.6 + 3^2.7 + \ldots$

15. Use the identity $\dfrac{1}{n^2} - \dfrac{1}{(n+1)^2} \equiv \dfrac{2n+1}{n^2(n+1)^2}$, to sum to n terms the series

$$\dfrac{3}{1^2.2^2} + \dfrac{5}{2^2.3^2} + \dfrac{7}{3^2.4^2} + \ldots$$

16. Find the following sums:

    (i) $\sum_1^n (2r-1)^2$;   (ii) $\sum_1^{2n} r(r+2)(r+5)$;   (iii) $\sum_n^{2n} r^2(2r+1)$.

O

17. Express each of the following functions in the form

$$\frac{A}{(r+1)(r+2)(r+3)} + \frac{B}{(r+2)(r+3)}$$

and hence obtain $\sum_1^n u_r$ in each case:

(i) $u_r = \dfrac{r}{(r+1)(r+2)(r+3)}$;   (ii) $u_r = \dfrac{1}{(r+1)(r+3)}$.

18. Find the sum $\sum_1^n r(r+1)(r+2)(2r+1)$.

19. If u_r is the rth term of a series, find the sum of n terms of the series in each of the following cases:

(i) $u_r = \dfrac{1}{2r(r+2)}$;   (ii) $u_r = \dfrac{r+1}{2r(r+2)(r+3)}$;   (iii) $u_r = \dfrac{1}{2r(r+3)}$.

20. If $\sum_1^n u_r = 3n^2 + 2n$, find u_r and $\sum_{n+1}^{2n} u_r$.

21. Prove that $\sum_1^n r(r+2)(r+4) = \frac{1}{4}n(n+1)(n+4)(n+5)$.

22. Sum to n terms each of the series:

(i) $1.5^2 + 5.9^2 + 9.13^2 + 13.17^2 + \ldots$;

(ii) $\dfrac{1}{1.3.4} + \dfrac{1}{2.4.5} + \dfrac{1}{3.5.6} + \dfrac{1}{4.6.7} + \ldots$

23. Find (i) $\sum_1^n \dfrac{1}{r(r+2)}$;   (ii) $\sum_1^n \dfrac{2r-1}{r(r+1)(r+2)}$;   (iii) $\sum_1^{2n} \dfrac{r+1}{r(r+2)(r+3)}$.

Trigonometrical series. Certain trigonometrical series can be summed by the difference method.

(i) $\sin \alpha + \sin (\alpha + \beta) + \sin (\alpha + 2\beta) + \ldots + \sin (\alpha + \overline{n-1}\beta)$.

Multiply throughout by $\sin \frac{1}{2}\beta$; then

$$u_r \sin \tfrac{1}{2}\beta = \sin (\alpha + \overline{r-1}\beta) \sin \tfrac{1}{2}\beta$$
$$= -\tfrac{1}{2}\{\cos (\alpha + \tfrac{1}{2}\overline{2r-1}\beta) - \cos (\alpha + \tfrac{1}{2}\overline{2r-3}\beta)\}$$
$$= -\tfrac{1}{2}\{f(r) - f(r-1)\}, \quad \text{where } f(r) = \cos (\alpha + \tfrac{1}{2}\overline{2r-1}\beta).$$
$$\therefore \ s_n \sin \tfrac{1}{2}\beta = -\tfrac{1}{2}\{f(n) - f(0)\}$$
$$= -\tfrac{1}{2}\{\cos (\alpha + \tfrac{1}{2}\overline{2n-1}\beta) - \cos (\alpha - \tfrac{1}{2}\beta)\}$$
$$= \sin \tfrac{1}{2}n\beta \sin (\alpha + \tfrac{1}{2}\overline{n-1}\beta).$$

I.e. $$s_n = \frac{\sin \tfrac{1}{2}n\beta \sin (\alpha + \tfrac{1}{2}\overline{n-1}\beta)}{\sin \tfrac{1}{2}\beta}.$$

(ii) $\cos \alpha + \cos (\alpha + \beta) + \cos (\alpha + 2\beta) + \ldots \cos (\alpha + \overline{n-1}\beta)$.

Using the method applied in (i) above,

$$s_n = \frac{\sin \frac{1}{2}n\beta \cos (\alpha + \frac{1}{2}\overline{n-1}\beta)}{\sin \frac{1}{2}\beta}.$$

It is interesting to note that the same result is obtained by treating α as variable and β as constant in (i) and then differentiating with respect to α.

Similarly, treating β as variable and α as constant and differentiating with respect to β will give the sums of the series

$\cos \alpha + 1 \cos (\alpha + \beta) + 2 \cos (\alpha + 2\beta) + \ldots + (n-1) \cos (\alpha + \overline{n-1}\beta)$,

$\sin \alpha + 1 \sin (\alpha + \beta) + 2 \sin (\alpha + 2\beta) + \ldots + (n-1) \sin (\alpha + \overline{n-1}\beta)$.

(iii) $\sum_{r=1}^{r=n} \sin^p (\alpha + \overline{r-1}\, \beta)$, $\sum_{r=1}^{r=n} \cos^p (\alpha + \overline{r-1}\, \beta)$.

These series can be summed by first converting the powers into multiple angles.

Ex. 4. *Sum the series* $\sin^2 \theta + \sin^2 2\theta + \ldots + \sin^2 n\theta$.

$$u_r = \sin^2 r\theta = \tfrac{1}{2}(1 - \cos 2r\theta).$$

$$\therefore \ s_n = \tfrac{1}{2}n - \tfrac{1}{2}\sum_{1}^{n} v_r, \text{ where } v_r = \cos 2r\theta.$$

But $\sin \tfrac{1}{2}(2\theta)v_r = \tfrac{1}{2}\{\sin (2r+1)\theta - \sin (2r-1)\theta\}$

$$= \tfrac{1}{2}\{f(r) - f(r-1)\}, \text{ where } f(r) = \sin (2r+1)\theta.$$

$$\therefore \ \sin \theta \sum_{1}^{n} v_r = \tfrac{1}{2}\{\sin (2n+1)\theta - \sin \theta\} = \cos (n+1)\theta \sin n\theta.$$

I.e. $$s_n = \tfrac{1}{2}\left\{ n - \frac{\cos (n+1)\theta \sin n\theta}{\sin \theta} \right\}.$$

Application of De Moivre's theorem. Series of the forms

$C = \cos \alpha + c \cos (\alpha + \beta) + c^2 \cos (\alpha + 2\beta) + \ldots + c^n \cos (\alpha + \overline{n-1}\beta)$,

$S = \sin \alpha + c \sin (\alpha + \beta) + c^2 \sin (\alpha + 2\beta) + \ldots + c^n \sin (\alpha + \overline{n-1}\beta)$,

can be summed by obtaining the value of $C + iS$.

Ex. 5. *Sum to n terms:*

(i) $1 + 2 \cos \theta + 4 \cos 2\theta + 8 \cos 3\theta + \ldots + 2^{n-1} \cos (n-1)\theta$;

(ii) $\cos \theta \sin \theta + \cos^2 \theta \sin 2\theta + \cos^3 \theta \sin 3\theta + \ldots + \cos^n \theta \sin n\theta$.

(i) Let $C = 1 + 2 \cos \theta + 4 \cos 2\theta + \ldots + 2^{n-1} \cos (n-1)\theta$,

and $S = 2 \sin \theta + 4 \sin 2\theta + \ldots + 2^{n-1} \sin (n-1)\theta$.

Writing $\cos\theta + i\sin\theta = z$ and noting that $\cos r\theta + i\sin r\theta = z^r$,

$$C + iS = 1 + 2z + 4z^2 + \ldots + 2^{n-1}z^{n-1}$$

$$= \frac{1 - (2z)^n}{1 - 2z}, \text{ the series being a G.P.,}$$

$$= \frac{(1 - 2^n z^n)(1 - 2/z)}{(1 - 2z)(1 - 2/z)} = \frac{1 - 2/z - 2^n z^n + 2^{n+1} z^{n-1}}{1 - 2(z + 1/z) + 4}$$

$$= \frac{1 - 2(\cos\theta - i\sin\theta) - 2^n(\cos n\theta + i\sin n\theta) + 2^{n+1}(\cos\overline{n-1}\,\theta + i\sin\overline{n-1}\,\theta)}{5 - 4\cos\theta}.$$

Equating real parts,

$$C = \frac{1 - 2\cos\theta - 2^n\cos n\theta + 2^{n+1}\cos\overline{n-1}\,\theta}{5 - 4\cos\theta}.$$

(ii) In this case the multiple angle terms are sines, so write

$$S = \cos\theta\sin\theta + \cos^2\theta\sin 2\theta + \cos^3\theta\sin 3\theta + \ldots + \cos^n\theta\sin n\theta,$$

$$C = \cos\theta\cos\theta + \cos^2\theta\cos 2\theta + \cos^3\theta\cos 3\theta + \ldots + \cos^n\theta\cos n\theta.$$

$$C + iS = z\cos\theta + z^2\cos^2\theta + z^3\cos^3\theta + \ldots + z^n\cos^n\theta,$$

$$= \frac{z\cos\theta(1 - z^n\cos^n\theta)}{1 - z\cos\theta}, \text{ where } z = \cos\theta + i\sin\theta,$$

$$= \frac{z\cos\theta(1 - z^n\cos^n\theta)\left(1 - \dfrac{\cos\theta}{z}\right)}{(1 - z\cos\theta)\left(1 - \dfrac{\cos\theta}{z}\right)}$$

$$= \frac{\cos\theta(\cos\theta + i\sin\theta)\{1 - \cos\theta(\cos\theta - i\sin\theta) - \cos^n\theta(\cos n\theta + i\sin n\theta) + \cos^{n+1}\theta(\cos\overline{n-1}\,\theta + i\sin\overline{n-1}\,\theta)\}}{1 - \cos\theta(2\cos\theta) + \cos^2\theta}.$$

Equating imaginary parts,

$$S = \frac{1}{\sin^2\theta}\left\{\begin{array}{l}\cos^2\theta(\cos\theta\sin\theta - \cos^n\theta\sin n\theta + \cos^{n+1}\theta\sin\overline{n-1}\,\theta) \\ + \cos\theta\sin\theta(1 - \cos^2\theta - \cos^n\theta\cos n\theta + \cos^{n+1}\theta\cos\overline{n-1}\,\theta)\end{array}\right\}$$

$$= \frac{1}{\sin^2\theta}\left\{\begin{array}{l}\cos\theta\sin\theta - \cos^{n+2}\theta(\sin n\theta - \cos\theta\sin\overline{n-1}\,\theta) \\ \qquad\qquad - \cos^{n+1}\theta\sin\theta(\cos n\theta - \cos\theta\cos\overline{n-1}\,\theta)\end{array}\right\}$$

$$= \frac{1}{\sin^2\theta}\left\{\begin{array}{l}\cos\theta\sin\theta - \cos^{n+2}\theta\sin\theta\cos\overline{n-1}\,\theta \\ \qquad\qquad + \cos^{n+1}\theta\sin\theta\sin\theta\sin\overline{n-1}\,\theta\end{array}\right\}$$

$$= \frac{1}{\sin^2\theta}\{\cos\theta\sin\theta(1 - \cos^n\theta[\cos\theta\cos\overline{n-1}\,\theta - \sin\theta\sin\overline{n-1}\,\theta])\}$$

$$= \cot\theta\{1 - \cos^n\theta\cos n\theta\}.$$

EXAMPLES 10b

Write down the rth terms of the following series and in each case find the sum to n terms:

1. $\sin \theta + \sin 2\theta + \sin 3\theta + \sin 4\theta + \ldots$

2. $\cos \theta + \cos 2\theta + \cos 3\theta + \cos 4\theta + \ldots$

3. $\sin \theta + \sin \frac{3}{2}\theta + \sin 2\theta + \sin \frac{5}{2}\theta + \ldots$

4. $\cos 2\theta + \cos 4\theta + \cos 6\theta + \cos 8\theta + \ldots$

5. $\sin \theta + \sin (\theta + \frac{1}{2}\pi) + \sin (\theta + \pi) + \sin (\theta + \frac{3}{2}\pi) \ldots$

6. $\cos \theta + \cos (\theta + \frac{2}{3}\pi) + \cos (\theta + \frac{4}{3}\pi) + \cos (\theta + 2\pi) + \ldots$

7. $1 + 2 \cos \theta + 4 \cos 2\theta + 8 \cos 3\theta + \ldots$

8. $1 + \frac{1}{2} \sin \theta + \frac{1}{4} \sin 2\theta + \frac{1}{8} \sin 3\theta + \ldots$

9. $1 - x \cos \theta + x^2 \cos 2\theta - x^3 \cos 3\theta + \ldots$

10. $\cos \theta - \cos 3\theta + \cos 5\theta - \cos 7\theta + \ldots$

11. Find the sums: (i) $\sum_{1}^{n} \sin^2 \frac{1}{2}r\alpha$; (ii) $\sum_{1}^{n} \sin \frac{1}{2}r\alpha \cos \frac{1}{2}r\alpha$.

12. Prove the result $\tan \theta = \cot \theta - 2 \cot 2\theta$ and deduce the sum to n terms of the series $\tan x + \frac{1}{2} \tan \frac{1}{2}x + \frac{1}{4} \tan \frac{1}{4}x + \frac{1}{8} \tan \frac{1}{8}x + \ldots$

13. Prove the result $\operatorname{cosec} 2x = \cot x - \cot 2x$ and deduce the sum to n terms of the series $\operatorname{cosec} x + \operatorname{cosec} 2x + \operatorname{cosec} 3x + \ldots$

14. Sum to n terms the series
$$\cos \theta \cos \theta + \cos^2 \theta \cos 2\theta + \cos^3 \theta \cos 3\theta + \ldots$$

15. Prove that $\dfrac{1}{\sin \theta} (\cot n\theta - \cot \overline{n+1}\,\theta) = \operatorname{cosec} n\theta \operatorname{cosec} \overline{n+1}\,\theta$, and hence find the sum $\sum_{1}^{n} \operatorname{cosec} (r\theta) \operatorname{cosec} (r+1)\theta$.

16. Prove that
$$1 + {}_nC_1 \cos \theta + {}_nC_2 \cos 2\theta + \ldots + {}_nC_n \cos n\theta = (2 \cos \tfrac{1}{2}\theta)^n \cos (\tfrac{1}{2}n\theta).$$

17. Sum to $2n$ terms the series
$$\sin \theta - \sin (\theta + \tfrac{1}{4}\pi) + \sin (\theta + \tfrac{1}{2}\pi) - \sin (\theta + \tfrac{3}{4}\pi) + \ldots$$

18. Use the result $\tan A \tan B = (\tan A - \tan B)/\tan (A - B) - 1$ to sum the series
$$\tan x \tan 2x + \tan 2x \tan 3x + \tan 3x \tan 4x + \ldots + \tan nx \tan \overline{n+1}\,x.$$

19. Sum the series
$$\cos \alpha + {}_nC_1 \cos (\alpha + \beta) + {}_nC_2 \cos (\alpha + 2\beta) + \ldots + {}_nC_n \cos (\alpha + n\beta).$$

20. Sum to n terms each of the series:
$$\text{(i) } \sinh x + \sinh 2x + \sinh 3x + \ldots;$$
$$\text{(ii) } \cosh x + \cosh 2x + \cosh 3x + \ldots$$

21. Prove by use of the identity $\sin^3 \theta = \frac{1}{4}(3 \sin \theta - \sin 3\theta)$, that the sum to n terms of the series $\sin^3 \theta + \frac{1}{3} \sin^3 3\theta + \frac{1}{9} \sin^3 9\theta + \ldots$ is
$$\tfrac{1}{4}(3 \sin \theta - \sin 3^n\theta/3^{n-1}).$$

22. Prove that $\tan^{-1}(x+1) - \tan^{-1}(x-1) = \tan^{-1} 2/x^2$ and deduce the sum to n terms of the series $\tan^{-1}\dfrac{2}{1^2} + \tan^{-1}\dfrac{2}{2^2} + \tan^{-1}\dfrac{2}{3^2} + \ldots$, all the angles being acute.

Power series. The sum s_n of n terms of the geometrical progression

$$a + ax + ax^2 + \ldots + ax^{n-1},$$

is obtained by finding the value of $s_n(1-x)$,

for
$$\begin{aligned}
s_n(1-x) &= a + ax + ax^2 \ldots + ax^{n-1}\\
&\quad - ax - ax^2 \ldots - ax^{n-1} - ax^n,\\
&= a - ax^n.
\end{aligned}$$

I.e.
$$s_n = a\frac{(1-x^n)}{1-x}.$$

This method of summation can be extended to power series in which the coefficient of x^r is a simple function of r.

The power series

$$a + (a+d)x + (a+2d)x^2 + \ldots + (a+\overline{n-1}\,d)x^{n-1},$$

where the coefficients are terms of an A.P. is of importance; its sum can be obtained by the method used to sum the G.P.

For
$$\begin{aligned}
s_n &= a + (a+d)x + (a+2d)x^2 + \ldots + (a+\overline{n-2}\,d)x^{n-2}\\
&\qquad\qquad\qquad\qquad\qquad\qquad + (a+\overline{n-1}\,d)x^{n-1}.
\end{aligned}$$

$$\begin{aligned}
xs_n &= ax + (a+d)x^2 + \ldots + (a+\overline{n-3}\,d)x^{n-2}\\
&\qquad\qquad + (a+\overline{n-2}\,d)x^{n-1} + (a+\overline{n-1}\,d)x^n.
\end{aligned}$$

$$\begin{aligned}
\therefore (1-x)s_n &= a + xd + x^2d + \ldots + x^{n-2}d + x^{n-1}d - (a+\overline{n-1}\,d)x^n,\\
&= a + \frac{xd(1-x^{n-1})}{1-x} - (a+\overline{n-1}\,d)x^n.
\end{aligned}$$

I.e.
$$s_n = \frac{a - (a+\overline{n-1}\,d)x^n}{1-x} + \frac{xd(1-x^{n-1})}{(1-x)^2}.$$

This method will apply when the coefficient of x^r is a linear function of r. If the coefficient of x^r is a quadratic function of r, it will be found that $s_n(1-x)^2$ reduces to a G.P. with extra terms at the beginning and end.

Ex. 6. *Sum to n terms each of the series:*

(i) $2 + 3 \cdot 2 + 4 \cdot 2^2 + 5 \cdot 2^3 + 6 \cdot 2^4 \ldots$;

(ii) $2 + 3x + 5x^2 + 8x^3 + 12x^4 + \ldots$

(i) This series is of the form

$$2 + 3x + 4x^2 + 5x^3 + \ldots,$$

where $x = 2$ and the coefficients are in A.P.

Write
$$s_n = 2 + 3 \cdot 2 + 4 \cdot 2^2 + 5 \cdot 2^3 + \ldots + (n+1)2^{n-1}.$$
$$2s_n = \qquad 2 \cdot 2 + 3 \cdot 2^2 + 4 \cdot 2^3 + \ldots + n2^{n-1} + (n+1)2^n.$$
$$\therefore (1-2)s_n = 2 + 2 + 2^2 + 2^3 + \ldots + 2^{n-1} - (n+1)2^n.$$
$$s_n = (n+1)2^n - 2 - 2(2^{n-1} - 1)$$
$$= n2^n.$$

(ii) The coefficient of $x^r = 2 + (1 + 2 + 3 + \ldots + \overline{r-1}) = 2 + \tfrac{1}{2}r(r-1)$
$$= \tfrac{1}{2}(r^2 - r + 4).$$

So it will be necessary to obtain $s_n(1-x)^2$.

$$s_n = 2 + 3x + 5x^2 + 8x^3 + \ldots + \tfrac{1}{2}(n^2 - n + 4)x^{n-1}.$$
$$(1-x)s_n = 2 + (x + 2x^2 + 3x^3 + \ldots + \overline{n-1}\,x^{n-1}) - \tfrac{1}{2}(n^2 - n + 4)x^n$$
$$= 2 - \tfrac{1}{2}(n^2 - n + 4)x^n + (x + 2x^2 + 3x^3 + \ldots + \overline{n-1}\,x^{n-1}).$$
$$(1-x)^2 s_n = \{2 - \tfrac{1}{2}(n^2 - n + 4)x^n\}(1-x) + (x + x^2 + x^3 + \ldots + x^{n-1}) - \overline{n-1}\,x^n$$
$$= \{2 - \tfrac{1}{2}(n^2 - n + 4)x^n\}(1-x) + \frac{x(1 - x^{n-1})}{1-x} - \overline{n-1}\,x^n.$$
$$\therefore \quad s_n = \frac{1}{1-x}\{2 - \tfrac{1}{2}(n^2 - n + 4)x^n\} + \frac{x(1 - x^{n-1})}{(1-x)^3} - \frac{\overline{n-1}\,x^n}{(1-x)^2}.$$

Binomial series and coefficients. When n is a positive integer, we write

$$(1+x)^n = c_0 + c_1 x + c_2 x^2 + \ldots + c_r x^r + \ldots + c_n x^n,$$

the coefficients $c_0, c_1, \ldots c_n$ being called *binomial coefficients.*
The values of the individual coefficients are, of course, known

$$c_0 = 1; \quad c_1 = n; \quad c_2 = \frac{n(n-1)}{2!}; \quad \ldots$$
$$c_r = \frac{n(n-1) \ldots (n-r+1)}{r!}; \quad \ldots \quad c_n = 1.$$

The summation of series involving these coefficients illustrates new methods, some of which can be applied more generally.

(i) *To prove* (a) $c_0 + c_1 + c_2 \ldots + c_n = 2^n$;
(b) $c_0 + c_2 + c_4 \ldots = c_1 + c_3 + c_5 + \ldots = 2^{n-1}$.

(a) This result follows by substituting $x = 1$ in the expansion of
$$(1+x)^n.$$

(b) In like manner, substituting $x = -1$ gives
$$0 = c_0 - c_1 + c_2 - c_3 + \ldots + (-1)^n c^n.$$
$$\therefore \sum \text{ even coefficients} = \sum \text{ odd coefficients} = \tfrac{1}{2}2^n = 2^{n-1}.$$

(ii) *Series involving multiples of the coefficients.* The methods of the calculus are useful in these cases.

As $\qquad (1+x)^n = c_0 + c_1 x + c_2 x^2 + \ldots + c_n x^n, \qquad$ . . . (i)

on differentiating with respect to x, we get

$$n(1+x)^{n-1} = c_1 + 2c_2 x + 3c_3 x^2 + \ldots + nc_n x^{n-1}.$$

Putting $x = 1$, gives the result

$$c_1 + 2c_2 + 3c_3 + \ldots + nc_n = n2^{n-1}.$$

Other series of this type can be summed by multiplying result (i) above by a suitable power of x before differentiating. If the multiples of the coefficients are fractional, integration can be used as illustrated in the following example.

Ex. 7. *Sum the series:* $\quad$ (i) $c_0 + 2c_1 + 3c_2 + \ldots + (n+1)c_n$;
$\qquad\qquad\qquad\qquad$ (ii) $c_0 + 3c_1 + 5c_2 + \ldots + (2n+1)c_n$;
$\qquad\qquad\qquad\qquad$ (iii) $c_0 + \frac{1}{2}c_1 + \frac{1}{3}c_2 + \ldots + \dfrac{1}{n+1}c_n.$

(i) It will be necessary to multiply the basic result by x before differentiation.

We have $\qquad x(1+x)^n = c_0 x + c_1 x^2 + c_2 x^3 + \ldots + c_n x^{n+1}.$

Differentiating with respect to x,

$$(1+x)^n + nx(1+x)^{n-1} = c_0 + 2c_1 x + 3c_2 x^2 + \ldots + (n+1)c_n.$$

Putting $x = 1$,

$$c_0 + 2c_1 + 3c_2 + \ldots + (n+1)c_n = 2^n + n2^{n-1} = 2^{n-1}(n+2).$$

(ii) This series can be written as the sum

$$c_0 + c_1 + c_2 + \ldots + c_n + 2(c_1 + 2c_2 + \ldots + nc_n).$$

Hence its sum $\qquad\qquad = 2^n + 2n2^{n-1} = 2^n(n+1).$

(iii) Integrating the basic result over the range $x = 0$ to $x = 1$,

$$\int_0^1 (1+x)^n \, dx = \int_0^1 (c_0 + c_1 x + c_2 x^2 + \ldots + c_n x^n) dx.$$

I.e. $\qquad \dfrac{1}{n+1}(2^{n+1} - 1) = c_0 + \frac{1}{2}c_1 + \frac{1}{3}c_2 + \ldots + \dfrac{1}{n+1}c_n.$

(iii) *Series involving powers or products of the coefficients.* Series of this type can often be summed by taking the product of two or more binomial series and picking out the required series as the coefficient of a particular term in the product.

E.g. consider the series

$\qquad$ (a) $c_0^2 + c_1^2 + c_2^2 + \ldots + c_n^2$;
$\qquad$ (b) $c_0 c_1 + c_1 c_2 + c_2 c_3 + \ldots + c_{n-1} c_n.$

(a) As $c_r = c_{n-r}$, the expansion

$$(1+x)^n = c_0 + c_1 x + c_2 x^2 + \ldots + c_n x^n$$

can be written

$$(1+x)^n = c_n + c_{n-1} x + c_{n-2} x^2 + \ldots + c_0 x^n.$$

In the product of these two series, the coefficient of x^n is

$$c_0{}^2 + c_1{}^2 + c_2{}^2 + \ldots + c_n{}^2.$$

$\therefore \ c_0{}^2 + c_1{}^2 + c_2{}^2 + \ldots + c_n{}^2 = $ coefficient of x^n in the expansion of
$$(1+x)^{2n}$$
$$= \frac{2n!}{n!\,n!}.$$

(b) The series $c_0 c_1 + c_1 c_2 + c_2 c_3 + \ldots + c_{n-1} c_n$ is the coefficient of x^{n-1} in the same product.

$$\therefore \ c_0 c_1 + c_1 c_2 + c_2 c_3 + \ldots + c_{n-1} c_n = \frac{2n!}{(n-1)!\,(n+1)!}.$$

Ex. 8. *Prove that* $c_1{}^2 + 2c_2{}^2 + 3c_3{}^2 + \ldots + nc_n{}^2 = (2n-1)!/(n-1)!(n-1)!.$

The summation of this series will require a combination of the methods used in types (ii) and (iii).

$$(1+x)^n = c_0 + c_1 x + c_2 x^2 + \ldots + c_n x^n.$$

Differentiating,

$$n(1+x)^{n-1} = c_1 + 2c_2 x + \ldots + nc_n x^{n-1} \quad . \quad . \quad (i)$$

Also $\quad (1+x)^n = c_n + c_{n-1} x + c_{n-2} x^2 + \ldots + c_1 x^{n-1} + c_0 x^n \quad . \quad (ii)$

The coefficient of x^{n-1} in the product of the series (i) and (ii) is

$$c_1{}^2 + 2c_2{}^2 + 3c_3{}^2 + \ldots + nc_n{}^2.$$

$\therefore \ c_1{}^2 + 2c_2{}^2 + 3c_3{}^2 + \ldots + nc_n{}^2 = $ coefficient of x^{n-1} in $n(1+x)^{2n-1}$
$$= \frac{n(2n-1)!}{(n-1)!(n)!} = \frac{(2n-1)!}{(n-1)!(n-1)!}.$$

EXAMPLES 10c

Sum each of the series 1–10 to n terms:

1. $1 + 2a + 3a^2 + 4a^3 + \ldots$

2. $1 - 2 + 3 - 4 + \ldots$

3. $2 + 4(\tfrac{1}{3}) + 6(\tfrac{1}{3})^2 + 8(\tfrac{1}{3})^3 + \ldots$

4. $2 + \dfrac{3}{2} + \dfrac{4}{2^2} + \dfrac{5}{2^3} + \ldots$

5. $1 - 2\cos\theta + 3\cos^2\theta - 4\cos^3\theta + \ldots$

6. $1 - 3x + 5x^2 - 7x^3 + \ldots$

7. $a + \tfrac{1}{2}(a+d) + \tfrac{1}{4}(a+2d) + \tfrac{1}{8}(a+3d) + \ldots$

8. $1 \cdot 3 + 4 \cdot 9 + 7 \cdot 27 + 10 \cdot 81 + \ldots$

9. $2 - 3 + 5 - 8 + 12 - \ldots$

10. $1 + 2x + 4x^2 + 7x^3 + 11x^4 + \ldots$

11. Sum the series: (i) $1 + 3x + 5x^2 + \ldots + (2n-1)x^{n-1}$;

                     (ii) $1 + 3x + 6x^2 + \ldots + \frac{1}{2}n(n+1)x^{n-1}$.

12. By equating coefficients of x^r in the identity $(1+x)^{n+1} \equiv (1+x)(1+x)^n$, prove that $_{n+1}C_r = {}_nC_r + {}_nC_{r-1}$.

13. Using a method similar to that of the previous example, prove that
$$_{n+2}C_r = {}_nC_r + 2{}_nC_{r-1} + {}_nC_{r-2}.$$

14. Sum the series: (i) $c_0 + 2c_1x + 3c_2x^2 + \ldots + (n+1)c_nx^n$;

                     (ii) $c_0 + 2^2c_1x + 3^2c_2x^2 + \ldots + (n+1)^2c_nx^n$.

15. Prove that: (i) $c_0 - 2c_1 + 3c_2 - \ldots + (-1)^n(n+1)c_n = 0$;

               (ii) $c_1 - 2c_2 + 3c_3 - \ldots + (-1)^{n+1}nc_n = 0$.

16. If n is a positive integer, prove that
$$x + x^2 + x^3 + \ldots + x^n = (x - x^{n+1})/(1-x).$$

By differentiating with respect to x, obtain the sums of the series

    (i) $1 + 2x + 3x^2 + \ldots + nx^{n-1}$;

    (ii) $1^2 + 2^2x + 3^2x^2 + \ldots + n^2x^{n-1}$.

17. When n is even, prove that
$$c_0 + c_2x^2 + c_4x^4 + \ldots + c_nx^n = \tfrac{1}{2}\{(1+x)^n + (1-x)^n\}.$$
Deduce the value of $c_0 + 2^2c_2 + 2^4c_4 + \ldots + 2^nc_n$ in this case.

18. Prove that $c_1 + 3c_3 + 5c_5 + \ldots = 2c_2 + 4c_4 + 6c_6 + \ldots = n2^{n-2}$.

19. Show that $c_0 - \frac{1}{2}c_1 + \frac{1}{3}c_2 + \ldots + (-1)^n \dfrac{1}{n+1}c_n = \dfrac{1}{n+1}$.

20. Find the sum of each of the following series:

    (i) $1^2c_1 + 2^2c_2 + 3^2c_3 + \ldots + n^2c_n$;

    (ii) $1 . 2c_1 + 2 . 3c_2 + 3 . 4c_3 + \ldots + n(n+1)c_n$.

21. Prove that
$$c_0^2 + 2c_1^2 + 3c_2^2 + \ldots + (n+1)c_n^2 = (n+2)(2n-1)!/(n-1)!n!.$$

22. Use the identity $(1-x)^n(1+x)^n \equiv (1-x^2)^n$ to find the value of $c_0^2 - c_1^2 + c_2^2 - \ldots + (-1)^nc_n^2$, if n is even.

23. Prove: (i) $\frac{1}{2}c_1 + \frac{1}{4}c_3 + \frac{1}{6}c_5 + \ldots + \dfrac{1}{2n}c_{2n-1} = (2^n - 1)/(n+1)$.

         (ii) $\dfrac{c_1}{c_0} + 2\dfrac{c_2}{c_1} + 3\dfrac{c_3}{c_2} + \ldots + n\dfrac{c_n}{c_{n-1}} = \frac{1}{2}n(n+1)$.

24. Use the identity $(1+x)^m(1+x)^n \equiv (1+x)^{m+n}$, to prove that
$$_mC_r + {}_mC_{r-1}{}_nC_1 + {}_mC_{r-2}{}_nC_2 + \ldots + {}_nC_r = {}_{m+n}C_r.$$

25. Prove that $c_0c_r - c_1c_{r-1} + c_2c_{r-2} - \ldots + (-1)^rc_rc_0 = 0$ if r is odd and $(-1)^{\frac{1}{2}r}c_{\frac{1}{2}r}$ if r is even.

26. Prove that the sum of $(n+1)$ terms of the series
$$ac_0 + (a+d)c_1 + (a+2d)c_2 + \ldots = 2^{n-1}(2a+nd),$$
where $c_0, c_1, c_2, \ldots$ are the binomial coefficients.

Mathematical induction. The *method of induction* is useful in establishing the validity of general results or theorems which admit of successive cases corresponding to the numbers 1, 2, 3, . . . *n*. The method, which *only applies to prove a stated result or one which can be conjectured from special cases*, is particularly valuable in dealing with finite series. Other applications of the method will also be demonstrated in the following worked examples.

Ex. 9. *Prove that the sum of the series*

$$1 \cdot 1! + 2 \cdot 2! + 3 \cdot 3! + \ldots n \cdot n! = (n+1)! - 1.$$

Let the sum to n terms be s_n and assume that $s_n = (n+1)! - 1$.
Then since the $(n+1)$th term is $(n+1) \cdot (n+1)!$,

$$s_{n+1} = (n+1)! - 1 + (n+1) \cdot (n+1)!$$
$$= (n+1)!(1+n+1) - 1 = (n+2)! - 1.$$

This is the same function of $(n+1)$ as s_n is of n, and therefore if the result is true for n terms it is also true for $(n+1)$ terms.

The result is clearly true when $n=1$, and hence it is true generally.

Ex. 10. *If u_n denotes the nth term of the series*

$$1 + \frac{2^2}{1(1+2 \cdot 2^2)} + \frac{3^2}{1(1+2 \cdot 2^2)(1+2 \cdot 3^2)} + \cdots,$$

prove that the sum of n terms is $\frac{1}{2}(3 - u_n/n^2)$.

Assume

$$s_n = \frac{1}{2}\left(3 - \frac{u_n}{n^2}\right),$$

then

$$s_{n+1} = \frac{1}{2}\left(3 - \frac{u_n}{n^2}\right) + u_{n+1},$$

$$= \frac{3}{2} - \frac{1}{2n^2} \cdot \frac{n^2}{1(1+2 \cdot 2^2) \ldots (1+2n^2)} +$$

$$\frac{(n+1)^2}{1(1+2 \cdot 2^2) \ldots (1+2n^2)(1+2\overline{n+1}^2)}$$

$$= \frac{3}{2} - \frac{1}{2 \cdot 1(1+2 \cdot 2^2) \ldots (1+2\overline{n+1}^2)}\{1 + 2\overline{n+1}^2 - 2\overline{n+1}^2\}$$

$$= \frac{3}{2} - \frac{u_{n+1}}{2(n+1)^2} = \frac{1}{2}\left(3 - \frac{u_{n+1}}{(n+1)^2}\right).$$

Hence if the result is true for n terms it is also true for $(n+1)$ terms.

But when $n=1$, $\qquad s_1 = 1 = \frac{1}{2}\left(3 - \frac{u_1}{1^2}\right).$

So the result is true successively for $n = 2, 3, 4, \ldots$

Ex. 11. *The terms of a sequence u_1, u_2, u_3, . . . are given by the following rules:* $u_1 = 1$; $u_2 = 4$; $u_3 = 9$; $u_n = 3u_{n-1} - 3u_{n-2} + u_{n-3}$ *for all values of $n \geqslant 4$. Prove that $u_n = n^2$.*

Assume the result is true for the values $n-2$, $n-1$, n;

i.e. $u_{n-2} = (n-2)^2$; $u_{n-1} = (n-1)^2$; $u_n = n^2$.

Then $u_{n+1} = 3u_n - 3u_{n-1} + u_{n-2}$
$$= 3n^2 - 3(n-1)^2 + (n-2)^2$$
$$= n^2 + 2n + 1 = (n+1)^2.$$

Hence if the result is true for three successive values of n it is also true for the next value.

But the result is true for $n = 1$, 2, 3, and so successively it is true for $n = 4$, 5, 6, . . .

Ex. 12. *If n is a positive integer, prove that $7^n(3n+1) - 1$ is always divisible by 9.*

Let $f(n) = 7^n(3n+1) - 1$,

then $f(n+1) = 7^{n+1}(3n+4) - 1$.

$$\therefore \ f(n+1) - f(n) = 7^{n+1}(3n+4) - 7^n(3n+1)$$
$$= 7^n(21n + 28 - 3n - 1) = 9 \cdot 7^n(2n+3).$$

I.e. $f(n+1) = f(n) + 9 \cdot 7^n(2n+3)$.

Hence if $f(n)$ is divisible by 9, so is $f(n+1)$.

But $f(1) = 7(4) - 1 = 27$ or $9 \cdot 3$.

Since the theorem is true for $n = 1$, it is true successively for $n = 2$, 3, 4, . . .

Ex. 13. *Prove that if $n \geqslant 1$, $\dfrac{d^n}{dx^n}[\log(x^2+1)] = 2(-1)^{n-1}(n-1)! \sin^n \theta \cos n\theta$ where $\cot \theta = x$.*

Assume

$$y_n = \frac{d^n}{dx^n}[\log(x^2+1)] = 2(-1)^{n-1}(n-1)! \sin^n \theta \cos n\theta, \text{ where } \cot \theta = x$$

Then

$$y_{n+1} = \frac{d}{dx}(y_n) = 2(-1)^{n-1}(n-1)! \frac{d}{dx}(\sin^n \theta \cos n\theta)$$

$$= 2(-1)^{n-1}(n-1)! \frac{d}{d\theta}(\sin^n \theta \cos n\theta) \frac{d\theta}{dx}$$

$$= 2(-1)^{n-1}(n-1)! \{n \sin^{n-1} \theta \cos \theta \cos n\theta - n \sin^n \theta \sin n\theta\}$$
$$\times \left(-\frac{1}{\operatorname{cosec}^2 \theta}\right)$$

$$= 2(-1)^n n! \{\sin^{n+1} \theta \cos \theta \cos n\theta - \sin^{n+2} \theta \sin n\theta\}$$

$$= 2(-1)^n n! \sin^{n+1} \theta \{\cos \theta \cos n\theta - \sin \theta \sin n\theta\}$$

$$= 2(-1)^n n! \sin^{n+1} \theta \cos \overline{n+1} \, \theta.$$

Hence if the result is true for the value n it is also true for the value $n+1$.

But
$$y_1 = \frac{2x}{x^2+1},$$

and when $n=1$, the given expression for y_n reduces to $2\cos\theta$, where $x=\cot\theta$; i.e. to $\frac{2x}{x^2+1}$.

Consequently, the result is true for $n=1$, and hence it is true successively for all integral values of n.

EXAMPLES 10d

Use the method of induction to prove the following results:

1. $1^2 + 3^2 + 5^2 + \ldots n$ terms $= \frac{1}{3}n(4n^2-1)$.

2. $\frac{1}{1 \cdot 2} + \frac{1}{2 \cdot 3} + \frac{1}{3 \cdot 4} + \ldots n$ terms $= \frac{n}{n+1}$.

3. $1^2 \cdot 1 + 2^2 \cdot 4 + 3^2 \cdot 7 + \ldots n$ terms $= \frac{1}{12}n(n+1)(9n^2+n-4)$.

4. $1^3 + 3^3 + 5^3 + \ldots n$ terms $= n^2(2n^2-1)$.

5. $\frac{1}{1 \cdot 2 \cdot 3} + \frac{1}{2 \cdot 3 \cdot 4} + \frac{1}{3 \cdot 4 \cdot 5} + \ldots n$ terms $= \frac{n(n+3)}{4(n+1)(n+2)}$.

6. $\frac{3}{1^2 \cdot 2^2} + \frac{5}{2^2 \cdot 3^2} + \frac{7}{3^2 \cdot 4^2} + \ldots n$ terms $= \frac{n(n+2)}{(n+1)^2}$.

7. $\sum_{1}^{n} r^4 = \frac{1}{30}n(n+1)(2n+1)(3n^2+3n-1)$.

8. $\sum_{1}^{n} \frac{(r+1)^2}{r(r+2)} = n + \frac{3}{4} - \frac{1}{2(n+1)} - \frac{1}{2(n+2)}$.

9. $\sum_{1}^{n} \frac{r^2+r-1}{(r+2)!} = \frac{1}{2} - \frac{n+1}{(n+2)!}$.

10. $\sum_{1}^{n} \frac{r2^r}{(r+2)!} = 1 - \frac{2^{n+1}}{(n+2)!}$.

11. $\frac{1}{n} + \frac{1}{n+1} + \frac{1}{n+2} + \ldots + \frac{1}{2n-1} = 1 - \frac{1}{2} + \frac{1}{3} - \frac{1}{4} + \ldots + \frac{1}{2n-1}$.

12. $1(n) + 2(n-1) + 3(n-2) + \ldots + n(1) = \frac{1}{6}n(n+1)(n+2)$.

13. Prove by induction that $x^{2n} - y^{2n}$ is divisible by $x+y$.

14. When n is a positive integer, prove that $10^n + 3 \cdot 4^{n+2} + 5$ is divisible by 9.

15. The terms of a sequence $u_1, u_2, u_3, \ldots$ are given by the rules:
$$u_1 = 2; \quad u_2 = 6; \quad u_n = 3u_{n-1} - 2u_{n-2}.$$
Prove that $\quad u_n = 2(2^n - 1)$.

16. Prove by induction that $\sum_{1}^{n}(r^3 + 3r^5) = \frac{1}{2}n^3(n+1)^3$.

17. If $f(n) \equiv 3^{4n+2} + 5^{2n+1}$, prove that $f(n+1) + 3f(n) = 28(3^{4n+3} + 5^{2n+1})$ and deduce that $f(n)$ is a multiple of 14.

18. Prove that the nth derivative of $1/(ax+b)$ is $(-1)^n n!\, a^n/(ax+b)^{n+1}$.

19. The terms of a sequence u_1, u_2, u_3, . . . are given by the rules:
$$u_1 = 3; \quad u_2 = 1; \quad u_n = 2u_{n-1} + 3u_{n-2}.$$
Prove that $\qquad u_n = 3^{n-1} + 2(-1)^{n-1}.$

20. If n is a positive integer, show that $4 \cdot 6^n + 5^{n+1}$ when divided by 20 leaves a remainder of 9.

21. Prove that $\dfrac{d^n}{dx^n}(e^x \sin x) = 2^{\frac{1}{2}n} e^x \sin (x + \frac{1}{4}n\pi).$

22. If $s_r = 1^r + 2^r + 3^r + \ . \ . \ . \ + n^r$, prove that:

(i) $s_3 - s_1{}^2 = 0$;   (ii) $s_5 + s_7 = 2s_1{}^4.$

23. A sequence is defined by $u_{r+2} + u_{r+1} - 12u_r = 0$ and $u_1 = 2$, $u_2 = 34$. Prove that $u_n = 2 \cdot 3^n + (-4)^n.$

24. Prove that $\dfrac{d^n}{dx^n}(x^2 e^{ax}) = a^{n-2} e^{ax}\{a^2 x^2 + 2nax + n(n-1)\}.$

MISCELLANEOUS EXAMPLES

1. Sum each of the following series to n terms:

(i) $1^3 + 4^3 + 7^3 + 10^3 + \ . \ . \ .;$

(ii) $1 \cdot 2^2 + 3 \cdot 3^2 + 5 \cdot 4^2 + 7 \cdot 5^2 + \ . \ . \ .;$

(iii) $1 \cdot 2 \cdot 4 + 2 \cdot 3 \cdot 5 + 3 \cdot 4 \cdot 6 + 4 \cdot 5 \cdot 7 + \ . \ . \ .$

2. Prove that
$$1^2(m) + 2^2(m-1) + 3^2(m-2) + \ . \ . \ . \ + m^2(1) = \tfrac{1}{12}m(m+1)^2(m+2).$$

3. The sum of n terms of a series is $\tfrac{1}{12}n(n+1)(3n^2 + 23n + 46)$, find the nth term of the series.

4. Find the sum of n terms of each of the series:

(i) $1 \cdot 3 \cdot 5 + 3 \cdot 5 \cdot 7 + 5 \cdot 7 \cdot 9 + \ . \ . \ .;$

(ii) $1 \cdot 3 \cdot 5 + 2 \cdot 4 \cdot 6 + 3 \cdot 5 \cdot 7 + \ . \ . \ .$

5. Prove that $c_0 c_2 + c_1 c_3 + c_2 c_4 + \ . \ . \ . \ + c_{n-2} c_n = (2n)!/(n+2)! \,(n-2)!.$

6. Find the sum of $2n$ terms of the series
$$1^2 - 3^2 + 5^2 - 7^2 + \ . \ . \ .$$

7. By expressing the nth term as a difference of two partial fractions find in each of the following cases the sum to n terms of the series:

(i) $\dfrac{1}{1 \cdot 3} + \dfrac{1}{2 \cdot 4} + \dfrac{1}{3 \cdot 5} + \ . \ . \ .;$

(ii) $\dfrac{3}{1^2 \cdot 2^2} + \dfrac{5}{2^2 \cdot 3^2} + \dfrac{7}{3^2 \cdot 4^2} + \ . \ . \ .$

8. Prove that $2 \cdot 7^n + 3 \cdot 5^n - 5$ is a multiple of 24.

9. Sum to n terms:

(i) $1 \cdot 2^2 + 2 \cdot 3^2 + 3 \cdot 4^2 + \ldots$;

(ii) $\dfrac{1}{1 \cdot 4} + \dfrac{1}{4 \cdot 7} + \dfrac{1}{7 \cdot 10} + \ldots$

10. Prove that, if n is even,

$$1 - \frac{1}{2} + \frac{1}{3} - \frac{1}{4} + \ldots - \frac{1}{n} = 2\left(\frac{1}{n+2} + \frac{1}{n+4} + \ldots + \frac{1}{2n}\right).$$

11. Sum to n terms, $\quad 1 + \dfrac{1}{2}\cos\theta + \dfrac{1}{2^2}\cos 2\theta + \dfrac{1}{2^3}\cos 3\theta + \ldots$

12. If u_r, the rth term of a series, is given by

$$u_r = 1^2 + 3^2 + 5^2 + \ldots (2r - 1)^2,$$

find $\displaystyle\sum_1^n u_r$.

13. Find the sum of the products of the integers $1, 2, 3, \ldots n$ taken two at a time and show that it is equal to half the excess of the sum of the cubes of the given integers over the sum of their squares.

14. Sum to n terms:

(i) $1 + 4x + 7x^2 + 10x^3 + \ldots$;

(ii) $1 + 4(3) + 8(3)^2 + 13(3)^3 + \ldots$

15. If the sum of n consecutive integers is kn, prove that the sum of their cubes is $kn\{k^2 + \frac{1}{4}(n^2 - 1)\}$.

16. If $u_r = r(2r + 3) + 3 \cdot 2^r$, find $\displaystyle\sum_1^n u_r$.

17. Evaluate: (i) $\displaystyle\sum_1^n \frac{1}{r(r+1)(r+2)}$;   (ii) $\displaystyle\sum_1^n \frac{1}{r(r+1)(r+2)(r+3)}$.

18. Find the sum of the squares of all the odd numbers less than 100 which are not multiples of 3.

19. Prove by induction that

$$1^3(1 + 3 \cdot 1^2) + 2^3(1 + 3 \cdot 2^2) + 3^3(1 + 3 \cdot 3^2) + \ldots n \text{ terms} = \tfrac{1}{2}n^3(n+1)^3.$$

20. If $c_0, c_1, c_2, \ldots c_n$ are the binomial coefficients, prove the results:

(i) $1 + 2c_1 + 4c_2 + 8c_3 + \ldots + 2^n c_n = 3^n$;

(ii) $1 + \dfrac{1}{3}c_1 + \dfrac{1}{3^2}c_2 + \dfrac{1}{3^3}c_3 + \ldots + \dfrac{1}{3^n}c_n = \left(\dfrac{4}{3}\right)^n.$

21. If $y = (1 + x)^2 \log(1 + x)$, prove that, if $n > 2$,

$$\frac{d^n y}{dx^n} = (-1)^{n-1} \frac{2 \cdot (n-3)!}{(1+x)^{n-2}}.$$

22. Express the rth term of the series $\dfrac{2}{3.5} - \dfrac{3}{5.7} + \dfrac{4}{7.9} - \dfrac{5}{9.11} + \cdots$, in partial fractions, and hence sum the series to n terms.

23. Sum to n terms:

    (i) $n(n+1) + (n+1)(n+2) + (n+2)(n+3) + \cdots$;

    (ii) $\dfrac{1}{n(n+1)} + \dfrac{1}{(n+1)(n+2)} + \dfrac{1}{(n+2)(n+3)} + \cdots$

24. Find the sum of n terms of the series whose rth term is $r(r+1)(2r+1)$.

25. Prove that the sum of n terms of the series:

$$\sin \theta + \sin (\theta + 2\phi) + \sin (\theta + 4\phi) + \cdots$$

is

$$\sin \{\theta + \overline{n-1}\phi\} \sin n\phi \operatorname{cosec} \phi.$$

26. If the sequence $u_1, u_2, u_3, \ldots$ is defined as follows:

$$u_1 = 1; \quad u_2 = 2; \quad 4u_{r+2} = u_r,$$

prove that

$$u_n = 5(\tfrac{1}{2})^n + 3(-\tfrac{1}{2})^n.$$

27. If $(1+x)^n = c_0 + c_1 x + c_2 x^2 + \cdots + c_n x^n$, $n > 1$, prove that:

    (i) $2c_1 - 3c_2 + 4c_3 - \cdots + (-1)^{n+1}(n+1)c_n = 1$;

    (ii) $c_0 + \tfrac{1}{2}c_1 + \tfrac{1}{3}c_2 + \cdots + \dfrac{1}{n+1} c_n = (2^{n+1} - 1)/(n+1)$.

28. Prove that the sum of n terms of the series

$$1 + \frac{2n-2}{2n-3} + \frac{(2n-2)(2n-4)}{(2n-3)(2n-5)} + \cdots$$

is $2n - 1$.

29. If u_r is the rth term of a series, find $\displaystyle\sum_1^n u_r$ in each of the following cases:

    (i) $u_r = r(r+2)(r+4)$;   (ii) $u_r = \dfrac{2r-1}{r(r+1)(r+2)}$.

30. Prove: (i) $\displaystyle\sum_1^n r \log \frac{r+1}{r} = \log \frac{(n+1)^n}{n!}$;

            (ii) $\displaystyle\sum_1^n (r^3 + 3r^5) = \tfrac{1}{2} n^3 (n+1)^3$.

31. Prove by induction that, if $n \geqslant 1$,

$$\frac{d^n}{dx^n} (x^n \log x) = n! \left\{ \log x + 1 + \tfrac{1}{2} + \cdots + \frac{1}{n} \right\}.$$

32. Sum to n terms:

    (i) $\dfrac{1}{1.2.3} + \dfrac{3}{2.3.4} + \dfrac{5}{3.4.5} + \dfrac{7}{4.5.6} + \cdots$;

    (ii) $1.n + 2(n-1) + 3(n-2) + 4(n-3) + \cdots + n.1$.

33. (i) The first of a set of n numbers in G.P. is a and the last is b; express the product of the n numbers in terms of a, b and n.

(ii) Defining a harmonic progression as a series the reciprocals of whose terms are in A.P., show that if the pth term of such a progression is q and the qth term is p, then the $(p+q)$th term is $pq/(p+q)$.

34. Find the sum of the first n terms of the series

$$\cos^3 0 - \tfrac{1}{3}\cos^3 30 + \tfrac{1}{9}\cos^3 90 - \tfrac{1}{27}\cos^3 270 + \ \cdots$$

35. If the sequence u_1, u_2, u_3, $\ldots$ is defined by $u_1 = 1$; $\ u_2 = 2$,

$$u_{r+2} + 4u_r = 4u_{r+1},$$

prove that $u_n = 2^{n-1}$.

36. Prove that $\dfrac{1}{2^2 - 1} + \dfrac{1}{4^2 - 1} + \dfrac{1}{6^2 - 1} + \ \cdots \ + \dfrac{1}{(2n)^2 - 1} = \dfrac{n}{2n+1}$.

37. If $\theta_p = \alpha + 2p\pi/n$, where $n > 2$, prove that:

(i) $\cos\theta_1 + \cos\theta_2 + \ \cdots \ + \cos\theta_n = 0$;

(ii) $\cos^2\theta_1 + \cos^2\theta_2 + \ \cdots \ + \cos^2\theta_n = \tfrac{1}{2}n$.

38. Prove by induction that

$$\frac{d^n}{dx^n}(e^{ax}\sin bx) = (a^2+b^2)^{\frac{1}{2}n}e^{ax}\sin\left(bx + n\tan^{-1}\frac{b}{a}\right).$$

39. Express $\dfrac{r^4 + 2r^3 + r^2 - 1}{r^2 + r}$ in the form $Ar^2 + Br + \dfrac{C}{r(r+1)}$; hence determine the sum $\displaystyle\sum_1^n \dfrac{r^4 + 2r^3 + r^2 - 1}{r^2 + r}$.

40. Sum to n terms:

(i) $\dfrac{1}{(1+x)(1+ax)} + \dfrac{a}{(1+ax)(1+a^2x)} + \dfrac{a^2}{(1+a^2x)(1+a^3x)} + \ \cdots$;

(ii) $1 + 3x + 6x^2 + 10x^3 + 15x^4 + \ \cdots$

CHAPTER XI

EXPANSIONS

Infinite series. A series in which the number of terms is allowed to increase without limit is an *infinite series*.

If u_r is the general term, then such a series can be denoted $\sum\limits_{1}^{\infty} u_r$.

Suppose $\qquad s_n = u_1 + u_2 + u_3 + \ldots + u_n,$

then if s_n tends to a definite limiting value s as n increases without limit or, as we say, tends to infinity, the infinite series is said to be *convergent* and s is referred to as its sum.

Infinite series fall into three main classes:

(*a*) series in which $s_n \longrightarrow$ a definite limit s as $n \longrightarrow \infty$—*convergent series*;

(*b*) series in which $s_n \longrightarrow \infty$ as $n \longrightarrow \infty$—*divergent series*;

(*c*) series in which s_n does not tend to a definite limit, finite or infinite, as $n \longrightarrow \infty$—*oscillating series*.

Some important infinite series will already be known; e.g.:

(i) $1 + \dfrac{x}{1!} + \dfrac{x^2}{2!} + \dfrac{x^3}{3!} + \ldots$;

(ii) $x - \dfrac{x^3}{3!} + \dfrac{x^5}{5!} - \dfrac{x^7}{7!} + \ldots$;

(iii) $x - \dfrac{x^2}{2} + \dfrac{x^3}{3} - \dfrac{x^4}{4} + \ldots$;

(iv) $1 + nx + \dfrac{n(n-1)}{2!} x^2 + \dfrac{n(n-1)(n-2)}{3!} x^3 + \ldots$, n not a positive integer.

Series (i) and (ii) are convergent for all values of x, and their sums are respectively e^x and $\sin x$.

Series (iii) is convergent only when $-1 < x \leqslant 1$, and in this case it has a sum $\log (1+x)$.

Series (iv) is convergent only when $-1 < x < 1$, in which case its sum is $(1+x)^n$.

Expansion of a function. The expansion of a function of x as an infinite power series of the form

$$a_0 + a_1 x + a_2 x^2 + \ldots + a_r x^r + \ldots$$

is an important mathematical process.

The expansions of several functions have already been met and made use of; it is the intention now to develop methods which will enable the expansions of a wider group of functions.

The principal methods of expanding a given function which will be dealt with are as follows:

  (i) by the use of known expansions and the application of ordinary algebraic and trigonometrical processes; e.g. partial fractions, factorisation;
  (ii) by use of Maclaurin's theorem;
  (iii) by differentiation or integration of a known series;
  (iv) by the formation and use of a differential equation.

As the basic theory of infinite series is beyond the scope of this book, *it is essential that the reader should realise that all the methods of expansion to be used depend on the initial assumption that it is possible to find an infinite series which is convergent, at least for some range of values of the variable x, with a sum equal to the given function.*

Algebraic and trigonometrical methods.   These methods, depending on a knowledge of the expansions of the basic functions $(1+x)^n$, e^x, $\log (1+x)$, $\sin x$, $\cos x$, $\sinh x$, $\cosh x$, are illustrated in the following examples.

Ex. 1.   *Expand* $\tan x$ *in powers of* x *as far as the term in* x^5.

$$\tan x = \frac{\sin x}{\cos x} = \frac{x - x^3/3! + x^5/5! - \ldots}{1 - x^2/2! + x^4/4! - \ldots},$$

$$= (x - \tfrac{1}{6}x^3 + \tfrac{1}{120}x^5 - \ldots)\{1 - \tfrac{1}{2}x^2(1 - \tfrac{1}{12}x^2 + \ldots)\}^{-1},$$

$$= (x - \tfrac{1}{6}x^3 + \tfrac{1}{120}x^5 - \ldots)\{1 + \tfrac{1}{2}x^2(1 - \tfrac{1}{12}x^2 + \ldots)$$
$$+ \tfrac{1}{4}x^4(1 - \tfrac{1}{12}x^2 + \ldots)^2 + \ldots\},$$

$$= (x - \tfrac{1}{6}x^3 + \tfrac{1}{120}x^5 - \ldots)\{1 + \tfrac{1}{2}x^2 + \tfrac{5}{24}x^4 - \ldots\},$$

$$= x + x^3(\tfrac{1}{2} - \tfrac{1}{6}) + x^5(\tfrac{5}{24} - \tfrac{1}{12} + \tfrac{1}{120}) \ldots$$

i.e. $\tan x = x + \tfrac{1}{3}x^3 + \tfrac{2}{15}x^5 \ldots$

Ex. 2.   *Obtain the coefficient of* $x^{3(2r-1)}$ *in the expansion of* $\log \dfrac{1-x+x^2}{1+x+x^2}$.

As $1 + x^3 = (1 + x)(1 - x + x^2);$ $(1 - x^3) = (1 - x)(1 + x + x^2);$

$$\log \frac{1-x+x^2}{1+x+x^2} = \log (1 + x^3) - \log (1 + x) - \log (1 - x^3) + \log (1 - x),$$

$$= \{\log (1 + x^3) - \log (1 - x^3)\} - \{\log (1 + x) - \log (1 - x)\},$$

$$= 2\left\{x^3 + \frac{1}{3}(x^3)^3 + \ldots + \frac{1}{2r-1}(x^3)^{2r-1} + \ldots\right\}$$

$$- 2\left\{x + \frac{1}{3}x^3 + \ldots + \frac{1}{2r-1}x^{2r-1} + \ldots + \frac{1}{3(2r-1)}x^{3(2r-1)} + \ldots\right\}$$

$\therefore$ Coefficient of $x^{3(2r-1)} = 2\left\{\dfrac{1}{2r-1} - \dfrac{1}{3(2r-1)}\right\} = \dfrac{4}{3(2r-1)}.$

Ex. 3. *Expand $e^{\cos^2 x}$ as far as the term in x^4.*

Write $\quad \cos^2 x = \frac{1}{2}(1 + \cos 2x).$

Then $\quad e^{\cos^2 x} = e^{\frac{1}{2}} \cdot e^{\frac{1}{2}\cos 2x}$

$$= e^{\frac{1}{2}} \cdot e^{\frac{1}{2}\{1 - \frac{1}{2}(2x)^2 + \frac{1}{24}(2x)^4 \dots \}}$$

$$= e \cdot e^{-x^2\{1 - \frac{1}{3}x^2 + \dots\}}$$

$$= e\{1 - x^2(1 - \frac{1}{3}x^2 + \dots) + \frac{1}{2}x^4(1 - \frac{1}{3}x^2 + \dots)^2 - \dots\},$$

$$= e\{1 - x^2 + \frac{5}{6}x^4 \dots\}.$$

EXAMPLES 11a

Obtain the following expansions as far as the terms shown:

1. $\cosh x = \frac{1}{2}(e^x + e^{-x}) = 1 + \dfrac{x^2}{2!} + \dfrac{x^4}{4!} + \dots$

2. $\sinh x = \frac{1}{2}(e^x - e^{-x}) = x + \dfrac{x^3}{3!} + \dfrac{x^5}{5!} + \dots$

3. $\sec x = 1 + \dfrac{x^2}{2!} + \dfrac{5x^4}{4!} + \dots$

4. $\dfrac{x}{\sin x} = 1 + \dfrac{x^2}{3!} + \dfrac{14x^4}{6!} + \dots$

5. $\log \cos x = -\frac{1}{2}x^2 - \frac{1}{12}x^4 - \frac{1}{48}x^6 \dots$

6. $\log \sec x = \frac{1}{2}x^2 + \frac{1}{12}x^4 + \frac{1}{48}x^6 + \dots$

7. $a^x = 1 + x \log a + \dfrac{(x \log a)^2}{2!} + \dfrac{(x \log a)^3}{3!} + \dots$

8. $\log (1 + e^x) = \log 2 + \frac{1}{2}x + \frac{1}{8}x^2 - \frac{1}{192}x^4 \dots$

9. $\cos^2 x = 1 - x^2 + \frac{1}{3}x^4 - \frac{2}{45}x^6 + \dots$

10. $\tan (\frac{1}{4}\pi + x) = 1 + 2x + 2x^2 + \frac{8}{3}x^3 + \dots$

11. $e^{x \sin x} = 1 + x^2 + \frac{1}{3}x^4 + \frac{1}{120}x^6 + \dots$

12. $\log \dfrac{\sin x}{x} = -\frac{1}{6}x^2 - \frac{1}{180}x^4 \dots$

13. Expand $\dfrac{x}{e^x - 1}$ as far as the term in x^4.

14. Show that, if powers of x above the fourth are neglected,

$$\frac{3 \sin x}{2 + \cos x} = x.$$

15. Prove that $\log (1 - x + x^2) = -x + \frac{1}{2}x^2 + \frac{2}{3}x^3 + \frac{1}{4}x^4 - \frac{1}{5}x^5 - \frac{1}{3}x^6 \dots$

16. Obtain the first three terms in the expansion of $\tanh x$ as a power series in x.

17. Express $\cos^4 x$ in multiple angles and deduce the first four terms in its expansion.

18. Expand $\sin 5x \cos x$ as far as the term in x^5.

19. Obtain the expansions of $(1 + \sin x)^{-1}$ and $(1 - \sin x)^{-1}$ as far as the terms in x^4 and deduce the first three terms in the expansion of $1/(1 - \sin^2 x)$.

20. Obtain the expansion of $\log \dfrac{1 + \cos x}{1 + \sin x}$ as far as the term in x^4.

Use the method of expansion to evaluate the following limits:

21. $\displaystyle\lim_{x \to 0} \dfrac{x \log (1 + x)}{1 - \cos x}$.

22. $\displaystyle\lim_{x \to 0} \dfrac{e^x - 1 + \log (1 - x)}{\sin^2 x}$.

23. $\displaystyle\lim_{x \to 0} \dfrac{\log (1 + \sin x) - x}{x^2}$.

Taylor's theorem. *If $f(x)$ is a function of x which is such that $f(x + h)$ can be expanded in a convergent series of positive integral powers of h, then*

$$f(x + h) = f(x) + hf'(x) + \frac{h^2}{2!} f''(x) + \frac{h^3}{3!} f'''(x) + \ \ldots$$

For assume

$$f(x + h) = a_0 + a_1 h + a_2 h^2 + a_3 h^3 + a_4 h^4 + \ \ldots, \quad . \quad . \quad \text{(i)}$$

where $a_0, a_1, a_2, \ldots$ are functions of x alone not containing h. Differentiating with respect to h and noting that

$$\frac{d}{dh} f(x + h) = \frac{d}{dX} f(X) \cdot \frac{dX}{dh}, \text{ where } X = x + h,$$

$$= f'(X) \cdot 1,$$

with similar results for higher derivatives, then

$$f'(X) = a_1 + 2a_2 h + 3a_3 h^2 + 4a_4 h^3 + \ \ldots \quad . \quad . \quad \text{(ii)}$$

Similarly, $\quad f''(X) = a_2 \cdot 2! + 3 \cdot 2a_3 h + 4 \cdot 3a_4 h^2 + \ \ldots \ . \quad . \quad \text{(iii)}$

$$f'''(X) = a_3 \cdot 3! + 4 \cdot 3 \cdot 2a_4 h + \ \ldots \quad . \quad . \quad \text{(iv)}$$

$$\cdot \quad \cdot \quad \cdot \quad \cdot \quad \cdot \quad \cdot \quad \cdot \quad \cdot \quad \cdot \quad \cdot$$

Putting $h = 0$ successively in (i), (ii), (iii), (iv), $\ldots$ gives

$$a_0 = f(x); \quad a_1 = f'(x); \quad a_2 = \frac{1}{2!} f''(x); \quad a_3 = \frac{1}{3!} f'''(x); \ \ldots$$

$$\therefore \ \mathbf{f(x + h) = f(x) + hf'(x) + \frac{h^2}{2!} f''(x) + \frac{h^3}{3!} f'''(x) + \ \ldots \ + \frac{h^r}{r!} f^r(x) + \ \ldots}$$

Ex. 4. *Use Taylor's theorem to derive the binomial expansion $(x + h)^n$.*

Take $\qquad\qquad\qquad\qquad f(x) = x^n.$

Then $\qquad f'(x) = nx^{n-1}; \quad f''(x) = n(n-1)x^{n-2}; \ \ldots$

$$\therefore \ (x + h)^n = x^n + nx^{n-1}h + \frac{n(n-1)}{2!} x^{n-2}h^2 + \ \ldots$$

Maclaurin's theorem. *If $f(x)$ can be expanded in a convergent series of positive integral powers of x, then*

$$f(x) = f(0) + xf'(0) + \frac{x^2}{2!}f''(0) + \frac{x^3}{3!}f'''(0) + \ldots$$

For assume

$$f(x) = a_0 + a_1x + a_2x^2 + a_3x^3 + a_4x^4 + \ldots, \qquad \text{(i)}$$

where a_0, a_1, a_2, a_3, $\ldots$ are constants.

Differentiating repeatedly with respect to x gives

$$f'(x) = a_1 + 2a_2x + 3a_3x^2 + 4a_4x^3 + \ldots \qquad \text{(ii)}$$

$$f''(x) = a_2 . 2! + 3 . 2a_3x + 4 . 3a_4x^2 + \ldots \qquad \text{(iii)}$$

$$f'''(x) = a_3 . 3! + 4 . 3 . 2a_4x + \ldots \qquad \text{(iv)}$$

$$\cdot \quad \cdot \quad \cdot \quad \cdot \quad \cdot \quad \cdot \quad \cdot \quad \cdot \quad \cdot \quad \cdot$$

Putting $x = 0$ in (i), (ii), (iii), (iv), $\ldots$, gives

$$a_0 = f(0); \quad a_1 = f'(0); \quad a_2 = \frac{1}{2!}f''(0); \quad a_3 = \frac{1}{3!}f'''(0); \ldots$$

$$\therefore \; \mathbf{f(x) = f(0) + xf'(0) + \frac{x^2}{2!}f''(0) + \frac{x^3}{3!}f'''(0) + \ldots + \frac{x^r}{r!}f^r(0) + \ldots}$$

N.B. (i) It will be noted that Maclaurin's theorem is the special case of Taylor's theorem with x replaced by 0 and h by x.

(ii) Unless the repeated differentiation is relatively simple as with such functions as e^x, $\cos x$, $\sin x$, $(1 + x)^n$, it is usually more convenient to use Maclaurin's theorem in conjunction with a differential equation derived from the function whose expansion is required. This procedure will be demonstrated in a later section.

Ex. 5. *Find the first three terms in the expansion of* $\log (1 + \tan x)$.

$f(x) = \log (1 + \tan x); \quad f(0) = 0.$

$f'(x) = \dfrac{\sec^2 x}{1 + \tan x}; \quad f'(0) = 1.$

$f''(x) = \dfrac{2 \sec^2 x \tan x(1 + \tan x) - \sec^4 x}{(1 + \tan x)^2} = \dfrac{\sec^2 x(\tan^2 x + 2 \tan x - 1)}{(1 + \tan x)^2}$

$\qquad = \sec^2 x - \dfrac{2 \sec^2 x}{(1 + \tan x)^2}; \quad f''(0) = -1.$

$f'''(x) = 2 \sec^2 x \tan x - \dfrac{4 \sec^2 x \tan x (1 + \tan x)^2 - 4 \sec^4 x(1 + \tan x)}{(1 + \tan x)^4};$

$$f'''(0) = 4.$$

$\therefore \; \log (1 + \tan x) = x - \tfrac{1}{2}x^2 + \tfrac{2}{3}x^3 \ldots$

EXAMPLES 11b

Use Maclaurin's theorem to obtain the following expansions:

1. $\cos^2 x = 1 - x^2 + \frac{1}{3}x^4 \ldots$

2. $\log(1 + x^2) = x^2 - \frac{1}{2}x^4 + \frac{1}{3}x^6 \ldots$

3. $\sinh x = x + \dfrac{1}{3!}x^3 + \dfrac{1}{5!}x^5 + \ldots$

4. $\cosh x = 1 + \dfrac{1}{2!}x^2 + \dfrac{1}{4!}x^4 + \ldots$

5. $e^{\sin x} = 1 + x + \frac{1}{2}x^2 - \frac{1}{8}x^4 \ldots$

6. $\dfrac{x}{\sin x} = 1 + \frac{1}{6}x^2 + \frac{7}{360}x^4 \ldots$

7. $\tan^{-1} x = x - \frac{1}{3}x^3 + \frac{1}{5}x^5 - \ldots$

8. $\sin^{-1} x = x + \frac{1}{6}x^3 + \frac{3}{40}x^5 \ldots$

Use Taylor's theorem to prove the following results:

9. $\cos(x + h) = \cos x + h \cos(x + \frac{1}{2}\pi) + \dfrac{1}{2!}h^2 \cos(x + \pi)$

$$+ \dfrac{1}{3!}h^3 \cos(x + \frac{3}{2}\pi) + \ldots$$

10. $\log \sin(x + h) = \log \sin x + h \cot x - \dfrac{1}{2}h^2 \operatorname{cosec}^2 x$

$$+ \dfrac{1}{3}h^3 \cot x \operatorname{cosec}^2 x \ldots$$

11. $\sin^{-1}(x + h) = \sin^{-1} x + \dfrac{h}{(1 - x^2)^{\frac{1}{2}}} + \dfrac{h^2}{2!}\dfrac{x}{(1 - x^2)^{\frac{3}{2}}} \ldots$

12. If $\tan y = \dfrac{1 + x}{1 - x}$, expand y as far as the term in x^3.

13. If $\log y = \tan^{-1} x$, find the coefficient of x^3 in the expansion of y by Maclaurin's theorem.

14. Use Taylor's theorem to obtain approximate values of: (i) $\log(1 \cdot 001)$; (ii) $\sin 30° \, 1'$; (iii) $\tan^{-1} 1 \cdot 02$.

15. If $\tan y = 1 + x + x^2$, show that $y = \frac{1}{4}\pi + \frac{1}{2}x + \frac{1}{4}x^2 \ldots$

16. If $f(x), g(x)$ are such that $f(a) = g(a) = 0$ and $g'(a) \neq 0$, prove that

$$\frac{f(a + h)}{g(a + h)} = \frac{f'(a) + \dfrac{1}{2!}hf''(a) + \dfrac{1}{3!}h^2 f'''(a) + \ldots}{g'(a) + \dfrac{1}{2!}hg''(a) + \dfrac{1}{3!}h^2 g'''(a) + \ldots}$$

Deduce that $\qquad \lim\limits_{x \to a} \dfrac{f(x)}{g(x)} = \dfrac{f'(a)}{g'(a)}.$

17. Use the result of the previous example to find the following limits:

(i) $\lim\limits_{x \to 0} \dfrac{\sin 2x}{x}$; (ii) $\lim\limits_{x \to 1} \dfrac{\log x}{1 - x}$; (iii) $\lim\limits_{x \to 2} \dfrac{x^3 - 2^3}{x^2 - 2^2}$; (iv) $\lim\limits_{x \to 0} \dfrac{\tan^{-1} x}{x}$.

18. By repeated use of the result in Question 16, obtain the limit, as $x \to 0$, of $\dfrac{x \cos x - \sin x}{x^3}$.

Expansion by differentiation or integration of a known series. From a known expansion it is possible by differentiation and integration to derive new expansions, for it can be shown that if a power series $\sum\limits_{}^{\infty} a_n x^n$ is convergent for some particular range of values of x and has a sum $s(x)$, then the series obtained by differentiation and integration are also convergent for the same range of values of x and have sums $s'(x)$ and $\int_0^x s(x)\,dx$ respectively.

Ex. 6. *Using the expansion of* $(1+x^2)^{-1}$ *derive the expansion of* $\tan^{-1} x$.

If $-1 < x < 1$, $(1+x^2)^{-1} = 1 - x^2 + x^4 - x^6 + \ \ldots$

Integrating with respect to x,

$$\tan^{-1} x = C + x - \tfrac{1}{3}x^3 + \tfrac{1}{5}x^5 - \tfrac{1}{7}x^7 + \ \ldots$$

Putting $x = 0$; $C = \tan^{-1} 0 = 0$, *assuming the principal value.*

$$\tan^{-1} x = x - \tfrac{1}{3}x^3 + \tfrac{1}{5}x^5 - \tfrac{1}{7}x^7 + \ \ldots$$

It can be shown that the expansion is also true for $x = 1$ and by using this value we have,

$$\tfrac{1}{4}\pi = 1 - \tfrac{1}{3} + \tfrac{1}{5} - \tfrac{1}{7} \ \ldots$$

and hence the value of π can be obtained to any degree of accuracy.

Ex. 7. *If* $y = \sinh^{-1} 2x \sqrt{(1+x^2)}$, *find* $\dfrac{dy}{dx}$ *and hence obtain the first three terms in the expansion of* y.

Let $y = \sinh^{-1} 2x \sqrt{(1+x^2)} = a_0 + a_1 x + a_2 x^2 + a_3 x^3 + a_4 x^4 + a_5 x^5 + \ \ldots$

Then $\dfrac{dy}{dx} = \dfrac{2}{\sqrt{(1+x^2)}} = a_1 + 2a_2 x + 3a_3 x^2 + 4a_4 x^3 + 5a_5 x^4 + \ \ldots$

But $\dfrac{2}{\sqrt{(1+x^2)}} = 2(1+x^2)^{-\frac{1}{2}} = 2\{1 - \tfrac{1}{2}x^2 + \tfrac{3}{8}x^4 \ \ldots\}.$

Comparing coefficients, $a_1 = 2;\quad a_3 = -\tfrac{1}{3};\quad a_5 = \tfrac{3}{20}; \ \ldots$
$$a_2 = 0;\quad a_4 = 0;\quad a_6 = 0; \ \ldots$$

Also $a_0 = \sinh^{-1} 0 = 0.$

$$\therefore\ \sinh^{-1} 2x \sqrt{(1+x^2)} = 2x - \tfrac{1}{3}x^3 + \tfrac{3}{20}x^5 \ \ldots$$

EXAMPLES 11c

Apply the processes of differentiation or integration to derive the following results.

1. From the expansion of $\sin x$ derive that of $\cos x$, and vice-versa.

2. Repeat Question 1 with the functions $\sinh x$, $\cosh x$.

3. From the expansion of $(1+x)^{-1}$ for $-1 < x < 1$, derive the expansions of: (i) $(1+x)^{-2}$;   (ii) $\log (1+x)$.

4. Expand $1/\sqrt{(1-x^2)}$ if $|x| < 1$ and deduce the expansions of $\sin^{-1} x$ and $\cos^{-1} x$, assuming principal values.

5. Use the expansion of $\sin^{-1} x$ to deduce the result

$$\frac{\pi}{6} = \frac{1}{2} + \frac{1}{2 \cdot 3 \cdot 2^3} + \frac{1 \cdot 3}{2 \cdot 4 \cdot 5 \cdot 2^5} + \cdots$$

6. Deduce the expansion of $\sinh^{-1} x$ from that of $1/\sqrt{(1 + x^2)}$, where $|x| < 1$.

7. Differentiate $\tan^{-1} \dfrac{2x}{1 - x^2}$ and use the result to obtain the expansion of the function if $-1 < x < 1$.

8. Use the method of the previous example to obtain the first three terms in the expansions of each of the following functions:

   (i) $\tan^{-1} \dfrac{1 + x}{1 - x}$;   (ii) $\sec^{-1} \dfrac{1}{1 - 2x^2}$;   (iii) $\sin^{-1} 2x\sqrt{(1 - x^2)}$.

9. Obtain the expansion $\tan^{-1} x = x - \frac{1}{3}x^3 + \frac{1}{5}x^5 - \frac{1}{7}x^7 + \cdots$; assuming it is true when $x = 1$, calculate the value of π correct to two decimal places.

10. If $-1 < x < 1$, sum the series $1 + x + x^2 + x^3 + \cdots$ Deduce the sums of the series:

      (i) $1 + 2x + 3x^2 + 4x^3 + \cdots$;
      (ii) $1 + x + \frac{1}{2}x^2 + \frac{1}{3}x^3 + \cdots$;

      (iii) $x + \dfrac{1}{1 \cdot 2}x^2 + \dfrac{1}{2 \cdot 3}x^3 + \cdots$

Expansion by the formation of a differential equation. This method depends on first obtaining a linear differential equation satisfied by the given function $f(x)$. Then by assuming

$$f(x) = a_0 + a_1 x + a_2 x^2 + \cdots$$

and substituting for $f(x), f'(x), f''(x) \ldots$ in this differential equation, a series of equations are obtained from which the coefficients $a_0, a_1, a_2, \ldots$, except one or two at the beginning, can be determined.

Ex. 8. *If* $y = \sin^{-1} x$, *prove that* $(1 - x^2)y_2 - xy_1 = 0$ *and hence obtain the first three terms in the expansion of* $\sin^{-1} x$.

$$y = \sin^{-1} x.$$

Differentiating, $y_1 = \dfrac{1}{\sqrt{(1 - x^2)}}$

i.e. $(1 - x^2)y_1^2 = 1.$

Differentiating again and dividing by $2y_1$,

$$(1 - x^2)y_2 - xy_1 = 0. \quad \cdots \cdots \cdots \quad \text{(i)}$$

Now assume $y = a_0 + a_1 x + a_2 x^2 + a_3 x^3 + a_4 x^4 + a_5 x^5 + \cdots,$

then $y_1 = a_1 + 2a_2 x + 3a_3 x^2 + 4a_4 x^3 + 5a_5 x^4 + \cdots,$

            $y_2 = 2a_2 + 3 \cdot 2a_3 x + 4 \cdot 3a_4 x^2 + 5 \cdot 4a_5 x^3 + \cdots$

Substituting in (i),

$$(1 - x^2)(2a_2 + 6a_3 x + 12a_4 x^2 + 20a_5 x^3 \cdots)$$
$$= x(a_1 + 2a_2 x + 3a_3 x^2 + 4a_4 x^3 + 5a_5 x^4 + \cdots).$$

Equating coefficients,
$$2a_2 = 0; \qquad a_2 = 0.$$
$$6a_3 = a_1; \qquad a_3 = \tfrac{1}{6}a_1.$$
$$-2a_2 + 12a_4 = 2a_2; \qquad a_4 = \tfrac{1}{3}a_2 = 0.$$
$$-6a_3 + 20a_5 = 3a_3; \qquad a_5 = \tfrac{9}{20}a_3.$$

But
$$a_0 = y(0) = 0; \qquad a_1 = y_1(0) = 1.$$
$$\therefore \; a_0 = a_2 = a_4 = 0; \qquad a_1 = 1, \; a_3 = \tfrac{1}{6}, \; a_5 = \tfrac{3}{40}.$$

I.e.
$$\sin^{-1} x = x + \tfrac{1}{6}x^3 + \tfrac{3}{40}x^5 + \; \ldots$$

More general method. A better method of obtaining the expansion of a function $f(x)$ requires a general relationship between the values of the derivatives of the function when $x = 0$.

The determination of this general relationship involves the use of *Leibnitz's theorem*. This theorem is a generalisation of the product rule in differentiation, and its basis is seen from the following, where u, v are functions of x and suffixes are used to denote differentiation with respect to x:

$$(uv)_1 = u_1 v + u v_1 \; \ldots \text{ the product rule.}$$
$$(uv)_2 = (u_1 v)_1 + (u v_1)_1,$$
$$= u_2 v + u_1 v_1 + u_1 v_1 + u v_2,$$
$$= u_2 v + 2u_1 v_1 + u v_2 = u_2 v + {}_2C_1 u_1 v_1 + u v_2.$$

Similarly,

$$(uv)_3 = u_3 v + 3u_2 v_1 + 3u_1 v_2 + u v_3 = u_3 v + {}_3C_1 u_2 v_1 + {}_3C_2 u_1 v_2 + u v_3.$$

. . . .

Generally, if n is a positive integer,

$$\mathbf{(uv)_n = u_n v + {}_nC_1 u_{n-1} v_1 + {}_nC_2 u_{n-2} v_2 + \; \ldots \; + {}_nC_r u_{n-r} v_r + \; \ldots \; + u v_n.}$$

This result is Leibnitz's theorem.

The use of this theorem in conjunction with Maclaurin's theorem to obtain the expansion of a function is illustrated in the following worked examples.

Ex. 9. *If* $y = e^{\tan^{-1} x}$, *prove that*
$$(1 + x^2)y_n - \{1 - 2(n-1)x\}y_{n-1} + (n-1)(n-2)y_{n-2} = 0$$
and hence find the first six terms in the expansion of y by Maclaurin's theorem.

$$y = e^{\tan^{-1} x},$$

differentiating,
$$y_1 = \frac{e^{\tan^{-1} x}}{1 + x^2} = \frac{y}{1 + x^2};$$

i.e.
$$(1 + x^2)y_1 = y.$$

To obtain the required differential equation it is necessary to differentiate the above result $(n-1)$ times.

By Leibnitz's theorem, the $(n-1)$th derivative of the product $(1+x^2)y_1$ is

$$(1+x^2)y_n + {}_{n-1}C_1 2xy_{n-1} + {}_{n-1}C_2 2y_{n-2},$$

subsequent terms vanishing.

$$\therefore \quad (1+x^2)y_n + 2(n-1)xy_{n-1} + (n-1)(n-2)y_{n-2} = y_{n-1}$$

or, $\quad (1+x^2)y_n - \{1 - 2(n-1)x\}y_{n-1} + (n-1)(n-2)y_{n-2} = 0.$

Putting $x = 0$,

$$y_n(0) - y_{n-1}(0) + (n-1)(n-2)y_{n-2}(0) = 0, \text{ true for } n \geqslant 2. \quad . \quad \text{(i)}$$

By Maclaurin's theorem,

$$y = y(0) + xy_1(0) + \frac{1}{2!}x^2y_2(0) + \ldots + \frac{1}{n!}x^n y_n(0) + \ldots$$

But, $\qquad y(0) = e^{\tan^{-1}0} = 1; \quad y_1(0) = y(0) = 1.$

Using result (i), $\qquad y_2(0) = y_1(0) - 0 = 1;$

$$y_3(0) = y_2(0) - 2y_1(0) = -1;$$
$$y_4(0) = y_3(0) - 6y_2(0) = -7;$$
$$y_5(0) = y_4(0) - 12y_3(0) = 5.$$

$$\therefore \quad y = 1 + x + \tfrac{1}{2}x^2 - \tfrac{1}{6}x^3 - \tfrac{7}{24}x^4 + \tfrac{1}{24}x^5 \ldots$$

Ex. 10. *Prove that* $\dfrac{\sinh^{-1} x}{\sqrt{(1+x^2)}} = x - \dfrac{2}{3}x^3 + \dfrac{2 \cdot 4}{3 \cdot 5}x^5 - \dfrac{2 \cdot 4 \cdot 6}{3 \cdot 5 \cdot 7}x^7 + \ldots$

Let $\qquad\qquad\qquad\qquad y = \dfrac{\sinh^{-1} x}{\sqrt{(1+x^2)}}$

i.e. $\qquad\qquad\qquad\qquad y^2(1+x^2) = (\sinh^{-1} x)^2.$

Differentiating with respect to x,

$$2yy_1(1+x^2) + 2xy^2 = \frac{2\sinh^{-1} x}{\sqrt{(1+x^2)}} = 2y.$$

Dividing by $2y$,

$$(1+x^2)y_1 + xy = 1. \quad . \quad . \quad . \quad . \quad . \quad \text{(i)}$$

Differentiating $(n-1)$ times by Leibnitz's theorem,

$$(1+x^2)y_n + (n-1)2xy_{n-1} + (n-1)(n-2)y_{n-2} + xy_{n-1} + (n-1)y_{n-2} = 0.$$

Putting $x = 0$,

$$y_n(0) + (n-1)^2 y_{n-2}(0) = 0. \quad . \quad . \quad . \quad . \quad \text{(ii)}$$

Also $\quad y(0) = 0$ and hence from (ii), $y_2 = y_4 = y_6 = \ldots = 0.$

From (i), $\quad y_1(0) = 1$ and hence from (ii),

$$y_3(0) = -2^2; \quad y_5(0) = 4^2 \cdot 2^2; \quad y_7(0) = -6^2 \cdot 4^2 \cdot 2^2, \text{ etc.}$$

By Maclaurin's theorem,

$$y = y(0) + xy_1(0) + \frac{1}{2!}x^2y_2(0) + \ldots + \frac{1}{r!}x^r y_r(0) + \ldots$$

$$\therefore \frac{\sinh^{-1} x}{\sqrt{(1+x^2)}} = x - \frac{2^2}{3!}x^3 + \frac{4^2 \cdot 2^2}{5!}x^5 - \frac{6^2 \cdot 4^2 \cdot 2^2}{7!}x^7 + \ldots$$

$$= x - \frac{2}{3}x^3 + \frac{2 \cdot 4}{3 \cdot 5}x^5 - \frac{2 \cdot 4 \cdot 6}{3 \cdot 5 \cdot 7}x^7 + \ldots$$

EXAMPLES 11d

1. If $y = (1+x)^n$, show that $(1+x)y_1 = ny$, and deduce the expansion of $(1+x)^n$.

2. If $\log y = \tan^{-1} x$, show that $(1+x^2)y_1 = y$, and hence obtain the first four terms in the expansion of y by Maclaurin's theorem.

3. If $y = \cos mx$, prove that $y_2 + m^2 y = 0$ and deduce the expansion of $\cos mx$.

Obtain linear differential equations with rational coefficients satisfied by the following functions and use them to derive the expansions of the functions:

4. e^{mx}.   **5.** 2^x.   **6.** $\log(1+x)$.   **7.** $\sin^{-1} x$.

8. $\sinh mx$.   **9.** $\cosh mx$.   **10.** $\tan^{-1} \dfrac{2x}{1-x^2}$.   **11.** $\sinh^{-1} x$.

12. If $y = \tan^{-1} x/(1+x^2)$, prove that $(1+x^2)^2 y_1 + 2x(1+x^2)y = 1$ and deduce the first three terms in the expansion of y as a power series.

13. If $y = (\sin^{-1} x)^2 = a_0 + a_1 x + a_2 x^2 + a_3 x^3 + \ldots$, prove that
$$(1-x^2)y_2 - xy_1 - 2 = 0$$
and deduce the values of a_0, a_1, a_2, a_3, a_4. Show also that
$$(1-x^2)y_{n+2} - x(2n+1)y_{n+1} - n^2 y_n = 0,$$
and hence prove that $(n+1)(n+2)a_{n+2} = n^2 a_n$.

14. If $\log y = \sin^{-1} x$, prove:
(i) $(1-x^2)y_2 - xy_1 - y = 0$;
(ii) $(1-x^2)y_{n+2} - (2n+1)xy_{n+1} - (n^2+1)y_n = 0$.
Deduce that if $y = a_0 + a_1 x + a_2 x^2 + \ldots$, then
$$(n+1)(n+2)a_{n+2} = (n^2+1)a_n.$$

15. If $y = (\sin^{-1} x)^2 = a_0 + a_1 x + a_2 x^2 + a_3 x^3 + \ldots$, prove that
$$(n+1)(n+2)a_{n+2} = n^2 a_n$$
and deduce that
$$(\sin^{-1} x)^2 = \frac{2x^2}{2!} + \frac{2^2}{4!} 2x^4 + \frac{2^2 \cdot 4^2}{6!} 2x^6 + \ldots$$

16. If $y = \sin(2 \sin^{-1} x) = a_0 + a_1 x + \dfrac{a_2}{2!} x^2 + \dfrac{a_3}{3!} x^3 + \ldots$, prove:
(i) $(1-x^2)y_2 - xy_1 + 4y = 0$;
(ii) $(1-x^2)y_{n+2} - (2n+1)xy_{n+1} + (4-n^2)y_n = 0$;
(iii) $a_{n+2} + (4-n^2)a_n = 0$.

17. Prove that $\log\{x + \sqrt{(x^2+1)}\} = x - \dfrac{1}{2}\dfrac{x^3}{3} + \dfrac{1 \cdot 3}{2 \cdot 4}\dfrac{x^5}{5} - \dfrac{1 \cdot 3 \cdot 5}{2 \cdot 4 \cdot 6}\dfrac{x^7}{7} + \ldots$

18. If $4xy_2 + 2y_1 + y = 0$ and $y = 1$ when $x = 0$, show that
$$y = 1 - \frac{x}{2!} + \frac{x^2}{4!} - \frac{x^3}{6!} \ldots = \cos \sqrt{x}.$$

19. If $(x - x^2)y_2 + (1 - x)y_1 - y = 0$, obtain y in the form
$$a_0 + a_1 x + a_2 x^2 + \ldots$$

20. If $2x(1 - x)y_2 + (1 - x)y_1 + 3y = 0$, prove that a particular solution is
$$y = 1 - 3x + \frac{3x^2}{1 \cdot 3} + \frac{3x^3}{3 \cdot 5} + \frac{3x^4}{5 \cdot 7} + \ldots$$

MISCELLANEOUS EXAMPLES

1. Obtain the first four terms in the expansion of $\log (1 - x + x^2)$.

2. Find the coefficient of x^r in the expansion of $1/e^{x+2}$.

3. Obtain the coefficient of x^{3r} in the expansion of $\cos^3 x$ if r is even.

4. Find the first three terms in the expansion of $\log (2 - \cos x)$ by Maclaurin's theorem.

5. Find the coefficient of x^{4n} in the expansion of $(1 - x + x^2 - x^3)^{-1}$ in ascending powers of x.

6. Use Maclaurin's theorem to show that
$$\log \sec x = \tfrac{1}{2}x^2 + \tfrac{1}{12}x^4 + \tfrac{1}{45}x^6 + \ldots$$

7. Obtain the first four terms in the expansion of $e^{x \sin x}$ as a power series.

8. If x is small, prove that $\tfrac{1}{2} \log \dfrac{1 + x}{1 - x} - \sin \{x\sqrt{(1 + x^2)}\} \simeq \tfrac{17}{30}x^5$.

9. If $\log y = \tan^{-1} \dfrac{2x}{1 - x^2}$, show that $(1 + x^2)y_1 = 2y$ and deduce the expansion of y as far as the term in x^5.

10. Prove by Maclaurin's theorem that
$$\log (1 + x \sin x) = x^2 - \tfrac{2}{3}x^4 \ldots$$

11. Expand $e^{\tan x}$ as far as the term in x^3.

12. Find the coefficients of x, x^2, x^3 in the expansion of $\dfrac{1}{\sqrt{(1 - 2x \cos \theta + x^2)}}$ in ascending powers of x.

13. Obtain the expansion of $\log \dfrac{1 + \cos x}{1 - \sin x}$ as far as the term in x^4.

14. Prove the results: (i) $\tan^{-1} x = x - \tfrac{1}{3}x^3 + \tfrac{1}{5}x^5 - \ldots$;

$\qquad$ (ii) $\dfrac{\pi}{4} = \tan^{-1} \tfrac{1}{2} + \tan^{-1} \tfrac{1}{3}$.

Deduce the value of π correct to 5 places of decimals.

15. Find the limit as x tends to zero of $(\tan x - x)/(x - \sin x)$.

16. Prove that if $y = \log \cos x$, then $y_3 + 2y_2 y_1 = 0$. Hence, or otherwise, obtain the Maclaurin expansion of $\log \cos x$ as far as the term in x^6.

17. Prove the results:

$\qquad$ (i) $e^{x \cos x} = 1 + x + \tfrac{1}{2}x^2 - \tfrac{1}{3}x^3 - \tfrac{11}{24}x^4 \ldots$;

$\qquad$ (ii) $(1 + x)^x = e^{x \log (1 + x)} = 1 + x^2 - \tfrac{1}{2}x^3 + \tfrac{5}{6}x^4 \ldots$

18. Expand $\log(1 + \sin x)$ as far as the term in x^5 and deduce the value of $\int_0^{\frac{1}{2}} \log(1 + \sin x)\,dx$ correct to 3 decimal places.

19. If $\log y = 1 + \frac{1}{2}x - \frac{1}{6}x^2 + \frac{1}{12}x^3 \ldots$, show that, as far as the term in x^3,
$$y = e(1 + \frac{1}{2}x - \frac{1}{24}x^2 + \frac{1}{48}x^3).$$

20. Prove that $\dfrac{x}{e^x - 1} = 1 - \dfrac{1}{2}x + \dfrac{1}{6}\dfrac{x^2}{2!} - \dfrac{1}{30}\dfrac{x^4}{4!} \cdots$

21. Calculate the limiting values of the following functions as $x \to 0$:

   (i) $\dfrac{1 - \cos x}{x^2}$;   (ii) $\dfrac{x}{\log(1 + x)}$;   (iii) $\dfrac{\tan^{-1} x}{\sin x}$;   (iv) $\dfrac{1}{x} - \cot x$.

22. Show that $\theta \cot \theta \simeq 1 - \frac{1}{3}\theta^2 - \frac{1}{45}\theta^5$, if θ is small.

23. If $y = \sin^{-1} x$, prove the results:

   (i) $(1 - x^2)y_2 - xy_1 = 0$;

   (ii) $(1 - x^2)y_{n+2} - (2n + 1)xy_{n+1} - n^2 y_n = 0$.

Expand y as a Maclaurin series as far as the term in x^5.

24. By writing $1 + x + x^2 + x^3 + x^4 = (1 - x^5)/(1 - x)$, obtain the result
$$\log(1 + x + x^2 + x^3 + x^4) = x + \frac{1}{2}x^2 + \frac{1}{3}x^3 + \frac{1}{4}x^4 - \frac{4}{5}x^5 + \frac{1}{6}x^6 + \ \cdots$$

25. If $\tan y = 1 + ax + bx^2$, expand y in terms of x as far as the term in x^3.

26. Express $(1 + x)^{1+x}$ in the form $e^{f(x)}$ and deduce the result
$$(1 + x)^{1+x} = 1 + x + x^2 + \frac{1}{2}x^3 + \ \cdots$$

27. Find constants a, b, c, d such that the coefficient of x^n in the expansion of $(a + bx + cx^2 + dx^3)/(1 - x)^4$ is n^3.

28. If $\log y = xy$, find the values of y_1 and y_2 when $x = 0$. Hence show that the Maclaurin expansion of y in powers of x is $y = 1 + x + \frac{3}{2}x^2 \ldots$

29. Find the limit, as x tends to zero, of $\dfrac{\log(1 + x \sin x)}{\cos x - 1}$.

30. If $y = xe^{-x} \cos x$, prove that $x^2 y_2 + 2x(x - 1)y_1 + 2(x^2 - x + 1)y = 0$ and deduce the first three terms in the expansion of y.

31. Prove that for $|x| < 1$:

   (i) $\displaystyle\sum_0^\infty x^n \cos n\theta = \dfrac{1 - x \cos \theta}{1 - 2x \cos \theta + x^2}$;

   (ii) $\displaystyle\sum_0^\infty x^n \sin n\theta = \dfrac{x \sin \theta}{1 - 2x \cos \theta + x^2}$.

32. Prove that $\left(\dfrac{1 + x}{1 - x}\right)^3 = 1 + 6x + 18x^2 + \ \cdots \ + (4n^2 + 2)x^n + \ \cdots$, if $|x| < 1$.

33. Evaluate the limits: (i) $\displaystyle\lim_{x \to 0} \dfrac{4^x - 3^x}{2^x - 1}$;   (ii) $\displaystyle\lim_{x \to 0} \dfrac{\log(e^x + e^{-x} - 1)}{\log \cos x}$.

34. Prove that $\left(1+\dfrac{1}{n}\right)^{n}=e\left(1-\dfrac{1}{2n}+\dfrac{11}{24n^{2}}-\dfrac{7}{16n^{3}}\cdots\right).$

35. Expand the function $\dfrac{3\sin x}{2+\cos x}$ in powers of x, up to, and including the term in x^{5}.

36. Show that, if $e^{x}\sin x=a_{0}+a_{1}x+\dfrac{1}{2!}a_{2}x^{2}+\ldots+\dfrac{1}{n!}a_{n}x^{n}+\ldots,$
then $a_{4n}=0$ and $a_{4n+1}=(-1)^{n}4^{n}$.

37. If $\{\cosh^{-1}(1+x)\}^{2}=a_{0}+a_{1}x+a_{2}x^{2}+\ldots+a_{n}x^{n}+\ldots,$ prove that
$$(n+1)(2n+1)a_{n+1}+n^{2}a_{n}=0.$$

38. If x is small, show that an approximate value of $[\log(1+x)]^{n}$ is
$$x^{n}-\tfrac{1}{2}nx^{n+1}+\tfrac{1}{24}n(3n+5)x^{n+2}.$$

39. Prove that: (i) $\displaystyle\sum_{1}^{\infty}\dfrac{4n-3}{n!}=e+3;$

(ii) $\log\tan\left(\dfrac{\pi}{4}+\dfrac{x}{2}\right)=\sin x+\tfrac{1}{3}\sin^{3}x+\tfrac{1}{5}\sin^{5}x+\ldots,$

if $0\leqslant x<\pi/2$.

40. If $y=\{x+\sqrt{(1+x^{2})}\}^{m}$, prove that:
(i) $(1+x^{2})y_{2}+xy_{1}-m^{2}y=0;$
(ii) $(1+x^{2})y_{n+2}+x(2n+1)y_{n+1}+(n^{2}-m^{2})y_{n}=0.$
Deduce that
$$y=1+mx+\dfrac{1}{2!}m^{2}x^{2}+\dfrac{1}{3!}m^{2}(m^{2}-1^{2})x^{3}+\dfrac{1}{4!}m^{2}(m^{2}-2^{n})x^{4}+\ldots$$

CHAPTER XII

SYSTEMATIC INTEGRATION.
PROPERTIES OF DEFINITE INTEGRALS

Basic theorems. There are two basic theorems of integration which together with a knowledge of the common standard forms enable the evaluation of a large number of integrals.

The first of the theorems can be expressed in the form

$$\int F\{f(x)\}f'(x)\,dx = \int F(u)\,du;$$

a result which follows from the substitution $u = f(x)$.

An important special case arises when $F(u) = \dfrac{1}{u}$.

Then $\displaystyle\int \frac{f'(x)}{f(x)}\,dx = \int \frac{du}{u} = \log u$ or $\log\{f(x)\} + c.$

Ex. 1. *Integrate:* (i) $\dfrac{\cos x}{4 + \sin^2 x}$; (ii) $\dfrac{1 - \tan x}{1 + \tan x}$; (iii) $\dfrac{x}{\sqrt{(1 + x^4)}}$; (iv) sech x.

(i) $\displaystyle\int \frac{\cos x\,dx}{4 + \sin^2 x} = \int \frac{du}{4 + u^2}$, where $u = \sin x$,

$$= \tfrac{1}{2}\tan^{-1}(\tfrac{1}{2}\sin x) + c.$$

(ii) $\displaystyle\int \frac{1 - \tan x}{1 + \tan x}\,dx = \int \frac{\cos x - \sin x}{\cos x + \sin x}\,dx = \log(\cos x + \sin x) + c.$

(iii) $\displaystyle\int \frac{x\,dx}{\sqrt{(1 + x^4)}} = \frac{1}{2}\int \frac{du}{\sqrt{(1 + u^2)}}$, where $u = x^2$,

$$= \tfrac{1}{2}\sinh^{-1}(x^2) + c.$$

(iv) $\displaystyle\int \text{sech } x\,dx = 2\int \frac{dx}{e^x + e^{-x}} = 2\int \frac{e^x\,dx}{e^{2x} + 1},$

$$= 2\int \frac{du}{u^2 + 1}, \text{ where } u = e^x,$$

$$= 2\tan^{-1}(e^x) + c.$$

The second theorem, *the theorem of integration by parts*, follows from the rule for differentiating a product and can be expressed in the form,

$$\int f'(x)\,F(x)\,dx = f(x)\,F(x) - \int f(x)\,F'(x)\,dx.$$

An important special case arises when $f'(x)=1$,

then $$\int F(x)\,dx = x\,F(x) - \int x\,F'(x)\,dx.$$

E.g. $$\int \log x\,dx = x \log x - \int x\,\frac{1}{x}\,dx = x \log x - x + c.$$

The method of integration by parts has wide applications and is particularly useful in dealing with integrals involving inverse functions, logarithmic functions and mixed functions such as $x^n \sin mx$.

Ex. 2. *Integrate:* (i) $\dfrac{\log x}{x^2}$; (ii) $x \sin x \cos x$; (iii) $\sec^{-1} x$.

(i) $$\int \frac{1}{x^2} \log x\,dx = \left(-\frac{1}{x}\right)\log x + \int \left(\frac{1}{x}\right)\frac{1}{x}\,dx = -\frac{1}{x}\log x - \frac{1}{x} + c.$$

(ii) Write $$\sin x \cos x = \tfrac{1}{2} \sin 2x.$$

Then
$$\int x \sin x \cos x\,dx = \tfrac{1}{2}\int x \sin 2x\,dx,$$
$$= \tfrac{1}{2}\{(-\tfrac{1}{2}\cos 2x)x + \tfrac{1}{2}\int \cos 2x\,dx\},$$
$$= -\tfrac{1}{4}x \cos 2x + \tfrac{1}{8}\sin 2x + c.$$

(iii)
$$\int \sec^{-1} x\,dx = (x)\sec^{-1} x - \int \frac{x\,.\,1\,dx}{x\sqrt{(x^2-1)}},$$
$$= x \sec^{-1} x - \cosh^{-1} x + c.$$

EXAMPLES 12a

Integrate the following functions with respect to x:

1. $\dfrac{x^2}{\sqrt{(1-x^3)}}$.

2. xe^{x^2}.

3. $\dfrac{\log x}{x}$.

4. $\cot 2x$.

5. $\dfrac{\tan x + 1}{\tan x - 1}$.

6. $\dfrac{\sinh^{-1} x}{\sqrt{(1+x^2)}}$.

7. $x\sqrt{(x^2+1)}$.

8. $(x-1)\sqrt{(x^2-2x+2)}$.

9. $x(x^2+a^2)^{\frac{1}{2}n}$.

10. $\dfrac{1}{\sqrt{x}}\cos \sqrt{x}$.

11. $x^2 e^{-x}$.

12. $\tan^{-1} x$.

13. $\sinh^{-1} x$.

14. $x \sin^{-1} x$.

15. $x^3 \tan^{-1} x$.

16. $\cos^{-1}\dfrac{1}{x}$.

17. $\dfrac{1}{x^2}\log (x^2+1)$.

18. $\cosh x \sin x$.

19. $(\log x)^2$.

20. $\dfrac{xe^x}{(x+1)^2}$.

Evaluate the following integrals:

21. $\displaystyle\int_0^1 \frac{x\,dx}{\sqrt{(4-x^2)}}$.

22. $\displaystyle\int_0^1 \frac{x^2\,dx}{\sqrt{(x^3+1)}}$.

23. $\displaystyle\int_1^2 \frac{3dx}{x\sqrt{(x^3+1)}}$, (let $x^3+1=u^2$).

24. $\displaystyle\int_1^e (x \log x)^2\,dx$.

Q

25. $\displaystyle\int_0^{\frac{1}{4}\pi} \frac{\sec^2 x \, dx}{2 + \tan^2 x}.$ **26.** $\displaystyle\int_0^{\frac{1}{2}\pi} \frac{x \, dx}{1 + \cos x}.$

27. $\displaystyle\int_0^{\frac{1}{2}\pi} \sqrt{(1 + \sin x)} \, dx,$ (let $\tan \frac{1}{2}x = t$).   **28.** $\displaystyle\int_0^1 \sin^{-1}\left(\frac{2x}{1 + x^2}\right) dx.$

29. Prove that $\displaystyle\int u \frac{d^2 v}{dx^2} \, dx = u \frac{dv}{dx} - v \frac{du}{dx} + \int v \frac{d^2 u}{dx^2} \, dx.$

30. Use the method of integration by parts to find:

     (i) $\displaystyle\int \cos 2\theta \log (1 + \tan \theta) \, d\theta;$ (ii) $\displaystyle\int e^x \frac{1 + \sin x}{1 + \cos x} \, dx.$

31. Prove that $\displaystyle\int_a^b \frac{\log x}{x} \, dx = \frac{1}{2} \log \left(\frac{b}{a}\right) \log (ab).$

32. Show that $\displaystyle\int_0^{\frac{1}{2}\pi} \frac{\sin x \cos x \, dx}{\cos^2 x + 3 \cos x + 2} = \log \frac{9}{8}.$

Important algebraic integrals

Two of the most important forms of algebraic integrals are those involving

     (i) rational functions;   (ii) the function $\sqrt{(ax^2 + bx + c)}.$

The former are integrated after first being expressed in partial fractions of the types

     (a) $\dfrac{A}{ax + b};$ (b) $\dfrac{B}{(ax + b)^n}, \ n \neq 1;$

     (c) $\dfrac{Cx + D}{ax^2 + bx + c};$ (d) $\dfrac{Ex + F}{(ax^2 + bx + c)^n}, \ n \neq 1.$

Type (a) integrates to a logarithm but care is required if the range of integration makes $(ax + b)$ negative as $\log x$ is not defined for $x < 0$.

E.g. $\displaystyle\int_{-2}^{-3} \frac{dx}{x - 1}$ does not equal $\Big[\log (x - 1) \Big]_{-2}^{-3}$, it equals

$$\int_{-2}^{-3} \frac{-dx}{1 - x} = \Big[\log (1 - x) \Big]_{-2}^{-3} = \log \frac{4}{3}.$$

Type (b) integrates to $\dfrac{-B}{a(n - 1)(ax + b)^{n-1}}.$

Type (c) is integrated by expressing the numerator in the form

$$P(2ax + b) + Q.$$

E.g. $\displaystyle\int \frac{3x + 1}{x^2 + x + 1} \, dx = \int \frac{\frac{3}{2}(2x + 1) - \frac{1}{2}}{x^2 + x + 1} \, dx,$

$$= \frac{3}{2} \log (x^2 + x + 1) - \frac{1}{2} \int \frac{dx}{(x + \frac{1}{2})^2 + \frac{3}{4}},$$

$$= \frac{3}{2} \log (x^2 + x + 1) - \frac{1}{\sqrt{3}} \tan^{-1} \frac{2x + 1}{\sqrt{3}} + c.$$

Type (d) is first dealt with in a similar manner to type (c) and the resulting integral $\int \dfrac{dx}{(ax^2+bx+c)^n}$ is evaluated by integrating $\int \dfrac{dx}{(ax^2+bx+c)^{n-1}}$ by parts.

E.g.　$\displaystyle\int \frac{x+1}{(1+x^2)^2}\,dx = \frac{1}{2}\int \frac{2x\,dx}{(1+x^2)^2} + \int \frac{dx}{(1+x^2)^2},$

$$= -\frac{1}{2(1+x^2)} + \int \frac{dx}{(1+x^2)^2}.$$

Then　$\displaystyle\int \frac{1 \cdot dx}{1+x^2} = (x)\frac{1}{1+x^2} + \int \frac{(x)\,2x\,dx}{(1+x^2)^2},$

$$= \frac{x}{1+x^2} + \int \frac{2(1+x^2)-2}{(1+x^2)^2}\,dx,$$

$$= \frac{x}{1+x^2} + 2\int \frac{dx}{1+x^2} - 2\int \frac{dx}{(1+x^2)^2}.$$

$\therefore\ \displaystyle\int \frac{dx}{(1+x^2)^2} = \frac{x}{2(1+x^2)} + \frac{1}{2}\int \frac{dx}{1+x^2},$

$$= \frac{x}{2(1+x^2)} + \tfrac{1}{2}\tan^{-1} x + c.$$

Hence　$\displaystyle\int \frac{x+1}{(1+x^2)}\,dx = -\frac{1}{2(1+x^2)} + \frac{x}{2(1+x^2)} + \tfrac{1}{2}\tan^{-1} x + c.$

Ex. 3. *Integrate:* (i) $\dfrac{x}{x^4+x^2+1}$;　(ii) $\dfrac{1}{x(x^2+1)^3}$.

(i) By the usual method,

$$\frac{x}{x^4+x^2+1} \equiv \frac{1}{2(x^2-x+1)} - \frac{1}{2(x^2+x+1)}.$$

$\therefore\ \displaystyle\int \frac{x\,dx}{x^4+x^2+1} = \frac{1}{2}\int \frac{dx}{x^2-x+1} - \frac{1}{2}\int \frac{dx}{x^2+x+1},$

$$= \frac{1}{\sqrt3}\tan^{-1}\frac{2x-1}{\sqrt3} - \frac{1}{\sqrt3}\tan^{-1}\frac{2x+1}{\sqrt3} + c.$$

(ii) The integral $\displaystyle\int \frac{dx}{x(x^2+1)^3}$ is simplified by writing $x^2 = u$.

$$\int \frac{dx}{x(x^2+1)^3} = \frac{1}{2}\int \frac{du}{u(u+1)^3}, \text{ where } x^2 = u.$$

But　$\dfrac{1}{u(u+1)^3} \equiv \dfrac{1}{u} - \dfrac{1}{u+1} - \dfrac{1}{(u+1)^2} - \dfrac{1}{(u+1)^3}.$

$\therefore\ \displaystyle\int \frac{du}{u(u+1)^3} = \log u - \log(u+1) + \frac{1}{u+1} + \frac{1}{2(u+1)^2},$

$$= \frac{2u+3}{2(u+1)^2} - \log\frac{u+1}{u}.$$

I.e.　$\displaystyle\int \frac{dx}{x(x^2+1)^3} = \frac{2x^2+3}{2(x^2+1)^2} - \log\frac{x^2+1}{x^2} + c.$

Integrals involving the function $\sqrt{(ax^2 + bx + c)}$

Special cases. If $a = 0$, the function reduces to $\sqrt{(bx + c)}$ and the substitution $bx + c = u^2$ will be effective.

If $b = 0$, the function reduces to one of the forms $\sqrt{(\alpha^2 - x^2)}$, $\sqrt{(\alpha^2 + x^2)}$, $\sqrt{(x^2 - \alpha^2)}$ and the respective substitutions $x = \alpha \sin \theta$, $x = \alpha \sinh \theta$, $x = \alpha \cosh \theta$ are usually effective.

General forms. Writing $R \equiv ax^2 + bx + c$, the following types of integral will be considered:

(a) $\displaystyle \int \frac{dx}{\sqrt{R}}$;   (b) $\displaystyle \int \frac{qx + r}{\sqrt{R}}\, dx$;   (c) $\displaystyle \int \sqrt{R}\, dx$;

(d) $\displaystyle \int (qx + r)\sqrt{R}\, dx$;   (e) $\displaystyle \int \frac{px^2 + qx + r}{\sqrt{R}}\, dx$;   (f) $\displaystyle \int \frac{dx}{(qx + r)\sqrt{R}}$.

Type (a). By completing the square for the function R, this integral can be expressed in one of the standard forms.

Ex. 4. *Integrate* $\dfrac{1}{\sqrt{\{(x - a)(x - b)\}}}$, $b > a$.

$$(x - a)(x - b) = x^2 - x(a + b) + ab,$$
$$= \{x - \tfrac{1}{2}(a + b)\}^2 + ab - \tfrac{1}{4}(a + b)^2,$$
$$= \{x - \tfrac{1}{2}(a + b)\}^2 - \tfrac{1}{4}(b - a)^2.$$

$$\therefore \int \frac{dx}{\sqrt{\{(x - a)(x - b)\}}} = \int \frac{du}{\sqrt{(u^2 - \alpha^2)}}, \text{ where } u = x - \tfrac{1}{2}(a + b); \ \alpha = \tfrac{1}{2}(b - a);$$

$$= \cosh^{-1}\frac{u}{\alpha} + c = \cosh^{-1}\frac{2x - (a + b)}{b - a} + c.$$

Type (b). This integral is dealt with by expressing the numerator in the form $A(2ax + b) + B$, where A, B are constants.

It should be noted that integrals of the form $\displaystyle \int \sqrt{\frac{x - a}{x - b}}\, dx$ reduce to this type when the *numerator* is rationalised.

Ex. 5. *Integrate* $\sqrt{\dfrac{x - 1}{x + 2}}$.

We have $\sqrt{\dfrac{x - 1}{x + 2}} = \dfrac{x - 1}{\sqrt{\{(x + 2)(x - 1)\}}} = \dfrac{x - 1}{\sqrt{(x^2 + x - 2)}}$.

$$\therefore \int \sqrt{\frac{x - 1}{x + 2}}\, dx = \frac{1}{2}\int \frac{2x + 1}{\sqrt{(x^2 + x - 2)}}\, dx - \frac{3}{2}\int \frac{dx}{\sqrt{\{(x + \frac{1}{2})^2 - \frac{9}{4}\}}},$$
$$= \sqrt{(x^2 + x - 2)} - \tfrac{3}{2}\cosh^{-1}\tfrac{1}{3}(2x + 1) + c.$$

Type (c). The integral $\displaystyle \int \sqrt{R}\, dx$ is evaluated by using the method of integration by parts with unity as one function.

Ex. 6. *Integrate* $\sqrt{(x^2+x+1)}$.

$$I = \int \sqrt{(x^2+x+1)}\,dx = x\sqrt{(x^2+x+1)} - \int \frac{x(2x+1)}{2\sqrt{(x^2+x+1)}}\,dx.$$

Now express the numerator $x(2x+1)$ in terms of (x^2+x+1) and its derivative $(2x+1)$.

We have, $\qquad x(2x+1) \equiv 2(x^2+x+1) - \frac{1}{2}(2x+1) - \frac{3}{2}.$

$$\therefore\ I = x\sqrt{(x^2+x+1)} - I + \frac{1}{4}\int \frac{2x+1}{\sqrt{(x^2+x+1)}}\,dx + \frac{3}{4}\int \frac{dx}{\sqrt{\{(x+\frac{1}{2})^2+\frac{3}{4}\}}}.$$

I.e. $\quad 2I = x\sqrt{(x^2+x+1)} + \frac{1}{2}\sqrt{(x^2+x+1)} + \frac{3}{4}\sinh^{-1}\frac{2x+1}{\sqrt{3}};$

$$I = \frac{1}{4}(2x+1)\sqrt{(x^2+x+1)} + \frac{3}{8}\sinh^{-1}\frac{2x+1}{\sqrt{3}} + c.$$

Type (d). By writing $qx+r$ in the form $A(2ax+b)+B$, where A, B are constants, this integral reduces to one of Type (c).

Ex. 7. *Integrate* $x\sqrt{(x^2+x+1)}$.

$$\int x\sqrt{(x^2+x+1)}\,dx = \frac{1}{2}\int (2x+1)\sqrt{(x^2+x+1)}\,dx - \frac{1}{2}\int \sqrt{(x^2+x+1)}\,dx.$$

But

$$\frac{1}{2}\int (2x+1)\sqrt{(x^2+x+1)}\,dx = \frac{1}{2}\int \sqrt{u}\,du, \text{ where } u = x^2+x+1,$$
$$= \frac{1}{3}u^{\frac{3}{2}} = \frac{1}{3}(x^2+x+1)^{\frac{3}{2}},$$

and

$$\frac{1}{2}\int \sqrt{(x^2+x+1)}\,dx = \frac{1}{8}(2x+1)\sqrt{(x^2+x+1)} + \frac{3}{16}\sinh^{-1}\frac{2x+1}{\sqrt{3}}, \text{ from Ex. 6.}$$

Hence

$$\int x\sqrt{(x^2+x+1)}\,dx = \frac{1}{3}(x^2+x+1)^{\frac{3}{2}} - \frac{1}{8}(2x+1)\sqrt{(x^2+x+1)}$$
$$- \frac{3}{16}\sinh^{-1}\frac{2x+1}{\sqrt{3}} + c.$$

Type (e). This integral is obtained by expressing the numerator in the form $A(ax^2+bx+c)+B(2ax+b)+C$, where A, B, C are constants. Of the resulting integrals one is immediately determinable and the others are respectively of types (c) and (a).

An integral of this form has been evaluated on the right-hand side of the working in Ex. 6 above.

Type (f). The integral $\int \dfrac{dx}{(qx+r)\sqrt{R}}$ is evaluated by using the substitution $qx+r = \dfrac{1}{t}$.

Note also that an integral of the form $\int \dfrac{dx}{(px^2+qx+r)\sqrt{R}}$ reduces to two integrals of type (f) if $1/(px^2+qx+r)$ can be expressed as the sum or difference of two real linear partial fractions.

Ex. 8. *Integrate:* (i) $\int \dfrac{dx}{(1+x)\sqrt{(1+2x-x^2)}}$; (ii) $\int \dfrac{dx}{(x^2-x-2)\sqrt{(x^2+1)}}$.

(i) Let $\qquad 1+x = \dfrac{1}{t}; \qquad dx = -\dfrac{1}{t^2}\,dt.$

Then $\qquad 1+2x-x^2 = 1 + 2\left(\dfrac{1}{t}-1\right) - \left(\dfrac{1}{t}-1\right)^2 = -2 + \dfrac{4}{t} - \dfrac{1}{t^2},$

$$= \dfrac{1}{t^2}(-1+4t-2t^2).$$

$$\therefore \int \frac{dx}{(1+x)\sqrt{(1+2x-x^2)}} = -\int \frac{dt}{\sqrt{(-1+4t-2t^2)}},$$

$$= -\frac{1}{\sqrt{2}} \int \frac{dt}{\sqrt{\{\frac{1}{2}-(t-1)^2\}}},$$

$$= -\frac{1}{\sqrt{2}} \sin^{-1} \sqrt{2}(t-1) + c,$$

$$= \frac{1}{\sqrt{2}} \sin^{-1} \frac{x\sqrt{2}}{1+x} + c.$$

(ii) We have $\qquad \dfrac{1}{x^2-x-2} = \dfrac{1}{3}\left(\dfrac{1}{x-2} - \dfrac{1}{x+1}\right).$

$$\therefore \int \frac{dx}{(x^2-x-2)\sqrt{x^2+1}} = \frac{1}{3}\int \frac{dx}{(x-2)(\sqrt{(x^2+1)}} - \frac{1}{3}\int \frac{dx}{(x+1)\sqrt{(x^2+1)}},$$

$$= \tfrac{1}{3}(I_1 - I_2).$$

Using the substitution $x - 2 = \dfrac{1}{t}$,

$$I_1 = -\int \frac{dt}{\sqrt{(5t^2+4t+1)}} = -\frac{1}{\sqrt{5}}\int \frac{dt}{\sqrt{\{(t+\frac{2}{5})^2+\frac{1}{25}\}}}$$

$$= -\frac{1}{\sqrt{5}} \sinh^{-1}(5t+2) = -\frac{1}{\sqrt{5}} \sinh^{-1}\frac{2x+1}{x-2}.$$

Similarly, by using the substitution $x + 1 = \dfrac{1}{t}$,

$$I_2 = -\frac{1}{\sqrt{2}} \sinh^{-1} \frac{1-x}{1+x}.$$

$$\therefore \int \frac{dx}{(x^2-x-2)\sqrt{(x^2+1)}} = \frac{1}{3}\left\{\frac{1}{\sqrt{2}} \sinh^{-1}\frac{1-x}{1+x} - \frac{1}{\sqrt{5}} \sinh^{-1}\frac{2x+1}{x-2}\right\} + c.$$

EXAMPLES 12b

Integrate the following functions:

1. $\dfrac{1}{x(x^2-1)}$.

2. $\dfrac{1}{(x-1)^2(x+1)}$.

3. $\dfrac{1}{(x^2+a^2)(x^2+b^2)}$.

4. $\dfrac{x^2}{(x-1)(x-3)}$.

5. $\dfrac{x}{(1+x^2)(1-x)}$.

6. $(x^2-1)^{-2}$.

7. $\dfrac{x}{x^3-1}$.

8. $\dfrac{1}{1+x+x^2+x^3}$.

9. $\dfrac{x+1}{x^3-x^2-6x}$.

10. $\dfrac{x^4}{x^2+1}$.

11. $\dfrac{(x+1)^2}{x^4+x^2+1}$.

12. $\dfrac{x^2+1}{x^4+1}$.

13. $\dfrac{1}{x^4+8x^2-9}$.

14. $\dfrac{1}{x(x^2+1)^2}$.

15. $\dfrac{x^2+1}{x^4-x^2+1}$.

16. $\dfrac{1}{(x^2+4)^2}$.

17. $\dfrac{1}{(x+1)\sqrt{(x+2)}}$.

18. $\dfrac{1}{x+\sqrt{(1-x)}}$.

19. $\sqrt{\dfrac{x}{x+1}}$.

20. $\dfrac{1}{\sqrt{(x-1)(3-x)}}$.

21. $\dfrac{x}{\sqrt{(x^2+2x+2)}}$.

22. $\sqrt{\{x(x+1)\}}$.

23. $\dfrac{x+1}{(x-1)\sqrt{(x+2)}}$.

24. $\dfrac{x^2}{\sqrt{(x^2+1)}}$.

25. $\dfrac{1}{x\sqrt{(x^2+1)}}$.

26. $\dfrac{1}{(x^2+2x+2)\sqrt{(x+1)}}$.

27. $\dfrac{1}{x\sqrt{(x^2+2x+3)}}$.

28. $\dfrac{1}{(x^2-1)\sqrt{(x^2+1)}}$.

29. $\dfrac{x}{(x^2+a^2)\sqrt{(x^2+b^2)}}$, $a^2>b^2$.

30. $\dfrac{1}{x}\sqrt{\dfrac{x-1}{x+1}}$.

31. $\dfrac{1}{(x^2-x)\sqrt{(1-x^2)}}$.

32. $\dfrac{1}{(x^2-1)^{\frac{3}{2}}}$.

33. Evaluate: (i) $\displaystyle\int_0^1 \dfrac{(x-1)\,dx}{(x+1)(x^2+1)}$; (ii) $\displaystyle\int_0^{\frac{1}{2}\pi} \dfrac{\cos x\,dx}{(1+\sin x)(2+\sin x)}$.

34. Integrate: (i) $\{(x-a)(x-b)\}^{-\frac{1}{2}}$; (ii) $\{(x-a)(b-x)\}^{-\frac{1}{2}}$, $b>a$.

35. Evaluate $\displaystyle\int_0^1 \dfrac{1+x^{\frac{1}{2}}}{1+x^{\frac{1}{3}}}\,dx$.

36. Prove that $\displaystyle\int_{-1}^2 \dfrac{dx}{(x+2)\sqrt{(2x^2+6x+5)}} = \log 2$.

37. Evaluate: (i) $\displaystyle\int_0^1 \left(\dfrac{x+3}{x+1}\right)^{\frac{1}{2}}dx$; (ii) $\displaystyle\int_a^b \sqrt{\{(b-x)(x-a)\}}\,dx$, where $0<a<b$.

38. By rationalising the denominator of the integrand, evaluate
$$\int \dfrac{dx}{x+\sqrt{(x^2+1)}}.$$

39. Prove that $\displaystyle\int_0^1 \dfrac{dx}{(1+e^x)(1+e^{-x})} = \tfrac{1}{2}\tanh\tfrac{1}{2}$.

40. Evaluate: (i) $\displaystyle\int_0^1 \dfrac{dx}{(x^2+2x+1)\sqrt{(x+1)}}$; (ii) $\displaystyle\int_{\frac{1}{2}}^1 \dfrac{dx}{x\sqrt{(5x^2-4x+1)}}$.

Trigonometric integrals. The following types of integrals will be considered:

(a) integral powers and products of sines and cosines;

(b) integral powers of tangent and cotangent;

(c) integral powers of secant and cosecant;

(d) the integral $\displaystyle\int \dfrac{dx}{a+b\cos x}$ and allied forms.

Powers and products of sines and cosines

The integrals $\int \sin^n x \, dx, \int \cos^n x \, dx.$ In the case where n *is an odd positive integer* these integrals are readily evaluated.

E.g. $\int \sin^5 x \, dx = \int \sin^4 x \sin x \, dx = -\int (1-c^2)^2 \, dc,$ where $c = \cos x,$

$$= -c + \tfrac{2}{3}c^3 - \tfrac{1}{5}c^5 + A,$$
$$= -\cos x + \tfrac{2}{3} \cos^3 x - \tfrac{1}{5} \cos^5 x + A.$$

In the case where n *is an even positive integer*, the integrals can be evaluated by expressing the integrand in terms of multiple angles either by elementary means or by use of De Moivre's theorem, but usually the general method given below, involving a reduction formula, is preferable.

$$\int \sin^n x \, dx = \int \sin^{n-1} x \sin x \, dx,$$

$$= (-\cos x) \sin^{n-1} x - \int (-\cos x)(n-1) \sin^{n-2} x \cos x \, dx,$$
$$\text{integrating by parts,}$$

$$= -\cos x \sin^{n-1} x + (n-1) \int \sin^{n-2} x(1 - \sin^2 x) \, dx,$$

$$= -\cos x \sin^{n-1} x + (n-1) \int \sin^{n-2} x \, dx - (n-1) \int \sin^n x \, dx.$$

$$\therefore n \int \sin^n x \, dx = -\cos x \sin^{n-1} x + (n-1) \int \sin^{n-2} x \, dx . \quad \text{(i)}$$

Similarly,

$$n \int \cos^n x \, dx = \sin x \cos^{n-1} x + (n-1) \int \cos^{n-2} x \, dx \quad . \quad \text{(ii)}$$

Negative integral powers of sine and cosine are best integrated by expressing them in terms of cosecant and secant respectively.

Ex. 9. *Integrate* $\sin^4 x$ *and evaluate* $\int_0^{\frac{1}{2}\pi} \cos^8 x \, dx.$

Using result (i) above,

$$4 \int \sin^4 x \, dx = -\cos x \sin^3 x + 3 \int \sin^2 x \, dx.$$

$$\therefore \quad \int \sin^4 x \, dx = \tfrac{1}{4}\{ -\cos x \sin^3 x + \tfrac{3}{2}(x - \tfrac{1}{2} \sin 2x)\} + c.$$

From result (ii) it follows that

$$\int_0^{\frac{1}{2}\pi} \cos^n x \, dx = \frac{n-1}{n} \int_0^{\frac{1}{2}\pi} \cos^{n-2} x \, dx.$$

$$\therefore \int_0^{\frac{1}{2}\pi} \cos^8 x\, dx = \tfrac{7}{8}\int_0^{\frac{1}{2}\pi} \cos^6 x\, dx = \tfrac{7}{8} \cdot \tfrac{5}{6} \int_0^{\frac{1}{2}\pi} \cos^4 x\, dx,$$

$$= \tfrac{7}{8} \cdot \tfrac{5}{6} \cdot \tfrac{3}{4} \int_0^{\frac{1}{2}\pi} \cos^2 x\, dx = \tfrac{7}{8} \cdot \tfrac{5}{6} \cdot \tfrac{3}{4} \Big[\tfrac{1}{2}x + \tfrac{1}{2}\sin 2x \Big]_0^{\frac{1}{2}\pi},$$

$$= \tfrac{7}{8} \cdot \tfrac{5}{6} \cdot \tfrac{3}{4} \cdot \tfrac{1}{2} \cdot \tfrac{1}{2}\pi = \tfrac{35}{256}\pi.$$

The integral $\int \sin^p x \cos^q x\, dx$, p and q integral.

If *at least one of the indices p, q is odd*, the integral is easily obtained.

E.g. $$\int \sin^6 x \cos^3 x\, dx = \int \sin^6 x \cos^2 x \cos x\, dx,$$

$$= \int s^6 (1 - s^2)\, ds, \quad \text{where } s = \sin x,$$

$$= \tfrac{1}{7}\sin^7 x - \tfrac{1}{9}\sin^9 x + c.$$

A second simple case arises *when p+q is a negative even integer*, immediate integration being effected in terms of tan *x* or cot *x*.

E.g. $$\int \frac{\cos^2 x}{\sin^6 x}\, dx = \int \frac{\cos^2 x}{\sin^2 x} \cdot \frac{1}{\sin^2 x} \cdot \frac{1}{\sin^2 x}\, dx,$$

$$= \int \cot^2 x \, \operatorname{cosec}^2 x \, \operatorname{cosec}^2 x\, dx,$$

$$= -\int C^2 (1 + C^2)\, dC, \quad \text{where } C = \cot x,$$

$$= -\tfrac{1}{3}\cot^3 x - \tfrac{1}{5}\cot^5 x + A.$$

In other cases the integral is evaluated by obtaining a reduction formula connecting it with either of the integrals $\int \sin^{p-2} x \cos^q x\, dx$ or $\int \sin^p x \cos^{q-2} x\, dx$.

$$\int \sin^p x \cos^q x\, dx$$

$$= \int (\cos^q x \sin x) \sin^{p-1} x\, dx,$$

$$= \left(-\frac{1}{q+1}\cos^{q+1} x \right) \sin^{p-1} x + \frac{p-1}{q+1}\int \cos^{q+1} x \sin^{p-2} x \cos x\, dx,$$

$$= -\frac{1}{q+1}\cos^{q+1} x \sin^{p-1} x + \frac{p-1}{q+1}\int \cos^q x (1 - \sin^2 x) \sin^{p-2} x\, dx,$$

$$= -\frac{1}{q+1}\cos^{q+1} x \sin^{p-1} x + \frac{p-1}{q+1}\int \sin^{p-2} x \cos^q x\, dx$$
$$-\frac{p-1}{q+1}\int \sin^p x \cos^q x\, dx.$$

$$\therefore (p+q)\int \sin^p x \cos^q x\, dx$$

$$= -\cos^{q+1} x \sin^{p-1} x + (p-1)\int \sin^{p-2} x \cos^q x\, dx. \qquad . \qquad \text{(iii)}$$

Similarly,

$$(p+q)\int \sin^p x \cos^q x \, dx$$

$$= \sin^{p+1} x \cos^{q-1} x + (q-1)\int \sin^p x \cos^{q-2} x \, dx. \quad . \quad . \quad \text{(iv)}$$

Ex. 10. *Integrate* $\dfrac{\sin^4 x}{\cos^2 x}.$

Using the reduction formula (iii) with $p=4$, $q=-2$.

$$2\int \frac{\sin^4 x}{\cos^2 x} \, dx = -\frac{\sin^3 x}{\cos x} + 3\int \frac{\sin^2 x}{\cos^2 x} \, dx,$$

$$= -\frac{\sin^3 x}{\cos x} + 3\int \tan^2 x \, dx,$$

$$= -\frac{\sin^3 x}{\cos x} + 3\int (\sec^2 x - 1) \, dx.$$

$$\therefore \int \frac{\sin^4 x}{\cos^2 x} \, dx = \frac{1}{2}\left\{ -\frac{\sin^3 x}{\cos x} + 3 \tan x - 3x \right\} + c.$$

Powers of tangent and cotangent. Any integral power of tangent or cotangent can be readily integrated.

We have $\quad \displaystyle\int \tan^n x \, dx = \int \tan^{n-2} x \, (\sec^2 x - 1) \, dx, \quad$ for $n \geqslant 2$.

I.e. $\quad \displaystyle\int \tan^n x \, dx = \frac{1}{n-1} \tan^{n-1} x - \int \tan^{n-2} x \, dx.$

Hence $\displaystyle\int \tan^n x \, dx$ can be reduced in terms of one or other of the integrals $\displaystyle\int \tan^2 x \, dx, \int \tan x \, dx,$

where $\quad \displaystyle\int \tan^2 x \, dx = \int (\sec^2 x - 1) \, dx = \tan x - x + c;$

$$\int \tan x \, dx = \int \frac{\sin x}{\cos x} \, dx = -\log \cos x \text{ or } \log \sec x + c.$$

Similarly, $\quad \displaystyle\int \cot^n x \, dx = -\frac{1}{n-1} \cot^{n-1} x - \int \cot^{n-2} x \, dx.$

Hence $\displaystyle\int \cot^n x \, dx$ can be reduced in terms of one or other of the integrals $\displaystyle\int \cot^2 x \, dx, \int \cot x \, dx,$

where $\quad \displaystyle\int \cot^2 x \, dx = \int (\operatorname{cosec}^2 x - 1) \, dx = -\cot x - x + c;$

$$\int \cot x \, dx = \int \frac{\cos x}{\sin x} \, dx = \log \sin x + c.$$

Ex. 11. *Integrate:* (*i*) $\tan^3 x$; (*ii*) $\cot^4 x$.

(i) $\displaystyle\int \tan^3 x \, dx = \int \tan x \, (\sec^2 x - 1) \, dx = \frac{1}{2} \tan^2 x + \log \cos x + c.$

(ii) $\displaystyle\int \cot^4 x \, dx = \int \cot^2 x \, (\operatorname{cosec}^2 x - 1) \, dx = -\frac{1}{3} \cot^3 x + \cot x + x + c.$

Powers of secant and cosecant.   *Even powers of secant and cosecant* can be integrated without difficulty.

For $\int \sec^2 x \, dx = \tan x + c;$

$$\int \sec^4 x \, dx = \int (1 + \tan^2 x) \sec^2 x \, dx = \tan x + \tfrac{1}{3} \tan^3 x + c;$$

$$\int \sec^6 x \, dx = \int (1 + t^2)^2 \, dt, \text{ where } t = \tan x,$$

$$= \tan x + \tfrac{2}{3} \tan^3 x + \tfrac{1}{5} \tan^5 x + c.$$

Generally, $\int \sec^{2n} x \, dx = \int (1 + t^2)^{n-1} \, dt, \text{ where } t = \tan x.$

Similarly, $\int \operatorname{cosec}^{2n} x \, dx = - \int (1 + c_0{}^2)^{n-1} \, dc_0, \text{ where } c_0 = \cot x.$

When n is odd, the integrals $\int \sec^n x \, dx$, $\int \operatorname{cosec}^n x \, dx$ are evaluated by obtaining reduction formulae as follows:

$$\int \sec^n x \, dx = \int \sec^2 x \sec^{n-2} x \, dx, \text{ assuming } n > 2,$$

$$= \tan x \sec^{n-2} x - (n-2) \int \tan x \sec^{n-3} x \, (\sec x \tan x) \, dx,$$

$$= \tan x \sec^{n-2} x - (n-2) \int \sec^{n-2} x \tan^2 x \, dx,$$

$$= \tan x \sec^{n-2} x - (n-2) \int \sec^{n-2} x \, (\sec^2 x - 1) \, dx.$$

$$\therefore \ (n-1) \int \sec^n x \, dx = \tan x \sec^{n-2} x + (n-2) \int \sec^{n-2} x \, dx.$$

Similarly,

$$(n-1) \int \operatorname{cosec}^n x \, dx = - \cot x \operatorname{cosec}^{n-2} x + (n-2) \int \operatorname{cosec}^{n-2} x \, dx.$$

These results are true for all integral values of $n > 2$, but need only be applied when n is odd.

Ex. 12. *Integrate:*   (*i*) $\sec^3 x$;   (*ii*) $\operatorname{cosec}^5 x$.
   (i) Using the general result above,

$$2 \int \sec^3 x \, dx = \tan x \sec x + \int \sec x \, dx,$$

$$\therefore \ \int \sec^3 x \, dx = \tfrac{1}{2} [\tan x \sec x + \log (\sec x + \tan x)] + c.$$

(ii) From the general result,

$$4\int \mathrm{cosec}^5 x\, dx = -\cot x\, \mathrm{cosec}^3 x + 3\int \mathrm{cosec}^3 x\, dx;$$

and $\quad 2\int \mathrm{cosec}^3 x\, dx = -\cot x\, \mathrm{cosec}\, x + \int \mathrm{cosec}\, x\, dx,$

$$= -\cot x\, \mathrm{cosec}\, x - \log\,(\mathrm{cosec}\, x + \cot x).$$

$$\therefore \int \mathrm{cosec}^{\,5} x\, dx = -\tfrac14 \cot x\, \mathrm{cosec}^3 x - \tfrac38 \cot x\, \mathrm{cosec}\, x$$
$$- \tfrac38 \log\,(\mathrm{cosec}\, x + \cot x) + c.$$

The integral $\displaystyle\int \frac{dx}{a+b\cos x}$ **and allied forms.** The integral $\displaystyle\int \frac{dx}{a+b\cos x}$ and such allied forms as

$$\int \frac{dx}{a+b\sin x}, \qquad\qquad \int \frac{dx}{a+b\tan x},$$

$$\int \frac{dx}{a+b\cos x + c\sin x}, \qquad \int \frac{A+B\cos x + C\sin x}{a+b\cos x + c\sin x}\, dx$$

are transformed into integrals of rational algebraic functions *by using the substitution*

$$t = \tan\tfrac12 x \quad whence \quad dx = \frac{2dt}{1+t^2};\ \cos x = \frac{1-t^2}{1+t^2};\ \sin x = \frac{2t}{1+t^2}.$$

Integrals of similar forms but involving one or more of the functions $\cos 2x$, $\sin 2x$, $\tan 2x$, $\cos^2 x$, $\sin^2 x$, $\tan^2 x$ can be evaluated by using the substitution $t = \tan x$.

Ex. 13. *Evaluate:* $(i) \displaystyle\int \frac{dx}{\cos \alpha + \cos x}$, *where* $0 < \alpha < \pi$; $(ii) \displaystyle\int \frac{d\theta}{a^2 \sin^2 \theta + b^2 \cos^2 \theta}$.

(i) Using the substitution $t = \tan\tfrac12 x$,

$$\int \frac{dx}{\cos \alpha + \cos x} = \int \frac{2dt}{\cos \alpha(1+t^2) + (1-t^2)} = 2\int \frac{dt}{(1+\cos \alpha) - t^2(1-\cos \alpha)},$$

$$= \frac{2}{1-\cos \alpha}\int \frac{dt}{a^2 - t^2}, \quad \text{where } a^2 = \frac{1+\cos \alpha}{1-\cos \alpha} = \cot^2 \tfrac12\alpha,$$

$$= \frac{1}{\sin^2 \tfrac12\alpha}\int \frac{1}{2a}\left(\frac{1}{a-t} + \frac{1}{a+t}\right) dt, \quad \text{where } a = \cot \tfrac12\alpha,$$

$$= \frac{1}{\sin \alpha}\ \log\ \frac{\cot \tfrac12\alpha + \tan \tfrac12 x}{\cot \tfrac12\alpha - \tan \tfrac12 x} + c.$$

(ii) Using the substitution $t = \tan \theta$,

then $\qquad d\theta = \dfrac{dt}{1+t^2};\quad \cos^2 \theta = \dfrac{1}{1+t^2};\quad \sin^2 \theta = \dfrac{t^2}{1+t^2}.$

$$\therefore \int \frac{d\theta}{a^2 \sin^2 \theta + b^2 \cos^2 \theta} = \int \frac{dt}{a^2 t^2 + b^2},$$

$$= \frac{1}{ab} \tan^{-1} \frac{at}{b} = \frac{1}{ab} \tan^{-1}\left(\frac{a \tan \theta}{b}\right) + c.$$

Hyperbolic integrals. Most of the integrals involving hyperbolic functions can be evaluated by methods similar to those used for the corresponding trigonometric integrals. Some hyperbolic integrals, however, are best evaluated by replacing the hyperbolic functions by exponential functions. Both methods are illustrated below.

Ex. 14. *Integrate:* (*i*) $\sinh^3 x$; (*ii*) $\tanh^4 x$.

(i) $\displaystyle\int \sinh^3 x \, dx = \int \sinh^2 x \sinh x \, dx,$

$\qquad = \displaystyle\int (c^2 - 1) \, dc, \text{ where } c = \cosh x,$

$\qquad = \tfrac{1}{3} \cosh^3 x - \cosh x + A.$

(ii) $\displaystyle\int \tanh^4 x \, dx = \int \tanh^2 x(1 - \operatorname{sech}^2 x) \, dx,$

$\qquad = \displaystyle\int \tanh^2 x \, dx - \tfrac{1}{3} \tanh^3 x,$

$\qquad = \displaystyle\int (1 - \operatorname{sech}^2 x) \, dx - \tfrac{1}{3} \tanh^3 x = x - \tanh x - \tfrac{1}{3} \tanh^3 x + c.$

Ex. 15. *Integrate:* (*i*) $\operatorname{sech} x$; (*ii*) $\dfrac{1}{a + b \cosh x}$, $a^2 < b^2$.

(i) $\displaystyle\int \operatorname{sech} x \, dx = 2 \int \frac{dx}{e^x + e^{-x}} = 2 \int \frac{e^x}{e^{2x} + 1} \, dx,$

$\qquad = 2 \tan^{-1}(e^x) + c.$

(ii) $\displaystyle\int \frac{dx}{a + b \cosh x} = 2 \int \frac{dx}{2a + b(e^x + e^{-x})} = 2 \int \frac{e^x \, dx}{be^{2x} + 2ae^x + b},$

$\qquad = 2 \displaystyle\int \frac{du}{bu^2 + 2au + b}, \text{ where } u = e^x,$

$\qquad = \dfrac{2}{b} \displaystyle\int \frac{du}{\left(u + \dfrac{a}{b}\right)^2 + \left(1 - \dfrac{a^2}{b^2}\right)}, \text{ where } 1 - \dfrac{a^2}{b^2} > 0,$

$\qquad = \dfrac{2}{\sqrt{(b^2 - a^2)}} \tan^{-1} \dfrac{bu + a}{\sqrt{(b^2 - a^2)}} + c$

or $\qquad = \dfrac{2}{\sqrt{(b^2 - a^2)}} \tan^{-1} \dfrac{be^x + a}{\sqrt{(b^2 - a^2)}} + c.$

EXAMPLES 12c

Integrate the following functions:

1. $\cos^5 x$.	**2.** $\sin^3 x \cos^2 x$.	**3.** $\sin 3x \cos x$.	**4.** $\tan^2 x$.
5. $\cos^4 x$.	**6.** $\sin^6 x$.	**7.** $\dfrac{\sin^3 x}{\cos^5 x}$.	**8.** $\sin 2x \cos^2 x$.
9. $\dfrac{1}{\sin^2 x \cos^2 x}$.	**10.** $\tan^5 x$.	**11.** $\cot^3 x$.	**12.** $\sin^4 x \cos^2 x$.
13. $\dfrac{1}{\cos^4 x}$.	**14.** $\sec^5 x$.	**15.** $\sin x \sin 2x \sin 3x$.	

16. $\tan x(1 + \sec x)$. **17.** $\dfrac{1}{5 + 4 \cos x}$. **18.** $\dfrac{5 \cos x + 6}{2 \cos x + \sin x + 3}$.

19. $\dfrac{\cos^2 x}{2 \cos^2 x + \sin^2 x}$. **20.** $\dfrac{1}{a^2 - b^2 \cos^2 x}$, $a > b$. **21.** $\dfrac{\sec x}{a + b \tan x}$.

22. $\dfrac{1}{a + b \tan x}$. **23.** $\dfrac{1}{(a \sin x + b \cos x)^2}$. **24.** $\dfrac{1}{\sin x(1 + \sin x)}$.

25. $\cosh^3 x$. **26.** $\cosh mx \cosh nx$. **27.** $\operatorname{sech}^3 x$.

28. $\cosh^4 x \sinh^3 x$. **29.** $\dfrac{1}{a \cosh x + b \sinh x}$, $a > b$.

30. $\dfrac{\sin x}{\sin(x - \alpha)}$. **31.** $\dfrac{1}{\sin x + \sin 2x}$. **32.** $\dfrac{\cos^2 2x}{\sin^4 x \cos^2 x}$.

Evaluate the following integrals:

33. $\displaystyle\int_0^{\frac{1}{4}\pi} \sin^4 x \, dx$. **34.** $\displaystyle\int_0^{\frac{1}{2}\pi} \cos^6 x \, dx$. **35.** $\displaystyle\int_0^{\frac{1}{3}\pi} \tan^3 x \, dx$.

36. $\displaystyle\int_0^{\frac{1}{2}\pi} \dfrac{a \cos x + b \sin x}{\cos x + \sin x} \, dx$ **37.** $\displaystyle\int_0^{\frac{1}{2}\pi} \dfrac{dx}{3 + 5 \cos x}$. **38.** $\displaystyle\int_0^{\frac{1}{4}\pi} \dfrac{d\theta}{\cos^2 \theta + 3 \sin^2 \theta}$.

39. $\displaystyle\int_0^{\frac{1}{2}\pi} \dfrac{dx}{a + b \sin x}$, $b > a$. **40.** $\displaystyle\int_0^{\frac{1}{4}\pi} \dfrac{\sin^2 x}{1 + \cos^2 x} \, dx$.

41. Evaluate $\displaystyle\int_0^{\theta} \dfrac{d\theta}{(1 + e \cos \theta)^2}$ by means of the substitution

$$\tan \tfrac{1}{2}\theta = \sqrt{\left(\dfrac{1 + e}{1 - e}\right)} \tan \tfrac{1}{2}\phi.$$

42. Prove that $\dfrac{1}{\pi}\displaystyle\int_0^{\pi} \dfrac{d\theta}{1 - \cos \theta \tanh \alpha} = \cosh \alpha$.

43. Evaluate: (i) $\displaystyle\int_0^{\frac{1}{2}\pi} \dfrac{x \, dx}{1 + \cos x}$; (ii) $\displaystyle\int_0^{\pi} \dfrac{x \, dx}{1 + \sin x}$; (iii) $\displaystyle\int_0^{\frac{1}{2}\pi} \dfrac{3 + 2 \cos x}{(3 + \cos x)^2} \, dx$.

Reduction formulae. Reduction formulae, used successively, are an important means of evaluating a considerable number of different types of integrals. By far the most common method of establishing them is by integration by parts and in some simple cases, as in the following example, the result follows directly.

Ex. 16. *Find a reduction formula for* $\displaystyle\int x^n \sin x \, dx$.

Let $$I_n = \int x^n \sin x \, dx.$$

Clearly, to reduce the power of x, the term x^n will have to be differentiated when integrating by parts.

We have $$I_n = - x^n \cos x + n \int x^{n-1} \cos x \, dx,$$

$$= - x^n \cos x + n \left\{ x^{n-1} \sin x - (n - 1) \int x^{n-2} \sin x \, dx \right\}.$$

I.e. $$I_n = x^{n-1}(n \sin x - x \cos x) - n(n - 1)I_{n-2}.$$

In some cases of establishing reduction formulae by the method of integration by parts the original integral I_n is made to appear on both sides of the equation. This procedure is demonstrated below.

Ex. 17. *Find a reduction formula for* $\int e^{ax} \sin^n x \, dx$, $a \neq 0$.

Clearly, in integrating by parts, the term $\sin^n x$ must be differentiated.

We have $\qquad I_n = \dfrac{1}{a} e^{ax} \sin^n x - \dfrac{n}{a} \int e^{ax} \sin^{n-1} x \cos x \, dx.$

The process will have to be repeated in order to obtain a term in $\cos^2 x$ on the R.H.S., as this can be replaced by $1 - \sin^2 x$.

$$I_n = \frac{1}{a} e^{ax} \sin^n x - \frac{n}{a} \left[\frac{1}{a} e^{ax} \sin^{n-1} x \cos x \right.$$
$$\left. - \frac{1}{a} \int e^{ax}\{(n-1) \sin^{n-2} x \cos^2 x - \sin^n x\} dx \right],$$

$$= \frac{1}{a} e^{ax} \sin^n x - \frac{n}{a} \left[\frac{1}{a} e^{ax} \sin^{n-1} x \cos x \right.$$
$$\left. - \frac{1}{a} \int e^{ax}\{(n-1) \sin^{n-2} x - n \sin^n x\} dx \right].$$

$\therefore \ (a^2 + n^2) I_n = e^{ax} \sin^{n-1} x\{a \sin x - n \cos x\} + n(n-1)I_{n-2}.$

Ex. 18. *If* $I_n = \displaystyle\int_0^a x^n (a^2 - x^2)^{\frac{1}{2}} dx$, *where* $n > 1$, *prove that*
$$(n+2)I_n = a^2(n-1)I_{n-2}$$
and hence evaluate I_4.

To reduce the power of x, the term in x^n must be differentiated, but to facilitate the integration of the term $(a^2 - x^2)^{\frac{1}{2}}$ the integrand is written $x^{n-1} . x(a^2 - x^2)^{\frac{1}{2}}$.

Then $\qquad I_n = \left[-\dfrac{1}{3}(a^2 - x^2)^{\frac{3}{2}} x^{n-1} \right]_0^a + \dfrac{1}{3} \displaystyle\int_0^a (a^2 - x^2)^{\frac{3}{2}}(n-1)x^{n-2} \, dx,$

$\qquad\qquad = 0 + \tfrac{1}{3}(n-1) \displaystyle\int_0^a (a^2 - x^2)(a^2 - x^2)^{\frac{1}{2}} x^{n-2} \, dx,$

$\qquad\qquad = \tfrac{1}{3}a^2(n-1)I_{n-2} - \tfrac{1}{3}(n-1)I_n.$

I.e. $\qquad\qquad (n+2)I_n = a^2(n-1)I_{n-2}.$

Substituting $n = 4$, $\qquad\qquad 6I_4 = 3a^2 I_2.$

Substituting $n = 2$, $\qquad\quad 4I_2 = a^2 I_0 = a^2 \displaystyle\int_0^a (a^2 - x^2)^{\frac{1}{2}} \, dx.$

The integral $\displaystyle\int_0^a (a^2 - x^2)^{\frac{1}{2}} \, dx$ is evaluated to $\tfrac{1}{4}a^2 \pi$ by use of the substitution $x = a \sin \theta$.

Hence $\qquad\qquad I_4 = \tfrac{1}{2}a^2 I_2 = \tfrac{1}{8}a^4 I_0 = \tfrac{1}{32}a^6 \pi.$

Ex. 19. *Connect* $I_{m,n} = \int \cos^m x \sin nx \, dx$ *with* $I_{m-1,n-1}$.

Clearly the term $\cos^m x$ must be differentiated in integrating by parts.

We have $\quad I_{m,n} = -\dfrac{1}{n} \cos nx \cos^m x - \dfrac{m}{n} \int \cos nx \sin x \cos^{m-1} x \, dx$.

The term $\sin(n-1)x$ is introduced on the R.H.S. by noting that

$$\cos nx \sin x = -\sin(nx - x) + \sin nx \cos x.$$

$\therefore \quad I_{m,n} = -\dfrac{1}{n} \cos nx \cos^m x - \dfrac{m}{n} \int \{\sin nx \cos x - \sin(n-1)x\} \cos^{m-1} x \, dx$.

I.e. $\qquad (m+n)I_{m,n} = -\cos nx \cos^m x + mI_{m-1,n-1}$.

Other methods of establishing reduction formulae are indicated in the worked examples which follow.

Ex. 20. *By differentiating the function* $\dfrac{b \sin x}{(a + b \cos x)^{n-1}}$, *establish the reduction formula* $\qquad (n-1)(a^2 - b^2)I_n - (2n-3)aI_{n-1} + (n-2)I_{n-2} = 0$,

where $I_n = \displaystyle\int_0^\pi \dfrac{dx}{(a + b \cos x)^n}$, $\quad a > b$.

$$\frac{d}{dx}\left\{ \frac{b \sin x}{(a + b \cos x)^{n-1}} \right\} = \frac{b \cos x}{(a + b \cos x)^{n-1}} + \frac{(n-1)b^2 \sin^2 x}{(a + b \cos x)^n}.$$

The numerators on the R.H.S. are expressed in terms of $(a + b \cos x)$ as follows:

$$b \cos x = (a + b \cos x) - a;$$
$$b^2 \sin^2 x = b^2 - b^2 \cos^2 x = b^2 - \{(a + b \cos x)^2 - 2a(a + b \cos x) + a^2\}.$$

$$\therefore \quad \frac{d}{dx}\left\{ \frac{b \sin x}{(a + b \cos x)^{n-1}} \right\} = -(n-2)\frac{1}{(a + b \cos x)^{n-2}} +$$
$$a(2n-3)\frac{1}{(a + b \cos x)^{n-1}} - (a^2 - b^2)(n-1)\frac{1}{(a + b \cos x)^n}.$$

Integrating with respect to x between the limits 0 to π,

$$\left[\frac{b \sin x}{(a + b \cos x)^{n-1}} \right]_0^\pi = -(n-2)I_{n-2} + a(2n-3)I_{n-1} - (a^2 - b^2)(n-1)I_n,$$

and the result follows as the L.H.S. is zero.

Ex. 21. *If* $I_n = \displaystyle\int_0^\pi \dfrac{\cos nx}{5 - 4 \cos x} dx$, *prove that* $2(I_n + I_{n-2}) = 5I_{n-1}$, *when* $n > 1$

$$2(I_n + I_{n-2}) = 2\int_0^\pi \frac{\cos nx + \cos(n-2)x}{5 - 4 \cos x} dx.$$

But $\qquad 2\{\cos nx + \cos(n-2)x\} = 4\cos(n-1)x \cos x,$
$$= -\cos(n-1)x\{(5 - 4\cos x) - 5\}.$$

$$\therefore \quad 2(I_n + I_{n-2}) = -\int_0^\pi \cos(n-1)x \, dx + 5I_{n-1}.$$

But $\displaystyle\int_0^\pi \cos(n-1)x \, dx = 0$, for $n > 1$ and hence the result follows.

EXAMPLES 12d

1. If $I_n = \int e^{ax} \cos^n x \, dx$, prove that
$$(a^2 + n^2)I_n = e^{ax} \cos^{n-1} x \, (a \cos x + n \sin x) + n(n-1)I_{n-2}$$
and evaluate $\int_0^{\frac{1}{2}\pi} e^{2x} \cos^4 x \, dx$.

2. If $I_n = \int_0^{\frac{1}{2}\pi} x^n \sin x \, dx$, prove that $I_n = n(\frac{1}{2}\pi)^{n-1} - n(n-1)I_{n-2}$.

3. Prove that $n\int_0^{\frac{1}{2}\pi} \cos^n x \, dx = (n-1)\int_0^{\frac{1}{2}\pi} \cos^{n-2} x \, dx$ and deduce the value of $\int_0^{\frac{1}{2}\pi} \cos^{10} x \, dx$.

4. If $I_n = \int_0^{\frac{1}{4}\pi} \tan^n \theta \, d\theta$, prove that $I_n + I_{n-2} = \dfrac{1}{n-1}$, for $n > 1$.

5. By differentiating the function $\sin^{p-1} x \cos^{q+1} x$, prove the result
$$(p+q)\int \sin^p x \cos^q x \, dx = -\sin^{p-1} x \cos^{q+1} x + (p-1)\int \sin^{p-2} x \cos^q x \, dx.$$

6. If $I_n = \int_0^1 (\log x)^n \, dx$, where n is a positive integer, prove that $I_n = -nI_{n-1}$ and deduce that $I_n = (-1)^n n!$.

7. Prove that $(m+n)\int_0^{\frac{1}{2}\pi} \sin^m x \cos^n x \, dx = (n-1)\int_0^{\frac{1}{2}\pi} \sin^m x \cos^{n-2} x \, dx$.

8. If $I_{m,n} = \int x^m(1+x^2)^{\frac{1}{2}n} \, dx$, where m, n are positive integers, prove that
$$(m+n+1)I_{m,n} = x^{m-1}(1+x^2)^{\frac{1}{2}n+1} - (m-1)I_{m-2,n}.$$

9. If $I_n = \int_0^1 x^n e^{x^2} \, dx$, prove that $I_n = \frac{1}{2}e - \frac{1}{2}(n-1)I_{n-2}$ and evaluate $\int_0^1 x^5 e^{x^2} \, dx$.

10. Prove that $\int \dfrac{\sin nx}{\sin x} \, dx = \dfrac{2 \sin (n-1)x}{n-1} + \int \dfrac{\sin (n-2)x}{\sin x} \, dx$ for $n \geqslant 2$, and deduce the value of $\int_{\frac{1}{4}\pi}^{\frac{1}{2}\pi} \dfrac{\sin 4x}{\sin x} \, dx$.

11. Find a reduction formula for $\int \dfrac{dx}{(x^2+1)^n}$ and evaluate $\int_0^1 \dfrac{dx}{(x^2+1)^3}$.

12. If n is a positive integer and $I_n = \int_0^1 x^n(1-x)^{\frac{1}{2}} \, dx$, prove that $(2n+3)I_n = 2nI_{n-1}$ and evaluate I_3.

13. Prove that $2^{n+1}\int_0^{\frac{1}{2}\pi} \cos^n x \cos nx \, dx = \pi$.

R

14. Find reduction formulae for the integrals:

$$\text{(i)} \int \sinh^n x \, dx; \quad \text{(ii)} \int \tanh^n x \, dx.$$

15. If $I_{m,\,n} = \int \dfrac{x^m \, dx}{(\log x)^n}$, prove that

$$(n-1)I_{m,\,n} = -\frac{x^{m+1}}{(\log x)^{n-1}} + (m+1)I_{m,\,n-1}.$$

16. If $X = x^2 + ax + a^2$, prove that

$$\int X^{\frac{1}{2}n} \, dx = \frac{2x+a}{2(n+1)} X^{\frac{1}{2}n} + \frac{3na^2}{4(n+1)} \int X^{\frac{1}{2}n-1} \, dx.$$

17. Investigate a reduction formula for $\int \dfrac{x^{2n+1} \, dx}{(1-x^2)^{\frac{1}{2}}}$.

18. Prove that, if $I_n = \int_0^{\frac{1}{2}\pi} \dfrac{dx}{(a+b\tan x)^n}$, $n > 1$, then

$$(a^2+b^2)I_n - 2aI_{n-1} + I_{n-2} = b/(n-1)a^{n-1}.$$

19. Find a reduction formula for $\int \dfrac{x}{\sin^n x} \, dx$, $n > 1$.

20. If $I_p = \int_0^1 \dfrac{x^p \, dx}{\sqrt{(x^q + 1)}}$, $p > q - 1$, prove that

$$(2p - q + 2)I_p + (2p - 2q + 2)I_{p-q} = 2\sqrt{2},$$

and hence show that $\displaystyle\int_0^1 \dfrac{x^8 \, dx}{\sqrt{(x^3+1)}} = \dfrac{1}{45}(14\sqrt{2} - 16)$.

General theorems on definite integrals.   In dealing with the properties of the definite integral $\displaystyle\int_a^b f(x) \, dx$, where $f(x)$ is assumed to be a finite continuous function in the range $a \leqslant x \leqslant b$, it is important to remember the alternative results:

$$\int_a^b f(x) \, dx = F(b) - F(a), \text{ where } F'(x) = f(x), \text{ or geometrically,}$$

$$\int_a^b f(x) \, dx = \text{the area under the curve } y = f(x) \text{ for } x \text{ between } a \text{ and } b.$$

Theorem I. $\displaystyle\int_a^b f(x) \, dx = \int_a^b f(y) \, dy.$

This result follows from the fact that each integral is equal to $F(b) - F(a)$, where $F(u)$ is the indefinite integral of $f(u)$.

Theorem II. $$\int_a^b f(x)\,dx = -\int_b^a f(x)\,dx.$$

This result also follows at once from the definition in terms of the indefinite integral.

Theorem III. $$\int_a^b f(x)\,dx = \int_a^c f(x)\,dx + \int_c^b f(x)\,dx.$$

With the previous notation,

$$\text{R.H.S.} = F(c) - F(a) + F(b) - F(c)$$
$$= F(b) - F(a) = \text{L.H.S.}$$

The result also follows directly from the geometrical definition of a definite integral.

Theorem IV. $$\int_0^a f(x)\,dx = \int_0^a f(a-x)\,dx.$$

Let $x = a - y$, then $dx = -dy$.

$$\therefore \int_0^a f(x)\,dx = -\int_a^0 f(a-y)\,dy,$$
$$= \int_0^a f(a-y)\,dy \quad \text{by theorem II,}$$
$$= \int_0^a f(a-x)\,dx \quad \text{by theorem I.}$$

This result has important applications in the evaluation of trigonometrical integrals of the forms

$$\int_0^\pi x\,\phi(\sin x)\,dx \quad \text{or} \quad \int_0^{2\pi} x\,\phi(\cos x)\,dx,$$

where $\phi(u)$ is an integrable function, as is illustrated in the following example.

Ex. 22. *Evaluate* $\int_0^\pi \dfrac{x \sin x}{1 + \cos^2 x}\,dx.$

By theorem IV,

$$\int_0^\pi \frac{x \sin x}{1 + \cos^2 x}\,dx = \int_0^\pi \frac{(\pi - x)\sin(\pi - x)}{1 + \cos^2(\pi - x)}\,dx,$$
$$= \int_0^\pi \frac{(\pi - x)\sin x}{1 + \cos^2 x}\,dx.$$

$$\therefore 2\int_0^\pi \frac{x \sin x}{1 + \cos^2 x}\,dx = \pi \int_0^\pi \frac{\sin x}{1 + \cos^2 x}\,dx,$$
$$= \pi \left[-\tan^{-1}(\cos x) \right]_0^\pi = \pi 2 \tan^{-1} 1.$$

I.e. $$\int_0^\pi \frac{x \sin x}{1 + \cos^2 x}\,dx = \tfrac{1}{4}\pi^2.$$

Theorem V. If $f(x) = f(2a - x)$, then $\int_0^{2a} f(x)\, dx = 2\int_0^a f(x)\, dx$.

For
$$\int_0^{2a} f(x)\, dx = \int_0^a f(x)\, dx + \int_a^{2a} f(x)\, dx.$$

Putting $x = 2a - y$ in the integral $\int_0^{2a} f(x)\, dx$, we get

$$\int_a^{2a} f(x)\, dx = -\int_a^0 f(2a - y)\ dy = \int_0^a f(2a - y)\, dy,$$

$$= \int_0^a f(y)\, dy \text{ as } f(2a - y) = f(y),$$

$$= \int_0^a f(x)\, dx.$$

$$\therefore \int_0^{2a} f(x)\, dx = 2\int_0^a f(x)\, dx.$$

Ex. 23. *Prove that* $\int_0^\pi \phi(\sin x)\, dx = 2\int_0^{\frac{1}{2}\pi} \phi(\sin x)\, dx$.

Putting $2a = \pi$ and noting that $\sin x = \sin(\pi - x)$, the result follows from theorem V.

Theorem VI. If $f(x) \geqslant \phi(x)$ in the range $a \leqslant x \leqslant b$, then

$$\int_a^b f(x)\, dx \geqslant \int_a^b \phi(x)\, dx.$$

As the ordinates of the curve $y = f(x)$ are greater than or equal to the corresponding ordinates of the curve $y = \phi(x)$ throughout the range $a \leqslant x \leqslant b$, it follows that the area under the former curve is greater than or equal to the area under the latter; hence the required result.

Ex. 24. *Prove that* $\frac{1}{2} < \int_0^1 \dfrac{dx}{\sqrt{(4 - x^2 + x^3)}} < \frac{1}{6}\pi$.

In the range $0 \leqslant x \leqslant 1$,

$$\frac{1}{\sqrt{4}} \leqslant \frac{1}{\sqrt{(4 - x^2 + x^3)}} \leqslant \frac{1}{\sqrt{(4 - x^2)}},$$

the equalities being true only at the end points $x = 0, 1$.

$$\therefore \int_0^1 \tfrac{1}{2}\, dx < \int_0^1 \frac{dx}{\sqrt{(4 - x^2 + x^3)}} < \int_0^1 \frac{dx}{\sqrt{(4 - x^2)}}$$

i.e.
$$\frac{1}{2} < \int_0^1 \frac{dx}{\sqrt{(4 - x^2 + x^3)}} < \frac{1}{6}\pi.$$

The logarithmic function. The logarithmic function $\log_e x$ can be defined by the relationship,

$$\log_e x = \int_1^x \frac{dt}{t} \text{ for } x > 0.$$

It is instructive to develop the simple properties of the function from this definition.

(i) **log xy = log x + log y.** For $\log xy = \int_1^{xy} \frac{dt}{t} = \int_1^x \frac{dt}{t} + \int_x^{xy} \frac{dt}{t}.$

In the latter integral using the substitution $t = xu$; $dt = x\,du$,

$$\int_x^{xy} \frac{dt}{t} = \int_1^y \frac{x\,du}{xu} = \int_1^y \frac{du}{u} = \int_1^y \frac{dt}{t}.$$

Hence $\qquad \log xy = \int_1^x \frac{dt}{t} + \int_1^y \frac{dt}{t} = \log x + \log y.$

(ii) **log x/y = log x − log y.** This result follows either as a corollary of (i) by writing $\log x = \log\left(\dfrac{x}{y}\right)y$ or by expressing $\int_1^{x/y} \frac{dt}{t}$ as

$\int_1^x \frac{dt}{t} + \int_x^{x/y} \frac{dt}{t}$ and using the substitution $t = x/u$ in the latter integral

(iii) **log xⁿ = n log x.** In the integral $\int_1^{x^n} \frac{dt}{t}$, let $t = u^n$; $dt = nu^{n-1}\,du.$

Then $\qquad \log x^n = \int_1^{x^n} \frac{dt}{t} = \int_1^x \frac{nu^{n-1}\,du}{u^n} = n\int_1^x \frac{du}{u} = n\log x.$

Ex. 25. *If $x > 0$, prove that* $\dfrac{x}{1+x} < \log(1+x) < x.$

We have $\qquad \log(1+x) = \int_1^{1+x} \frac{dt}{t}.$

Now as $x > 0$, the maximum and minimum values of the integrand $\dfrac{1}{t}$ in the range integration are 1 and $1/(1+x)$ respectively,

$$\therefore \int_1^{1+x} \frac{dt}{1+x} < \int_1^{1+x} \frac{dt}{t} < \int_1^{1+x} dt.$$

Remembering that x is constant here, the variable of integration being t,

$$\int_1^{1+x} \frac{dt}{1+x} = \frac{1}{1+x}\int_1^{1+x} dt = \frac{x}{1+x}; \qquad \int_1^{1+x} dt = x.$$

Hence the required inequalities.

EXAMPLES 12e

1. Show geometrically that $\displaystyle\int_0^{\frac{1}{2}\pi} \sin\theta \, d\theta > \int_0^{\frac{1}{2}\pi} \sin^2\theta \, d\theta$.

2. Without evaluating the integrals show that: (i) $\displaystyle\int_{-\frac{1}{2}}^{\frac{1}{2}} \frac{dx}{1-x^2}$ is positive;
(ii) $\displaystyle\int_1^2 (1-x^2)^3 \, dx$ is negative.

3. Use theorem IV to evaluate: (i) $\displaystyle\int_0^\pi x \sin x \, dx$; (ii) $\displaystyle\int_0^\pi x \cos^2 x \, dx$.

4. Show geometrically that: (i) $\displaystyle\int_0^\pi \sin^3 x \, dx = 2 \int_0^{\frac{1}{2}\pi} \sin^3 x \, dx$;

(ii) $\displaystyle\int_0^{2\pi} \sin^2 x \, dx = 4 \int_0^{\frac{1}{2}\pi} \sin^2 x \, dx$.

5. Prove that $\displaystyle\frac{1}{\sqrt{2}} < \int_0^1 \frac{dx}{\sqrt{(1+x^3)}} < 1$.

6. Without evaluating the integrals prove:

(i) $\displaystyle\int_0^{\frac{1}{2}\pi} \sin x \, dx = \int_0^{\frac{1}{2}\pi} \cos x \, dx$;

(ii) $\displaystyle\int_0^\pi \cos^3 x \, dx = -\int_0^\pi \cos^3 x \, dx = 0$.

7. If $f(x) < 0$ in the range $a \leqslant x \leqslant b$, show that $\displaystyle\int_a^b \{f(x)\}^n \, dx$ is negative or positive according as n is odd or even.

8. Evaluate: (i) $\displaystyle\int_0^\pi x \sin^3 x \, dx$; (ii) $\displaystyle\int_0^{2\pi} x \cos^3 x \, dx$.

9. If $m \leqslant f(x) \leqslant M$ in the range $a \leqslant x \leqslant b$, prove that
$$m(b-a) \leqslant \int_a^b f(x) \, dx \leqslant M(b-a).$$

10. Use the result of the previous question to establish the following results:

(i) $\displaystyle 0 < \int_0^{\frac{1}{4}\pi} x \tan x \, dx < \tfrac{1}{16}\pi^2$; (ii) if $n > 0$, $\displaystyle\frac{1}{2} < \int_0^1 \frac{dx}{x^n+1} < 1$.

11. Without evaluating the integrals prove that:

(i) $\displaystyle\int_0^\pi \sin^n x \, dx = 2 \int_0^{\frac{1}{2}\pi} \sin^n x \, dx$;

(ii) if n is a positive integer, $\displaystyle\int_0^\pi \sin^n x \, dx > \int_0^\pi \sin^{n+1} x \, dx$.

12. Prove that $\displaystyle\int_{-\frac{1}{4}\pi}^{\frac{1}{4}\pi} \tan^n\theta \, d\theta = 0$ if n is an odd integer.

13. Evaluate the integrals: (i) $\displaystyle\int_0^{2\pi} x \cos^2 x \, dx$; (ii) $\displaystyle\int_0^{\frac{1}{2}\pi} x \sin^2 2x \, dx$.

14. Prove geometrically that $\int_{-a}^{a} xe^{-x^2}\,dx = 0$.

15. Show that $I = \int_{2}^{3} \dfrac{dx}{(x^2-1)^{\frac{3}{2}}} > \int_{2}^{3} \dfrac{dx}{x^3}$ and deduce that $I > \frac{5}{72}$.

16. Prove: (i) $\int_{0}^{\pi} x\phi(\sin x)\,dx = \frac{1}{2}\pi\int_{0}^{\pi} \phi(\sin x)\,dx$;

(ii) $\int_{0}^{\pi} x\phi(\cos^2 x)\,dx = \frac{1}{2}\pi\int_{0}^{\pi} \phi(\cos^2 x)\,dx$.

17. Evaluate $\int_{0}^{\pi} \dfrac{x\sin x}{2+\cos^2 x}\,dx$ and show that $\int_{0}^{2\pi} \dfrac{x\cos x}{1+\sin^2 x}\,dx = 0$.

18. Prove: (i) $0 < \int_{0}^{\frac{1}{4}\pi} \tan^{n+1} x\,dx < \int_{0}^{\frac{1}{4}\pi} \tan^n x\,dx$, if n is a positive integer; (ii) $e^{-1} < \int_{0}^{1} e^{-x^2}\,dx < 1$.

19. Show that $\int_{0}^{\frac{1}{2}\pi} \log\sin x\,dx = \int_{0}^{\frac{1}{2}\pi} \log\cos x\,dx$ and deduce the results:

(i) $2\int_{0}^{\frac{1}{2}\pi} \log\sin x\,dx = \int_{0}^{\frac{1}{2}\pi} \log\sin 2x\,dx - \frac{1}{2}\pi\log 2$;

(ii) $\int_{0}^{\frac{1}{2}\pi} \log\sin 2x\,dx = \frac{1}{2}\int_{0}^{\pi} \log\sin x\,dx = \int_{0}^{\frac{1}{2}\pi} \log\sin x\,dx$;

(iii) $\int_{0}^{\frac{1}{2}\pi} \log\sin x\,dx = -\frac{1}{2}\pi\log 2$.

20. If $\beta > 0$, prove that $\log x < \dfrac{x^\beta - 1}{\beta}$, $x > 0$. [*Hint*: $\dfrac{1}{t} < \dfrac{1}{t^{1-\beta}}$ when $t > 1$.]

Infinite integrals. Some consideration will now be given to definite integrals which involve infinity. The two cases which will be dealt with in an elementary manner are:

(i) definite integrals in which the range is infinite;
(ii) definite integrals in which the integrand becomes infinite at some point within the range of integration.

Infinite range of integration. The *integral to infinity* $\int_{a}^{\infty} f(x)\,dx$ is defined by the relationship

$$\int_{a}^{\infty} f(x)\,dx = \lim_{N \to \infty} \int_{a}^{N} f(x)\,dx,$$

where N is a large positive number.

It is implicit in this definition that the limit exists, and we are interested here only in the cases where the limit is finite and the corresponding integrals are *convergent*. In other cases the limit will be infinite and the corresponding integrals *divergent*, and in others no limit will exist.

Similarly, $\qquad \displaystyle\int_{-\infty}^{b} f(x)\,dx = \lim_{N \to \infty} \int_{-N}^{b} f(x)\,dx.$

To illustrate the evaluation of an infinite integral take the integral

$$\int_{0}^{\infty} e^{-x}\,dx.$$

We have $\qquad \displaystyle\int_{0}^{N} e^{-x}\,dx = \left[-e^{-x} \right]_{0}^{N} = 1 - e^{-N},$

and $\qquad \displaystyle\lim_{N \to \infty} e^{-N} = \lim_{N \to \infty} \frac{1}{1 + N + \frac{1}{2}N^2 \ldots} = 0.$

$$\therefore \int_{0}^{\infty} e^{-x}\,dx = \lim_{N \to \infty} \int_{0}^{N} e^{-x}\,dx = 1.$$

Ex. 26. *Evaluate:* (i) $\displaystyle\int_{-\infty}^{0} \frac{dx}{1+x^2}$; (ii) $\displaystyle\int_{0}^{\infty} e^{-x}\cos x\,dx$; (iii) $\displaystyle\int_{0}^{\infty} x^2 e^{-x}\,dx.$

(i) $\displaystyle\int_{-N}^{0} \frac{dx}{1+x^2} = \tan^{-1} 0 - \tan^{-1}(-N)$, where the inverse tangent is taken as the principal value.

So $\qquad \tan^{-1} 0 = 0; \qquad \displaystyle\lim_{N \to \infty} \tan^{-1}(-N) = -\tfrac{1}{2}\pi.$

$$\therefore \int_{-\infty}^{0} \frac{dx}{1+x^2} = \lim_{N \to \infty} \int_{-N}^{0} \frac{dx}{1+x^2} = 0 - (-\tfrac{1}{2}\pi) = \tfrac{1}{2}\pi.$$

(ii) Either by parts, or by taking the integrand as the real part of $e^{x(-1+i)}$, the indefinite integral of $e^{-x}\cos x$ is found to be $\frac{1}{2}e^{-x}(\sin x - \cos x)$.

$$\therefore \int_{0}^{N} e^{-x}\cos x\,dx = \tfrac{1}{2}e^{-N}(\sin N - \cos N) - \tfrac{1}{2}(-1).$$

But $\quad \displaystyle\lim_{N \to \infty} e^{-N} = 0,$ and hence $\quad \displaystyle\lim_{N \to \infty} e^{-N}(\sin N - \cos N) = 0.$

$$\therefore \int_{0}^{\infty} e^{-x}\cos x\,dx = \lim_{N \to \infty} \int_{0}^{N} e^{-x}\cos x\,dx = \tfrac{1}{2}.$$

(iii) By parts,

$$\int_{0}^{N} x^2 e^{-x}\,dx = \left[-e^{-x}\cdot x^2 \right]_{0}^{N} + 2\int_{0}^{N} e^{-x} x\,dx,$$

$$= -e^{-N}\cdot N^2 + 2\left\{ \left[-e^{-x}\cdot x \right]_{0}^{N} + \int_{0}^{N} e^{-x}\,dx \right\},$$

$$= -e^{-N}(N^2 + 2N) + 2 - 2e^{-N}.$$

As $e^{N} = 1 + N + \dfrac{1}{2!}N^2 + \dfrac{1}{3!}N^3 + \ldots$, and N is positive it follows that

$e^{N} > \dfrac{1}{3!} N^3.$

$$\therefore \lim_{N \to \infty} e^{-N}\cdot N^2 = \lim_{N \to \infty} \frac{N^2}{e^{N}} \leqslant \lim_{N \to \infty} \frac{N^2}{\frac{1}{6}N^3} = 0.$$

Similarly, $\lim\limits_{N \to \infty} Ne^{-N} = 0$ and also $\lim\limits_{N \to \infty} e^{-N} = 0,$

hence $\displaystyle\int_0^\infty x^2 e^{-x}\, dx = \lim_{N \to \infty} \int_0^N x^2 e^{-x}\, dx = 2.$

Infinite integrand. Suppose the function $f(x) \to \infty$ as $x \to c,$ where $a \leqslant c \leqslant b,$ then the definite integral $\displaystyle\int_a^b f(x)\, dx$ is defined by the relationship,

$$\int_a^b f(x)\, dx = \lim_{\alpha \to 0} \int_a^{c-\alpha} f(x)\, dx + \lim_{\beta \to 0} \int_{c+\beta}^b f(x)\, dx,$$

where $\alpha,\ \beta$ are small positive constants, and the limits are assumed to exist.

In the special case where c is equal to a or b only one limiting value is required.

Take, for example, the integral $\displaystyle\int_0^1 \frac{dx}{\sqrt{x}},$ where the integrand becomes infinite at the lower limit.

We have $\displaystyle\int_\alpha^1 \frac{dx}{\sqrt{x}} = 2(1 - \alpha^{\frac12}),$ α being a small positive constant.

As $\alpha \to 0,$ $\alpha^{\frac12} \to 0.$

$$\therefore \int_0^1 \frac{dx}{\sqrt{x}} = \lim_{\alpha \to 0} \int_\alpha^1 \frac{dx}{\sqrt{x}} = 2.$$

Ex. 27. *Evaluate:* (i) $\displaystyle\int_0^1 \frac{dx}{\sqrt{(1-x^2)}};$ (ii) $\displaystyle\int_0^2 \frac{dx}{\sqrt{\{x(2-x)\}}}.$

(i) In this integral, the integrand is infinite at the upper limit $x = 1.$

Consider $\displaystyle\int_0^{1-\alpha} \frac{dx}{\sqrt{(1-x^2)}},$ where α is a small positive constant.

$$\int_0^{1-\alpha} \frac{dx}{\sqrt{(1-x^2)}} = \left[\sin^{-1} x \right]_0^{1-\alpha} = \sin^{-1}(1-\alpha) - 0.$$

As $\alpha \to 0,$ $\sin^{-1}(1-\alpha),$ assumed the principal value $\to \frac12 \pi.$

$$\therefore \int_0^1 \frac{dx}{\sqrt{(1-x^2)}} = \lim_{\alpha \to 0} \int_0^{1-\alpha} \frac{dx}{\sqrt{(1-x^2)}} = \frac12 \pi.$$

(ii) Here the integrand is infinite at both limits.

We have $\displaystyle\int_\alpha^{2-\beta} \frac{dx}{\sqrt{x(2-x)}} = \int_\alpha^{2-\beta} \frac{dx}{\sqrt{\{1-(x-1)^2\}}} = \left[\sin^{-1}(x-1) \right]_\alpha^{2-\beta}.$

$$= \sin^{-1}(1-\beta) - \sin^{-1}(\alpha-1).$$

As $\beta \to 0,$ $\sin^{-1}(1-\beta) \to \frac12\pi;$ as $\alpha \to 0,$ $\sin^{-1}(\alpha-1) \to -\frac12\pi.$

$$\therefore \int_0^2 \frac{dx}{\sqrt{\{x(2-x)\}}} = \pi.$$

Ex. 28. *Evaluate:* (i) $\displaystyle\int_0^2 \frac{dx}{(x-1)^{\frac{2}{3}}}$; (ii) $\displaystyle\int_0^\infty \frac{dx}{(x+1)\sqrt{x}}$.

(i) The integrand becomes infinite at the point $x=1$.

Here $\displaystyle\int_0^{1-\alpha} \frac{dx}{(x-1)^{\frac{2}{3}}}\, dx + \int_{1+\beta}^2 \frac{dx}{(x-1)^{\frac{2}{3}}} = \left[3(x-1)^{\frac{1}{3}}\right]_0^{1-\alpha} + \left[3(x-1)^{\frac{1}{3}}\right]_{1+\beta}^2$

$$= 3(-\alpha)^{\frac{1}{3}} - 3(-1) + 3(1) - 3\beta^{\frac{1}{3}}.$$

As $\alpha \to 0$, $(-\alpha)^{\frac{1}{3}} \to 0$ and as $\beta \to 0$ so does $\beta^{\frac{1}{3}}$.

$$\therefore \int_0^2 \frac{dx}{(x-1)^{\frac{2}{3}}} = 6.$$

(ii) This integral involves two infinities, the upper limit is infinite and the integrand is infinite when $x=0$.

So consider the integral $\displaystyle\int_\alpha^N \frac{dx}{(x+1)\sqrt{x}}$.

Let $\sqrt{x} = u$, then $\dfrac{dx}{2\sqrt{x}} = du$ and the limits become $\sqrt{\alpha}$, $\sqrt{N}$.

$$\text{Integral} = \int_{\sqrt{\alpha}}^{\sqrt{N}} \frac{2\,du}{u^2+1} = 2(\tan^{-1}\sqrt{N} - \tan^{-1}\sqrt{\alpha}).$$

But as $N \to \infty$, $\tan^{-1}\sqrt{N} \to \frac{1}{2}\pi$ and as $\alpha \to 0$, $\tan^{-1}\sqrt{\alpha} \to 0$.

$$\therefore \int_0^\infty \frac{dx}{(x+1)\sqrt{x}} = \frac{1}{2}\pi.$$

EXAMPLES 12f

1. Evaluate: (i) $\displaystyle\int_0^\infty e^{-2x}\,dx$; (ii) $\displaystyle\int_{-\infty}^0 e^x\,dx$.

2. Find the values of the integrals $\displaystyle\int_2^\infty \frac{dx}{4+x^2}$, $\displaystyle\int_{-\infty}^2 \frac{dx}{4+x^2}$, $\displaystyle\int_{-\infty}^\infty \frac{dx}{4+x^2}$.

3. Using integration by parts, or otherwise, evaluate:

(i) $\displaystyle\int_0^\infty e^{-x}\cos x\,dx$; (ii) $\displaystyle\int_0^\infty e^{-x}\sin x\,dx$.

4. If $n<-1$, prove that $\displaystyle\int_1^\infty x^n\,dx = -\frac{1}{n+1}$.

5. Using the expansion of e^x, show that, if N is positive, $e^N > \frac{1}{2}N^2$ and deduce that $Ne^{-N} \to 0$ as $N \to \infty$. Evaluate the integral $\displaystyle\int_0^\infty xe^{-x}\,dx$.

6. Prove that $\displaystyle\int_0^\infty e^{-2x}\cos 3x\,dx = \frac{2}{13}$.

7. Evaluate: (i) $\displaystyle\int_0^2 \frac{dx}{\sqrt{(4-x^2)}}$; (ii) $\displaystyle\int_2^4 \frac{dx}{\sqrt{(x^2-4)}}$.

8. Find the value of the integral $\int_{-1}^{1} x^{-\frac{4}{3}} dx$.

9. Evaluate: (i) $\int_{1}^{\infty} \frac{dx}{(x+2)\sqrt{x}}$; (ii) $\int_{0}^{\infty} \frac{dx}{(x+2)\sqrt{x}}$.

10. Evaluate: (i) $\int_{0}^{2} \frac{dx}{\sqrt{(4x-x^2)}}$; (ii) $\int_{0}^{4} \frac{dx}{\sqrt{(4x-x^2)}}$.

11. Find the value of the integral $\int_{0}^{\infty} x^3 e^{-2x} dx$.

12. Evaluate: (i) $\int_{-\infty}^{\infty} \frac{dx}{x^2 - 2x + 2}$; (ii) $\int_{1}^{2} \frac{dx}{\sqrt{\{(x-1)(2-x)\}}}$.

13. Evaluate: (i) $\int_{0}^{\infty} xe^{-x^2} dx$; (ii) $\int_{0}^{\infty} (x^2 + 3x)e^{-x} dx$;

(iii) $\int_{0}^{\infty} \frac{dx}{\cosh x + \sinh x}$.

14. Prove that $\int_{a}^{b} \frac{dx}{\{(x-a)(b-x)\}^{\frac{1}{2}}} = \pi$.

15. Evaluate the integral $\int_{0}^{\infty} (1 + x^2)^{-\frac{3}{2}} dx$, using the substitution $x = \tan \theta$.

16. If $a > b$, find the value of $\int_{0}^{\infty} \frac{dx}{a \cosh x + b \sinh x}$.

17. If $I_n = \int_{0}^{\infty} x^n e^{-x} dx$, where n is a positive integer, establish the reduction formula $I_n = nI_{n-1}$ and deduce the value of I_n.

18. Use the substitution $x = a \cos^2 \theta + b \sin^2 \theta$ to evaluate the integral

$$\int_{a}^{b} \frac{x \, dx}{\sqrt{\{(x-a)(b-x)\}}}, \quad 0 < a < b.$$

19. Prove that $\int_{-\infty}^{\infty} \operatorname{sech} x \, dx = \pi$.

20. Evaluate: (i) $\int_{0}^{1} \sqrt{\frac{x+1}{1-x}} \, dx$; (ii) $\int_{-1}^{1} \frac{x^2}{\sqrt{(1-x^2)}} \, dx$.

21. Prove that $\int_{0}^{\infty} \frac{dx}{x^2 + 2x \cos \theta + 1} = \frac{\theta}{\sin \theta}$ if $0 < \theta < \pi$.

22. If $I_n = \int_{0}^{\infty} \frac{dx}{(x^2 + 1)^n}$, where n is an integer > 1, prove that

$$2(n-1)I_n = (2n-3)I_{n-1},$$

and find the value of I_3.

MISCELLANEOUS EXAMPLES

1. Integrate:

(i) $\dfrac{1}{x^2 - 4x + 3}$;   (ii) $\dfrac{1}{\sqrt{(x^2 - 4x + 3)}}$;   (iii) $\dfrac{x}{\sqrt{(x^2 - 4x + 3)}}$.

2. Show that $\displaystyle\int_0^{\frac{1}{4}\pi} \sec^3 \theta \, d\theta = \tfrac{1}{2}[\log (\sqrt{2} + 1) + \sqrt{2}]$.

3. Evaluate: (i) $\displaystyle\int_0^1 \left(\dfrac{x}{1 - x}\right)^{\frac{1}{2}} dx$;   (ii) $\displaystyle\int_0^1 \dfrac{x^2 + x + 1}{\sqrt{(x^2 + 2x + 3)}} \, dx$.

4. Integrate $\cosh ax \cos bx$ with respect to x.

5. Integrate:

(i) $\dfrac{x^3}{(x^2 + 1)(x - 2)}$;   (ii) $(x + a)(x + b)^{\frac{1}{3}}$;   (iii) $\dfrac{1}{x^2 \sqrt{(x^2 + 1)}}$.

6. Evaluate:

(i) $\displaystyle\int_0^{\frac{1}{4}\pi} \tan^3 x \, dx$;   (ii) $\displaystyle\int_0^{\frac{1}{6}\pi} \sin x \tan x \, dx$;   (iii) $\displaystyle\int_0^{\frac{1}{2}\pi} \sin^5 x \, dx$.

7. Integrate the functions: (i) $\tan^{-1} x$;   (ii) $(\sinh^{-1} x)^2$.

8. Evaluate $\displaystyle\int_0^{\alpha} \dfrac{d\theta}{5 + 3 \cos \theta}$ when: (i) $\alpha = \pi$;   (ii) $\alpha = 2\pi$.

9. Evaluate: (i) $\displaystyle\int_2^{\infty} \dfrac{dx}{x\sqrt{x}}$;   (ii) $\displaystyle\int_{-1}^1 \sqrt{\dfrac{x + 3}{x + 1}} \, dx$.

10. Integrate: (i) $\operatorname{cosech} x$;   (ii) $e^{\sin^{-1} x}$;   (iii) $x^3 e^{-x^2}$.

11. If $I_n = \displaystyle\int_0^1 (\log x)^n \, dx$, n a positive integer, prove that $I_n = -nI_{n-1}$, and deduce that $I_n = (-1)^n n!$.

12. Prove that the integrals $\displaystyle\int_0^1 x^7 (1 - x)^8 \, dx$, $\displaystyle\int_0^1 x^8 (1 - x)^7 \, dx$ are equal.

Show further that each integral is equal to $\tfrac{1}{2} \displaystyle\int_0^1 x^7 (1 - x)^7 \, dx$.

13. Use the result $\displaystyle\int_0^a f(x) \, dx = \int_0^a f(a - x) \, dx$ to evaluate the integrals:

(i) $\displaystyle\int_0^{\pi} \dfrac{x \sin x \, dx}{1 + 2 \cos^2 x}$;   (ii) $\displaystyle\int_0^{\pi} \dfrac{x \, dx}{2 + \tan^2 x}$;   (iii) $\displaystyle\int_0^{2\pi} \dfrac{x \, dx}{2 + \cos x}$.

14. Find a reduction formula for $\displaystyle\int_0^1 (1 + x^2)^{n + \frac{1}{2}} \, dx$ and evaluate the integral when $n = 2$.

15. Integrate $x^{\frac{1}{2}} \sqrt{(1 + x^3)}$ with respect to x.

16. Prove: (i) $\displaystyle\int_0^{\frac{1}{2}\pi} \dfrac{dx}{2 + \cos x} = \dfrac{\pi}{3\sqrt{3}}$;   (ii) $\displaystyle\int_0^{\frac{1}{2}\pi} \dfrac{dx}{5 + 4 \cos x + 3 \sin x} = \dfrac{1}{6}$.

17. Use the substitution $\tan \theta = t^2$ to evaluate the integral $\displaystyle\int_0^{\frac{1}{4}\pi} \sqrt{\tan \theta} \, d\theta$.

18. Evaluate: (i) $\displaystyle\int_0^1 \frac{dx}{(1+x)\sqrt{(1+2x)}}$; (ii) $\displaystyle\int_0^1 \frac{dx}{(x-2)\sqrt{(x^2+1)}}$.

19. If n is a positive integer and $I_n = \displaystyle\int_0^1 x^n(1-x)^{\frac{1}{2}}\,dx$, prove that

$(2n+3)I_n = 2nI_{n-1}$ and evaluate I_2.

20. Prove that $\displaystyle\int_0^\pi \frac{\cos^2 x\,dx}{a^2\cos^2 x + b^2\sin^2 x} = \frac{\pi}{a(a+b)}$.

21. Defining $\log_e x = \displaystyle\int_1^x \frac{dt}{t}$, prove geometrically that $\log_e x \leqslant x - 1$.

22. Prove that

$$\int \cos^m x \sin nx\,dx = -\frac{\cos^m x \cos nx}{m+n} + \frac{m}{m+n}\int \cos^{m-1} x \sin (n-1)x\,dx$$

and deduce that $\displaystyle\int_0^{\frac{1}{2}\pi} \cos^4 x \sin 6x\,dx = \frac{1}{5}$.

23. Evaluate the integrals: (i) $\displaystyle\int_0^1 \frac{dx}{x+\sqrt{(1-x)}}$; (ii) $\displaystyle\int_{-1}^1 \frac{x^4\,dx}{\sqrt{(1-x^2)}}$.

24. Evaluate: (i) $\displaystyle\int_0^{\frac{1}{2}\pi} \frac{dx}{1+\sin\alpha \sin x}, 0<\alpha<\frac{1}{2}\pi$; (ii) $\displaystyle\int_0^\pi \frac{d\theta}{5+3\cos^2\theta}$.

25. If $f(x) = f(a-x)$, prove that $2\displaystyle\int_0^a xf(x)\,dx = a\int_0^a f(x)\,dx$, and hence prove

that $\displaystyle\int_0^{\frac{1}{2}\pi} \frac{x\sin x\cos x}{\sin^4 x + \cos^4 x}\,dx = \frac{1}{4}\pi^2$.

26. Evaluate the integrals: (i) $\displaystyle\int_0^1 (1+x^2)\tan^{-1} x\,dx$; (ii) $\displaystyle\int_0^\infty \frac{x\tan^{-1} x}{(1+x^2)^2}\,dx$.

27. If $0<a<b$, prove that $\displaystyle\int_a^b \frac{dx}{x\sqrt{\{(x-a)(b-x)\}}} = \frac{\pi}{\sqrt{(ab)}}$.

28. Evaluate: (i) $\displaystyle\int_0^\pi \frac{dx}{5-3\cos x}$; (ii) $\displaystyle\int_0^{\frac{1}{2}\pi} \frac{dx}{(2-\cos x)(3-\cos x)}$.

29. If $0<k<1$, integrate $\dfrac{1}{(1-kt)\sqrt{(1-t^2)}}$ with respect to t.

30. If $I_n = \displaystyle\int_0^\infty x^n e^{-x^2}\,dx$, $n \geqslant 2$, prove that $2I_n = (n-1)I_{n-2}$ and deduce

the value of I_5.

31. Evaluate the integrals: (i) $\displaystyle\int_6^7 \sqrt{\frac{x-3}{x-6}}\,dx$; (ii) $\displaystyle\int_{\frac{1}{2}}^1 \frac{\sqrt{(1-x^2)}}{x}\,dx$.

32. Prove that $\displaystyle\int_0^\infty \frac{dx}{x^2+2x\cos\alpha+1} = \frac{\alpha}{\sin\alpha}$, $0<\alpha<\pi$ and evaluate

$$\int_0^\infty \frac{dx}{x^4+2x^2\cos\alpha+1}.$$

33. If $I_n = \int_0^{\frac{1}{4}\pi} \tan^n \theta \, d\theta$, prove that $I_n + I_{n-2} = \dfrac{1}{n-1}$ for n integral and >1.

Show further that $\dfrac{1}{2(n+1)} < I_n < \dfrac{1}{2(n-1)}$.

34. Prove that $\int_0^{\frac{1}{2}\pi} \cos x \log (\cos x) \, dx = \log 2 - 1$.

35. If $b > a > 0$, show that $\int_0^{\pi} \dfrac{\sin \theta \, d\theta}{\sqrt{(a^2 + b^2 - 2ab \cos \theta)}} = \dfrac{2}{b}$.

36. Evaluate $\int_{\sqrt{2}}^{\infty} \dfrac{dx}{(x^2 - 1)\sqrt{(1 + x^2)}}$.

37. If $I_n = \int \dfrac{x^n \, dx}{\sqrt{(x^2 + 2ax + b)}}$, $n \geqslant 0$, prove the result

$$nI_n + (2n+1)aI_{n-1} + (n-1)bI_{n-2} = x^{n-1}\sqrt{(x^2 + 2ax + b)}.$$

38. Use the result $\int_0^a f(x) \, dx = \int_0^a f(a-x) \, dx$ to evaluate the integrals:

(i) $\int_0^{\theta} \log (1 + \tan \theta \tan x) \, dx$, $0 < \theta < \frac{1}{2}\pi$;   (ii) $\int_0^{\pi} \dfrac{x \sin^3 x}{1 + \cos^2 x} \, dx$.

39. Evaluate: (i) $\int_a^b (x-a)^{\frac{3}{2}}(b-x)^{\frac{3}{2}} \, dx$;   (ii) $\int_0^{\pi} \dfrac{x \sin x \, dx}{\sqrt{(1 - a^2 \sin^2 x)}}$, $|a| < 1$.

40. Prove that $\int_0^1 \dfrac{\sqrt{(1-x^2)}}{1+x^2} \, dx = \frac{1}{2}\pi(\sqrt{2} - 1)$ and deduce the result

$$\tfrac{1}{2}\pi(\sqrt{2} - 1) < \int_0^1 \dfrac{\sqrt{(1-x^2)}}{1+x^4} \, dx < \tfrac{1}{4}\pi.$$

41. Find a reduction formula for $I_n = \int_1^{\infty} \dfrac{dx}{x^n \sqrt{(x^2 - 1)}}$ and evaluate the integral when $n = 1$, $n = 2$.

42. Prove that $\int_0^a f(x) \, dx = \frac{1}{2}\int_0^a \{f(x) + f(a-x)\} \, dx$ and evaluate the integral

$$\int_0^1 \dfrac{dx}{(x^2 - x + 1)(e^{2x-1} + 1)}.$$

CHAPTER XIII

FURTHER PROPERTIES OF PLANE CURVES

Plane curves expressed in polar coordinates. Let $P(r, \theta)$ and $Q(r + \delta r, \theta + \delta\theta)$ be neighbouring points on the curve $r = f(\theta)$ (Fig. 78).

Take A as a fixed point on the curve and let the arc lengths AP, PQ be s, δs respectively.

If PR is perpendicular to OQ, then

$$RQ \simeq \delta r; \quad RP \simeq r\delta\theta; \quad \text{chord } PQ \simeq \delta s.$$

By Pythagoras, $(\delta s)^2 \simeq (r\delta\theta)^2 + (\delta r)^2.$

$$\therefore \left(\frac{\delta s}{\delta\theta}\right)^2 \simeq r^2 + \left(\frac{\delta r}{\delta\theta}\right)^2.$$

In the limit as $Q \to P$,

$$\left(\frac{ds}{d\theta}\right)^2 = r^2 + \left(\frac{dr}{d\theta}\right)^2.$$

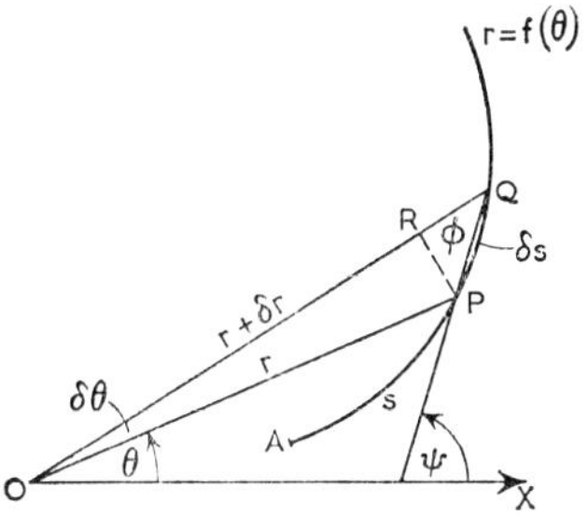

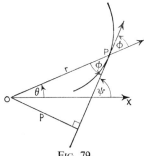

FIG. 78.

Let angle $OQP = \phi$,

then

$$\tan\phi \simeq r\frac{\delta\theta}{\delta r}; \quad \sin\phi \simeq r\frac{\delta\theta}{\delta s}; \quad \cos\phi \simeq \frac{\delta r}{\delta s}.$$

In the limit as $Q \to P$, ϕ becomes the angle between the radius vector and tangent at P and we have the results:

$$\tan\varphi = r\frac{d\theta}{dr}; \quad \sin\varphi = r\frac{d\theta}{ds}; \quad \cos\varphi = \frac{dr}{ds}.$$

Sign convention. ϕ is measured positive in the counterclockwise direction from $\overrightarrow{OP}$ to the direction of the tangent for increasing values of θ (Fig. 79).

When $\tan\phi$ is negative, ϕ will be a positive obtuse angle.

If ψ is the angle from the initial line OX to the tangent at P,

$$\psi = \theta + \varphi = \theta + \tan^{-1} r\frac{d\theta}{dr}.$$

Perpendicular from origin to tangent. In Fig. 79 if p is the length of the perpendicular from O to the tangent at P,

$$p = r\sin\phi.$$

FIG. 79.

261

To express p in terms of r, we write

$$\frac{1}{p^2} = \frac{1}{r^2}\cosec^2\phi = \frac{1}{r^2}(1 + \cot^2\phi),$$

$$= \frac{1}{r^2}\left\{1 + \frac{1}{r^2}\left(\frac{dr}{d\theta}\right)^2\right\}.$$

I.e.
$$\mathbf{\frac{1}{p^2} = \frac{1}{r^2} + \frac{1}{r^4}\left(\frac{dr}{d\theta}\right)^2}.\qquad .\quad .\quad .\quad .\quad .\quad \text{(i)}$$

This result is often expressed in the form,

$$\mathbf{\frac{1}{p^2} = u^2 + \left(\frac{du}{d\theta}\right)^2}, \quad \text{where } u = \frac{1}{r}.$$

By eliminating θ between the equation (i) and the equation of the curve $r = f(\theta)$, an equation connecting p and r is obtained. This is known as *the pedal equation* and is useful in dealing with curvature.

The locus of the foot of the perpendicular from O to a tangent is called the *pedal curve*.

Ex. 1. *For the curve* $\dfrac{2a}{r} = 1 - \cos\theta$, *prove that:*

      (*i*) $\phi = \pi - \tfrac{1}{2}\theta$;   (*ii*) $p = a\cosec\tfrac{1}{2}\theta$;   (*iii*) $p^2 = ar$.

(i)
$$\frac{2a}{r} = 1 - \cos\theta.$$

Differentiating with respect to θ,

$$-\frac{2a}{r^2}\frac{dr}{d\theta} = \sin\theta.$$

$$\therefore\ r\frac{d\theta}{dr} = -\frac{2a}{r\sin\theta} = -\frac{1-\cos\theta}{\sin\theta}.$$

I.e.
$$\tan\phi = -\tan\tfrac{1}{2}\theta = \tan(\pi - \tfrac{1}{2}\theta),$$
$$\phi = \pi - \tfrac{1}{2}\theta.$$

(ii)
$$p = r\sin\phi = r\sin\tfrac{1}{2}\theta,$$
$$= \frac{2a\sin\tfrac{1}{2}\theta}{1-\cos\theta} = \frac{a}{\sin\tfrac{1}{2}\theta}.$$

I.e.
$$p = a\cosec\tfrac{1}{2}\theta.$$

(iii) We have
$$p^2 = a^2\cosec^2\tfrac{1}{2}\theta,$$

but
$$r = \frac{2a}{1-\cos\theta} = \frac{a}{\sin^2\tfrac{1}{2}\theta}.$$

$$\therefore\ \cosec^2\tfrac{1}{2}\theta = \frac{r}{a},$$

and
$$p^2 = a^2\cdot\frac{r}{a} = ar.$$

Ex. 2. *Show that the curves* $r^4 = a^4 \sec(4\theta + \alpha)$, $r^4 = b^4 \sec(4\theta + \beta)$ *intersect at an angle independent of the constants a, b.*

To find the angle of intersection we require the difference between the values of ϕ at a common point.

For the curve $r^4 = a^4 \sec(4\theta + \alpha)$,

taking logarithms and differentiating with respect to θ,

$$4\frac{1}{r}\frac{dr}{d\theta} = 4\tan(4\theta + \alpha).$$

I.e. $\cot\phi = \tan(4\theta + \alpha)$; $\quad \frac{1}{2}\pi - \phi = 4\theta + \alpha$.

Similarly, if ϕ' refers to the second curve, $\frac{1}{2}\pi - \phi' = 4\theta + \beta$.

∴ The angle between the tangents to the curves at a point of intersection

$$= \phi \sim \phi' = \beta \sim \alpha.$$

Arc length and area of surface of revolution. Integrating the result

$$\left(\frac{ds}{d\theta}\right)^2 = r^2 + \left(\frac{dr}{d\theta}\right)^2,$$

we have $\quad s = \pm \int_\alpha^\beta \sqrt{\left\{r^2 + \left(\frac{dr}{d\theta}\right)^2\right\}}\, d\theta,$

where s is the arc length AB and α, β are the vectorial angles of A, B respectively (Fig. 80).

s is taken as positive in the direction determined by θ increasing.

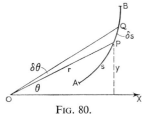

Fig. 80.

Area of surface swept out by the element of arc δs in one revolution about the initial line $OX \approx 2\pi y \delta s$.

∴ **Area of surface of revolution of arc AB**

$$= 2\pi \int_\alpha^\beta r \sin\theta \sqrt{\left\{r^2 + \left(\frac{dr}{d\theta}\right)^2\right\}}\, d\theta.$$

Ex. 3. *Show that the polar equation of a circle radius a with pole on the circumference and a diameter as initial line is* $r = 2a\cos\theta$. *Deduce that the circumference of the circle is* $2\pi a$ *and by rotating the circle about the initial line, establish that the surface area of a sphere, radius a, is* $4\pi a^2$.

Let $P(r, \theta)$ be any point on the circle centre C, radius a.

Then $\quad OP = OA\cos\theta$,

i.e. $\quad r = 2a\cos\theta$.

For the complete circle, θ varies from 0 to π.

∴ Circumference $= \displaystyle\int_0^\pi \sqrt{\left\{r^2 + \left(\frac{dr}{d\theta}\right)^2\right\}}\, d\theta,$

$$= \int_0^\pi 2a\sqrt{(\cos^2\theta + \sin^2\theta)}\, d\theta,$$

$$= 2a\int_0^\pi d\theta = 2a\pi.$$

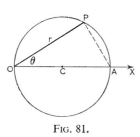

Fig. 81.

S

If the semicircle $r = 2a \cos \theta$, $\theta = 0$ to $\frac{1}{2}\pi$, is rotated about OX,

$$\text{area of surface of revolution} = 2\pi \int_0^{\frac{1}{2}\pi} r \sin \theta \sqrt{\left\{r^2 + \left(\frac{dr}{d\theta}\right)^2\right\}} d\theta,$$

$$= 4a^2\pi \int_0^{\frac{1}{2}\pi} \sin 2\theta \, d\theta = 4\pi a^2.$$

I.e. Surface area of sphere $= 4\pi a^2$.

EXAMPLES 13a

Find ϕ and p in terms of r, θ for each of the following curves:

1. $r = a \cos \theta$.   **2.** $r = a \sin \theta$.

3. $r \sin \theta = a$.   **4.** $r = e^{\theta \cot \alpha}$.

5. $r = a(1 - \cos \theta)$.   **6.** $r \sin^2 \frac{1}{2}\theta = a$.

7. $r^2 = a^2 \sin 2\theta$.   **8.** $r(1 + 2 \cos \theta) = 4$.

9. Find the points of intersection of the curves $r = \sin \theta$, $r = 1 - \sin \theta$ and the angles at which they intersect.

10. For the curve $\theta = \frac{1}{a}\sqrt{(r^2 - a^2)} - \cos^{-1} \frac{a}{r}$, prove that $\cos \phi = \frac{a}{r}$.

11. Prove that the pedal equation of the curve $r^2 = a^2 \cos 2\theta$ is $r^3 = a^2 p$.

12. Find a point on the curve $r^2 = 4 \cos 2\theta$ at which the angle between the radius vector and the tangent is $\frac{3}{4}\pi$.

13. For the cardioid $r = a(1 + \cos \theta)$, prove the following results:

    (i) $\phi = \frac{1}{2}\pi + \frac{1}{2}\theta$;   (ii) $\psi = \frac{1}{2}\pi + \frac{3}{2}\theta$;

    (iii) $p = 2a \cos^3 \frac{1}{2}\theta$;   (iv) $2ap^2 = r^3$.

14. Find the angle at which the line $\theta = \frac{1}{3}\pi$ meets the curve $r = a(1 + \cos \theta)$ at the point of intersection other than the origin.

15. Prove that the curves $r^2 \cos \theta = a^2$, $r^2 \sin \theta = -b^2$ intersect orthogonally.

16. Prove that the pedal equation of the ellipse $x^2/a^2 + y^2/b^2 = 1$ is $a^2b^2 = p^2(a^2 + b^2 - r^2)$, when the origin is the centre of the curve.

17. Taking the focus as pole and the axis as initial line, establish the polar equation of a parabola in the form $r(1 - \cos \theta) = 2a$. Deduce the pedal equation $p^2 = ar$.

18. Find the coordinates of the foot of the perpendicular from the origin to the tangent at the point $(4, \frac{1}{3}\pi)$ on the curve $r = 2(1 + 2 \cos \theta)$.

19. With the usual notation, show that the coordinates (r', θ') of P' the foot of the perpendicular from O to the tangent at P on the curve $f(r, \theta) = 0$ are given by $r' = r \sin \phi$; $\theta' = \theta + \phi - \frac{1}{2}\pi$.

20. With the notation of the previous example, find the polar equation of the locus of P' in the following cases:

    (i) $r = a \cos \theta$;   (ii) $r^2 = a^2 \cos 2\theta$;   (iii) $r(1 - \cos \theta) = 2a$.

21. Find the locus of the foot of the perpendicular from the centre to a tangent for the hyperbola $x^2/a^2 - y^2/b^2 = 1$.

22. Prove that the curve $r = ae^{\theta \cot \alpha}$, where a, α are constants, has the property that it cuts all radii vectors at a constant angle. Show also that the pedal curve has a similar property.

23. Find the arc length of the curve $r = 2a \cos (\theta - \frac{1}{4}\pi)$ between $\theta = \frac{1}{4}\pi$ and $\theta = \frac{1}{2}\pi$.

24. For the curve $r - a(1 + \cos \theta)$, prove that $\dfrac{ds}{d\theta} = 2a \cos \frac{1}{2}\theta$ and deduce the perimeter of the curve.

25. Find the arc length of the curve $r = ae^{m\theta}$ between $\theta = \alpha$ and $\theta = \beta$.

26. Show that in the curve $r\theta = a$, $p^{-2} = r^{-2} + a^{-2}$.

27. Find the total length of the curve $r = a(1 - \cos \theta)$.

28. Show that the tangents at the ends of a chord of the cardioid $r = a(1 + \cos \theta)$, which passes through the pole, are at right angles.

29. For the curve $r \cos^3 \theta = a \sin^2 \theta$, prove that

$$\frac{ds}{d\theta} = a \tan \theta \sec^2 \theta (4 + 9 \tan^2 \theta)^{\frac{1}{2}}.$$

Use the substitution $\tan^2 \theta = t$ to obtain s in terms of θ and show that the arc length between $\theta = 0$ and $\theta = \tan^{-1} \frac{1}{3}\sqrt{5}$ is $\frac{19}{27}a$.

30. Show that the area of the surface obtained by revolving the curve $r = a(1 + \cos \theta)$ about the line $\theta = 0$ is $\frac{32}{5}\pi a^2$.

31. The arc of the curve $r(1 + \cos \theta) = 2a$ between $\theta = 0$ and $\theta = \frac{1}{2}\pi$ is rotated about the initial line, show that the area of the curved surface generated is $\frac{8}{3}\pi a^2(\sqrt{8} - 1)$.

Polar form of radius of curvature. We have $\psi = \theta + \phi$,

so

$$\frac{d\psi}{ds} = \frac{d\theta}{ds} + \frac{d\phi}{ds}.$$

But

$$\tan \phi = r\frac{d\theta}{dr} = r \left/ \frac{dr}{d\theta} \right.,$$

$$\therefore \quad \sec^2 \phi \frac{d\phi}{ds} = \frac{d}{d\theta}\left(r \left/ \frac{dr}{d\theta}\right.\right) \times \frac{d\theta}{ds} = \frac{d\theta}{ds}\left\{\frac{\left(\dfrac{dr}{d\theta}\right)^2 - r\dfrac{d^2r}{d\theta^2}}{\left(\dfrac{dr}{d\theta}\right)^2}\right\}.$$

$$\therefore \quad \left\{1 + \frac{r^2}{\left(\dfrac{dr}{d\theta}\right)^2}\right\}\frac{d\phi}{ds} = \frac{d\theta}{ds}\left\{\frac{\left(\dfrac{dr}{d\theta}\right)^2 - r\dfrac{d^2r}{d\theta^2}}{\left(\dfrac{dr}{d\theta}\right)^2}\right\} \quad \text{as } \sec^2 \phi = 1 + \tan^2 \phi.$$

So
$$\frac{d\phi}{ds} = \frac{d\theta}{ds} \left\{ \frac{\left(\frac{dr}{d\theta}\right)^2 - r\frac{d^2r}{d\theta^2}}{\left(\frac{dr}{d\theta}\right)^2 + r^2} \right\},$$

and hence
$$\frac{d\psi}{ds} = \frac{1}{\left\{r^2 + \left(\frac{dr}{d\theta}\right)^2\right\}^{\frac{1}{2}}} \left\{ \frac{r^2 + 2\left(\frac{dr}{d\theta}\right)^2 - r\frac{d^2r}{d\theta^2}}{r^2 + \left(\frac{dr}{d\theta}\right)^2} \right\}.$$

I.e.   **Radius of curvature** $\rho = \dfrac{\mathbf{ds}}{\mathbf{d\psi}} = \dfrac{\left\{\mathbf{r}^2 + \left(\dfrac{\mathbf{dr}}{\mathbf{d\theta}}\right)^2\right\}^{\frac{3}{2}}}{\mathbf{r}^2 + 2\left(\dfrac{\mathbf{dr}}{\mathbf{d\theta}}\right)^2 - \mathbf{r}\dfrac{\mathbf{d^2r}}{\mathbf{d\theta^2}}}.$

Ex. 4. *Find the radius of curvature of the equiangular spiral* $r = ae^{\theta \cot \alpha}$ *at the point* (r, θ).

We have $\dfrac{dr}{d\theta} = a \cot \alpha \, e^{\theta \cot \alpha} = r \cot \alpha;$ $\dfrac{d^2r}{d\theta^2} = r \cot^2 \alpha.$

$$\therefore \left\{r^2 + \left(\frac{dr}{d\theta}\right)^2\right\}^{\frac{3}{2}} = \{r^2(1 + \cot^2 \alpha)\}^{\frac{3}{2}} = r^3 \operatorname{cosec}^3 \alpha;$$

and $r^2 + 2\left(\dfrac{dr}{d\theta}\right)^2 - r\dfrac{d^2r}{d\theta^2} = r^2(1 + 2\cot^2 \alpha - \cot^2 \alpha) = r^2 \operatorname{cosec}^2 \alpha.$

$$\therefore \rho = \frac{r^3 \operatorname{cosec}^3 \alpha}{r^2 \operatorname{cosec}^2 \alpha} = r \operatorname{cosec} \alpha.$$

Radius of curvature—pedal form.   Let $P(r, \theta)$ and $Q(r + \delta r, \theta + \delta\theta)$ be neighbouring points on the curve $f(r, \theta) = 0$ (Fig. 82).

Let OR, OS the perpendiculars from the origin on to the tangents at P and Q be of lengths p and $p + \delta p$ respectively.

If the tangents at P and Q make angles ψ, $\psi + \delta\psi$ with the initial line OX, it follows that

$$\angle TUS = \delta\psi.$$

We have
$$TS \simeq OS - OR \simeq \delta p; \quad UT \simeq PR \simeq r \cos \phi;$$
so from triangle TUS,

$$\delta\psi \simeq \frac{TS}{UT} \simeq \frac{\delta p}{r \cos \phi},$$

i.e. $\dfrac{\delta p}{\delta\psi} \simeq r \cos \phi.$

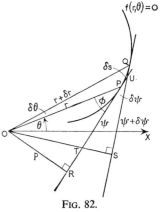

Fig. 82.

In the limit as $Q \to P$, this result becomes

$$\frac{\mathbf{dp}}{\mathbf{d\psi}} = \mathbf{r} \cos \boldsymbol{\varphi} = \mathbf{PR}.$$

Hence, $$\rho = \frac{ds}{d\psi} = \frac{ds}{dp} \cdot \frac{dp}{d\psi} = \frac{ds}{dr} \cdot \frac{dr}{dp} \cdot r \cos \phi.$$

But $$\frac{ds}{dr} = \frac{1}{\cos \phi},$$

$$\therefore \rho = r \frac{dr}{dp}.$$

Ex. 5. *For the curve* $r^2 \cos 2\theta = a^2$, *prove that* $\rho = r^3/a^2$ *numerically.*

It will be simpler to obtain the pedal equation of the curve and then use the pedal form for the radius of curvature.

We have $$r^2 = a^2 \sec 2\theta,$$

$$2r \frac{dr}{d\theta} = 2a^2 \sec 2\theta \tan 2\theta.$$

I.e. $$\tan \phi = \frac{r^2}{a^2 \sec 2\theta \tan 2\theta} = \cot 2\theta;$$

$$\phi = \tfrac{1}{2}\pi - 2\theta.$$

$$\therefore \ p = r \sin \phi = r \cos 2\theta = \frac{a^2}{r}.$$

Radius of curvature, $$\rho = r \frac{dr}{dp} = -\frac{a^2 r}{p^2} = -\frac{r^3}{a^2}.$$

I.e. $$\rho = \frac{r^3}{a^2} \text{ numerically.}$$

Ex. 6. *Prove that* $\rho = p + \dfrac{d^2p}{d\psi^2}.$

Referring to Fig. 82, $$OP^2 = OR^2 + PR^2;$$

i.e. $$r^2 = p^2 + \left(\frac{dp}{d\psi}\right)^2.$$

Differentiating w.r.t. p, $$2r \frac{dr}{dp} = 2p + \frac{d}{d\psi}\left(\frac{dp}{d\psi}\right)^2 \cdot \frac{d\psi}{dp}$$

$$= 2p + 2 \frac{d^2p}{d\psi^2}.$$

$$\therefore \ \rho = r \frac{dr}{dp} = p + \frac{d^2p}{d\psi^2}.$$

EXAMPLES 13b

Find the radius of curvature of each of the following curves at the point stated:

1. $r = 2\theta$; $\theta = \tfrac{1}{4}\pi$.
2. $r = a \cos \theta$; $\theta = \tfrac{1}{3}\pi$.
3. $r = a \sin 2\theta$; $\theta = \tfrac{1}{4}\pi$.
4. $r = a(1 - \cos \theta)$; $\theta = \pi$.
5. $r = a(2 + \cos \theta)$; $\theta = \tfrac{1}{2}\pi$.
6. $r = ae^\theta$; $\theta = 0$.
7. $p = ar^3$; $r = 2$.
8. $pr^2 = a^3$; $r = 1$.
9. $r^2 = p(a - p)$; $p = 0$.
10. $a^2b^2 = (b^2 + a^2 - r^2)p^2$; $r = a$.
11. $r^2 = a^2 \sin 2\theta$; $r = a$.
12. $r^2 \cos \theta = a^2$; $r = a\sqrt{2}$.

13. By first obtaining the pedal equation or otherwise, prove that for the cardioid $r = a(1 + \cos \theta)$, $\rho = \frac{4}{3}a \cos \frac{1}{2}\theta$.

14. Find the pedal equation of the parabola $2a = r(1 + \cos \theta)$ and deduce the result, $a^{\frac{1}{2}}\rho = 2r^{\frac{3}{2}}$.

15. For the curve $r = a \sec 2\theta$, prove that $\rho = r^4/3p^3$ numerically.

16. Show that the radius of curvature of the curve $r = a \sin n\theta$ at the origin is $\frac{1}{2}na$.

17. For the curve $r^2 = a^2 \cos 2\theta$, prove that $3r\rho = a^2$.

18. In Fig. 83, C is the centre of curvature of the point P; the radius vector OP meets the circle of curvature again in Q. PQ is called *the chord of curvature* through the pole. Prove the results

$$PQ = 2\rho \sin \phi = 2p \frac{dr}{dp}.$$

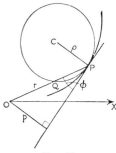

Fig. 83.

19. Show that the length of the chord of curvature through the pole of the curve $r^2 = a^2 \cos 2\theta$ is $\frac{2}{3}r$.

20. For the equiangular spiral $r = ae^{\theta \cot \alpha}$, prove that the centre of curvature is at the point where the perpendicular to the radius vector through the pole meets the normal.

21. For any curve, prove the result $\rho = \dfrac{r}{\sin \phi \left(1 + \dfrac{d\phi}{d\theta}\right)}$ and deduce the ordinary formula for ρ in terms of r and θ.

22. Prove that in an ellipse, centre C, semi-axes a, b, the radius of curvature at any point P is given by $\rho = \dfrac{a^2b^2}{p^3}$, where p is the perpendicular from C on the tangent at P.

23. Show that the pedal equation of a curve for which $\rho = p$ is of the form $r^2 = p^2 + a^2$, where a is a constant.

24. For a given curve which passes through the pole, $3r\rho = a^2$; find the pedal equation of the curve and verify that its polar equation is $r^2 = a^2 \sin 2\theta$.

Area of a closed curve. Suppose the curve is given in parametric Cartesian coordinates $x = f(t)$; $y = g(t)$.

Referring to Fig. 84, imagine the curve to be described in a counterclockwise direction starting and finishing at A.

Let the value of t vary from t_0 to T_0 where, as A corresponds to the two parameters t_0, T_0,

$$f(t_0) = f(T_0) \quad \text{and} \quad g(t_0) = g(T_0).$$

To illustrate this point take the ellipse $x = 1 + 4 \cos t$, $y = 3 \sin t$; the curve is completely described when t varies from 0 to 2π, the point A corresponding to $t = 0$ and $t = 2\pi$.

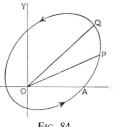

Fig. 84.

Now the sectorial area $OPQ = \frac{1}{2}\int_{\alpha}^{\beta} r^2\, d\theta$, where α, β are the vectorial angles of P and Q respectively.

But as $x = r \cos\theta$, $\quad \dfrac{dx}{dt} = \dfrac{dr}{dt}\cos\theta - r\sin\theta\,\dfrac{d\theta}{dt}$ . . . . . (i)

Also as $y = r\sin\theta$, $\quad \dfrac{dy}{dt} = \dfrac{dr}{dt}\sin\theta + r\cos\theta\,\dfrac{d\theta}{dt}$ . . . . . (ii)

Multiplying (i) by y or $r\sin\theta$, (ii) by x or $r\cos\theta$ and subtracting (i) from (ii),

$$x\,\frac{dy}{dt} - y\,\frac{dx}{dt} = r^2\,\frac{d\theta}{dt}(\cos^2\theta + \sin^2\theta) = r^2\,\frac{d\theta}{dt};$$

i.e. $\qquad \displaystyle\int\left(x\,\frac{dy}{dt} - y\,\frac{dx}{dt}\right)dt = \int r^2\,\frac{d\theta}{dt}\,dt = \int r^2\,d\theta.$

$\therefore$ Sectorial area $OPQ = \frac{1}{2}\displaystyle\int_{t_1}^{t_2}\left(x\,\frac{dy}{dt} - y\,\frac{dx}{dt}\right)dt,$

where t_1, t_2 are the parameters of P, Q.

Hence the area of the closed curve

$$= \frac{1}{2}\int_{t_0}^{T_0}\left(x\,\frac{dy}{dt} - y\,\frac{dx}{dt}\right)dt.$$

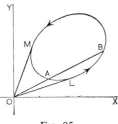

FIG. 85.

In a case where O lies outside the closed curve as in Fig. 85, suppose that in travelling completely around the curve from A to A in a counterclockwise direction, t varies from t_0 to T_0 and let the parameters of L, M, where OL, OM are the bounding radii vectores, be l, m.

Then, remembering that areas measured in the direction of θ increasing, that is counterclockwise, are positive and those measured in the opposite direction are negative, it follows that

$$\frac{1}{2}\int_{t_0}^{l}\left(x\,\frac{dy}{dt} - y\,\frac{dx}{dt}\right)dt = -\,\text{area } OLA;$$

$$\frac{1}{2}\int_{l}^{m}\left(x\,\frac{dy}{dt} - y\,\frac{dx}{dt}\right)dt = +\,\text{area } OLBM;$$

and $\qquad \dfrac{1}{2}\displaystyle\int_{m}^{T_0}\left(x\,\frac{dy}{dt} - y\,\frac{dx}{dt}\right)dt = -\,\text{area } OAM.$

Hence

$$\frac{1}{2}\int_{t_0}^{T_0}\left(x\,\frac{dy}{dt} - y\,\frac{dx}{dt}\right)dt = -\,\text{area } OLA + \text{area } OLBM - \text{area } OAM$$

$$= \text{area of the closed curve.}$$

So in all cases, **the area of a closed curve** $x = f(t)$, $y = g(t)$

$$= \tfrac{1}{2} \int_{t_0}^{T_0} \left(x\, \frac{dy}{dt} - y\, \frac{dx}{dt} \right) dt,$$

the limits being such that the integral is taken round the curve in a counterclockwise direction.

Ex. 7. *Find the area of the ellipse* $x = a \cos t$, $y = b \sin t$.

The curve is traced out by the point t when t varies from 0 to 2π.

$$\therefore \text{ Area} = \tfrac{1}{2} \int_0^{2\pi} \left(x\, \frac{dy}{dt} - y\, \frac{dx}{dt} \right) dt = \tfrac{1}{2} ab \int_0^{2\pi} (\cos^2 t + \sin^2 t) dt,$$

$$= \tfrac{1}{2} ab \int_0^{2\pi} dt = \pi ab.$$

Ex. 8. *By putting* $y = tx$, *obtain the parametric equations of the curve* $x^3 + y^3 = 3axy$ *and find the area of the loop of the curve described when t varies from 0 to ∞.*

Substituting $y = tx$, $x^3 + t^3 x^3 = 3atx^2$

i.e. $x = \dfrac{3at}{1 + t^3}$; $y = \dfrac{3at^2}{1 + t^3}$.

A sketch of the curve is given in Fig. 86; the origin O corresponds to $t = 0$ and $t = \infty$, and the loop is given by values of t between 0 and ∞.

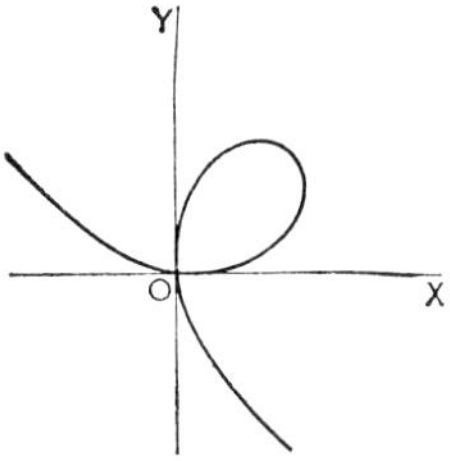

$$\text{Area of loop} = \tfrac{1}{2} \int_0^{\infty} \left(x\, \frac{dy}{dt} - y\, \frac{dx}{dt} \right) dt.$$

Now $\dfrac{dx}{dt} = \dfrac{3a(1 - 2t^3)}{(1 + t^3)^2}$; $\dfrac{dy}{dt} = \dfrac{3at(2 - t^3)}{(1 + t^3)^2}$.

$$\therefore \ x\, \frac{dy}{dt} - y\, \frac{dx}{dt} = \frac{9a^2 t^2}{(1 + t^3)^2},$$

and $\displaystyle \int \left(x\, \frac{dy}{dt} - y\, \frac{dx}{dt} \right) dt = 3a^2 \int \frac{du}{u^2}$, where $u = 1 + t^3$,

$$= -\frac{3a^2}{1 + t^3}.$$

Hence,   area of loop $= \displaystyle \lim_{N \to \infty} \tfrac{1}{2} \int_0^{N} \left(x\, \frac{dy}{dt} - y\, \frac{dx}{dt} \right) dt,$

$$= \tfrac{3}{2} a^2 - \tfrac{3}{2} a^2 \lim_{N \to \infty} \frac{1}{1 + N^3},$$

$$= \tfrac{3}{2} a^2.$$

FIG. 86.

Theorems of Pappus

I. *If a plane area revolves about an axis in its plane not intersecting it, the volume of revolution is equal to the area multiplied by the length of the path of its centre of gravity.*

Let the area A be rotated about the axis OX and let the ordinate of G, the centre of gravity of the area, be $\bar{y}$.

Imagine A to be divided into a large number of very small elements of area of which the element δA at P is typical.

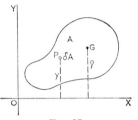

Then
$$\bar{y} = \lim_{\delta A \to 0} \frac{\sum y\,\delta A}{\sum \delta A};$$

i.e.
$$A\bar{y} = \int y\,dA,$$

where the integration extends to the whole area.

FIG. 87.

But the volume swept out by δA in one revolution $\simeq 2\pi y\,\delta A$.

$$\therefore \text{ Volume of revolution} = 2\pi \int y\,dA = 2\pi \bar{y}\,A,$$
$$= \text{Area} \times \text{ length of path of } G.$$

II. *If an arc of a plane curve revolves about an axis in its plane not intersecting it, the area of the surface of revolution is equal to the length of the arc multiplied by the length of the path of the centre of gravity of the arc.*

Let the arc, length s, be rotated about the axis OX and let the ordinate of G, the centre of gravity of the arc, be $\bar{y}$.

Imagine the arc to be split up into a large number of very small elements of length of which δs at P is typical.

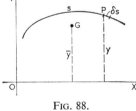

Then
$$\bar{y} = \lim_{\delta s \to 0} \frac{\sum y\,\delta s}{\sum \delta s};$$

i.e.
$$s\bar{y} = \int y\,ds,$$

FIG. 88.

where the integration extends to the whole arc.

But the area swept out by δs in one revolution $\simeq 2\pi y\,\delta s$.

$$\therefore \text{ Area of surface of revolution} = 2\pi \int y\,ds = 2\pi \bar{y}\,s,$$
$$= \text{Length of arc}$$
$$\times \text{length of path of } G.$$

Ex. 9. *Use the theorems of Pappus to determine the centres of gravity of:* (*i*) *a uniform semicircular area;* (*ii*) *a semicircular arc.*

(i) Imagine a semicircular area, radius r, to rotate about its bounding diameter AB, the volume swept out being a sphere, radius r.
We have

$$\tfrac{4}{3}\pi r^3 = \text{volume of revolution} = \tfrac{1}{2}\pi r^2 \cdot 2\pi\bar{y}.$$

I.e. $$\bar{y} = \frac{4r}{3\pi}.$$

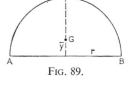

FIG. 89.

∴ The centre of gravity of the semicircular area lies on the radius of symmetry at a distance of $\dfrac{4r}{3\pi}$ from the centre.

(ii) Let a semicircular arc, radius r, rotate about the diameter AB, the area swept out being the curved surface area of a sphere, radius r.
We have

$$4\pi r^2 = \text{area of surface of revolution} = \pi r \cdot 2\pi\bar{y}.$$

I.e. $$\bar{y} = \frac{2r}{\pi}.$$

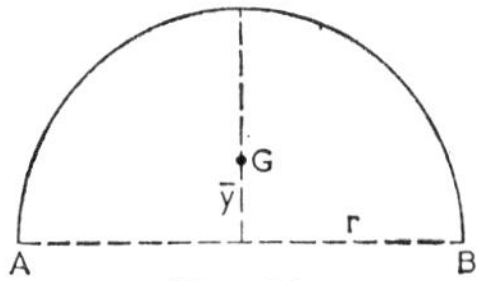

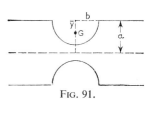

FIG. 90.

∴ The centre of gravity of the semicircular arc is on the radius of symmetry and at a distance of $\dfrac{2r}{\pi}$ from the centre.

Ex. 10. *A groove of semicircular section, radius b, is cut round a cylinder of radius a, find the volume removed and the area of surface of the groove.*

Volume removed = area of semicircle × length of path of its C.G.,

$$= \tfrac{1}{2}\pi b^2 \cdot 2\pi\left(a - \frac{4b}{3\pi}\right),$$

$$= \pi^2 a b^2 - \tfrac{4}{3}\pi b^3.$$

Area of groove = length of semicircular arc × length of path of its C.G.,

$$= \pi b \cdot 2\pi\left(a - \frac{2b}{\pi}\right),$$

$$= 2\pi^2 ab - 4\pi b^2.$$

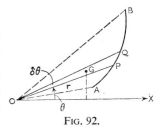

FIG. 91.

Volume of revolution of a sectorial area.

Consider the sectorial area OAB to be divided up into infinitesimal elements such as OPQ (Fig. 92).

The centre of gravity of the element OPQ is two-thirds of the way down the median from O and in a revolution about OX this point moves a distance $2\pi(\tfrac{2}{3}r\sin\theta)$.

FIG. 92.

Hence the volume swept out by the element $\simeq \frac{1}{2} r^2 \delta\theta \cdot \frac{4}{3}\pi r \sin\theta$.

$$\therefore \textbf{ The volume of revolution} = \tfrac{2}{3}\pi \int_\alpha^\beta \mathbf{r}^3 \sin\theta \, d\theta,$$

where α, β are the vectorial angles of A and B.

EXAMPLES 13c

1. Find the area of the ellipse $x = 1 + 3 \cos t$, $y = 2 \cos t$.

2. Prove that the area of the closed curve $x = 4 \cos t - 5$, $y = 4 \sin t + 6$ is 16π.

3. If P is the point $(at^2, 2at)$ on the parabola $y^2 = 4ax$ and O is the vertex, find the area bounded by the curve and the chord OP.

4. The triangle ABC, right-angled at B, is rotated about BC to generate the surface of a right circular cone; $BC = h$, $AB = r$. Deduce from Pappus' theorems the formulae for the volume and curved surface area of a circular cone.

5. If P is the point $(at^2, 2at)$ and PQ a focal chord of the parabola $y^2 = 4ax$, prove that the area enclosed between the curve and PQ is

$$\tfrac{1}{3}a^2\left(t^3 + \frac{1}{t^3}\right) + a^2\left(t + \frac{1}{t}\right).$$

6. A curtain ring has an external diameter of 6 cm and its cross-section is a circle of diameter 1 cm; find its volume and surface area.

7. A semicircular bend of iron pipe has a mean radius of 10 cm and an internal pipe diameter of 5 cm. If the thickness of the iron is $\frac{1}{2}$ cm, calculate the external curved surface area and the volume of the metal.

8. Sketch the curve $x = a \cos^3 t$, $y = a \sin^3 t$ and prove that its total area is $\frac{3}{8}\pi a^2$.

9. Sides BC, CA, AB of triangle ABC are of lengths 5 cm, 4 cm, 3 cm respectively. The triangle is rotated about an axis parallel to BC and 4 cm from it on the side remote from A. Find the volume and surface area of the resulting solid.

10. The cross-section of a solid circular tyre consists of a rectangle with sides 6 cm and 4 cm surmounted by a semicircle of diameter 6 cm. If the external radius of the tyre is 30 cm, find the surface area of the tyre.

11. Show that the curve $x = a \sin 2t$, $y = a \sin t$ consists of two equal loops and that the area of either is $\frac{4}{3}a^2$.

12. By writing $y = tx$, obtain the parametric equation of the curve $ay^2 = x^2(a - x)$ in the form $x = a(1 - t^2)$, $y = at(1 - t^2)$ and deduce that the area of the loop between $t = -1$ and $t = 1$ is $\frac{8}{15}a^2$.

13. The segment of the parabola $y^2 = 4ax$ bounded by the double ordinate $x = h$ is rotated about the y-axis. Find the area of the segment and the volume of revolution; deduce the distance of the C.G. of the area from the vertex.

14. Prove that the parametric equations of the curve $\left(\dfrac{x}{a}\right)^{\frac{2}{3}} + \left(\dfrac{y}{b}\right)^{\frac{2}{3}} = 1$ can be expressed in the form $x = a\cos^5 t$, $y = b\sin^5 t$. Hence find the total area of the curve.

15. The figure bounded by a quadrant of a circle radius a and the tangents at its ends revolves about one of these tangents. Prove that the volume of the solid generated is $(\frac{5}{3} - \frac{1}{2}\pi)\pi a^3$.

16. Find the volume of the solid formed by the revolution of the curve $r = a(1 + \cos\theta)$ about the initial line.

17. Find the area of the loop $(-1 \leqslant t \leqslant 1)$ of the curve

$$x = \frac{1 - t^2}{1 + t^2}, \quad y = \frac{t(1 - t^2)}{1 + t^2}.$$

18. The minor segment of a circle of radius a cut off by a chord of length $2a\sin\alpha$ is rotated about the diameter parallel to the chord. Find the volume of the solid of revolution and deduce the distance of the centre of gravity of the segment from the bounding chord.

19. Find the area common to the two ellipses $x = a\cos\theta$, $y = b\sin\theta$; $x = b\cos\theta$, $y = a\sin\theta$, $a \neq b$.

20. Prove that the complete area of the curve traced out by the point $(2a\cos t + a\cos 2t, 2a\sin t - a\sin 2t)$ is $2\pi a^2$.

21. Find the volume of the solid formed by the revolution about the initial line of the loop of the curve $r^3 = a^3\theta\cos\theta$ between $\theta = 0$ and $\theta = \frac{1}{2}\pi$.

22. Show that the area cut off from the curve $x^3 = ay^2$ by the chord joining the points $(at_1{}^2, at_1{}^3)$, $(at_2{}^2, at_2{}^3)$ is $\frac{1}{10}a^2(t_1 \sim t_2)^3(t_1{}^2 + 3t_1t_2 + t_2{}^2)$.

MISCELLANEOUS EXAMPLES

1. Show that in the curve $r = a(1 - \cos\theta)$, the angle between the radius vector and the tangent is $\frac{1}{2}\theta$.

2. Show that the curvatures of the curves $r = a\theta$, $r\theta = a$ are in the ratio $3 : 1$ at their common points.

3. Prove that the circumference of the cardioid $r = a(1 + \cos\theta)$ is $8a$.

4. Trace the curve $r = 1 + 2\cos\theta$, showing that it consists of two loops. What area is represented by the integral $\frac{1}{2}\displaystyle\int_0^{2\pi} r^2\,d\theta$? Find the areas of the separate loops.

5. Find the acute angle between the tangents drawn to the curve $2a = r(1 + \cos\theta)$ at the points where $\theta = \frac{1}{6}\pi$ and $\theta = \frac{1}{3}\pi$.

6. Show that in the curve $r\cos m\theta = a$, $\dfrac{1}{p^2} = \dfrac{1 - m^2}{r^2} + \dfrac{m^2}{a^2}$.

7. Sketch the curve $x = t^2 + 1$, $y = t(t^2 - 4)$. Show that it has a loop and find the area of this loop.

8. Trace the curve $r \cos \theta = a \sin 3\theta$ and prove that the area of a loop is $\frac{1}{8}a^2(9\sqrt{3} - 4\pi)$.

9. Prove that the radius of curvature of the curve $r = a(1 - \cos \theta)$ is $\frac{4}{3}a \sin \frac{1}{2}\theta$.

10. Show that the area of the ellipse $b^2x^2 + a^2y^2 = a^2b^2$ is πab. A ring is formed by the rotation of the ellipse about the line $y = c$, $c > b$; find the volume of the ring.

11. Prove that the curves $r = a(1 + \cos \theta)$, $r = b(1 - \cos \theta)$ cut orthogonally.

12. Show that the tangents to the curve $r = a(1 - \cos \theta)$ at the points θ, $\frac{1}{3}\pi + \theta$, $\frac{2}{3}\pi + \theta$, $\pi + \theta$, from a rectangle.

13. A semicircular groove of diameter 1 cm is cut in a solid right circular cone of base radius 6 cm and height 8 cm, the groove being mid-way between the vertex and the base. Find the volume removed and the curved surface area of the groove.

14. Find the coordinates of each of the points on the curve $r = \cos 2\theta - \cos \theta$ at which the tangent is at right angles to the radius vector.

15. Find the pedal equation of the curve $r^2 \cos 2\theta = a^2$ and deduce that the numerical value of the radius of curvature is $|r^3/a^2|$.

16. Show that the length of the arc of that part of the cardioid $r = a(1 + \cos \theta)$ which lies on the side of the line $4r \cos \theta = 3a$ remote from the pole is equal to $4a$.

17. Find the area included between the two loops of the curve $r = a(2 \cos \theta + \sqrt{3})$.

18. Trace the curve $x = \cos 2t$, $y = \sin 3t$ and find the area of the loop.

19. The equation of a curve is $r = a + bf(\theta)$, where a is small compared with b, show that approximately $\cot \phi = \dfrac{f'(\theta)}{f(\theta)} \left\{ 1 - \dfrac{a}{bf(\theta)} \right\}$.

20. With the usual notation, show that in the curve with pedal equation $p^2 = r^2 - a^2$, arc length $s = \frac{1}{2}\dfrac{r^2}{a} + \text{const.}$

21. By writing $y = tx$, obtain the parametric equations of the curve $x^5 + y^5 = 5ax^2y^2$ and determine the area of the loop $t = 0$ to $t = \infty$.

22. If the curve $r = a + b \cos \theta$, $a > b$, rotates about the initial line, show that the volume generated is $\frac{4}{3}\pi a(a^2 + b^2)$.

23. Starting from the Cartesian equation of an ellipse, deduce that its pedal equation with respect to a focus as pole is $\dfrac{b^2}{p^2} = \dfrac{2a}{r} - 1$, $b < a$.

24. Show that the chord of curvature through the pole of the curve $r = ae^{m\theta}$ is of length $2r$.

25. Express the equation of the curve $(x^2 + y^2)^2 - 2ax(x^2 + y^2) - a^2y^2 = 0$ in polar coordinates, and hence obtain the radius of curvature at the point $(2a, 0)$.

26. Prove that the curves $r^2 \cos (2\theta - \alpha) = a^2 \sin 2\alpha$, $r^2 = 2a^2 \sin (2\theta + \alpha)$ cut orthogonally.

27. Find the pedal equation of the curve $r^m = a^m \cos m\theta$ and prove that
$$\rho = \frac{a^m}{(m+1)r^{m-1}}.$$

28. Sketch the curve $r^2 = a^2 \sin \theta$ and find the maximum breadth of a loop.

29. A loop of the curve $r^2 = a^2 \cos \theta$ is rotated about the initial line, prove that: (i) the volume of revolution is $\frac{4}{15}\pi a^3$; (ii) the C.G. of the volume is at a distance $\frac{15}{32}a$ from the pole.

30. If A be the area of the cardioid $r = a(1 + \cos \theta)$ and V the volume generated when the curve revolves about the initial line, prove that $9V = 16aA$.

31. Find the area of the curve $x = \sin^2 t$, $y = \sin^3 t \cos t$.

32. The normal to the curve $r^2 = a^2 \cos 2\theta$ at a point P meets the initial line at G. Prove that, if r is the distance of P from the pole, $PG = a^2r/(a^2 + 2r^2)$.

33. Show that the curve $x = (t-1)e^{-t}$, $y = tx$ has a loop and prove that its area is $\frac{1}{8}e^{-2}$.

34. P, P' are neighbouring points on a plane curve and PQ, $P'Q$ are drawn perpendicular to OP, OP' respectively. Show that as $P' \to P$, angle $POQ \to \frac{1}{2}\pi - \phi$, where ϕ is the angle between OP and the tangent at P, and the length $PQ \to \dfrac{dr}{d\theta}$.

35. If C is the centre of curvature at any point P on the curve $r^n = a^n \cos n\theta$ and if CN is the perpendicular from C to OP, where O is the pole, prove that $NP : OP = 1 : (n+1)$.

36. Sketch the curve $r = a \cos^3 \frac{1}{3}\theta$ and show that its total length is $\frac{3}{2}\pi a$.

37. Sketch the curve $x = a \sin 2t$, $y = b \cos^3 t$, where a and $b > 0$, and show that its total area is $\frac{16}{5}ab$.

38. Show that if the area lying within the curve $r = 2a(1 + \cos \theta)$ and outside the curve $r(1 + \cos \theta) = 2a$, is rotated about the line $\theta = 0$, then the volume generated is $18\pi a^3$.

39. If C is the centre of curvature at P for the curve $r^3 = 2ap^2$, prove that: (i) $PC = \frac{2}{3}\sqrt{(2ar)}$; (ii) $OC = \frac{1}{3}\sqrt{(8ar - 3r^2)}$.

40. A chord of a circle of radius r subtends an angle 2α at the centre; the minor segment cut off by this chord is revolved about the chord through an angle of 2π. Prove that the volume of the solid formed is
$$2\pi r^3(\sin \alpha - \tfrac{1}{3}\sin^3 \alpha - \alpha \cos \alpha).$$

41. Prove that the volume of the wedge-shaped solid cut off from a right circular cylinder of unlimited length and radius a by a plane through the centre of the base making an angle α with the base is $\frac{2}{3}a^3 \tan \alpha$.

CHAPTER XIV

ALGEBRAIC GEOMETRY
OF THE PLANE AND STRAIGHT LINE

Rectangular Cartesian coordinates. Let $X'OX$, $Y'OY$ be two perpendicular straight lines intersecting in O and let $Z'OZ$ be a third straight line through O, perpendicular to the plane containing $X'OX, Y'OY$ (Fig. 93). For ease of interpretation this latter plane can be thought of as horizontal in which event, $Z'OZ$ would be a vertical line.

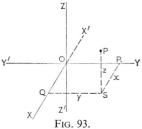

FIG. 93.

The mutually perpendicular lines $X'OX$, $Y'OY$, $Z'OZ$ determine three mutually perpendicular planes YOZ, ZOX, XOY, *the coordinate planes.*

Taking O as origin and the convention that displacements in the directions OX, OY, OZ are positive and those in directions OX', OY', OZ' negative, scales can be taken on each of the axes $X'OX$—the x-axis, $Y'OY$—the y-axis and $Z'OZ$—the z-axis.

The perpendicular distances of a point P in space from each of the coordinate planes YOZ, ZOX, XOY are the x, y and z coordinates of P; these distances are respectively RS, QS and PS (Fig. 93).

One set of values of x, y, z uniquely determines a point in space.

Notation. The point with x, y and z coordinates equal respectively to a, b and c is written (a, b, c).

Three-dimensional loci. If P is a variable point with coordinates (x, y, z), then the equation of the locus of P is the equation connecting the variables x, y, z.

Any equation of the form $f(x, y, z) = 0$ will represent a surface, and the intersection of two such surfaces $f_1(x, y, z) = 0$, $f_2(x, y, z) = 0$ will represent a curve. Consequently, in three dimensions a surface, such as a plane or a sphere, will be represented by one equation while a curve, and a straight line is included in this class, will be represented by two equations.

E.g. referring to Fig. 93, as all points of the plane YOZ have an x-coordinate of zero, the equation of YOZ is $x = 0$.

Similarly, the other coordinate planes ZOX, XOY have equations $y = 0$, $z = 0$.

The axis OX is determined by the planes ZOX, XOY, and hence it has the equations: $y = 0$, $z = 0$.

Similarly, the equations of OY are $z = 0$, $x = 0$ and of OZ, $x = 0$, $y = 0$.

Fundamental results. Employing the methods used in two-dimensional coordinate geometry, the following important results are readily obtained:

(i) *the distance between the points* $P_1(x_1, y_1, z_1)$, $P_2(x_2, y_2, z_2)$ *is*

$$\sqrt{\{(x_1 - x_2)^2 + (y_1 - y_2)^2 + (z_1 - z_2)^2\}};$$

(ii) *the coordinates of the point dividing the line* P_1P_2 *in the ratio* $m:n$ *are*

$$\left\{\frac{mx_2 + nx_1}{m+n}, \frac{my_2 + ny_1}{m+n}, \frac{mz_2 + nz_1}{m+n}\right\},$$

m or n being taken as negative if the division is external;

(iii) *the coordinates of the mid-point of* P_1P_2 *are*

$$\{\tfrac{1}{2}(x_1 + x_2), \tfrac{1}{2}(y_1 + y_2), \tfrac{1}{2}(z_1 + z_2)\}.$$

Ex. 1. *Find the distance between the points* $(2, 0, 1)$, $(-1, 2, -3)$.

$$\text{Distance} = \sqrt{\{3^2 + (-2)^2 + 4^2\}} = \sqrt{29}.$$

Ex. 2. *Find the coordinates of the point P dividing the line joining the points* $(3, 1, 0)$, $(-2, 2, 3)$ *in the ratio* $2:1$.

$$x \text{ coordinate} = \frac{1(3) + 2(-2)}{2+1} = -\tfrac{1}{3};$$

Similarly, y coordinate $= \tfrac{5}{3}$; z coordinate $= 2$.

I.e. P is the point $(-\tfrac{1}{3}, \tfrac{5}{3}, 2)$.

Ex. 3. *Find the coordinates of the points in which the surface* $3x - y + 2z = 6$ *meets the coordinate axes.*

The surface meets the x-axis, where $y = z = 0$.

Hence $3x = 6$, $x = 2$.

So the point of intersection with the x-axis is $(2, 0, 0)$.

Similarly, the points of intersection with the y- and z-axes are $(0, -6, 0)$, $(0, 0, 3)$ respectively.

Ex. 4. *Find the coordinates of the point in which the line joining the points* $A(0, 0, 1)$, $B(1, 0, 0)$ *meets the surface* $2x + y + z + 1 = 0$.

The coordinates of any point P on AB can be expressed as

$$\left\{\frac{0 + \lambda(1)}{1 + \lambda}, \frac{0 + \lambda(0)}{1 + \lambda}, \frac{1 + \lambda(0)}{1 + \lambda}\right\}; \quad \text{i.e.} \quad \left(\frac{\lambda}{1+\lambda}, 0, \frac{1}{1+\lambda}\right);$$

in fact, these are the coordinates of the point dividing the line in the ratio $\lambda : 1$.
The point P lies on the given surface if

$$\frac{2\lambda}{1+\lambda} + 0 + \frac{1}{1+\lambda} + 1 = 0; \quad \text{i.e.} \quad \lambda = -\tfrac{2}{3}.$$

Hence P is the point $(-2, 0, 3)$.

Ex. 5. *Find the equation of the locus of a point P which moves such that its distance from the point $A(1, 0, 1)$ is twice its distance from the point $B(-1, 0, -1)$.*

We have $\quad PA^2 = (x-1)^2 + y^2 + (z-1)^2; \quad PB^2 = (x+1)^2 + y^2 + (z+1)^2$, where P is the point (x, y, z).

$$\therefore \quad (x-1)^2 + y^2 + (z-1)^2 = 4\{(x+1)^2 + y^2 + (z+1)^2\}$$

i.e. $\qquad\qquad\qquad\qquad 0 = 3(x^2 + y^2 + z^2) + 10x + 10z + 6.$

This is the equation of the locus of P.

EXAMPLES 14a

1. Write down the coordinates of the six points which lie on the coordinate axes and are distant one unit from the origin.

2. Show approximately on diagrams the positions of the points: $(0, 0, 2)$; $(0, -1, 0)$; $(3, 0, 0)$; $(1, 1, 0)$; $(-2, 1, 0)$; $(2, 0, 1)$; $(0, 1, 1)$; $(1, 1, 1)$; $(-2, 1, -1)$; $(1, -2, 2)$.

3. Obtain the distance of each of the following points from the origin: $(1, 1, 0)$; $(2, 0, -1)$; $(-2, 0, -1)$; $(-2, 3, 1)$; $(0, 4, 3)$; $(\sqrt{2}, 1, 1)$.

4. Find the distance between each of the following pairs of points: (i) $(2, 0, 0)$, $(1, 2, 3)$; (ii) $(3, 0, -1)$, $(1, 2, 1)$; (iii) $(-2, -1, 1)$, $(0, 2, -2)$; (iv) $(a, -a, 0)$, $(-a, 0, a)$.

5. Find the coordinates of the point which divides the line joining the origin to the point $(3, 4, -2)$ in the ratio $1:2$.

6. Show that the mid-point of the line joining the points $(4, -2, 3)$, $(1, -1, 1)$ coincides with the mid-point of the line joining the points $(2, -4, 0)$, $(3, 1, 4)$.

7. Find the coordinates of the points in which the surface $x^2 + y^2 + z^2 = 4$ meets the x-axis.

8. What are the equations of the curve in which the surface $2x^2 + y^2 - z^2 = 1$ meets the plane $z = 0$?

9. Find the coordinates of the point in which the line joining the points $(1, 1, 1)$, $(2, 0, 3)$ meets the surface $x + 2y - z = 1$.

10. Find the ratio in which the line joining the points $(2, 1, -1)$, $(3, 2, 2)$ is divided by the plane $x = 0$.

11. What is the equation of the locus of a point which moves such that its distance from the plane $x = 0$ is twice its distance from the plane $z = 0$?

12. Obtain the equation of the locus of a point which moves equidistant from the origin and the point $(2, 2, 2)$.

13. Prove that the coordinates of the centroid of the triangle with vertices (x_1, y_1, z_1), (x_2, y_2, z_2), (x_3, y_3, z_3) are

$$\{\tfrac{1}{3}(x_1 + x_2 + x_3), \tfrac{1}{3}(y_1 + y_2 + y_3), \tfrac{1}{3}(z_1 + z_2 + z_3)\}.$$

14. A, B, C, D are the points $(1, 1, 1)$, $(1, -1, 1)$, $(1, 1, -1)$, $(-1, 1, 1)$. Write down the coordinates of the centroids G_1, G_2, G_3, G_4, of triangles BCD, DCA, ADB, ABC respectively and show that the lines AG_1, BG_2, CG_3, DG_4 are concurrent in a point which divides each of them in the ratio $3:1$.

T

15. Write down the coordinates of the mid-point M of the line joining the points $(\alpha, m\alpha, c)$, $(\beta, -m\beta, -c)$, where m, c are constants, and prove that the locus of M is the coordinate plane $z = 0$.

16. Write down the coordinates of the point P which divides the line joining the points $(\alpha, m\alpha, c)$, $(\beta, -m\beta, -c)$ in the constant ratio $\lambda : 1$. Prove that the locus of P is a plane parallel to the plane $z = 0$.

17. Find the equation of the locus of a point which moves such that its distance from the origin is constant and equal to two. What is the nature of the locus?

18. Prove that the surface $(x - 2)^2 + (y - 1)^2 + (z + 2)^2 = 5$ touches the x-axis at the point $(2, 0, 0)$.

19. Find the point of intersection of the straight lines $3y - x = 1$, $z = 0$; $y + 2x = 5$, $z = 0$.

20. Show that the point $(1, 1, 1)$ is the centre of the sphere passing through the origin and the points $(2, 0, 0)$, $(0, 2, 0)$, $(0, 0, 2)$.

Direction of a straight line. The direction of the straight line $\overrightarrow{PQ}$, joining P to Q, is determined by the angles the line makes with the positive directions of the coordinate axes OX, OY, OZ.

If these angles are α, β, γ respectively, then $\cos\alpha$, $\cos\beta$, $\cos\gamma$ are called *the direction-cosines* of $\overrightarrow{PQ}$ and are usually denoted by the letters l, m, n, although on occasions these letters are used to represent three numbers which are proportional to the direction-cosines.

Taking a line OA of unit length through the origin and parallel to $\overrightarrow{PQ}$ (Fig. 94), then the angles XOA, YOA, ZOA are respectively equal to α, β, γ. By dropping perpendiculars from A

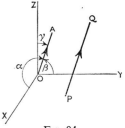

FIG. 94.

on to the three axes in turn, it follows that the coordinates of A are $(\cos\alpha, \cos\beta, \cos\gamma)$ or (l, m, n).

$$\therefore \quad l^2 + m^2 + n^2 = OA^2 = 1;$$

i.e.
$$l^2 + m^2 + n^2 = 1.$$

Hence *the sum of the squares of the direction-cosines of any straight line is unity.*

Parallel lines. Clearly parallel lines have the same direction-cosines.

Direction-cosines of the straight line joining two given points. Let P_1, P_2 be the points (x_1, y_1, z_1), (x_2, y_2, z_2).

Referring to Fig. 95, in which the rectangular parallelopiped with edges parallel to the coordinate axes and with P_1P_2 as a diagonal has been drawn, it

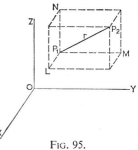

FIG. 95.

follows that the direction-cosines of $\overrightarrow{P_1P_2}$ are the cosines of angles $\overset{\bullet}{L}P_1P_2$, MP_1P_2, NP_1P_2 respectively.

I.e. the direction-cosines are $\dfrac{P_1L}{P_1P_2}$, $\dfrac{P_1M}{P_1P_2}$, $\dfrac{P_1N}{P_1P_2}$,

or $\qquad\qquad\qquad \dfrac{x_2-x_1}{r}$, $\dfrac{y_2-y_1}{r}$, $\dfrac{z_2-z_1}{r}$,

where $\qquad\qquad r = \sqrt{\{(x_2-x_1)^2+(y_2-y_1)^2+(z_2-z_1)^2\}}$.

Ex. 6. *Find the direction-cosines of the straight line joining the points* $P(2, -1, 3)$, $Q(4, 2, 0)$.

$$r = \text{length } PQ = \sqrt{22}.$$

$\therefore$ Direction-cosines of $\overrightarrow{PQ}$ are $\dfrac{4-2}{\sqrt{22}}$, $\dfrac{2-(-1)}{\sqrt{22}}$, $\dfrac{0-3}{\sqrt{22}}$;

i.e. $\qquad\qquad\qquad \dfrac{2}{\sqrt{22}}$, $\dfrac{3}{\sqrt{22}}$, $\dfrac{-3}{\sqrt{22}}$.

Angle between two straight lines. In the case of lines which do not intersect, the angle between them is defined as the angle between lines drawn through any point parallel to them.

Suppose the angle between two lines P_1Q_1, P_2Q_2 which have direction-cosines l_1, m_1, n_1; l_2, m_2, n_2 respectively is θ (Fig. 96).

Let OA_1, OA_2 be unit lines through the origin respectively parallel to P_1Q_1, P_2Q_2.

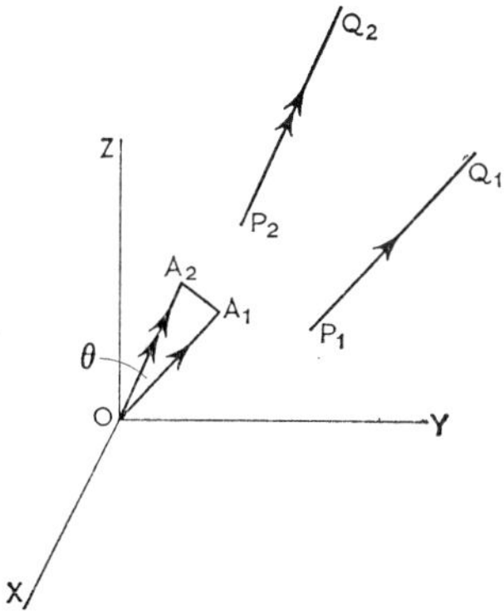

Then $\qquad$ angle $A_1OA_2 = \theta$

and by the cosine rule,

$$A_1A_2{}^2 = 2 - 2\cos\theta.$$

But as the coordinates of A_1, A_2 are (l_1, m_1, n_1), (l_2, m_2, n_2) respectively,

$$A_1A_2{}^2 = (l_1-l_2)^2+(m_1-m_2)^2+(n_1-n_2)^2.$$

FIG. 96.

$$\therefore (l_1-l_2)^2+(m_1-m_2)^2+(n_1-n_2)^2 = 2-2\cos\theta,$$

$$(l_1{}^2+m_1{}^2+n_1{}^2)+(l_2{}^2+m_2{}^2+n_2{}^2)-2(l_1l_2+m_1m_2+n_1n_2)=2-2\cos\theta.$$

But $\qquad\qquad l_1{}^2+m_1{}^2+n_1{}^2 = l_2{}^2+m_2{}^2+n_2{}^2 = 1,$

hence $\qquad\qquad \mathbf{\cos\theta = l_1l_2 + m_1m_2 + n_1n_2.}$

As an important special case, it follows that the lines with direction-cosines l_1, m_1, n_1; l_2, m_2, n_2 *are perpendicular if* $l_1l_2+m_1m_2+n_1n_2=0$.

Ex. 7. *If* $ABCDA'B'C'D'$ *is a rectangular parallelopiped with* $AB = a$, $BC = b$, $AA' = c$, *find the cosine of the angle between the diagonals* BD', $B'D$.

Taking edges AB, AD, AA' as coordinate axes (Fig. 97), then the coordinates of B, D' are respectively $(a, 0, 0)$, $(0, b, c)$.

Hence the direction-cosines of BD' are

$$\frac{-a}{\sqrt{(a^2 + b^2 + c^2)}}, \quad \frac{b}{\sqrt{(a^2 + b^2 + c^2)}}, \quad \frac{c}{\sqrt{(a^2 + b^2 + c^2)}}.$$

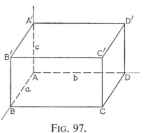

Similarly, the direction-cosines of $B'D$ are

$$\frac{-a}{\sqrt{(a^2 + b^2 + c^2)}}, \quad \frac{b}{\sqrt{(a^2 + b^2 + c^2)}}, \quad \frac{-c}{\sqrt{(a^2 + b^2 + c^2)}}.$$

So, if θ is the angle between BD' and $B'D$,

$$\cos \theta = l_1 l_2 + m_1 m_2 + n_1 n_2 = \frac{a^2 + b^2 - c^2}{a^2 + b^2 + c^2}.$$

Fig. 97.

Direction ratios. If l, m, n are the direction-cosines of a straight line, then any three numbers p, q, r which are in the ratios $l : m : n$ are called *direction ratios*.

As

$$\frac{l}{p} = \frac{m}{q} = \frac{n}{r} = k, \text{ say,}$$

then

$$l = kp; \quad m = kq; \quad n = kr.$$

But

$$l^2 + m^2 + n^2 = 1, \quad \text{hence} \quad k = \pm \frac{1}{\sqrt{(p^2 + q^2 + r^2)}}.$$

I.e. $l = \pm \dfrac{p}{\sqrt{(p^2 + q^2 + r^2)}}$; $m = \pm \dfrac{q}{\sqrt{(p^2 + q^2 + r^2)}}$; $n = \pm \dfrac{r}{\sqrt{(p^2 + q^2 + r^2)}}.$

If θ is the angle between two lines with direction ratios $p_1 : q_1 : r_1$; $p_2 : q_2 : r_2$, it follows that

$$\cos \theta = \frac{p_1 p_2 + q_1 q_2 + r_1 r_2}{\sqrt{\{(p_1^2 + q_1^2 + r_1^2)(p_2^2 + q_2^2 + r_2^2)\}}}.$$

N.B. *The lines with direction ratios* $p_1 : q_1 : r_1$; $p_2 : q_2 : r_2$ *are*

(i) *parallel, if* $\dfrac{p_1}{p_2} = \dfrac{q_1}{q_2} = \dfrac{r_1}{r_2}$;

(ii) *perpendicular, if* $p_1 p_2 + q_1 q_2 + r_1 r_2 = 0$.

Ex. 8. *The direction ratios of two lines are* $p_1 : q_1 : r_1$; $p_2 : q_2 : r_2$, *find the direction ratios of a line which is perpendicular to each of the given lines.*

Let the direction ratios of the common perpendicular be $p : q : r$.

Then

$$pp_1 + qq_1 + rr_1 = 0,$$
$$pp_2 + qq_2 + rr_2 = 0.$$

Solving,

$$\frac{p}{q_1 r_2 - q_2 r_1} = \frac{-q}{p_1 r_2 - p_2 r_1} = \frac{r}{p_1 q_2 - p_2 q_1}.$$

I.e.

$$p : q : r = (q_1 r_2 - q_2 r_1) : (r_1 p_2 - r_2 p_1) : (p_1 q_2 - p_2 q_1).$$

Ex. 9. *If a line OP is perpendicular to each of two intersecting lines OA, OB, show that it is perpendicular to any line through O in the plane AOB.*

Take O as the origin and let OA, OB be of unit length (Fig. 98).

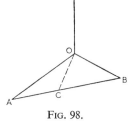

If the direction-cosines of OA, OB are l_1, m_1, n_1; l_2, m_2, n_2, then the coordinates of A, B are (l_1, m_1, n_1), (l_2, m_2, n_2) respectively.

The coordinates of any point C on the line AB can be expressed as

$$\left(\frac{l_1+\lambda l_2}{1+\lambda}, \frac{m_1+\lambda m_2}{1+\lambda}, \frac{n_1+\lambda n_2}{1+\lambda}\right).$$

Hence the direction ratios of OC are $l_1+\lambda l_2 : m_1+\lambda m_2 : n_1+\lambda n_2$.

Fig. 98.

If l, m, n are the direction-cosines of OP,

$$ll_1 + mm_1 + nn_1 = 0 \quad \text{and} \quad ll_2 + mm_2 + nn_2 = 0.$$
$$\therefore \; l(l_1+\lambda l_2) + m(m_1+\lambda m_2) + n(n_1+\lambda n_2) = 0$$

and in consequence, OP is perpendicular to OC.

EXAMPLES 14b

1. What are the direction-cosines of the axes OX, OY, OZ?

2. Show that the direction-cosines of the lines in the plane $z=0$ which bisect the angles between the x- and y-axes are $1/\sqrt{2}$, $\pm 1/\sqrt{2}$, 0.

3. If l, m, n are the direction-cosines of a line and $l=1/\sqrt{2}$, $m=-1/2$, find the possible values of n.

4. Find the direction-cosines of the line joining the origin to each of the following points: (i) $(1, 1, 1)$; (ii) $(2, 3, 4)$; (iii) $(0, 1, -1)$; (iv) (a, b, c).

5. Find the cosine of the angle between the lines joining the origin to the points $(4, 1, 3)$, $(2, 3, 1)$.

6. If the direction ratios of a line are $2 : -5 : 1$, find its direction-cosines.

7. Find the direction-cosines of the line $\overrightarrow{PQ}$ in each of the following cases:
(i) $P(1, 0, 1)$, $Q(3, 1, 2)$; (ii) $P(2, -1, 0)$, $Q(1, 2, 3)$; (iii) $P(1, -1, 1)$, $Q(-1, 1, -1)$; (iv) $P(-3, 2, -1)$, $Q(-4, -1, -2)$; (v) $P(a, 0, -a)$, $Q(2a, -a, 2a)$.

8. If the lines with direction ratios $1 : 3 : -2$, $2 : -1 : r$ are perpendicular, find the value of r.

9. Show that four lines can be drawn through the origin each equally inclined to the coordinate axes and find the direction-cosines of these lines.

10. Find the angles of the triangle with vertices $(0, 1, -1)$, $(1, 2, 3)$, $(2, 3, 1)$.

11. A straight rod is held with one end in the corner of a room. If it makes angles of $60°$ and $45°$ with the lines of intersection of the floor and the walls, find the angle it makes with the vertical.

12. Show that the direction ratios of any line drawn in the coordinate plane $z=0$ will be of the form $l : m : 0$ and write down similar results for lines in each of the other coordinate planes.

13. A line OP through the origin has direction-cosines l, m, n. If Q is the projection of P on the plane $z=0$, find the direction-cosines of the line OQ. Deduce that, if LM is a line in the plane $z=0$ perpendicular to OP, then LM is also perpendicular to OQ.

14. Find the size of angle A of the triangle with vertices $A(-1, 0, 1)$, $B(1, 2, 0)$, $C(2, -1, 2)$ and deduce the area of the triangle.

15. A tetrahedron has vertices $A(0,1,0)$, $B(0,0,2)$, $C(1,1,0)$, $D(-1,0,-1)$. Find the acute angle between the opposite edges AB, CD.

The plane. *Definition.* Suppose that P and Q are any two points in a surface, then the surface is a plane if all points of the straight line PQ lie in it.

The general equation of the first degree. Consider the equation $ax+by+cz+d=0$ and let $P(x_1, y_1, z_1)$, $Q(x_2, y_2, z_2)$ be any two points in the surface represented by this equation.

Then
$$ax_1+by_1+cz_1+d=0,$$
$$ax_2+by_2+cz_2+d=0.$$

Multiplying these equations by $\dfrac{n}{m+n}$ and $\dfrac{m}{m+n}$ respectively and adding,

$$a\frac{nx_1+mx_2}{m+n}+b\frac{ny_1+my_2}{m+n}+c\frac{nz_1+mz_2}{m+n}+d=0.$$

This equation shows that if P and Q are points of the surface so also is any point of PQ.

Hence the equation $ax+by+cz+d=0$, where a, b, c, d are constants, represents a plane.

Conversely, the general equation of a plane can be taken as

$$ax+by+cz+d=0.$$

This equation contains three independent constants, and consequently it follows that, in general, a plane will be uniquely determined by three conditions.

E.g. a plane is uniquely determined by three non-collinear points;
a plane is uniquely determined by two intersecting straight lines.

Plane determined by three given points. The equation of any plane passing through the point (x_1, y_1, z_1) can be written

$$a(x-x_1)+b(y-y_1)+c(z-z_1)=0.$$

This plane also contains the points (x_2, y_2, z_2), (x_3, y_3, z_3) if

$$a(x_2-x_1)+b(y_2-y_1)+c(z_2-z_1)=0,$$
$$a(x_3-x_1)+b(y_3-y_1)+c(z_3-z_1)=0.$$

Eliminating the ratios $a : b : c$ from the three equations gives

$$\begin{vmatrix} x-x_1 & y-y_1 & z-z_1 \\ x_2-x_1 & y_2-y_1 & z_2-z_1 \\ x_3-x_1 & y_3-y_1 & z_3-z_1 \end{vmatrix} = 0, \text{ the equation of}$$
the required plane.

Ex. 10. *Find the equation of the plane determined by the points* $(-1, 0, 1)$, $(2, 1, -1)$, $(1, 2, 1)$.

Required equation is
$$\begin{vmatrix} x+1 & y & z-1 \\ 3 & 1 & -2 \\ 2 & 2 & 0 \end{vmatrix} = 0,$$

$$4(x+1) - 4y + 4(z-1) = 0,$$

i.e.
$$x - y + z = 0.$$

Perpendicular form of the equation of a plane. In Fig. 99, ABC is a plane and ON is the perpendicular drawn to it from the origin.

Let the length of ON be p and let its direction-cosines be l, m, n; then N is the point (lp, mp, np).

If $P(x, y, z)$ is any point of the plane, the direction ratios of NP are

$$(x - lp) : (y - mp) : (z - np)$$

and as NP is perpendicular to ON,

$$l(x - lp) + m(y - mp) + n(z - np) = 0,$$
or, $\quad lx + my + nz = p(l^2 + m^2 + n^2) = p.$

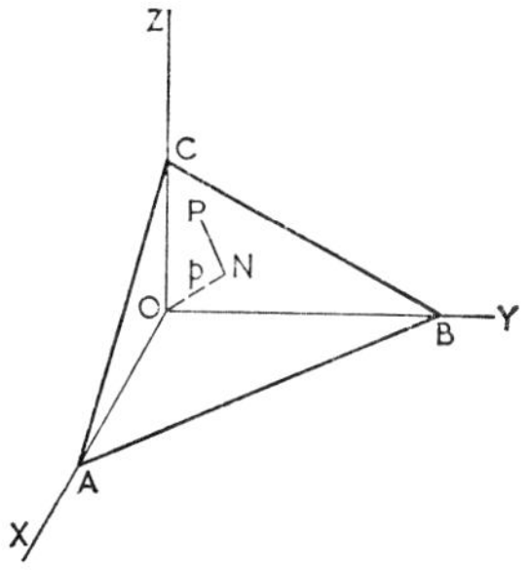

FIG. 99.

Hence **the equation of the plane is**

$$lx + my + nz = p,$$

where p, the length of the perpendicular from the origin, is usually taken as positive.

To express the equation $ax + by + cz + d = 0$ in the perpendicular form. Dividing throughout by $\sqrt{(a^2 + b^2 + c^2)}$ in order to make the sum of the squares of the coefficients of x, y, z unity, the equation can be written

$$\frac{a}{\sqrt{(a^2+b^2+c^2)}} x + \frac{b}{\sqrt{(a^2+b^2+c^2)}} y + \frac{c}{\sqrt{(a^2+b^2+c^2)}} z$$
$$= \frac{-d}{\sqrt{(a^2+b^2+c^2)}}, \text{ if } d \text{ is negative,}$$

or $\quad -\dfrac{a}{\sqrt{(a^2+b^2+c^2)}} x - \dfrac{b}{\sqrt{(a^2+b^2+c^2)}} y - \dfrac{c}{\sqrt{(a^2+b^2+c^2)}} z$
$$= \frac{d}{\sqrt{(a^2+b^2+c^2)}}, \text{ if } d \text{ is positive.}$$

In both cases, the equation is reduced to the form

$$lx + my + nz = p.$$

N.B. (i) *the length of the perpendicular from the origin to the plane* $ax + by + cz + d = 0$ *is* $\pm \dfrac{d}{\sqrt{(a^2 + b^2 + c^2)}}$, *the sign being chosen to make the expression positive;*

(ii) *the direction ratios of the normal to the plane from the origin are* $a : b : c$;

(iii) *from* (*ii*), *the equation of any plane parallel to* $ax + by + cz + d = 0$ *is of the form* $ax + by + cz + \lambda = 0$;

(iv) *if* θ *is an angle between the planes* $a_r x + b_r y + c_r z + d_r = 0$, $r = 1, 2$, *then* $\cos \theta = \pm \dfrac{a_1 a_2 + b_1 b_2 + c_1 c_2}{\sqrt{\{(a_1^2 + b_1^2 + c_1^2)(a_2^2 + b_2^2 + c_2^2)\}}}$.

Ex. 11. *Find the equation of the plane parallel to the plane* $3x - 2y + z - 1 = 0$ *and passing through the point* $(-1, 2, 1)$. *Also find the distance between the two planes.*

Any plane parallel to the given plane has the equation

$$3x - 2y + z + \lambda = 0.$$

As this plane contains the point $(-1, 2, 1)$,

$$-3 - 4 + 1 + \lambda = 0; \quad \lambda = 6.$$

I.e. equation of required plane is $3x - 2y + z + 6 = 0$.

Length of perpendicular from the origin on to the given plane is $\dfrac{1}{\sqrt{14}}$ and the direction-cosines of the perpendicular are $\dfrac{3}{\sqrt{14}}, \dfrac{-2}{\sqrt{14}}, \dfrac{1}{\sqrt{14}}$.

Length of perpendicular from the origin on to the parallel plane is $\dfrac{6}{\sqrt{14}}$ and the direction-cosines of the perpendicular are $\dfrac{-3}{\sqrt{14}}, \dfrac{2}{\sqrt{14}}, \dfrac{-1}{\sqrt{14}}$.

Hence the perpendiculars from the origin are in opposite directions and so the distance between the planes $= \dfrac{1}{\sqrt{14}} + \dfrac{6}{\sqrt{14}} = \sqrt{\tfrac{7}{2}}$.

The length of the perpendicular from a point to a plane. Take the equation of the plane as

$$lx + my + nz = p \quad \cdot \quad \cdot \quad \cdot \quad \cdot \quad \cdot \quad \text{(i)}$$

and let (x', y', z') be the coordinates of the given point P.

The equation of the plane parallel to (i) and passing through P is

$$lx + my + nz = lx' + my' + nz' = p', \text{ say} \quad \cdot \quad \cdot \quad \text{(ii)}$$

Now if ON, ON' are the perpendiculars from the origin to the planes (i) and (ii) respectively and PL is the perpendicular from P to the given plane (Fig. 100),

then
$$PL = ON - ON' = p - p',$$
$$= p - (lx' + my' + nz').$$

FIG. 100.

Hence the length of the perpendicular from any point on to the plane $lx + my + nz = p$ is obtained by substituting the coordinates of the point in the expression $p - (lx + my + nz)$.

If the equation of the plane is $ax + by + cz + d = 0$, then the length of the perpendicular from the point (x', y', z') is

$$\pm \frac{ax' + by' + cz' + d}{\sqrt{(a^2 + b^2 + c^2)}},$$

the sign being chosen to make the perpendicular from the origin positive.

Other important results on the plane. Following the methods used in dealing with the straight line in two-dimensional geometry, the following results for the plane are readily established:

(i) if $ax + by + cz + d = 0$ is a given plane and (x', y', z') any point, then the expression $ax' + by' + cz' + d$ is positive for all points on one side of the plane and negative for all points on the other side;

(ii) the equations of the planes which bisect the angles between the two planes $a_1x + b_1y + c_1z + d_1 = 0$, $a_2x + b_2y + c_2z + d_2 = 0$ are

$$\frac{a_1x + b_1y + c_1z + d_1}{\sqrt{(a_1{}^2 + b_1{}^2 + c_1{}^2)}} = \pm \frac{a_2x + b_2y + c_2z + d_2}{\sqrt{(a_2{}^2 + b_2{}^2 + c_2{}^2)}};$$

(iii) the equation of a plane passing through the line of intersection of the planes $a_1x + b_1y + c_1z + d_1 = 0$, $a_2x + b_2y + c_2z + d_2 = 0$ is of the form

$$a_1x + b_1y + c_1z + d_1 + \lambda(a_2x + b_2y + c_2z + d_2) = 0.$$

Ex. 12. *Find the equation of the plane passing through the line of intersection of the planes $x + y + z - 1 = 0$, $2x - z = 0$ and perpendicular to the plane $4x - y - 2z = 0$.*

The equation of the plane is of the form

$$x + y + z - 1 + \lambda(2x - z) = 0;$$

i.e.
$$x(1 + 2\lambda) + y + z(1 - \lambda) - 1 = 0.$$

This plane is perpendicular to the plane $4x - y - 2z = 0$ if
$$4(1 + 2\lambda) - 1 - 2(1 - \lambda) = 0; \quad \text{i.e. } \lambda = -\tfrac{1}{10}.$$
$\therefore$ Required equation is
$$10(x + y + z - 1) - (2x - z) = 0,$$
or,
$$8x + 10y + 11z - 10 = 0.$$

EXAMPLES 14c

1. Find the coordinates of the points in which the axes meet the plane $x - 2y + 3z = 6$.

2. Show that the plane $\dfrac{x}{a} + \dfrac{y}{b} + \dfrac{z}{c} = 1$ makes intercepts a, b, c on the coordinate axes.

3. Find the equation of the plane determined by each of the following sets of three points: (i) $(0, 0, 0)$, $(1, 1, 1)$, $(2, 0, 3)$; (ii) $(1, 0, 0)$, $(2, 1, 0)$, $(-1, -1, 2)$; (iii) $(2, -1, 1)$, $(-1, -3, 1)$, $(-2, 3, -1)$.

4. The normal to a plane from the origin has unit length and direction ratios $1 : -2 : -2$. Find the equation of the plane.

5. For each of the following planes find the length and the direction-cosines of the perpendicular from the origin: (i) $x = 2$; (ii) $z = -1$; (iii) $3x - 4y = 10$; (iv) $2x - y + 2z = 6$; (v) $x - y + z = \sqrt{3}$; (vi) $2x + 5y + 3z = 0$; (vii) $5x - 7y - 6z + 3 = 0$.

6. Find the equation of the plane through the origin parallel to the plane $x - 2y + 2z - 9 = 0$. What is the distance between these parallel planes?

7. Show that the points $(4, 5, 1)$, $(-4, 4, 4)$, $(0, -1, -1)$, $(3, 9, 4)$ are coplanar.

8. Find the acute angle between each of the following pairs of planes: (i) $z = 0$, $x - z = 0$; (ii) $x = 0$, $x + y + z = 1$; (iii) $x - 2z = 0$, $2y - z = 0$; (iv) $x + y + z = 1$, $5x - y - 4z = 4$.

9. Obtain the equation of the plane through the point $(1, 0, 1)$ and through the line of intersection of the planes $x - y + 2z = 1$, $2x + y - z = 0$.

10. In each of the following cases find the numerical length of the perpendicular from the point stated to the given plane: (i) $(1, 0, 0)$, $x + y - z = 1$; (ii) $(0, -1, 1)$, $2x - y = 3$; (iii) $(1, 1, 1)$, $3x - 2y + z = 4$; (iv) $(-2, 1, -1)$, $5x - 7y + 3z = 0$.

11. Show that the points $(1, -1, 3)$, $(3, 3, 3)$ are equidistant from the plane $5x + 2y - 7z + 9 = 0$ and on opposite sides of it.

12. Are the points $(1, -1, 1)$, $(-3, 2, 2)$ on the same or opposite sides of the plane $x - 2y + z = 3$?

13. Find the equation of the plane through $(1, 1, 1)$ and the line of intersection of the planes $x - 2y - z + 1 = 0$, $3x - y + 4z + 3 = 0$.

14. If A is the point $(1, -2, 2)$, find the equation of the plane drawn through A perpendicular to the line joining A to the origin.

15. Show that the three planes $2x - y + z + 1 = 0$, $x + y - 3z - 2 = 0$, $x - 5y + 11z + 8 = 0$ intersect in a straight line.

16. Find the equation of the plane which bisects perpendicularly the line joining the points $(1, 0, -1)$, $(2, 2, 1)$.

17. Find the point of intersection of the planes $2x + y + z = 0$, $x - 3y + 2z = 3$, $3x - y - z = -5$.

18. Obtain the equations of the planes: (i) passing through the x-axis and the point $(1, 2, 3)$; (ii) passing through the y-axis inclined at an angle of $30°$ to the plane $z = 0$.

19. Find the equation of the plane through the points $(1, -1, 2)$, $(2, 1, -1)$ perpendicular to the plane $x + y + z = 1$.

20. The plane $2x - y + 2z + 8 = 0$ is rotated through $90°$ about its line of intersection with the plane $x + y - z + 2 = 0$. Find the equation of the plane in its new position.

21. Find the equation of the plane through the points $(0, 1, 1)$, $(-2, 1, -1)$ and parallel to the line joining the origin to the point $(2, 1, 1)$.

22. Find the equation of the planes which bisect the angles between the planes $3x + 4y - 2$, $2x - y - 2z = 1$.

23. The vertices of a tetrahedron are $A(0, 0, 0)$, $B(3, 4, 0)$, $C(2, -1, 0)$, $D(1, 2, 3)$. Find: (i) the equations of the four plane faces; (ii) the length of the perpendicular from C to face ABD; (iii) the angle between faces ABD, BCD.

24. Determine the distance between the parallel planes $x - 3y + z - 2 = 0$, $2x - 6y + 2z + 3 = 0$.

The straight line. A straight line is determined by the intersection of two planes and consequently will be represented by a pair of linear equations of the form

$$a_1x + b_1y + c_1z + d_1 = 0 = a_2x + b_2y + c_2z + d_2.$$

Any set of values of x, y, z which satisfy the two equations simul-taneously will give the coordinates of a point on the line.

The above form of the equations of a straight line is not particularly useful and the symmetrical form in terms of the direction-cosines of the line and the coordinates of a point on it has more general application.

Symmetrical form of the equations of a straight line. Consider a straight line drawn through the point $A(\alpha, \beta, \gamma)$ with direction-cosines l, m, n.

Take $P(x, y, z)$ as a variable point on the line and let $AP = r$.

Referring to Fig. 101, in which a rect-angular parallelopiped has been drawn with AP as a diagonal and with edges parallel to the coordinate axes,

$$AL = AP \cos\angle LAP = lr;$$

but $AL = x - \alpha$, therefore $x - \alpha = lr$.

Similarly, $y - \beta = mr$; $z - \gamma = nr$.

Hence $\dfrac{x - \alpha}{l} = \dfrac{y - \beta}{m} = \dfrac{z - \gamma}{n} = r$,

the equations of the straight line.

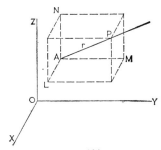

Fɪɢ. 101.

If the direction ratios of the line are given as $a:b:c$, then the equations will be

$$\frac{x-\alpha}{a}=\frac{y-\beta}{b}=\frac{z-\gamma}{c}=\frac{r}{\sqrt{(a^2+b^2+c^2)}}=\lambda, \text{ say.}$$

Any point on this line will have coordinates $(\alpha+\lambda a,\ \beta+\lambda b,\ \gamma+\lambda c)$.

Equations of the straight line joining the points (x_1, y_1, z_1), (x_2, y_2, z_2).

The direction ratios of the line are $(x_2-x_1):(y_2-y_1):(z_2-z_1)$.

$\therefore$ The equations of the line are

$$\frac{x-x_1}{x_2-x_1}=\frac{y-y_1}{y_2-y_1}=\frac{z-z_1}{z_2-z_1}.$$

Ex. 13. *Find the direction-cosines of the line with equations $x+y-z+1=0$, $4x+y-2z+2=0$ and obtain the equations of the line in the symmetrical form.*

Let the direction-cosines of the line be in the ratios $p:q:r$.

Now normals to the two planes which determine the line have direction ratios $1:1:-1$; $4:1:-2$ and as the line of intersection is perpendicular to each of these directions, we have

$$p+q-r=0; \quad 4p+q-2r=0.$$
$$\therefore\ p:q:r=-1:-2:-3=1:2:3.$$

I.e. the direction-cosines of the line are $\dfrac{1}{\sqrt{14}}$, $\dfrac{2}{\sqrt{14}}$, $\dfrac{3}{\sqrt{14}}$.

To find the symmetrical form of the equations, the coordinates of a point on the line must be determined; the point of intersection with plane $z=0$ will suffice.

Putting $z=0$ in the equation of the line, we have

$$x+y+1=0; \quad 4x+y+2=0.$$

Solving, $\qquad\qquad x=-\tfrac{1}{3},\ y=-\tfrac{2}{3}.$

So a point on the line has coordinates $(-\tfrac{1}{3},\ -\tfrac{2}{3}, 0)$.

Hence the equations of the line are

$$\frac{x+\tfrac{1}{3}}{1}=\frac{y+\tfrac{2}{3}}{2}=\frac{z}{3}=\frac{r}{\sqrt{14}},$$

where r is the distance of the point (x, y, z) from the point $(-\tfrac{1}{3},\ -\tfrac{2}{3}, 0)$.

Ex. 14. *Find the point of intersection of the line* $\dfrac{x-1}{2}=\dfrac{y+3}{-1}=\dfrac{z+1}{3}$ *and the plane* $3x-y-z=11$.

Writing $\qquad\qquad \dfrac{x-1}{2}=\dfrac{y+3}{-1}=\dfrac{z+1}{3}=k,$

then $\qquad\qquad x=1+2k,\ y=-3-k,\ z=-1+3k.$

Substituting in the equation of the plane,

$$3(1+2k)-(-3-k)-(-1+3k)=11; \quad \text{i.e. } k=1.$$

So the point of intersection has coordinates $(3, -4, 2)$.

Ex. 15. *Find the length of the perpendicular from the point* $P(5, 2, -1)$ *to the line* $(x-1)/2 = y/1 = z/3.$

Writing $\qquad \dfrac{x-1}{2} = \dfrac{y}{1} = \dfrac{z}{3} = k,$ $\qquad$ then any point Q of the line has coordinates $(1+2k, k, 3k).$

The direction ratios of PQ are $(2k-4):(k-2):(3k+1).$

$\therefore$ PQ is perpendicular to the given line if

$$2(2k-4)+1(k-2)+3(3k+1)=0; \quad \text{i.e.} \quad k=\tfrac{1}{2}.$$

Hence Q, the foot of the perpendicular from P to the line, is the point $(2, \tfrac{1}{2}, 1\tfrac{1}{2}).$

So the perpendicular distance $PQ = \sqrt{\{3^2+(\tfrac{3}{2})^2+(-\tfrac{5}{2})^2\}} = \tfrac{1}{2}\sqrt{70}.$

Ex. 16. *Find the image,* Q, *of the point* $P(2, 1, -2)$ *in the plane* $x-2y+2z=5.$

Let PN be the perpendicular from P to the plane.

Then, as P is on the same side of the plane as the origin, the direction-cosines of $\overrightarrow{PN}$ are $\tfrac{1}{3}, -\tfrac{2}{3}, \tfrac{2}{3}$ and so its equations are

$$\dfrac{x-2}{\tfrac{1}{3}} = \dfrac{y-1}{-\tfrac{2}{3}} = \dfrac{z+2}{\tfrac{2}{3}} = r, \quad . \quad . \quad . \quad . \quad . \quad \text{(i)}$$

where r is the distance of the point (x, y, z) on the line from P measured in the direction $\overrightarrow{PN}.$

$$\text{Distance } PN = \pm\dfrac{2-2-4-5}{\sqrt{(1^2+2^2+2^2)}} = 3 \text{ numerically.}$$

$\therefore$ Distance $PQ = 2PN = 6.$

So taking $r=6$ in the equations (i),

$$x=4, \quad y=-3, \quad z=2.$$

I.e. $\qquad\qquad\qquad Q$ is the point $(4, -3, 2).$

EXAMPLES 14d

1. Write down the equations of the axes $OX, OY, OZ.$

2. What are the equations of a line passing through the origin and making equal angles with the positive directions of the axes?

3. Express the equations of the following lines in the symmetrical form and hence obtain the direction-cosines of each line: (i) $2x=y=z$; (ii) $x-1=2y=3z$; (iii) $x+1=2y+3=-z-1$; (iv) $3x-2=1-y=-4z.$

4. Express the equations of the following lines in the symmetrical form: (i) $x-y=1, y-2z=2$; (ii) $2x-z=0, x+y+z=1$; (iii) $x-y-z=1, y-2z=0.$

5. Write down the equations of the lines joining the following pairs of points:

(i) $(0, 0, 0), (2, 1, 3)$; (ii) $(1, -1, 0), (2, 0, 3)$; (iii) $(3, -1, 2), (-1, 1, -2).$

6. Find the direction-cosines of the line of intersection of the planes $x-y+z=1, 2x+y-z+2=0.$

7. Write down the equations of the line through the point (α, β, γ) and equally inclined to the positive directions of the coordinate axes.

8. Find the coordinates of the point of intersection of the line $x/1 = (y-1)/2 = (z+1)/-2$ and the plane $x+y-z=1$.

9. Find the equation of the plane passing through the line $x-z=0=2x+y$ and the point $(1, 2, 2)$.

10. Determine the equation of the plane containing the line
$$x/2 = (y-1)/-1 = (z+2)/3$$
and passing through the origin.

11. Find the coordinates of the foot of the perpendicular from the origin to the line $x/2 = -y/1 = (z-3)/-2$ and deduce the length of the perpendicular.

12. Find the angle between the lines $2x-1 = y+1 = 1-z$, $x = 2y+3 = z+2$.

13. If l is the line $(x-1)/2 = y/3 = (z-3)/4$ and P the point $(0, 1, -1)$, find the equation of the plane which contains l and P and also the equation of the plane through l perpendicular to this plane.

14. Find the perpendicular distance of the point $(1, 0, -2)$ from the line $(x-2)/3 = y/2 = (z+1)/-1$.

15. Obtain the equation of the line through the point $(1, 1, 1)$ perpendicular to the plane $2x-y-2z-3=0$.

16. Find the equation of the plane containing the line
$$(x-4)/3 = (y-2)/4 = (z-1)/2$$
and perpendicular to the plane $9x+8y+2z-1=0$. Hence write down the equations of the orthogonal projection of the given line on the given plane.

17. Find the coordinates of the point in which the line joining the points $(2, -1, 0)$, $(1, 1, 2)$ is met by the perpendicular drawn from the origin.

18. Find the equations of the two planes containing the line
$$\tfrac{1}{2}x = \tfrac{1}{6}(y+2) = z-2$$
which are inclined at $45°$ to the plane $x-y=0$.

19. Find the image of the point $(-1, 2, 2)$ in the plane $2x+y-2z=2$.

20. Determine the coordinates of the point in which the line
$$x-1 = y/2 = (z+1)/3$$
meets the plane $z=0$. Find also the coordinates of the image of the point $(1, 0, -1)$ in the plane $z=0$ and deduce the equations of the image of the given line in the plane $z=0$.

21. Find the acute angle between the common line of the planes $x+2y-6z+13=0$, $2x-2y-3z+8=0$ and the line joining the points $(4, -1, 1)$, $(2, 1, 2)$.

22. The vertices of a tetrahedron are $A(0, 0, 0)$, $B(2, 0, 0)$, $C(3, 2, 0)$, $D(1, 1, -1)$. Find: (i) the angle between AB and the face ACD; (ii) the equation of the perpendicular from A to the face BCD; (iii) the length of the perpendicular from B to AD.

23. Find the equations of the line of intersection of the planes $x-y+2z-1=0$, $z=0$. Assuming that the axis of z is vertical, find the direction-cosines of a line of greatest slope of the plane $x-y+2z-1=0$.

Coplanar lines. Two lines will be coplanar if either they intersect or are parallel.

To find the condition that two lines intersect. Let the equations of the lines be

$$\frac{x-\alpha}{l}=\frac{y-\beta}{m}=\frac{z-\gamma}{n}; \quad \frac{x-\alpha'}{l'}=\frac{y-\beta'}{m'}=\frac{z-\gamma'}{n'}.$$

If the lines intersect they will lie in a plane, and since this plane passes through the point (α, β, γ), its equation can be taken as

$$a(x-\alpha)+b(y-\beta)+c(z-\gamma)=0. \quad \ldots \quad \text{(i)}$$

As the point $(\alpha', \beta', \gamma')$ also lies on this plane,

$$a(\alpha'-\alpha)+b(\beta'-\beta)+c(\gamma'-\gamma)=0. \quad \ldots \quad \text{(ii)}$$

Since the normal to the plane is perpendicular to both lines,

$$al+bm+cn=0. \quad \ldots \ldots \quad \text{(iii)}$$

$$al'+bm'+cn'=0. \quad \ldots \ldots \quad \text{(iv)}$$

Eliminating the ratios $a:b:c$ from equations (ii), (iii), (iv) gives the required condition

$$\begin{vmatrix} \alpha'-\alpha & \beta'-\beta & \gamma'-\gamma \\ l & m & n \\ l' & m' & n' \end{vmatrix}=0.$$

When this condition is satisfied, the equation of the plane containing the lines is obtained by eliminating the ratios $a:b:c$ from equations (i), (iii), (iv).

Equation of plane is
$$\begin{vmatrix} x-\alpha & y-\beta & z-\gamma \\ l & m & n \\ l' & m' & n' \end{vmatrix}=0.$$

Ex. 17. *Show that the two lines* $x-2=2y-6=3z$, $4x-11=4y-13=3z$ *intersect and find the equation of the plane determined by them.*

Writing the equation of the lines in the forms

$$\frac{x-2}{1}=\frac{y-3}{\frac{1}{2}}=\frac{z}{\frac{1}{3}}; \quad \frac{x-\frac{11}{4}}{\frac{1}{4}}=\frac{y-\frac{13}{4}}{\frac{1}{4}}=\frac{z}{\frac{1}{3}},$$

then
$$\begin{vmatrix} \alpha'-\alpha & \beta'-\beta & \gamma'-\gamma \\ l & m & n \\ l' & m' & n' \end{vmatrix}=\begin{vmatrix} \frac{3}{4} & \frac{1}{4} & 0 \\ 1 & \frac{1}{2} & \frac{1}{3} \\ \frac{1}{4} & \frac{1}{4} & \frac{1}{3} \end{vmatrix}=\frac{3}{4}(\frac{1}{12})-\frac{1}{4}(\frac{3}{12})=0.$$

Hence the lines are coplanar, and so they intersect, as clearly they are not parallel.

Equation of plane containing the lines is

$$\begin{vmatrix} x-2 & y-3 & z \\ 1 & \frac{1}{2} & \frac{1}{3} \\ \frac{1}{4} & \frac{1}{4} & \frac{1}{3} \end{vmatrix}=0; \quad \text{i.e.} \quad \begin{vmatrix} x-2 & y-3 & z \\ 6 & 3 & 2 \\ 3 & 3 & 4 \end{vmatrix}=0.$$

Simplifying, $\qquad 2x-6y+3z+14=0.$

Skew lines. Lines which are not coplanar, that is they neither intersect nor are parallel, are said to be *skew*.

To show that two skew lines have a common perpendicular. Suppose AB, CD are the two skew lines (Fig. 102).

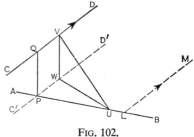

Through any point L of AB draw a line LM parallel to CD; let the orthogonal projection of CD on the plane ALM be $C'D'$.

If P is the point of intersection of AB, $C'D'$ and Q is the point of CD of which P is the projection, then PQ is perpendicular to both the given lines.

Fig. 102.

For, as QP is a perpendicular to the plane ALM,

$$\angle QPB = \angle QPD' = 90°.$$

But the plane ALM is parallel to CD, and so $C'D'$ is parallel to CD.

$$\therefore \quad \angle PQC = \angle QPD' = 90°.$$

Hence PQ is the common perpendicular to the skew lines.
If U, V are any two points other than P, Q, on the separate lines, then

$$PQ < UV.$$

For, referring to Fig. 102, where W is the projection of V on the plane ALM, it is clear in the right-angled triangle UVW that $WV <$ hypotenuse UV.

Also as $PQVW$ is a rectangle, $WV = PQ$.

Hence $PQ < UV.$

I.e. *the common perpendicular is the shortest distance between the two skew lines.*

Shortest distance between two skew lines with given equations. Let the equations of the skew lines AB, CD be

$$\frac{x-\alpha}{l} = \frac{y-\beta}{m} = \frac{z-\gamma}{n}; \quad \frac{x-\alpha'}{l'} = \frac{y-\beta'}{m'} = \frac{z-\gamma'}{n'}.$$

Then, if the direction-cosines of the common perpendicular PQ are in the ratios $\lambda : \mu : \nu$,

$$l\lambda + m\mu + n\nu = 0,$$
$$l'\lambda + m'\mu + n'\nu = 0.$$
$$\therefore \quad \lambda : \mu : \nu = (mn' - m'n) : (nl' - n'l) : (lm' - l'm).$$

But the equation of the plane through AB parallel to CD (plane ALM in Fig. 102) is

$$\lambda(x-\alpha)+\mu(y-\beta)+\nu(z-\gamma)=0. \quad . \quad . \quad . \quad \text{(i)}$$

Hence $PQ=$ perpendicular from $(\alpha'\ \beta', \gamma')$ to the plane (i),

$$=\frac{\lambda(\alpha'-\alpha)+\mu(\beta'-\beta)+\nu(\gamma'-\gamma)}{\sqrt{\{\lambda^2+\mu^2+\nu^2\}}} \text{ numerically,}$$

$$=\frac{(\alpha'-\alpha)(mn'-m'n)+(\beta'-\beta)(nl'-n'l)+(\gamma'-\gamma)(lm'-l'm)}{\sqrt{\{(mn'-m'n)^2+(nl'-n'l)^2+(lm'-l'm)^2\}}}.$$

This result can be expressed more conveniently in the form

$$\mathbf{PQ}=\begin{vmatrix} \boldsymbol{\alpha'-\alpha} & \boldsymbol{\beta'-\beta} & \boldsymbol{\gamma'-\gamma} \\ \mathbf{l} & \mathbf{m} & \mathbf{n} \\ \mathbf{l'} & \mathbf{m'} & \mathbf{n'} \end{vmatrix}\div\sqrt{\{(\mathbf{mn'-m'n})^2+(\mathbf{nl'-n'l})^2+(\mathbf{lm'-l'm})^2\}}.$$

The equation of the plane QAB containing the common perpendicular and the line AB is of the form

$$p(x-\alpha)+q(y-\beta)+r(z-\gamma)=0. \quad . \quad . \quad . \quad \text{(i)}$$

As a normal to this plane is perpendicular to both AB and PQ,

$$pl+qm+rn=0, \quad . \quad . \quad . \quad . \quad . \quad \text{(i)}$$

and $$p(mn'-m'n)+q(nl'-n'l)+r(lm'-l'm)=0. \quad . \quad . \quad \text{(ii)}$$

Eliminating the ratios $p:q:r$ from equations (i), (ii), (iii) we obtain *the equation of the plane QAB in the form*

$$\begin{vmatrix} x-\alpha & y-\beta & z-\gamma \\ l & m & n \\ mn'-m'n & nl'-n'l & lm'-l'm \end{vmatrix}=0.$$

Similarly, *the equation of the plane PCD is*

$$\begin{vmatrix} x-\alpha' & y-\beta' & z-\gamma' \\ l' & m' & n' \\ mn'-m'n & nl'-n'l & lm'-l'm \end{vmatrix}=0.$$

Ex. 18. *Find the shortest distance between the lines* $x=y+2=6z-6$, $x+1=2y=-12z$.

The equations of the lines in the standard form are

$$\frac{x}{6}=\frac{y+2}{6}=\frac{z-1}{1}; \quad \frac{x+1}{12}=\frac{y}{6}=\frac{z}{-1}.$$

$\therefore$ The shortest distance between them is the numerical value of

$$\begin{vmatrix} 1 & -2 & 1 \\ 6 & 6 & 1 \\ 12 & 6 & -1 \end{vmatrix}\div\sqrt{\{(-12)^2+(18)^2+(-36)^2\}}.$$

On evaluation this expression is equal to -2 and so the shortest distance between the lines is 2 units.

U

Ex. 19. *Points P, Q on the lines*

$$(x-1)/2 = y/1 = (z+3)/-1, \quad (x+2)/3 = (y-2)/-2 = z/1$$

respectively are such that PQ is the shortest distance between the two lines, find the coordinates of P and Q.

The equations of the lines can be written

$$\frac{x-1}{2} = \frac{y}{1} = \frac{z+3}{-1} = \lambda; \quad \frac{x+2}{3} = \frac{y-2}{-2} = \frac{z}{1} = \mu.$$

Hence P can be taken as the point $(1+2\lambda, \lambda, -3-\lambda)$ and Q as the point $(-2+3\mu, 2-2\mu, \mu)$.

So the direction ratios of PQ are $(-3-2\lambda+3\mu):(2-\lambda-2\mu):(3+\lambda+\mu)$ and as PQ is perpendicular to each of the given lines,

$$2(-3-2\lambda+3\mu)+1(2-\lambda-2\mu)-1(3+\lambda+\mu)=0,$$

and
$$3(-3-2\lambda+3\mu)-2(2-\lambda-2\mu)+1(3+\lambda+\mu)=0.$$

I.e.
$$-7-6\lambda+3\mu=0; \quad -10-3\lambda+14\mu=0.$$

Solving,
$$\lambda = -\tfrac{68}{75}, \quad \mu = \tfrac{13}{25}.$$

∴ P, Q are the points $(-\tfrac{61}{75}, -\tfrac{68}{75}, -\tfrac{157}{75})$, $(-\tfrac{11}{25}, \tfrac{24}{25}, \tfrac{13}{25})$ respectively.

Ex. 20. *Find the equations of the transversal through the point* $(2, 1, 3)$ *which intersects each of the lines* $x=y=z$, $x-1=y+2=(z+1)/3$.

The required line is common to the two planes which pass through the given point and contain each of the given lines.

Writing the equations $x=y=z$ in the form $x-y=0$, $y-z=0$, it follows that the equation of any plane containing this line can be expressed as

$$x-y+\lambda(y-z)=0.$$

This plane passes through the point $(2, 1, 3)$ if $\lambda = \tfrac{1}{2}$.

∴ The equation of the plane through the given point and the line $x=y=z$

is
$$2x-y-z=0.$$

In like manner, the equation of the plane through the given point and the second line is found to be

$$5x+y-2z-5=0.$$

So the equations of the required transversal can be written

$$2x-y-z=0=5x+y-2z-5.$$

Simplified form for the equations of two skew lines. Let PQ be the common perpendicular of the skew lines AB, CD (Fig. 103).

Through O, the mid-point of PQ, draw lines $A'B'$, $C'D'$ respectively parallel to AB, CD, and take the bisectors of the angles between these lines as the axes of x and y with OQ as the axis of z.

Let $PQ=2c$ and angle $B'OC'$, the angle between the skew lines $=2\alpha$.

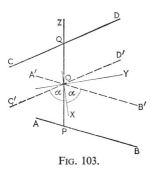

FIG. 103.

Then the equations of $A'B'$, $C'D'$ are respectively

$$y = x \tan \alpha, \ z = 0; \quad y = -x \tan \alpha, \ z = 0.$$

Hence the equations of AB, CD are respectively

$$\mathbf{y = mx, \ z = -c; \quad y = -mx, \ z = c,}$$

where $m = \tan \alpha$.

Ex. 21. *Points L, M taken on each of two perpendicular skew lines are such that LM is of constant length $2l$. Prove that the locus of the mid-point N of LM is a circle.*

If $2c$ is the shortest distance between the skew lines ($c < l$), the equations of the lines can be taken as

$$y = x, \ z = -c; \quad y = -x, \ z = c. \quad [\text{As } 2\alpha = 90°, \ m = 1.]$$

So L, M can be taken as the points $(\alpha, \alpha, -c)$, $(\beta, -\beta, c)$ respectively.

$$\therefore \ N \text{ is the point } (\tfrac{1}{2}\overline{\alpha + \beta}, \ \tfrac{1}{2}\overline{\alpha - \beta}, \ 0).$$

So N lies in the plane $z = 0$ and its x, y coordinates are

$$x = \tfrac{1}{2}(\alpha + \beta), \quad y = \tfrac{1}{2}(\alpha - \beta).$$

But $LM = 2l$,

$$\therefore \ (\alpha - \beta)^2 + (\alpha + \beta)^2 + (2c)^2 = 4l^2.$$

I.e.
$$4y^2 + 4x^2 + 4c^2 = 4l^2$$

or
$$x^2 + y^2 = l^2 - c^2.$$

So the equations of the locus of N are

$$x^2 + y^2 = l^2 - c^2, \quad z = 0 \text{—a circle.}$$

EXAMPLES 14e

1. Show that the following pairs of lines are coplanar and in each case find the equation of the plane in which they lie:

(i) $x - 1 = y - 1 = (z - 2)/-3, \ x + 2 = y + 2 = z$;

(ii) $x/1 = (y + 2)/3 = (z - 1)/2, \ (x - 2)/-3 = (y - 1)/-3 = z/4$;

(iii) $x/2 = (y - 1)/-2 = (z - 1)/-10, \ (x + 1)/2 = (y - 2)/1 = (z - 6)/-4$.

2. Find the common point of the intersecting lines

$$(x - 5)/4 = (y - 7)/4 = (z + 3)/-5, \ (x - 8)/7 = y - 4 = (z - 5)/3.$$

3. Obtain the equation of the plane passing through the points $(0, -1, 1)$, $(2, -11, 1)$ and parallel to a line with direction ratios $2 : -1 : 1$. What is the equation of the plane determined by the parallel lines

$$x/2 = (y + 1)/-1 = z - 1, \ (x - 2)/2 = (y + 11)/-1 = z - 1?$$

4. Find the shortest distance between each of the following pairs of skew lines:

(i) $x=y=0$, $x-1=y=z$;

(ii) $y=z=0$, $(x-2)/2=y/-1=(z+1)/3$;

(iii) $x/3=y/4=z/-12$, $(x-1)/4=(y+2)/-2=(z-\frac{1}{2})/3$;

(iv) $x=y-2=6z-12$, $x-2=2y=-12z$.

5. If PQ is the common perpendicular of the two lines

$$x-10=(y-9)/3=(z+2)/-2, \quad (x+1)/2=(y-12)/4=z-5,$$

find: (i) the coordinates of P and Q; (ii) the equations of PQ.

6. Find the equations of the straight line through the point $(2, 1, 3)$ which intersects each of the lines $x=-y=2z$, $x-2=y-3=(z+2)/3$.

7. Write down a simple form for the equations of two skew lines inclined at an angle of $60°$ with distance apart 2 units.

8. Points $L(\alpha, \alpha, -c)$, $M(\beta, -\beta, c)$ are taken on the perpendicular skew lines $y=x$, $z=-c$; $y=-x$, $z=c$ such that $LM=\sqrt{2}PQ$, where PQ is the common perpendicular. Prove that $\alpha^2+\beta^2=2c^2$.

9. Prove that the shortest distances between the diagonals of a rectangular parallelopiped and the edges which they do not meet are $bc/\sqrt{(b^2+c^2)}$, $ca/\sqrt{(c^2+a^2)}$, $ab/\sqrt{(a^2+b^2)}$, where a, b, c are the lengths of the edges.

10. The vertices of a tetrahedron are $A(0, 1, 0)$, $B(2, 0, 1)$, $C(1, 1, 3)$, $D(-1, 2, -1)$. Find the shortest distance between the edges AB, CD.

11. Find the ratio in which the shortest distance between the axis of z and the line joining the points $P(2, 2, 1)$, $Q(3, -3, -1)$ divides the line PQ.

12. Find the equation of the plane through the line

$$(x-1)/2=y+2=(z-2)/3$$

parallel to the line $x/2=y/-2=z$. By writing down the length of the perpendicular from the origin to this plane, obtain the perpendicular distance between the two given lines.

13. Find the direction ratios of the line through the point $(1, 0, 0)$ which intersects each of the lines $x-1=(y+1)/2=(z-2)/3$ and

$$(x+2)/3=y-3=(z+1)/2.$$

14. Obtain the equation of the plane determined by the parallel lines $\frac{1}{2}(x+1)=y-3=\frac{1}{3}(z-4)$, $\frac{1}{2}(x-2)=y+1=\frac{1}{3}(z+1)$.

15. If P, Q are points on each of two skew lines, prove that the point R which divides PQ in a constant ratio lies in a plane parallel to the two lines.

16. Variable points on each of two skew lines are a constant distance apart, prove that the line joining them makes a constant angle with the common perpendicular of the two lines.

17. A line of constant length has its extremities on two fixed non-intersecting straight lines; show that the locus of its mid-point is an ellipse.

18. A rectangular trapdoor $ABCD$, $AB=4$ m, $BC=8$ m, which can turn about AB occupies the horizontal position $ABCD$ when closed and the position $ABC'D'$ when opened. If the door is opened through an angle of $60°$ find the shortest distance between the lines AC', BD.

Some properties of the tetrahedron

   (i) *The joins of the mid-points of opposite edges are concurrent and bisect each other.*

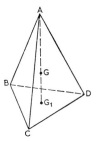

For taking the vertices A, B, C, D (Fig. 104) with coordinates (x_r, y_r, z_r), $r = 1, 2, 3, 4$ respectively it is easily established that the coordinates of the mid-point of the line joining each pair of mid-points of opposite edges are

$$[\tfrac{1}{4}(x_1+x_2+x_3+x_4), \quad \tfrac{1}{4}(y_1+y_2+y_3+y_4),$$
$$\tfrac{1}{4}(z_1+z_2+z_3+z_4)],$$

and the result follows.

   (ii) *The joins of the vertices to the centroids of the opposite faces are concurrent.*

FIG. 104.

The centroid G_1 of triangle BCD has coordinates

$$[\tfrac{1}{3}(x_2+x_3+x_4), \tfrac{1}{3}(y_2+y_3+y_4), \tfrac{1}{3}(z_2+z_3+z_4)].$$

So the point G on AG_1 which is such that the ratio $G_1G : GA = 1 : 3$ (Fig. 104) has coordinates

$$[\tfrac{1}{4}(x_1+x_2+x_3+x_4), \tfrac{1}{4}(y_1+y_2+y_3+y_4), \tfrac{1}{4}(z_1+z_2+z_3+z_4)].$$

As the coordinates of G are symmetrical in the coordinates of the four vertices of the tetrahedron, it follows that G lies on each join of a vertex to the centroid of the opposite face and so the result required.

N.B. It will be noted from (i) that G is also the point of concurrence of the lines joining the mid-points of opposite edges.

   (iii) *If two pairs of opposite edges are perpendicular, so also is the third pair.*

If BC is perpendicular to AD,

$$(x_3-x_2)(x_4-x_1)+(y_3-y_2)(y_4-y_1)+(z_3-z_2)(z_4-z_1)=0.$$

If AC is perpendicular to BD,

$$(x_3-x_1)(x_4-x_2)+(y_3-y_1)(y_4-y_2)+(z_3-z_1)(z_4-z_2)=0.$$

Subtracting these equations and noting that

$$(x_3-x_2)(x_4-x_1)-(x_3-x_1)(x_4-x_2)=x_2x_3-x_2x_4-x_1x_3+x_1x_4,$$
$$=(x_2-x_1)(x_3-x_4), \quad \text{with similar}$$
$$\text{results in } y \text{ and } z,$$

we have $\quad (x_2-x_1)(x_3-x_4)+(y_2-y_1)(y_3-y_4)+(z_2-z_1)(z_3-z_4)=0.$

$$\therefore \ AB, \ CD \text{ are perpendicular.}$$

(iv) *If a pair of opposite edges are equal, then the lines joining the mid-points of the other two pairs of edges are perpendicular.*

For suppose that $$AB = CD,$$

then $$(x_2 - x_1)^2 + \text{etc.} = (x_4 - x_3)^2 + \text{etc.}$$

I.e. $$[(x_2 - x_1)^2 - (x_4 - x_3)^2] + \text{etc.} = 0,$$

$$[\overline{x_2 + x_3} - \overline{x_1 + x_4}][\overline{x_2 + x_4} - \overline{x_1 + x_3}] + \text{etc.} = 0. \quad . \quad . \quad \text{(i)}$$

But the direction ratios of the line joining the mid-points of *AC, BD*

are $$[\overline{x_2 + x_4} - \overline{x_1 + x_3}] : [\overline{y_2 + y_4} - \overline{y_1 + y_3}] : [\overline{z_2 + z_4} - \overline{z_1 + z_3}]$$

and those of the line joining the mid-points of *AD, BC* are

$$[\overline{x_2 + x_3} - \overline{x_1 + x_4}] : [\overline{y_2 + y_3} - \overline{y_1 + y_4}] : [\overline{z_2 + z_3} - \overline{z_1 + z_4}].$$

Hence by equation (i) above, these lines are perpendicular.

(v) *If two pairs of opposite edges are equal, then the join of the mid-points of the other pair is the common perpendicular of these two edges.*

For suppose that $AB = CD$, then from (iv) above

$$[\overline{x_2 + x_3} - \overline{x_1 + x_4}][\overline{x_2 + x_4} - \overline{x_1 + x_3}] + \text{etc.} = 0. \quad . \quad . \quad \text{(i)}$$

Similarly, if $BC = AD$,

$$[\overline{x_3 + x_4} - \overline{x_2 + x_1}][\overline{x_1 + x_3} - \overline{x_2 + x_4}] + \text{etc.} = 0. \quad . \quad . \quad \text{(ii)}$$

Adding equations (i) and (ii) and noting the common factor $\overline{x_1 + x_3} - \overline{x_2 + x_4}$,

$$[\overline{x_1 + x_3} - \overline{x_2 + x_4}][\overline{2x_4 - x_2}] + \text{etc.} = 0.$$

Hence the line joining the mid-point of edges *AC, BD* is perpendicular to *BD*.

Similarly by subtracting equations (i) and (ii), it follows that the line joining these mid-points is also perpendicular to *AC*.

MISCELLANEOUS EXAMPLES

1. Find the perpendicular distance of the origin from the plane containing the points $(1, -2, 0)$, $(-3, 0, 1)$, $(2, 2, 2)$.

2. What are the direction-cosines of the line with equations
$$(x - 1)/2 = (y + 2)/-6 = z/3 ?$$
Find the coordinates of the point of intersection of this line and the plane $2x - y = 0$.

3. Find the equation of the locus of a point which moves such that its distances from the points $(-1, 3, 2)$, $(2, 0 \ -1)$ are equal.

4. Determine whether the points $(3, 3, -1)$, $(1, -1, 2)$ lie on the same or opposite sides of the plane $x - 3y - 2z = 5$.

5. Find the acute angle between the lines $(x-1)/3 = y + 2 = (z+1)/2$ and $x/-2 = (y-1)/3 = z - 2$.

6. Prove that the planes $5x - 3y + 4z - 1 = 0$, $8x + 3y + 5z - 4 = 0$, $x + 15y - 2z - 8 = 0$ have a common line of intersection and find the inclination of this line to the axis of z.

7. Find the ratio in which the line joining the points $(0, 1, 1)$, $(3, 2, -3)$ is divided by the plane $x - y - 2z = 1$.

8. Find the angles of the triangle whose vertices are the points $(0, 1, 1)$, $(2, -1, 2)$, $(1, 3, 3)$.

9. Prove that the locus of a point whose distances from two given planes are in a constant ratio is a plane.

10. Find the acute angle between the two lines whose direction-cosines are given by the equations $l + m + n = 0$, $l^2 + m^2 - n^2 = 0$.

11. Show that the equations $x = 3r + 2$, $y = 2r - 1$, $z = \frac{1}{2}r + 3$ represent a straight line. Find the angle between this line and the plane $2x + 2y + 2z = 19$.

12. Find the equation of the plane through $(1, 4, 3)$ perpendicular to the line of intersection of the planes $3x + 4y + 7z + 4 = 0$, $x - y + 2z + 3 = 0$.

13. Show that the line $x/a = y/b = z/c$ is parallel to the plane $lx + my + nz - p = 0$, if $la + mb + nc = 0$. If this condition is satisfied, what is the shortest distance between the line and the plane?

14. If l is the line $(x-2)/2 = (y-1)/3 = (z-4)/6$ and P is the point $(2, -1, 2)$ find: (i) the equation of the plane containing P and l; (ii) the equation of the plane through l perpendicular to this plane.

15. Prove that the perpendicular distance of a vertex of a cube of side a from a diagonal which does not pass through the vertex is $a\sqrt{\frac{2}{3}}$.

16. Find: (i) the equation of the plane containing the axis of z and the point $(2, -3, 1)$; (ii) the equation of the plane passing through the points $(0, 1, 0)$, $(1, 1, 1)$, $(2, -3, 1)$. Also find the angle of intersection of these two planes.

17. Find the shortest distance between the skew lines
$3x - 3 = 4y + 8 = 12z$, $-21x + 84 = 7y + 35 = 6z - 30$.

18. Prove that the lines

$$(x-3)/2 = (y+1)/-3 = (z-4)/6, \quad (x-1)/1 = y/4 = (z+2)/3$$

are coplanar and find the coordinates of their common point.

19. Find the equation of the plane through $A(-1, 1, 1)$ and $B(1, -1, 1)$ perpendicular to the plane $x + 2y + 2z = 5$. Find also a point P on the common section of these planes such that AP and BP make equal angles with the normal at P to the plane $x + 2y + 2z = 5$.

20. If A is a fixed point on a straight line through the origin equally inclined to the three axes, prove that any plane through A will intercept lengths on the axes the sum of whose reciprocals is constant.

21. Find the acute angle between the common line of the planes $x+y-z=1$, $2x-3y+z=2$ and the line joining the points $(3, -1, 2)$, $(4, 0, -1)$. Find also the equations of a line through the origin which is perpendicular to both the given lines.

22. Show that the lines of intersection of the three planes $x+y+z=1$, $5x-y-4z=4$, $4x+2y+z=8$ are parallel and prove that the planes form a prism whose cross-section is a right-angled triangle.

23. Find the equations of the line through the point $(1, 2, 3)$ which intersects each of the lines $x=y=z$, $x-4=y-5=(z+1)/2$.

24. Find the equation of the planes which bisect at right angles three edges of the tetrahedron with vertices $(1, 2, 3)$, $(3, 2, -1)$, $(-1, 1, 2)$, $(1, -1, -2)$ and hence determine the coordinates of the centre of the circumscribing sphere of the tetrahedron.

25. Find, in the symmetrical form, the equations of the line of intersection of the planes $x-2y+3z=1$, $2x-3y+z=3$. Hence find the coordinates of the point on this line which is nearest the origin.

26. Two edges AB, CD of a tetrahedron $ABCD$ are perpendicular. Prove that the distance between the mid-points of AC and BD is equal to the distance between the mid-points of AD and BC.

27. Find the equations of the line through the point $(1, 2, 3)$ which cuts the line $x+1=2y-4=z+4$ and is parallel to the plane $x+5y+z=0$.

28. Find the equation of the plane which contains the line
$$\tfrac{1}{2}(x-1) = -y-1 = \tfrac{1}{4}(z-3)$$
and is perpendicular to the plane $x+2y+z=12$. Deduce the direction-cosines of the projection of the given line on the given plane.

29. Show that the plane which contains the parallel lines
$$x-3 = -\tfrac{1}{4}(y-2) = \tfrac{1}{5}(z-1), \quad x-2 = -\tfrac{1}{4}(y+3) = \tfrac{1}{5}(z+1)$$
has the equation $11x-y-3z=28$. What is the distance between the parallel lines?

30. Two skew lines AP, BQ inclined at $60°$ are intersected by their common perpendicular at A, B respectively; P, Q are points on the lines such that AQ is perpendicular to BP. Prove that $AP \cdot BQ = 2AB^2$.

31. The equations of two lines are $x=y+2a=6z-6a$, $x+a=2y=-12z$, show that the shortest distance between the lines is $2a$ and find the equations of the line along which it lies.

32. Find the equations of the three planes which pass through the line of intersection of two of the planes $x+y+z+3=0$, $2x+y+2z+5=0$, $x+3y+2z+6=0$ and are perpendicular to the third. Prove that the planes so obtained have a common line of intersection and that the plane through the origin perpendicular to this line is $7x+5y-2z=0$.

33. Assuming the axis of z is vertical, find the inclination to the horizontal of the plane through the points $(0, 0, 0)$, $(2, 4, -1)$, $(3, 2, 2)$. Also find the direction ratios of a line of greatest slope of the plane.

34. Prove that the equation of the plane through $x/l = y/m = z/n$ and perpendicular to the plane containing $x/m = y/n = z/l$, $x/n = y/l = z/m$ is $x(m - n) + y(n - l) + z(l - m) = 0$.

35. Find the direction-cosines of the line through the origin which intersects each of the lines $(x - 1)/2 = (y - 2)/3 = (z - 3)/4$ and
$$(x + 2)/4 = (y - 3)/3 = (z - 4)/2.$$

36. If $ABCD$ is a tetrahedron in which AB, CD are perpendicular, prove that $AC^2 + BD^2 = AD^2 + BC^2$. If also AC, BD are perpendicular, prove that $BC^2 + AD^2 = CA^2 + BD^2 = AB^2 + CD^2$.

37. The inclination to the horizontal of two intersecting perpendicular lines are α, β. If the plane determined by the lines is inclined at an angle θ to the horizontal, prove that $\sin^2 \theta = \sin^2 \alpha + \sin^2 \beta$.

38. Lines are drawn to intersect the lines $y - mx = 0 = z - c$, $y + mx = 0 = z + c$ and to make a constant angle with the z-axis. Show that, if $-1 < m < 1$, the locus of their mid-points is an ellipse of eccentricity $(1 - m^4)^{\frac{1}{2}}$.

39. The ends of a straight line lie on two fixed planes which are at right angles to each other and the straight line subtends a right angle at each of two given points; show that the locus of its mid-point is a plane.

40. If two opposite edges of a tetrahedron are equal in length and are at right-angles to the line joining their mid-points, show that the other two pairs of edges have the same properties.

CHAPTER XV

THE SPHERE

The equation of a sphere. Let $P(x, y, z)$ be any point on the surface of a sphere centre the point $A(a, b, c)$ and radius r.

Then as
$$AP^2 = r^2,$$
$$(x-a)^2 + (y-b)^2 + (z-c)^2 = r^2. \quad . \quad . \quad . \quad \text{(i)}$$

This is the equation of the sphere centre (a, b, c), radius r.
Conversely the general equation
$$x^2 + y^2 + z^2 + 2ux + 2vy + 2wz + d = 0, \quad . \quad . \quad \text{(ii)}$$

which can be expressed in the form
$$(x+u)^2 + (y+v)^2 + (z+w)^2 = u^2 + v^2 + w^2 - d$$

is the equation of a sphere centre $(-u, -v, -w)$, radius $\sqrt{(u^2 + v^2 + w^2 - d)}$.

For the sphere to be real, $u^2 + v^2 + w^2 \geqslant d$.

Ex. 1. *Find the centre and radius of the sphere*
$$x^2 + y^2 + z^2 - 2x + 4y - z + 1 = 0.$$
The equation can be written
$$(x-1)^2 + (y+2)^2 + (z - \tfrac{1}{2})^2 = \tfrac{17}{4}.$$
So the centre of the sphere is the point $(1, -2, \tfrac{1}{2})$ and the radius is $\tfrac{1}{2}\sqrt{17}$.

Ex. 2. *Show that the spheres* $x^2 + y^2 + z^2 - 2x + 2y - 4z - 19 = 0$, $x^2 + y^2 + z^2 + 4x - 10y + 25 = 0$ *touch each other externally.*

The centres of the spheres are the points $(1, -1, 2)$, $(-2, 5, 0)$ and the radii are 5 and 2 respectively.
Distance between the centres $= \sqrt{(3^2 + 6^2 + 2^2)} = 7$,
$$= \text{sum of radii.}$$
Hence the spheres touch externally.

Sphere passing through four points. In the equation of a sphere, equation (ii) above, there are four constants u, v, w, d, and consequently, in general, four points will uniquely determine a sphere as substitution of the coordinates of each of the points in equation (ii) will lead to four equations in four unknowns. Clearly a special case arises when the four points are coplanar and concyclic, as in this event only three of the equations will be independent.

Ex. 3. *Find the equation of the sphere which passes through the points* $(0, 0, 1), (-1, 2, 2), (1, 3, 0), (2, -1, -3)$.

Let the equation of the sphere be

$$x^2 + y^2 + z^2 + 2ux + 2vy + 2wz + d = 0.$$

Since this equation is satisfied by the coordinates of the four points,

$$1 + 2w + d = 0, \quad \ldots \ldots \quad \text{(i)}$$
$$9 - 2u + 4v + 4w + d = 0, \quad \ldots \ldots \quad \text{(ii)}$$
$$10 + 2u + 6v + d = 0, \quad \ldots \ldots \quad \text{(iii)}$$
$$14 + 4u - 2v - 6w + d = 0. \quad \ldots \ldots \quad \text{(iv)}$$

Subtracting equation (i) from equations (ii), (iii), (iv) in turn,

$$-2u + 4v + 2w + 8 = 0,$$
$$2u + 6v - 2w + 9 = 0,$$
$$4u - 2v - 8w + 13 = 0.$$

Solving these equations, $u = \frac{53}{10}$, $v = -\frac{17}{10}$, $w = \frac{47}{10}$ and substituting in (i), $d = -\frac{52}{5}$.

Hence the equation of the sphere is

$$5(x^2 + y^2 + z^2) + 53x - 17y + 47z - 52 = 0.$$

EXAMPLES 15a

1. Obtain the equations of the spheres with the following centres and radii:

(i) centre $(0, 0, 0)$, radius 1; (ii) centre $(0, 0, 0)$, radius $\sqrt{3}$;
(iii) centre $(1, 0, -1)$, radius 1; (iv) centre $(-1, 1, 2)$, radius 3;
(v) centre $(3, -1, -4)$, radius $\sqrt{5}$; (vi) centre (a, a, a), radius $2a$.

2. Find the centre and radius of each of the following spheres:

(i) $x^2 + y^2 + z^2 = 3$; (ii) $x^2 + y^2 + z^2 - 4x = 0$;
(iii) $x^2 + y^2 + z^2 + 2x - 4y + 6z - 2 = 0$;
(iv) $x^2 + y^2 + z^2 - 3x + 2y + z - 1 = 0$;
(v) $2(x^2 + y^2 + z^2) - 6x + 2y - 5z + 1 = 0$;
(vi) $a(x^2 + y^2 + z^2) + 2bx - 2cy + d = 0$.

3. Find the equation of the sphere centre $(1, 1, 1)$ which touches the coordinate planes.

4. Find the equation of the sphere centre $(-2, 1, -1)$ which touches the plane $x + y + z = 2$.

5. Show that the plane $y - z + 3 = 0$ touches the sphere

$$x^2 + y^2 + z^2 - 4x + 2y + 3 = 0$$

at the point $(2, -2, 1)$.

6. Find the equations of the diameter of the sphere

$$x^2 + y^2 + z^2 + 2x - 8y + 6z = 0$$

which passes through the origin. What are the coordinates of the other end of this diameter?

7. Find the equation of the sphere centre $(1, -1, 2)$ which passes through the point $(2, 0, -1)$.

8. Prove that the plane $2x - y - 2z = 9$ does not meet the sphere $x^2 + y^2 + z^2 - 8 = 0$ in real points.

9. Find the equations of the diameter of the sphere
$$x^2 + y^2 + z^2 - 3x + 4y - 2z - 13 = 0$$
of which one end is the point $(1, 2, -1)$. Also find the coordinates of the other end of the diameter.

10. Find the equations of the normal to the sphere
$$x^2 + y^2 + z^2 - 4y + 6z - 1 = 0$$
which passes through the origin.

11. Prove that the spheres
$$x^2 + y^2 + z^2 + 2x - 4y - 2z - 3 = 0, \quad x^2 + y^2 + z^2 - 4x + 8y - 6z + 13 = 0$$
touch each other externally.

12. Prove that the square of the length of the tangent from the point (x', y', z') to the sphere $x^2 + y^2 + z^2 = r^2$ is $x'^2 + y'^2 + z'^2 - r^2$.

13. If $A(x_1, y_1, z_1)$, $B(x_2, y_2, z_2)$ are the extremities of a diameter of a sphere and $P(x, y, z)$ is any point on the sphere, use the fact that AP, BP are perpendicular to obtain the equation of the sphere in the form
$$(x - x_1)(x - x_2) + (y - y_1)(y - y_2) + (z - z_1)(z - z_2) = 0.$$

14. Find the equation of the sphere which passes through each of the following sets of four points:

   (i) $(1, 0, 0)$, $(0, 1, 0)$, $(0, 0, 1)$, $(1, 2, 1)$;

   (ii) $(0, 0, 0)$, $(0, 1, 2)$, $(3, 0, 1)$, $(-2, -1, 0)$;

   (iii) $(1, 0, -1)$, $(2, 1, 0)$, $(-1, 2, 1)$, $(0, -2, -2)$.

15. Find the centre and radius of the circumsphere of the tetrahedron with vertices $(0, 0, 0)$, $(4, 2, 0)$, $(-2, 4, 2)$, $(2, 4, 0)$.

16. Find the equation of the circumscribing sphere of the tetrahedron formed by the coordinate planes and the plane $x + y + z = p$.

Tangent plane to a sphere. Let the point $P(x', y', z')$ lie on the sphere
$$x^2 + y^2 + z^2 + 2ux + 2vy + 2wz + d = 0.$$

Then the centre C of the sphere is the point $(-u, -v, -w)$, and as CP is normal to the tangent plane at P, the direction ratios of the latter are
$$x' + u : y' + v : z' + w.$$

Hence the equation of the tangent plane at P is
$$(x' + u)(x - x') + (y' + v)(y - y') + (z' + w)(z - z') = 0,$$
i.e. $\quad xx' + yy' + zz' + ux + vy + wz = x'^2 + y'^2 + z'^2 + ux' + vy' + wz'.$ \quad (i)

But as P lies on the sphere,

$$x'^2 + y'^2 + z'^2 + 2ux' + 2vy' + 2wz' + d = 0,$$

or $\qquad x'^2 + y'^2 + z'^2 + ux' + vy' + wz' = -ux' - vy' - wz' - d.$

$\therefore$ Equation (i) can be written as

$$\mathbf{xx'} + \mathbf{yy'} + \mathbf{zz'} + \mathbf{u(x + x')} + \mathbf{v(y + y')} + \mathbf{w(z + z')} + \mathbf{d} = \mathbf{0}.$$

The condition that the plane $lx + my + nz = p$ is a tangent plane to the sphere

$$x^2 + y^2 + z^2 + 2ux + 2vy + 2wz + d = 0$$

is obtained by equating the perpendicular distance of the centre of the sphere from the plane to the radius of the sphere.

The condition is found to be

$$(lu + mv + nw + p)^2 = (l^2 + m^2 + n^2)(u^2 + v^2 + w^2 - d).$$

Ex. 4. *Find the equations of the tangent planes to the sphere*

$$x^2 + y^2 + z^2 - 2x + 4y + 2z + 2 = 0$$

which can be drawn through the x-axis.

Any plane passing through the x-axis has the equation

$$y + \lambda z = 0. \quad . \quad . \quad . \quad . \quad . \quad . \quad . \quad \text{(i)}$$

As the centre C of the sphere is the point $(1, -2, -1)$, the length of the perpendicular from C to the plane (i) is

$$\pm \frac{-2 - \lambda}{\sqrt{(1 + \lambda^2)}}.$$

The radius of the sphere $= \sqrt{(1^2 + 2^2 + 1^2 - 2)} = 2$.
Hence the plane (i) is tangential to the sphere if

$$\pm \frac{2 + \lambda}{\sqrt{(1 + \lambda^2)}} = 2; \quad \text{i.e. } (2 + \lambda)^2 = 4(1 + \lambda^2).$$

$$\lambda = 0, \tfrac{4}{3}.$$

So the tangent planes are $\quad y = 0, \quad 3y + 4z = 0$.

Ex. 5. *Show that the plane $x - 2y + 2z = 9$ touches the sphere $x^2 + y^2 + z^2 = 9$ and find the coordinates of the point of contact.*

The perpendicular from the centre $(0, 0, 0)$ of the sphere on the plane is of length 3 units and is equal to the radius of the sphere.

Hence the plane touches the sphere.

Also the direction-cosines of this perpendicular are $\tfrac{1}{3}, -\tfrac{2}{3}, \tfrac{2}{3}$; so if (x, y, z) is the point of contact,

$$(x - 0)/\tfrac{1}{3} = (y - 0)/-\tfrac{2}{3} = (z - 0)/\tfrac{2}{3} = 3; \quad \text{i.e. } x = 1, y = -2, z = 2.$$

$\therefore$ The point of contact has coordinates $(1, -2, 2)$.

Ex. 6. *A variable sphere is drawn touching two given planes and passing through a given point P. Prove that the sphere passes through the reflection point of P in the plane which is the locus of the centre of the sphere.*

Take the given planes with equations $z = \pm my$, then the centre of the variable sphere will lie in the plane $z = 0$.

Let the centre of the sphere be the point $(\alpha, \beta, 0)$ and let P have coordinates (a, b, c).

Then the radius of the sphere = length of perpendicular from $(\alpha, \beta, 0)$ to the plane $z + my = 0$,

$$= m\beta/\sqrt{(1 + m^2)}.$$

$\therefore$ Equation of sphere is

$$(x - \alpha)^2 + (y - \beta)^2 + z^2 = m^2\beta^2/(1 + m^2)$$

and as it passes through P,

$$(a - \alpha)^2 + (b - \beta)^2 + c^2 = m^2\beta^2/(1 + m^2).$$

This latter equation is also the condition that the sphere passes through $(a, b, -c)$, the reflection point of P in the plane $z = 0$.

To find the length of the tangent lines from a given point to a sphere. Let $P(x_1, y_1, z_1)$ be the given point and $C(-u, -v, -w)$ the centre of the sphere

$$x^2 + y^2 + z^2 + 2ux + 2vy + 2wz + d = 0.$$

Then the square of the length of a tangent line from P to the sphere

$$= CP^2 - (\text{radius})^2,$$
$$= (x_1 + u)^2 + (y_1 + v)^2 + (z_1 + w)^2 - (u^2 + v^2 + w^2 - d),$$
$$= \mathbf{x_1}^2 + \mathbf{y_1}^2 + \mathbf{z_1}^2 + \mathbf{2ux_1} + \mathbf{2vy_1} + \mathbf{2wz_1} + \mathbf{d}.$$

N.B. If this expression is negative, P lies inside the sphere.

Ex. 7. *Find the length of the tangent lines from the point $(4, -2, 3)$ to the sphere $2(x^2 + y^2 + z^2) - 3x + 4y - 8z + 2 = 0$.*

The equation of the sphere must be written with unity coefficients of x^2, y^2, z^2;

i.e. $$x^2 + y^2 + z^2 - \tfrac{3}{2}x + 2y - 4z + 1 = 0.$$

Then $$(\text{tangent})^2 = 4^2 + (-2)^2 + (3)^2 - \tfrac{3}{2}(4) + 2(-2) - 4(3) + 1$$
$$= 8.$$

$\therefore$ Length of tangent $= 2\sqrt{2}$.

EXAMPLES 15b

In each of the examples 1 to 6, write down the equation of the tangent plane to the given sphere at the point stated.

1. $x^2 + y^2 + z^2 = 3$, $(1, -1, 1)$.   **2.** $x^2 + y^2 + z^2 = 9$, $(-1, 2, 2)$.

3. $x^2 + y^2 + z^2 = 49$, $(6, -3, -2)$.   **4.** $x^2 + y^2 + z^2 - 4x + 2y = 0$, $(2, 1, -1)$.

5. $x^2 + y^2 + z^2 - 3x + 4y - 2z - 7 = 0$, $(-1, 0, 3)$.

6. $2(x^2 + y^2 + z^2) - 8x + 3y - 2z - 6 = 0$, $(2, 2, 0)$.

7. Prove that the plane $2x - 3y + z = 14$ touches the sphere $x^2 + y^2 + z^2 = 14$ and find the equation of the parallel tangent plane.

8. Show that the plane $2x + 2y - z = 1$ touches the sphere $9(x^2 + y^2 + z^2) = 1$ and find the coordinates of the point of contact.

9. For what values of p is the plane $x + 2y - 2z = p$ tangential to the sphere $x^2 + y^2 + z^2 - 2x + 4z - 4 = 0$?

10. Find the equations of the tangent planes to the sphere
$$x^2 + y^2 + z^2 + 4x - 2y + 2z = 0$$
which are parallel to the plane $x + y + z = 0$.

11. In each of the following cases find the length of the tangents from the point stated to the given sphere:

    (i) $(2, 3, 0)$, $x^2 + y^2 + z^2 = 1$;   (ii) $(-1, -2, 1)$, $x^2 + y^2 + z^2 - 4x = 0$;

    (iii) $(1, 4, -1)$, $x^2 + y^2 + z^2 - 3x + y + 5z - 1 = 0$;

    (iv) $(2, 2, 2)$, $2(x^2 + y^2 + z^2) + 6x - y + 3z - 4 = 0$.

12. Determine whether the point $(3, -1, -2)$ lies inside or outside the sphere $x^2 + y^2 + z^2 - 7x + y - 4z + 1 = 0$.

13. Find the locus of a point from which the tangents to the two spheres $x^2 + y^2 + z^2 - 1 = 0$, $x^2 + y^2 + z^2 - 4x - y + z - 1 = 0$ are equal in length.

14. Prove that the plane $7x - 10y + 4z - 117 = 0$ touches the sphere $x^2 + y^2 + z^2 - 3x + 4y - 2z - 34 = 0$ and find the coordinates of the point of contact.

15. Find the equations of the tangent planes to the sphere
$$x^2 + y^2 + z^2 - 4x - 10y + 9 = 0$$
which intersect in the x-axis.

16. Find the equations of the tangent planes to the sphere
$$x^2 + y^2 + z^2 + 2x - 4y + 6z - 7 = 0$$
which intersect in the line $6x - 3y - 23 = 0 = 3z + 2$.

Plane section of a sphere. Without loss of generality the plane can be taken as the coordinate plane $z=0$ and the sphere as

$$x^2 + y^2 + z^2 + 2ux + 2vy + 2wz + d = 0.$$

The common points of the plane and sphere lie on the curve defined by the equations

$$z = 0, \quad x^2 + y^2 + 2ux + 2vy + d = 0.$$

These equations clearly represent a circle in the plane $z=0$, centre $(-u, -v, 0)$.

Hence *a plane section of a sphere is a circle whose centre is the foot of the perpendicular from the centre of the sphere on the plane.*

Common points of two spheres. Suppose the spheres

$$S_1 \equiv x^2 + y^2 + z^2 + 2u_1x + 2v_1y + 2w_1z + d_1 = 0;$$
$$S_2 \equiv x^2 + y^2 + z^2 + 2u_2x + 2v_2y + 2w_2z + d_2 = 0,$$

meet in real points.

Then the equation $L \equiv S_1 - S_2 = 0$, represents a plane passing through the common points of S_1 and S_2.

Consequently as the common points of the spheres S_1 and S_2 are also the common points of one of these spheres and the plane L, it follows that the common points of the two spheres lie on a circle.

Equations of a circle. Since a circle is the curve of intersection of a sphere and a plane, the most general form of its equations are

$$x^2 + y^2 + z^2 + 2ux + 2vy + 2wz + d = 0,$$
$$lx + my + nz - p = 0.$$

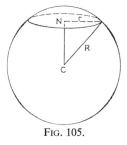

FIG. 105.

If C is the centre $(-u, -v, -w)$ of the sphere, N the centre of the circle, R the radius of the sphere and r the radius of the circle,

$$r^2 = R^2 - CN^2 \quad \text{(Fig. 105)},$$
$$= u^2 + v^2 + w^2 - d - \frac{(lu + mv + nw + p)^2}{l^2 + m^2 + n^2}.$$

The coordinates of N can be found from the intersection of the normal CN and the plane.

Ex. 8. *Find the centre and radius of the circle passing through the points* $(-1, 0, 0)$, $(0, 2, 0)$, $(0, 0, 3)$.

The equation of the plane containing the three points is

$$\begin{vmatrix} x+1 & y & z \\ 1 & 2 & 0 \\ 1 & 0 & 3 \end{vmatrix} = 0; \quad \text{i.e.} \quad 6x - 3y - 2z + 6 = 0.$$

We now find the equation of the sphere passing through the three given points and any other convenient point not coplanar with them; in this case, the origin is a suitable fourth point.

The equation of the sphere passing through the points $(0, 0, 0)$, $(-1, 0, 0)$, $(0, 2, 0)$, $(0, 0, 3)$ is found to be

$$x^2 + y^2 + z^2 + x - 2y - 3z = 0.$$

The centre of this sphere is the point $C(-\frac{1}{2}, 1, \frac{3}{2})$ and its radius is $\sqrt{\frac{7}{2}}$.

The centre of the circle is the foot of the perpendicular from C to the plane $6x - 3y - 2z + 6 = 0$.

$$\text{Length of this perpendicular} = \frac{3}{7}.$$

In finding the equation of the perpendicular *from* C to the plane $6x - 3y - 2z + 6 = 0$ it is important to note that

(i) the direction-cosines of the perpendicular from the origin to this plane are $-\frac{6}{7}, \frac{3}{7}, \frac{2}{7}$;

(ii) the point C is on the opposite side of the plane from the origin.

Hence the direction-cosines of the perpendicular *from* C to the plane are $\frac{6}{7}, -\frac{3}{7}, -\frac{2}{7}$ and the equations of the perpendicular are

$$\frac{x + \frac{1}{2}}{\frac{6}{7}} = \frac{y - 1}{-\frac{3}{7}} = \frac{z - \frac{3}{2}}{-\frac{2}{7}} = r,$$

where r is measured from C towards the plane.

Taking $r = \frac{3}{7}$, it follows that $x = -\frac{13}{98}$, $y = \frac{40}{49}$, $z = \frac{135}{98}$.

So the centre of the circle is the point $(-\frac{13}{98}, \frac{40}{49}, \frac{135}{98})$.

Also $\qquad$ (radius of circle)$^2 = \frac{7}{2} - (\frac{3}{7})^2 = \frac{325}{98}$.

I.e. $\qquad\qquad$ radius of circle $= \sqrt{\frac{325}{98}}$.

Equation of a sphere passing through a given circle. Suppose the circle has the equations

$$x^2 + y^2 + z^2 + 2ux + 2vy + 2wz + d = 0, \quad . \quad . \quad \text{(i)}$$

$$lx + my + nz - p = 0. \quad . \quad . \quad . \quad . \quad \text{(ii)}$$

Then the equation

$$x^2 + y^2 + z^2 + 2ux + 2vy + 2wz + d + \lambda(lx + my + nz - p) = 0 \quad \text{(iii)}$$

represents a sphere passing through the given circle. For clearly the equation represents a sphere for all values of the parameter λ and any values of x, y, z which simultaneously satisfy equations (i) and (ii) must also satisfy equation (iii).

X

Ex. 9. *A circle, centre* (2, 3, 0) *and radius* 1, *is drawn in the plane* $z = 0$. *Find the equation of the sphere which passes through this circle and through the point* (1, 1, 1).

The equation of the sphere, centre (2, 3, 0) radius 1, is

$$(x - 2)^2 + (y - 3)^2 + z^2 = 1;$$

i.e. $x^2 + y^2 + z^2 - 4x - 6y + 12 = 0.$

∴ The equations of the circle can be written

$$x^2 + y^2 + z^2 - 4x - 6y + 12 = 0; \quad z = 0.$$

∴ Any sphere passing through this circle has the equation

$$x^2 + y^2 + z^2 - 4x - 6y + 12 + \lambda z = 0.$$

As this passes through the point (1, 1, 1), $\lambda = -5$.
Hence the equation of the required sphere is

$$x^2 + y^2 + z^2 - 4x - 6y - 5z + 12 = 0.$$

System of spheres passing through the common points of two spheres.
Let the equations of the spheres be

$$S_1 \equiv x^2 + y^2 + z^2 + 2u_1 x + 2v_1 y + 2w_1 z + d_1 = 0,$$
$$S_2 \equiv x^2 + y^2 + z^2 + 2u_2 x + 2v_2 y + 2w_2 z + d_2 = 0.$$

Then the equation $L \equiv S_1 - S_2 = 0,$

represents the plane passing through the common points of the two spheres.

Now the equation $S_1 + \lambda L = 0$

represents a sphere for all values of the parameter λ and as it is satisfied by values of x, y, z which simultaneously satisfy the equations $S_1 = 0$, $L = 0$, it must be the equation of a sphere through the common points of S_1 and L, that is, the common points of S_1 and S_2.

Hence the equation of the system of spheres passing through the common points of the spheres $S_1 = 0$, $S_2 = 0$ is

$$\mathbf{S_1 + \lambda L = 0,}$$

where $L \equiv S_1 - S_2$.

Alternatively the system can be represented by either of the equations

$$S_2 + \lambda L = 0,$$
or $S_1 + \lambda S_2 = 0.$

Special case. If S_1, S_2 touch each other at a point A, then $L = 0$ is the equation of the common tangent plane at A and the equation

$$S_1 + \lambda L = 0$$

represents a system of spheres touching the given spheres at A.

Ex. 10. *Find the equation of the least sphere which passes through the common points of the spheres* $x^2 + y^2 + z^2 - 8 = 0$, $x^2 + y^2 + z^2 - 2x + 4y - 5z = 0$.

The equation of the plane of intersection of the two spheres is

$$2x - 4y + 5z - 8 = 0.$$

Hence the equation of any sphere passing through the common points of the two spheres can be written

$$x^2 + y^2 + z^2 - 8 + \lambda(2x - 4y + 5z - 8) = 0.$$

The centre of this sphere is the point $(-\lambda, 2\lambda, -\frac{5}{2}\lambda)$ and for the sphere of least radius this centre must lie in the plane of intersection.

$$\therefore\ 2(-\lambda) - 4(2\lambda) + 5(-\frac{5}{2}\lambda) - 8 = 0; \quad \lambda = -\frac{16}{45},$$

and the required sphere has the equation

$$45(x^2 + y^2 + z^2) - 32x + 64y - 80z - 232 = 0.$$

Ex. 11. *Find the equation of the sphere which touches the sphere* $x^2 + y^2 + z^2 = 6$ *at the point* $(1, 2, -1)$ *and passes through the point* $(3, -2, 2)$.

The tangent plane to the given sphere at the point $(1, 2, -1)$ is

$$x + 2y - z = 6,$$

so the equation of any sphere touching the given sphere at this point is

$$x^2 + y^2 + z^2 - 6 + \lambda(x + 2y - z - 6) = 0.$$

This sphere passes through the point $(3, -2, 2)$ if

$$11 - 9\lambda = 0; \quad \text{i.e.} \quad \lambda = \frac{11}{9}.$$

Hence the equation of the required sphere its

$$9(x^2 + y^2 + z^2) + 11x + 22y - 11z - 120 = 0.$$

EXAMPLES 15c

1. Find the equation of the sphere which passes through the circle $x^2 + y^2 + z^2 - 4 = 0$, $x + y + z - 1 = 0$ and through the point $(2, 2, 0)$.

2. Find the radius of the sphere which passes through the origin and contains the circle $x^2 + y^2 + z^2 - 4x + 1 = 0$, $y = 1$.

3. The centre of a circle lying in the plane $z = 0$ is the point $(2, 3, 0)$ and its radius is unity. Find the centre of the sphere which passes through this circle and the point $(4, 3, 2)$.

4. Find the coordinates of the point in which the common plane of the spheres $x^2 + y^2 + z^2 + 2x - 4z - 3 = 0$, $x^2 + y^2 + z^2 - 2y + 2z - 7 = 0$ meets the axis of x. Prove that the tangents to the spheres from this point are equal in length.

5. Show that the spheres

$$x^2 + y^2 + z^2 + 2x - 4z - 20 = 0, \quad x^2 + y^2 + z^2 - 2x - 2y - 2 = 0$$

touch each other internally. Find also the equation of the common tangent plane and the coordinates of the point of contact.

6. Show that the equation of a sphere passing through the circle $x^2 + z^2 - 4x + 6z = 0$, $y = 1$ is of the form $x^2 + y^2 + z^2 - 4x + 6z - 1 + \lambda(y - 1) = 0$. Deduce the equation of the sphere of which the given circle is a great circle.

7. Find the equations of the spheres of radius 5 units which pass through the circle $x^2 + y^2 + 2x - 4y - 11 = 0$, $z = 2$.

8. Determine the equation of the sphere passing through the common points of the spheres $2(x^2 + y^2 + z^2) - 9x = 0$, $x^2 + y^2 + z^2 - 4x + y - 3 = 0$ and also through the point $(0, -1, 2)$.

9. Find the centre and radius of the sphere which has the circle $x^2 + y^2 + z^2 = 9$, $x + 2y - z = 2$ as a great circle.

10. Obtain the equation of the tangent plane to the sphere

$$x^2 + y^2 + z^2 - 2x - 4 = 0$$

at the point $(0, 2, 0)$, and hence obtain the equation of the sphere which touches the given sphere at this point and passes through the origin.

11. Find the equations of the spheres which pass through the circle $x^2 + y^2 + z^2 - 4x + 2y - z + 5 = 0$, $y - z = 0$ and touch the plane $z = 0$.

12. A sphere is drawn on the line $A(1, 1, 1)$, $B(2, 3, 3)$ as diameter; find the equations of the spheres of radius 2 units which touch this sphere at A.

13. Find the equation of the sphere of minimum radius which can be drawn through the common points of the spheres $x^2 + y^2 + z^2 - 16 = 0$, $x^2 + y^2 + z^2 + 4x + 2y - 2z = 0$.

14. Find the centre of the circumcircle of the triangle with vertices $(3, 0, 0)$, $(0, 2, 0)$, $(0, 0, 4)$.

15. Find the equations of the spheres which pass through the circle $x^2 + z^2 - 2x + 2z - 2 = 0$, $y = 0$ and touch the plane $y - z = 7$.

16. Determine the centre and radius of the circle which is the section of the sphere $x^2 + y^2 + z^2 = 169$ by the plane $2x + y + 2z = 15$.

17. Obtain the coordinates of the centre of the circle which passes through the points $(0, 0, 0)$, $(3, 0, -1)$, $(1, 2, 0)$.

18. Show that the circles

$$x^2 + y^2 + z^2 - 4 = 0, \ 2x - y + z = 0;$$

$$x^2 + y^2 + z^2 - 2x + y - z - 2 = 0, \ 4x - 2y + 2z - 1 = 0$$

are sections of the same sphere and find the equation of this sphere.

MISCELLANEOUS EXAMPLES

1. Find the equation of the sphere which passes through the points $(0, 1, 0)$, $(0, 0, 1)$ $(-2, -1, -1)$, $(2, 2, 0)$.

2. Two spheres have equations $x^2 + y^2 + z^2 + 6x - 2y - 2z - 15 = 0$, $x^2 + y^2 + z^2 + 2x - 6y + 6 = 0$; show that one lies entirely inside the other.

3. Find the equation of the tangent plane at the origin to the sphere $x^2 + y^2 + z^2 + 2ux + 2vy + 2wz = 0$.

4. The plane $4x - y + z = 3$ is tangential to a sphere with centre $(-3, 1, -2)$. Find the equation of the sphere and the coordinates of the point of contact.

5. Show that the sphere $x^2 + y^2 + z^2 - 4x + 3y - z + 4 = 0$ touches the x-axis and find the coordinates of the point of contact.

6. Find the equations of the diameter of the sphere

$$x^2 + y^2 + z^2 - 4x + 4y + 2z - 7 = 0$$

which passes through the origin and the coordinates of its extremities.

7. Find the equation of the sphere which has its centre at the point $(8, 3, 2)$ and which touches the line $(x + 1)/2 = (y - 12)/4 = z - 5$.

8. The equations of the chord PQ of the sphere $x^2 + y^2 + z^2 - 3x - y - 8 = 0$ are $(x + 1)/2 = y/-2 = z - 1$. Find the coordinates of the mid-point of PQ.

9. Show that the locus of a point from which equal tangents can be drawn to each of the three spheres $x^2 + y^2 + z^2 = 1$, $x^2 + y^2 + z^2 + 2x - 2y + 2z - 1 = 0$, $x^2 + y^2 + z^2 - x + 4y - 6z - 2 = 0$ is the line $(x - 1)/2 = (y - 2)/5 = (z - 1)/3$.

10. Find the equation of the sphere which touches the plane $x + y + z = 3$ at the point $(1, 1, 1)$ and passes through the point $(3, 4, 2)$.

11. Find the areas of the circles in which the sphere

$$x^2 + y^2 + z^2 - 3x - 4y - 2z - 4 = 0$$

meets the coordinate planes.

12. Find the centre and radius of the section of the sphere $x^2 + y^2 + z^2 + 3x - 2y - 5 = 0$ by the plane $x - y + z + 1 = 0$.

13. Find the equations of the spheres which pass through the circle $x^2 + y^2 + z^2 - 2x - 4y = 0$, $x + 2y + 3z = 8$ and touch the plane $4x + 3y = 25$.

14. Spheres are drawn to pass through the points $(2, 0, 0)$, $(8, 0, 0)$ and to touch the axes of y and z. Find the equations of these spheres.

15. Find the equation of the locus of a point which moves such that its distances from the fixed points $(-a, 0, 0)$, $(a, 0, 0)$ are in the constant ratio $\lambda : 1$, where $\lambda > 1$. Show that the locus is a sphere and find its centre and radius.

16. Find the equation of the sphere which touches the coordinate planes and the plane $x + 2y + 2z - 8 = 0$ and is enclosed by these planes.

17. Find the equation of the sphere which has its centre in the positive quadrant of the xy-plane and which cuts the planes $x = 0$, $y = 0$, $z = 0$ in circles of radii 3, 4, 5 units respectively.

18. Two spheres are said to cut orthogonally when the radii to one of their common points are at right angles; prove that the spheres

$$x^2 + y^2 + z^2 - 2x + 3y + z - 2 = 0, \quad x^2 + y^2 + z^2 - 3x - 2y - 4z = 0$$

have this property.

19. Find equations of the circumcircle and the coordinates of the circumcentre of the triangle with vertices $(2, 0, 0)$, $(0, -2, 0)$, $(0, 0, 3)$.

20. Find the radius of the sphere which has the circle $x^2 + y^2 + z^2 = 9$, $x - 2y + 2z = 5$ as a great circle.

21. Obtain the equation of the sphere which touches the sphere $x^2 + y^2 + z^2 + 2x - 6y + 1 = 0$ at the point $(1, 2, -2)$ and passes through the origin.

22. Show that the circles

$$2(x^2 + y^2 + z^2) - 3x + 8y - 6z = 0, 2x - y - 3z - 1 = 0;$$
$$x^2 + y^2 + z^2 + 2y - 4z - 2 = 0, \ x - y - z - 1 = 0$$

are sections of the same sphere and find the equation of this sphere.

23. Find the centres of the two spheres which touch the plane $3x + 4z = 47$ at the point $(5, 4, 8)$ and which also touch the sphere $x^2 + y^2 + z^2 = 1$.

24. Find the equation of the sphere of minimum radius which passes through the points $(1, 0, 0)$, $(0, 1, 0)$, $(0, 0, 1)$.

25. A sphere is inscribed in the tetrahedron whose faces are the planes $x = 0$, $y = 0$, $z = 0$, $2x + 6y + 3z = 14$; find its centre and radius and write down its equation.

26. Find the equation of the sphere with centre $(5, -2, 3)$ which touches the line $(x - 1)/6 = (y + 1)/2 = (z - 12)/-3$. Find also the area of the circle of intersection of this sphere and the plane passing through the given line and the point $(0, -3, 0)$.

27. Determine the area of the circle of intersection of the spheres $x^2 + y^2 + z^2 - 2x + 3y + z - 2 = 0$, $x^2 + y^2 + z^2 - 3x - 2y - 4z = 0$.

28. Prove that the spheres $x^2 + y^2 + z^2 + 2u_1x + 2v_1y + 2w_1z + d_1 = 0$, $x^2 + y^2 + z^2 + 2u_2x + 2v_2y + 2w_2z + d_2 = 0$ cut orthogonally if

$$2(u_1u_2 + v_1v_2 + w_1w_2) = d_1 + d_2.$$

29. Find the equations of the tangent planes to the sphere

$$x^2 + y^2 + z^2 - 2x + 4y - 6z + 10 = 0$$

which intersect in the line $\dfrac{3x + 1}{6} = \dfrac{3y - 10}{-6} = \dfrac{z}{3}$. Find also the acute angle between these two planes.

30. OX, OY, OZ are three mutually perpendicular axes. Through a point P three mutually perpendicular lines are drawn, one passing through a fixed point C on OZ while the others intersect OX, OY respectively. Show that the locus of P is a sphere with centre C.

31. Find the equation of the circumscribing sphere of the tetrahedron whose faces are the planes $x = 0 = y = z$, $x + 2y + 3z = 4$.

32. Show that, in general, two spheres can be drawn to contain a given circle and touch a given plane.

CHAPTER XVI

PARTIAL DIFFERENTIATION

Functions of more than one variable. Consideration will now be given to the process of differentiation when applied to functions of more than one variable.

Suppose, for example, that $f(x, y)$ is a function of the variables x, y

and write $\qquad\qquad u = f(x, y)$.

Now let x increase by a small amount h while y remains unchanged in value, then the increase in u

$$= f(x+h, y) - f(x, y).$$

So the average rate of increase of u with respect to x

$$= \frac{f(x+h, y) - f(x, y)}{h}.$$

The limit of $\dfrac{f(x+h, y) - f(x, y)}{h}$ as $h \to 0$, if it exists, is called *the partial differential coefficient or partial derivative of u with respect to x* and is denoted by one of the symbols $\dfrac{\partial u}{\partial x}$, $\dfrac{\partial f}{\partial x}$, u_x or f_x.

Similarly, if the limit $\lim\limits_{k \to 0} \dfrac{f(x, y+k) - f(x, y)}{k}$ exists, it is *the partial derivative of u with respect to y*.

These definitions, involving the constancy of one variable whilst a change is taking place in the other, presuppose the independence of the variables x, y.

Moreover, the definitions can readily be extended to a function of any number of independent variables.

If $\qquad\qquad u = f(x_1, x_2, x_3 \ldots x_n)$,

then $\dfrac{\partial u}{\partial x_1} = \lim\limits_{h_1 \to 0} \dfrac{f(x_1 + h_1, x_2, x_3, \ldots x_n) - f(x_1, x_2, x_3, \ldots x_n)}{h_1}$,

$\qquad\qquad\qquad\qquad\qquad$ assuming that the limit exists,

and similarly for $\dfrac{\partial u}{\partial x_2}$, $\dfrac{\partial u}{\partial x_3}$, $\ldots \dfrac{\partial u}{\partial x_n}$.

It is clear that the process of the partial differentiation of a function $f(x_1, x_2, \ldots x_n)$ with respect to one of the variables, say x_1, is identical with that of the ordinary differentiation of the same function in which only x_1 is treated as variable and x_2, x_3, . . . x_n are treated as constants.

E.g. if $\qquad u = x^3 y^2$,

$$\frac{\partial u}{\partial x} = 3x^2 y^2, \text{ treating } y \text{ as a constant,}$$

and $\qquad \dfrac{\partial u}{\partial y} = 2x^3 y, \text{ treating } x \text{ as a constant.}$

It follows further that all the rules for the differentiation of a function of one variable hold good in partial differentiation.

E.g. using the function of a function rule,

if $\qquad u = \log (x^2 + y^2 + z^2),$

$$\frac{\partial u}{\partial x} = \frac{1}{x^2 + y^2 + z^2} \frac{\partial}{\partial x} (x^2 + y^2 + z^2) = \frac{2x}{x^2 + y^2 + z^2}.$$

Similarly, $\qquad \dfrac{\partial u}{\partial y} = \dfrac{2y}{x^2 + y^2 + z^2}; \ \dfrac{\partial u}{\partial z} = \dfrac{2z}{x^2 + y^2 + z^2}.$

Ex. 1. *Find* $\dfrac{\partial u}{\partial x}, \dfrac{\partial u}{\partial y}$ *if* (i) $u = xye^{xy}$; (ii) $u = \sin^{-1} \dfrac{x}{y}, \ |y| > |x|.$

(i) Using the product rule,

$$\frac{\partial u}{\partial x} = e^{xy} \frac{\partial}{\partial x} (xy) + xy \frac{\partial}{\partial x} e^{xy}$$

$$= e^{xy} y + xy \cdot ye^{xy}, \text{ treating } y \text{ as a constant,}$$

$$= ye^{xy}(1 + xy).$$

Similarly, $\qquad \dfrac{\partial u}{\partial y} = xe^{xy}(1 + xy).$

(ii) Using the function of a function rule,

$$\frac{\partial u}{\partial x} = \frac{1}{\sqrt{\left(1 - \left(\dfrac{x}{y}\right)^2\right)}} \frac{\partial}{\partial x} \left(\frac{x}{y}\right) = \frac{1}{\sqrt{\left(1 - \left(\dfrac{x}{y}\right)^2\right)}} \cdot \frac{1}{y}$$

$$= \frac{1}{\sqrt{(y^2 - x^2)}}.$$

Similarly, $\qquad \dfrac{\partial u}{\partial y} = \dfrac{1}{\sqrt{\left(1 - \left(\dfrac{x}{y}\right)^2\right)}} \left(-\frac{x}{y^2}\right) = -\frac{x}{y\sqrt{(y^2 - x^2)}}.$

Ex. 2. *If* $u = \phi(y + ax) + \phi(y - ax)$, *where* ϕ *is any differentiable function, prove that* $u_x = 0$ *when* $x = 0$.

To obtain the partial derivative of $\phi(y + ax)$ with respect to x, think of $y + ax$ as a single variable, say v.

Then by the function of a function rule,

$$\frac{\partial}{\partial x} \phi(y+ax) = \frac{d}{dv} \phi(v) \cdot \frac{\partial}{\partial x} (y+ax) = a\phi'(v).$$

∴ When $x=0$, $\quad \dfrac{\partial}{\partial x} \phi(y+ax) = a\phi'(y).$

Also $\qquad \dfrac{\partial}{\partial x} \phi(y-ax) = -a\phi'(w)$, where $w=y-ax.$

∴ When $x=0$, $\quad \dfrac{\partial}{\partial x} \phi(y-ax) = -a\phi'(y).$

Hence $\qquad (u_x)_{x=0} = a\phi'(y) - a\phi'(y) = 0.$

Function of two variables. Geometrical interpretation of partial derivatives. Consider the surface with equation

$$z = f(x, y).$$

Let $PQRS$ be the element of this surface bounded by the planes

$$x=x_1, \quad x=x_1+h, \quad y=y_1, \quad y=y_1+k$$

where h, k are small (Fig. 106).

The coordinates of P, Q, R, S are respectively

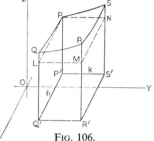

FIG. 106.

$\{x_1, y_1, f(x_1, y_1)\}, \{x_1+h, y_1, f(x_1+h, y_1)\}, \{x_1+h, y_1+k_1, f(x_1+h, y_1+k)\},$
$\{x_1, y_1+k, f(x_1, y_1+k)\}.$

Now the value of $\dfrac{\partial z}{\partial x}$ at $P = \lim\limits_{h \to 0} \dfrac{f(x_1+h, y_1) - f(x_1, y_1)}{h}$; but from the

diagram, $\qquad \dfrac{f(x_1+h, y_1) - f(x_1, y_1)}{h} = \dfrac{QQ' - PP'}{P'Q'} = \dfrac{QL}{PL}$

$$= \text{gradient of chord } PQ.$$

In the limit as $Q \to P$ or $h \to 0$,

the gradient of chord $PQ \to$ the gradient of the curve PQ at P.

Hence the value of $\dfrac{\partial z}{\partial x}$ at P, that is when $x=x_1$, $y=y_1$,

$\quad = $ the gradient at P of the curve of intersection of the surface
$$z=f(x, y) \text{ and the plane } y=y_1.$$

Similarly, $\left(\dfrac{\partial z}{\partial y} \right)_{x_1, y_1}$ gives the gradient at P of the curve

$$z=f(x, y), \ x=x_1.$$

Ex. 3. *At the point* $(1, 2, 2)$ *on the surface* $z = x^2 y$, *find the gradients of the curves of intersection of the surface and the planes* $y = 2$, $x = 1$.

The required gradients are given by the values of $\dfrac{\partial z}{\partial x}, \dfrac{dz}{\partial y}$ when $x = 1$, $y = 2$.

As $\dfrac{\partial z}{\partial x} = 2xy$; $\dfrac{\partial z}{\partial y} = x^2$, the gradients are 4 and 1 respectively.

Higher partial derivatives. If u is a function of x, y, z, . . . the partial derivatives $\dfrac{\partial u}{\partial x}, \dfrac{\partial u}{\partial y}, \dfrac{\partial u}{\partial z}$, . . will also be functions of $x, y, z, ..$ and consequently can be differentiated partially with respect to $x, y, z, \ldots$ The second order derivatives obtained are denoted as follows:

$$\frac{\partial}{\partial x}\left(\frac{\partial u}{\partial x}\right) = \frac{\partial^2 u}{\partial x^2} \text{ or } u_{xx}; \qquad \frac{\partial}{\partial y}\left(\frac{\partial u}{\partial x}\right) = \frac{\partial^2 u}{\partial y\,\partial x} \text{ or } u_{yx};$$

$$\frac{\partial}{\partial x}\left(\frac{\partial u}{\partial y}\right) = \frac{\partial^2 u}{\partial x\,\partial y} \text{ or } u_{xy}; \qquad \frac{\partial}{\partial y}\left(\frac{\partial u}{\partial y}\right) = \frac{\partial^2 u}{\partial y^2} \text{ or } u_{yy}.$$

There is a similar notation for partial derivatives of third and higher orders.

Ex. 4. *If* $u = x^2 \log y$, *verify that* $\dfrac{\partial^2 u}{\partial x\,\partial y} = \dfrac{\partial^2 u}{\partial y\,\partial x}$.

We have
$$\frac{\partial u}{\partial x} = 2x \log y; \qquad \frac{\partial u}{\partial y} = \frac{x^2}{y}.$$

$$\therefore \frac{\partial^2 u}{\partial x\,\partial y} = \frac{\partial}{\partial x}\left(\frac{x^2}{y}\right) = \frac{2x}{y}; \qquad \frac{\partial^2 u}{\partial y\,\partial x} = \frac{\partial}{\partial y}(2x \log y) = \frac{2x}{y}.$$

I.e.
$$\frac{\partial^2 u}{\partial x\,\partial y} = \frac{\partial^2 u}{\partial y\,\partial x}.$$

Order of partial differentiation. The result of example 4 above illustrates a general principle that the order in which successive partial differentiations are carried out is immaterial in the final result for a wide range of functions.

E.g.
$$\frac{\partial^2}{\partial x^2}\left(\frac{\partial u}{\partial y}\right) = \frac{\partial}{\partial y}\left(\frac{\partial^2 u}{\partial x^2}\right) = \frac{\partial^2}{\partial x\,\partial y}\left(\frac{\partial u}{\partial x}\right).$$

Ex. 5. *If* $u = \log(x^2 + y^2)$, *find the value of* $x^2\dfrac{\partial^2 u}{\partial x^2} + 2xy\dfrac{\partial^2 u}{\partial x\,\partial y} + y^2\dfrac{\partial^2 u}{\partial y^2}$.

$$\frac{\partial u}{\partial x} = \frac{2x}{x^2 + y^2}; \qquad \frac{\partial u}{\partial y} = \frac{2y}{x^2 + y^2}.$$

$$\frac{\partial^2 u}{\partial x^2} = \frac{2(x^2 + y^2) - 2x(2x)}{(x^2 + y^2)^2} = \frac{2(y^2 - x^2)}{(x^2 + y^2)^2}; \qquad \frac{\partial^2 u}{\partial x\,\partial y} = \frac{-4xy}{(x^2 + y^2)^2};$$

$$\frac{\partial^2 u}{\partial y^2} = \frac{2(x^2 + y^2) - 2y(2y)}{(x^2 + y^2)^2} = \frac{2(x^2 - y^2)}{(x^2 + y^2)^2}.$$

$$\therefore x^2\frac{\partial^2 u}{\partial x^2} + 2xy\frac{\partial^2 u}{\partial x\,\partial y} + y^2\frac{\partial^2 u}{\partial y^2} = \frac{2x^2(y^2 - x^2) - 8x^2y^2 + 2y^2(x^2 - y^2)}{(x^2 + y^2)^2},$$

$$= -\frac{2(x^4 + 2x^2y^2 + y^4)}{(x^2 + y^2)^2} = -2.$$

EXAMPLES 16a

Find $\dfrac{\partial z}{\partial x}$ and $\dfrac{\partial z}{\partial y}$ in the following cases:

1. $z = x^4 y$.

2. $z = \dfrac{x}{y}$.

3. $z = x \sin y$.

4. $z = y^2 \log x$.

5. $z = x^3 y + y^3 x$.

6. $z = \cos xy$.

7. $z = e^{x^2 y}$.

8. $z = \tan^{-1} \dfrac{x}{y}$.

9. $z = xy \tan xy$.

10. $z = \dfrac{xy}{x+y}$.

11. $z = (x^2 + y^2)^n$.

12. $z = x^y$, $x > 0$.

13. Find the gradient of the curve of intersection of the surface $z = xy^2$ and the plane $y = 2$ at the point $(1, 2, 4)$.

14. Find the gradient of the curve $z = \sin xy$, $x = 1$ at the point where $y = \frac{1}{4}\pi$.

15. If $u = \log\{(x^2 + 1)(y^2 + 1)\}$, prove that $u_x = u_y$ when $x = y$.

16. Given that $z = x^3 y^2$, find the values of $\dfrac{\partial z}{\partial x}$, $\dfrac{\partial z}{\partial y}$ when $x = 1$, $y = 2$.

17. Find $\dfrac{\partial^2 z}{\partial x^2}$, $\dfrac{\partial^2 z}{\partial x\, \partial y}$, $\dfrac{\partial^2 z}{\partial y\, \partial x}$, $\dfrac{\partial^2 z}{\partial y^2}$ in each of the following cases:

(i) $z = 2x^4 y^2$; (ii) $z = \cos(x^2 y)$; (iii) $z = \log(x^2 + y^2)$; (iv) $z = e^x \sin y$.

18. For the following functions verify that $\dfrac{\partial^2 z}{\partial x\, \partial y} = \dfrac{\partial^2 z}{\partial y\, \partial x}$:

(i) $z = \log(x + y)$; (ii) $z = \sin^{-1} \dfrac{y}{x}$; (iii) $z = \dfrac{x^3 + y^3}{x^2 + y^2}$; (iv) $z = e^{\sin^{-1}(xy)}$.

19. If $u = \log(x^2 + y^2 + z^2)$, verify that $\dfrac{\partial^2 u}{\partial x^2} + \dfrac{\partial^2 u}{\partial y^2} + \dfrac{\partial^2 u}{\partial z^2} = \dfrac{2}{x^2 + y^2 + z^2}$.

20. Find the equations of the tangent to the circle $x^2 + y^2 + z^2 = 4$, $x = 1$ at the point $(1, \sqrt{2}, 1)$.

21. Find the value of $\dfrac{\partial^2 z}{\partial x\, \partial y}$ at the point $(1, 1, -1)$ on the surface $x^3 y^4 z^2 = 1$.

22. If $xyz = 1$, find the values of $\dfrac{\partial z}{\partial x}$, $\dfrac{\partial z}{\partial y}$, $\dfrac{\partial x}{\partial z}$, $\dfrac{\partial y}{\partial z}$, $\dfrac{\partial y}{\partial x}$, $\dfrac{\partial x}{\partial y}$.

23. If $r^2 = x^2 + y^2$, show that $\dfrac{\partial r}{\partial x} = \dfrac{x}{r}$, $\dfrac{\partial r}{\partial y} = \dfrac{y}{r}$.

24. Verify that, when $u = x^3 + y^3 + 3xyz$, $\quad x\dfrac{\partial u}{\partial x} + y\dfrac{\partial u}{\partial y} + z\dfrac{\partial u}{\partial x} = 3u$.

25. If $u = \dfrac{x^2 + y^2}{x + y}$, prove the results:

(i) $x\dfrac{\partial u}{\partial x} + y\dfrac{\partial u}{\partial y} = u$; (ii) $x^2 \dfrac{\partial^2 u}{\partial x^2} + 2xy\dfrac{\partial^2 u}{\partial x\, \partial y} + y^2 \dfrac{\partial^2 u}{\partial y^2} = 0$.

26. Prove that the equation $\dfrac{\partial^2 v}{\partial x^2} + \dfrac{\partial^2 v}{\partial y^2} = 0$ is satisfied by the function $v = \tan^{-1} y/x$.

27. If z is a function of x and y, show that the general solution of the differential equation $\dfrac{\partial z}{\partial x} = x + y$ is $z = \frac{1}{2}x^2 + xy + \lambda(y)$, where $\lambda(y)$ is an arbitrary function of y.

28. Solve the following differential equations where in each case z is a function of x and y:

(i) $\dfrac{\partial z}{\partial x} = 0$;   (ii) $\dfrac{\partial z}{\partial y} = 0$;   (iii) $\dfrac{\partial z}{\partial x} = 2x$;   (iv) $\dfrac{\partial z}{\partial y} = x \sin y$;

(v) $\dfrac{\partial^2 z}{\partial x^2} = 0$;   (vi) $\dfrac{\partial^2 z}{\partial x^2} = \sin x$;   (vii) $\dfrac{\partial^2 z}{\partial x\, \partial y} = 0$;   (viii) $\dfrac{\partial^2 z}{\partial x\, \partial y} = 2xy$.

29. If $\tan \theta = \dfrac{y}{x}$, find $\dfrac{\partial \theta}{\partial x}$ and $\dfrac{\partial \theta}{\partial y}$.

30. If $\log z = \sin \dfrac{x}{y}$, prove that $x\,\dfrac{\partial z}{\partial x} + y\,\dfrac{\partial z}{\partial y} = 0$.

31. Given that $x^2 + y^2 + z^2 = 1$, prove that $\dfrac{\partial x}{\partial y} \cdot \dfrac{\partial y}{\partial z} \cdot \dfrac{\partial z}{\partial x} = -1$.

32. Given that $xy^2z^3 = \text{constant}$, show that $\dfrac{\partial x}{\partial y} \cdot \dfrac{\partial y}{\partial z} \cdot \dfrac{\partial z}{\partial x} = -1$.

33. If $f(x, y)$ is a polynomial of degree n in x, y, prove that $\dfrac{\partial^2 f}{\partial x\, \partial y} = \dfrac{\partial^2 f}{\partial y\, \partial x}$.

34. If $r = \sqrt{(x^2 + y^2 + z^2)}$, prove that $\dfrac{\partial^2 r}{\partial x^2} = \dfrac{1}{r} - \dfrac{x^2}{r^3}$ and by writing down the

corresponding results for $\dfrac{\partial^2 r}{\partial y^2}$ and $\dfrac{\partial^2 r}{\partial z^2}$ deduce that $\dfrac{\partial^2 r}{\partial x^2} + \dfrac{\partial^2 r}{\partial y^2} + \dfrac{\partial^2 r}{\partial z^2} = \dfrac{2}{r}$.

Small changes. It is already known that if u is a function of a variable x, then the increase δu in u arising from a small increase δx in x is given approximately by

$$\delta u \simeq \frac{du}{dx}\, \delta x.$$

This result will now be extended to functions of more than one variable.

Suppose that $\qquad\qquad u = f(x, y)$,

and that x, y increase by small amounts δx, δy.

Then $u + \delta u = f(x + \delta x, y + \delta y)$.

$$\delta u = f(x + \delta x, y + \delta y) - f(x, y),$$
$$= f(x + \delta x, y + \delta y) - f(x, y + \delta y) + f(x, y + \delta y) - f(x, y).$$

But $\displaystyle\lim_{\delta x \to 0} \frac{f(x + \delta x, y + \delta y) - f(x, y + \delta y)}{\delta x} = f_x(x, y + \delta y)$

and hence

$$f(x + \delta x, y + \delta y) - f(x, y + \delta y) \simeq f_x(x, y + \delta y)\, \delta x \simeq f_x(x, y)\, \delta x.$$

Similarly, $f(x, y + \delta y) - f(x, y) \simeq f_y(x, y)\, \delta y$.

$$\therefore\ \ \delta u \simeq f_x(x, y)\, \delta x + f_y(x, y)\, \delta y.$$

or $\delta u \simeq \dfrac{\partial u}{\partial x}\, \delta x + \dfrac{\partial u}{\partial y}\, \delta y,$

where the partial derivatives have values arising from the original values of x, y.

Extending this result,

if
$$u = f(x_1, x_2, x_3, \ldots x_n),$$
$$\delta u \simeq \frac{\partial u}{\partial x_1}\, \delta x_1 + \frac{\partial u}{\partial x_2}\, \delta x_2 + \frac{\partial u}{\partial x_3}\, \delta x_3 + \ldots + \frac{\partial u}{\partial x_n}\, \delta x_n.$$

Ex. 6. *If $z = x^3 y^2$, find the approximate percentage error in z arising from percentage errors of $0\cdot1$ and $0\cdot2$ in x, y respectively.*

In finding percentage errors it is convenient, if possible, to take logarithms before differentiation.

We have
$$\log z = 3 \log x + 2 \log y.$$

Writing $\log z = u$,
$$u = 3 \log x + 2 \log y$$
$$\therefore \ \delta u \simeq 3\frac{\delta x}{x} + 2\frac{\delta y}{y}.$$

But
$$\delta u \simeq \frac{\delta z}{z},$$

so
$$\frac{\delta z}{z} \simeq 3\frac{\delta x}{x} + 2\frac{\delta y}{y}.$$

I.e.
$$100\,\frac{\delta z}{z} \simeq 3(\cdot1) + 2(\cdot2) = 0\cdot7.$$

Hence the percentage error in z is approximately $0\cdot7$.

Ex. 7. *ABC is an acute-angled triangle with fixed base BC. If δb, δc, δA, δB are small increments in b, c, A, B respectively when the vertex A is given a small displacement δx parallel to BC, prove* (i) *$c\delta b + b\delta c + bc \cot A\, \delta A \simeq 0$;* (ii) *$c\delta B + \sin B\delta x \simeq 0$.*

(i) The area Δ of triangle ABC will remain constant; i.e. $\delta\Delta = 0$.

Now
$$\Delta = \tfrac{1}{2}bc \sin A,$$
$$\therefore \ \delta\Delta \simeq \tfrac{1}{2}(c \sin A\, \delta b + b \sin A\, \delta c + bc \cos A\, \delta A).$$

I.e.
$$0 \simeq c \sin A\, \delta b + b \sin A\, \delta c + bc \cos A\, \delta A$$

or,
$$c\delta b + b\delta c + bc \cot A\, \delta A \simeq 0.$$

(ii) If D is the foot of the altitude AD (Fig. 107), the increment in BD is δx, and consequently BD can be taken as x.

But $\quad AD = BD \tan B$

i.e. $\quad$ constant $= x \tan B$.
$$\therefore \ 0 \simeq \tan B\, \delta x + x \sec^2 B\, \delta B$$

or $\quad 0 \simeq \sin B \cos B\, \delta x + x\, \delta B.$

But $\quad x = c \cos B,$
$$\therefore \ 0 \simeq \sin B \cos B\, \delta x + c \cos B\, \delta B,$$

i.e. $\quad 0 \simeq \sin B\, \delta x + c\, \delta B.$

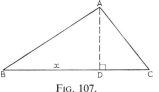

Fig. 107.

EXAMPLES 16b

In each of the following cases write down the approximate increase in z due to small increases h, k in x and y:

1. $z = x^3$.　　　　**2.** $z = xy^2$.　　　　**3.** $z = \dfrac{x}{y}$.

4. $z = x \sin y$.　　　**5.** $z = \log (x^2 + y^2)$.　　　**6.** $z = e^{x+y}$.

7. $z = (x + y)^n$.　　　**8.** $z = \tan^{-1} (xy)$.

9. If $u = x^5 y^4$, find an approximate value for u when $x = 2 \cdot 001$, $y = 0 \cdot 999$.

10. Find an expression for the approximate increase in the volume V of a circular cone due to increases δr, δh in the base radius r and height h.

11. Using the formula $\Delta = \frac{1}{2} bc \sin A$, express $\delta \Delta$ in terms of δb, δc, δA and deduce an approximate value for Δ when $b = 5 \cdot 02$ cm, $c = 3 \cdot 99$ cm, $A = 30°$.

12. If $u = x^m y^m$, show that $\dfrac{\delta u}{u} \simeq m \dfrac{\delta x}{x} + n \dfrac{\delta y}{y}$.

13. Find the approximate value for the percentage increase in the volume of a circular cylinder when the radius increases by $0 \cdot 5 \%$ and the height decreases by $0 \cdot 2 \%$.

14. If $z = x^4 y^5$, find the percentage increase in z due to percentage increases of $0 \cdot 5$, $0 \cdot 3$ in x, y respectively.

15. Obtain approximate values for: (i) $\sin 30° 1'$; (ii) $\sqrt{\{(3 \cdot 001)^2 + (4 \cdot 003)^2\}}$; (iii) $2bc \cos A$ when $b = 5 \cdot 01$, $c = 1 \cdot 98$, $A = 60°2'$.

16. The measured lengths 5 cm, 13 cm respectively of the base radius and slant height of a right circular cone are liable to maximum errors of $0 \cdot 1$ cm. Estimate the maximum error in the calculated volume.

17. The area Δ of a triangle is given in terms of b, c, A. Prove that
$$\frac{\delta \Delta}{\Delta} \simeq \frac{\delta b}{b} + \frac{\delta c}{c} + \cot A \; \delta A.$$

18. The formula $c^2 = a^2 + b^2 - 2ab \cos C$ is used to calculate c with $a = 2 \cdot 5$ cm, $b = 4$ cm, $c = 27°$. If C is correct but a, b are each in error by 2%, find the approximate percentage error in c.

19. If $I = k \dfrac{\cos \theta}{r^2}$ where k is a constant, prove that the percentage decrease in I due to increases δr, $\delta \theta$ in r, θ is approximately $100(\tan \theta \; \delta \theta + 2 \; \delta r / r)$.

20. A loaded beam with dimensions l, b, t is supported at the ends; the sag s at the mid-point is given by $s = \dfrac{kl^3}{bt^3}$, where k is a constant.

If there are errors δl, δb, δt in the values of l, b, t respectively, find the approximate error in the calculated value of s.

21. The area Δ of a triangle ABC is given in terms of c, A, B; prove the results
$$\frac{\partial \Delta}{\partial A} = \frac{1}{2} b^2; \qquad \frac{\partial \Delta}{\partial B} = \frac{1}{2} a^2; \qquad \frac{\partial^2 \Delta}{\partial A \, \partial B} = 2 \frac{\Delta}{\sin^2 C}.$$

Show also that the error in Δ due to small errors α, β in A, B respectively is approximately $\dfrac{1}{2} \dfrac{\partial^2 \Delta}{\partial A \, \partial B} \sin C \left[\dfrac{\sin B}{\sin A} \alpha + \dfrac{\sin A}{\sin B} \beta \right]$.

Differentials. If u is a function of x, then with the usual notation,

$$\delta u \simeq \frac{du}{dx} \, \delta x. \quad . \quad . \quad . \quad . \quad . \quad . \quad \text{(i)}$$

Differentials du, dx are defined as quantities, either finite or infinitesimally small, whose ratio is exactly equal to the differential coefficient $\frac{du}{dx}$ and instead of the approximate equation (i) we have the exact result

$$du = \frac{du}{dx} \, dx.$$

In the case where u is a function of two variables x, y,

$$\delta u \simeq \frac{\partial u}{\partial x} \, \delta x + \frac{\partial u}{\partial y} \, \delta y.$$

Differentials du, dx, dy are defined by the exact relationship

$$du = \frac{\partial u}{\partial x} \, dx + \frac{\partial u}{\partial y} \, dy.$$

Generally, *if u is a function of variables $x_1, x_2, \ldots x_n$,*

$$d\mathbf{u} = \frac{\partial \mathbf{u}}{\partial \mathbf{x_1}} \, d\mathbf{x_1} + \frac{\partial \mathbf{u}}{\partial \mathbf{x_2}} \, d\mathbf{x_2} + \ldots + \frac{\partial \mathbf{u}}{\partial \mathbf{x_n}} \, d\mathbf{x_n}.$$

Ex. 8. *In triangle ABC if a, b, c vary and R, the circumradius, is constant, prove* (i) $\dfrac{da}{\cos A} + \dfrac{db}{\cos B} + \dfrac{dc}{\cos C} = 0$ *and deduce* (ii) $\dfrac{\partial a}{\partial b} = -\dfrac{\cos A}{\cos B};\ \dfrac{\partial a}{\partial c} = -\dfrac{\cos A}{\cos C}.$

(i) As $\qquad\qquad a = 2R \sin A$ and R is constant,

$$da = 2R \cos A \, dA; \quad \text{i.e. } dA = \frac{1}{2R} \frac{da}{\cos A}.$$

Similarly, $\qquad dB = \dfrac{1}{2R} \dfrac{db}{\cos B};\qquad\qquad dC = \dfrac{1}{2R} \dfrac{dc}{\cos C}.$

But $\qquad\qquad\qquad A + B + C = \pi,$

$$\therefore \ dA + dB + dC = 0.$$

Hence $\qquad\qquad \dfrac{da}{\cos A} + \dfrac{db}{\cos B} + \dfrac{dc}{\cos C} = 0.$

(ii) As a, b, c vary in such a way that R is constant, a may be regarded as a function of b and c.

$$\therefore \ da = \frac{\partial a}{\partial b} \, db + \frac{\partial a}{\partial c} \, dc.$$

But from (i) above, $\qquad da = -\dfrac{\cos A}{\cos B} \, db - \dfrac{\cos A}{\cos C} \, dc.$

$$\therefore \ \frac{\partial a}{\partial b} = -\frac{\cos A}{\cos B};\ \frac{\partial a}{\partial c} = -\frac{\cos A}{\cos C}.$$

Total differential coefficient. Suppose that u is a function of x and y where x, y are each functions of t; so u is in fact a function of the single variable t.

The methods developed for dealing with a function of two variables can be applied to give a rule for obtaining the differential coefficient $\dfrac{du}{dt}$.

For we have
$$\delta u \simeq \frac{\partial u}{\partial x}\,\delta x + \frac{\partial u}{\partial y}\,\delta y.$$

Dividing throughout by δt and proceeding to the limit as $\delta t \to 0$, it follows that

$$\frac{du}{dt} = \frac{\partial u}{\partial x}\frac{dx}{dt} + \frac{\partial u}{\partial y}\frac{dy}{dt}. \qquad \cdot \quad \cdot \quad \cdot \quad \cdot \quad \cdot \quad \text{(i)}$$

This result can be extended to the case where u is a function of $x_1, x_2, \ldots x_n$, where $x_1, x_2, \ldots x_n$ are each functions of t, to give

$$\frac{du}{dt} = \frac{\partial u}{\partial x_1}\frac{dx_1}{dt} + \frac{\partial u}{\partial x_2}\frac{dx_2}{dt} + \ldots + \frac{\partial u}{\partial x_n}\frac{dx_n}{dt}. \qquad \cdot \quad \cdot \quad \text{(ii)}$$

Ex. 9. *If $u = x^2 + y^2$ where $x = (1 - t^2)/(1 + t^2)$, $y = 2t/(1 + t^2)$, prove that $\dfrac{du}{dt} = 0$.*

We have
$$\frac{du}{dt} = \frac{\partial u}{\partial x}\frac{dx}{dt} + \frac{\partial u}{\partial y}\frac{dy}{dt},$$

$$= 2x \cdot \frac{-4t}{(1 + t^2)^2} + 2y \cdot \frac{2(1 - t^2)}{(1 + t^2)^2},$$

$$= \frac{1}{(1 + t^2)^3}\{-8t(1 - t^2) + 8t(1 - t^2)\} = 0.$$

Important special cases

(a) $u = f(x, y)$, *where y is a function of x.*

Replacing t by x in formula (i),
$$\frac{du}{dx} = \frac{\partial u}{\partial x}\frac{dx}{dx} + \frac{\partial u}{\partial y}\frac{dy}{dx},$$

i.e.
$$\frac{du}{dx} = \frac{\partial f}{\partial x} + \frac{\partial f}{\partial y}\frac{dy}{dx}. \qquad \cdot \quad \cdot \quad \cdot \quad \cdot \quad \cdot \quad \text{(iii)}$$

(b) $0 = f(x, y)$ *or y an implicit function of x.*

Using the result (iii) with $u = \dfrac{du}{dx} = 0$, we have

$$0 = \frac{\partial f}{\partial x} + \frac{\partial f}{\partial y}\frac{dy}{dx}.$$

I.e.
$$\frac{dy}{dx} = -\frac{\partial f}{\partial x} \Big/ \frac{\partial f}{\partial y}. \qquad \cdot \quad \cdot \quad \cdot \quad \cdot \quad \cdot \quad \text{(iv)}$$

This latter result is useful in the differentiation of implicit functions.

E.g. if $\qquad x^3 \sin y + y \cos x = 0,$

$$\frac{dy}{dx} = -\frac{3x^2 \sin y - y \sin x}{x^3 \cos y + \cos x}.$$

It is instructive to use the results (iii) and (iv) to obtain an expression for $\dfrac{d^2y}{dx^2}$ in terms of partial derivatives when $f(x, y) = 0$.

Write $\qquad \dfrac{\partial f}{\partial x} = p; \quad \dfrac{\partial f}{\partial y} = q; \quad \dfrac{\partial^2 f}{\partial x^2} = r; \quad \dfrac{\partial^2 f}{\partial x \, \partial y} = s; \quad \dfrac{\partial^2 f}{\partial y^2} = t.$

Then $\qquad \dfrac{dy}{dx} = -\dfrac{p}{q},$

so $\qquad \dfrac{d^2y}{dx^2} = \dfrac{d}{dx}\left(-\dfrac{p}{q}\right) = \left(-q\,\dfrac{dp}{dx} + p\,\dfrac{dq}{dx}\right)\Big/ q^2.$

Now p is a function of x and y, where y is a function of x, so using result (iii),

$$\frac{dp}{dx} = \frac{\partial p}{\partial x} + \frac{\partial p}{\partial y}\frac{dy}{dx},$$

$$= r + s\left(-\frac{p}{q}\right) = (qr - ps)/q.$$

Similarly, $\qquad \dfrac{dq}{dx} = \dfrac{\partial q}{\partial x} + \dfrac{\partial q}{\partial y}\dfrac{dy}{dx} = (qs - pt)/q.$

$$\therefore \frac{d^2y}{dx^2} = \{-q(qr - ps) + p(qs - pt)\}/q^3,$$

$$= (2pqs - p^2t - q^2r)/q^3.$$

Ex. 10. If $x^2/a^2 + y^2/b^2 = 1$, prove (i) $\dfrac{dy}{dx} = -\dfrac{b^2x}{a^2y}$; (ii) $\dfrac{d^2y}{dx^2} = -\dfrac{b^4}{a^2y^3}.$

Writing $f(x, y) \equiv \dfrac{x^2}{a^2} + \dfrac{y^2}{b^2} - 1$; then $p = \dfrac{2x}{a^2}, \quad q = \dfrac{2y}{b^2}.$

$$\therefore \frac{dy}{dx} = -\frac{p}{q} = -\frac{b^2x}{a^2y}.$$

Also $\qquad r = \dfrac{2}{a^2}; \quad s = 0; \quad t = \dfrac{2}{b^2}.$

$$\therefore \frac{d^2y}{dx^2} = \frac{2pqs - p^2t - q^2r}{q^3},$$

$$= \left\{-\left(\frac{2x}{a^2}\right)^2\left(\frac{2}{b^2}\right) - \left(\frac{2y}{b^2}\right)^2\left(\frac{2}{a^2}\right)\right\}\Big/\left(\frac{2y}{b^2}\right)^3,$$

$$= -\frac{b^4}{a^2y^3}\left\{\frac{x^2}{a^2} + \frac{y^2}{b^2}\right\} = -\frac{b^4}{a^2y^3}.$$

Y

Ex. 11. *If $f(p, t, v) = 0$, prove that*

$$\left(\frac{dp}{dt}\right)_{v \text{ const.}} \times \left(\frac{dt}{dv}\right)_{p \text{ const.}} \times \left(\frac{dv}{dp}\right)_{t \text{ const.}} = -1.$$

We have $\qquad\qquad 0 = f_p \, dp + f_t \, dt + f_v \, dv.$

So when v is constant, $\quad dv = 0$ and

$$\left(\frac{dp}{dt}\right)_{v \text{ const.}} = -\frac{f_t}{f_p}.$$

Similarly, $\qquad \left(\frac{dt}{dv}\right)_{p \text{ const.}} = -\frac{f_v}{f_t}; \quad \left(\frac{dv}{dp}\right)_{t \text{ const.}} = -\frac{f_p}{f_v},$

and hence by multiplication the required result follows.

Ex. 12. *Given $y = f(x, z)$, $z = g(x, y)$, prove that $\dfrac{dy}{dx} = \dfrac{f_x + f_z g_x}{1 - f_z g_y}.$*

We have $\qquad\qquad dy = f_x \, dx + f_z \, dz,$

$$dz = g_x \, dx + g_y \, dy.$$

$$\therefore \ dy = f_x \, dx + f_z(g_x \, dx + g_y \, dy),$$

$$dy(1 - f_z g_y) = dx(f_x + f_z g_x).$$

I.e. $\qquad\qquad \dfrac{dy}{dx} = \dfrac{f_x + f_z g_x}{1 - f_z g_y}.$

Total partial derivative. Suppose $u = f(x, y)$, where x, y are each functions of the variables ξ, η.

Let ξ increase by $\delta\xi$ while η remains constant and let $\delta x, \delta y$ be the corresponding increases in x, y.

Then $\qquad\qquad \delta u \simeq \dfrac{\partial u}{\partial x} \, \delta x + \dfrac{\partial u}{\partial y} \, \delta y,$

so $\qquad\qquad \dfrac{\delta u}{\delta \xi} \simeq \dfrac{\partial u}{\partial x} \dfrac{\delta x}{\delta \xi} + \dfrac{\partial u}{\partial y} \dfrac{\delta y}{\delta \xi}.$

As $\qquad \delta\xi \to 0, \quad \dfrac{\delta u}{\delta \xi} \to \dfrac{\partial u}{\partial \xi}; \quad \dfrac{\delta x}{\delta \xi} \to \dfrac{\partial x}{\partial \xi}; \quad \dfrac{\delta y}{\delta \xi} \to \dfrac{\partial y}{\partial \xi}.$

$$\therefore \ \dfrac{\partial u}{\partial \xi} = \dfrac{\partial u}{\partial x} \dfrac{\partial x}{\partial \xi} + \dfrac{\partial u}{\partial y} \dfrac{\partial y}{\partial \xi},$$

and similarly, $\qquad \dfrac{\partial u}{\partial \eta} = \dfrac{\partial u}{\partial x} \dfrac{\partial x}{\partial \eta} + \dfrac{\partial u}{\partial y} \dfrac{\partial y}{\partial \eta}.$

Generally, if $\qquad u = f(x_1, x_2, \ldots x_n)$

where $x_1, x_2, \ldots x_n$ are each functions of $\xi_1, \xi_2, \ldots,$

then $\qquad \dfrac{\partial u}{\partial \xi_1} = \dfrac{\partial u}{\partial x_1} \dfrac{\partial x_1}{\partial \xi_1} + \dfrac{\partial u}{\partial x_2} \dfrac{\partial x_2}{\partial \xi_1} + \ldots + \dfrac{\partial u}{\partial x_n} \dfrac{\partial x_n}{\partial \xi_1},$

$$\dfrac{\partial u}{\partial \xi_2} = \dfrac{\partial u}{\partial x_1} \dfrac{\partial x_1}{\partial \xi_2} + \dfrac{\partial u}{\partial x_2} \dfrac{\partial x_2}{\partial \xi_2} + \ldots + \dfrac{\partial u}{\partial x_n} \dfrac{\partial x_n}{\partial \xi_2}.$$

. . . .

Ex. 13. *If $u=f(x, y)$, where $x=r\cos\theta$, $y=r\sin\theta$, express $\dfrac{\partial u}{\partial x}$, $\dfrac{\partial u}{\partial y}$ in terms of r, θ, $\dfrac{\partial u}{\partial r}$, $\dfrac{\partial u}{\partial \theta}$.*

We have
$$\frac{\partial u}{\partial r}=\frac{\partial u}{\partial x}\frac{\partial x}{\partial r}+\frac{\partial u}{\partial y}\frac{\partial y}{\partial r},$$

and
$$\frac{\partial u}{\partial \theta}=\frac{\partial u}{\partial x}\frac{\partial x}{\partial \theta}+\frac{\partial u}{\partial y}\frac{\partial y}{\partial \theta}.$$

But $\dfrac{\partial x}{\partial r}=\cos\theta$; $\dfrac{\partial y}{\partial r}=\sin\theta$; $\dfrac{\partial x}{\partial \theta}=-r\sin\theta$; $\dfrac{\partial y}{\partial \theta}=r\cos\theta$.

$$\therefore \frac{\partial u}{\partial r}=\cos\theta\,\frac{\partial u}{\partial x}+\sin\theta\,\frac{\partial u}{\partial y},$$

$$\frac{\partial u}{\partial \theta}=-r\sin\theta\,\frac{\partial u}{\partial x}+r\cos\theta\,\frac{\partial u}{\partial y}.$$

Solving these equations for $\dfrac{\partial u}{\partial x}$, $\dfrac{\partial u}{\partial y}$, gives

$$\frac{\partial u}{\partial x}=\cos\theta\,\frac{\partial u}{\partial r}-\frac{\sin\theta}{r}\frac{\partial u}{\partial \theta}; \quad \frac{\partial u}{\partial y}=\sin\theta\,\frac{\partial u}{\partial r}+\frac{\cos\theta}{r}\frac{\partial u}{\partial \theta}.$$

Ex. 14. *If $u=f(x-y, y-z, z-x)$, prove that $\dfrac{\partial u}{\partial x}+\dfrac{\partial u}{\partial y}+\dfrac{\partial u}{\partial z}=0$.*

Let $\qquad p=x-y,\quad q=y-z,\quad r=z-x,$

then $\qquad u=f(p, q, r).$

$$\therefore \frac{\partial u}{\partial x}=\frac{\partial u}{\partial p}\frac{\partial p}{\partial x}+\frac{\partial u}{\partial q}\frac{\partial q}{\partial x}+\frac{\partial u}{\partial r}\frac{\partial r}{\partial x},$$

$$=\frac{\partial u}{\partial p}(1)+\frac{\partial u}{\partial q}(0)+\frac{\partial u}{\partial r}(-1),$$

$$=\frac{\partial u}{\partial p}-\frac{\partial u}{\partial r}.$$

Similarly $\qquad \dfrac{\partial u}{\partial y}=-\dfrac{\partial u}{\partial p}+\dfrac{\partial u}{\partial q}; \quad \dfrac{\partial u}{\partial z}=-\dfrac{\partial u}{\partial q}+\dfrac{\partial u}{\partial r}.$

$$\therefore \frac{\partial u}{\partial x}+\frac{\partial u}{\partial y}+\frac{\partial u}{\partial z}=0.$$

Homogeneous functions

Definition. A homogeneous function of the nth degree in the variables x, y, z is one which can be written in the form $x^n F\left(\dfrac{y}{x}, \dfrac{z}{x}\right)$.

E.g. $\quad x^3+y^3+z^3-3xyz \equiv x^3\left\{1+\left(\dfrac{y}{x}\right)^3+\left(\dfrac{z}{x}\right)^3-3\left(\dfrac{y}{x}\right)\left(\dfrac{z}{x}\right)\right\}$

is a homogeneous function of degree three.

Euler's theorem

If u is a homogeneous function of degree n in x, y, z then

$$x\frac{\partial u}{\partial x} + y\frac{\partial u}{\partial y} + z\frac{\partial u}{\partial z} = nu.$$

For $\qquad u = x^n F\left(\frac{y}{x}, \frac{z}{x}\right),$

$$= x^n F(\xi, \eta), \text{ where } \xi = \frac{y}{x},\ \eta = \frac{z}{x}.$$

$$\therefore\ \frac{\partial u}{\partial x} = nx^{n-1} F + x^n\left\{\frac{\partial F}{\partial \xi}\frac{\partial \xi}{\partial x} + \frac{\partial F}{\partial \eta}\frac{\partial \eta}{\partial x}\right\},$$

$$= nx^{n-1} F + x^n\left\{\frac{\partial F}{\partial \xi}\left(-\frac{y}{x^2}\right) + \frac{\partial F}{\partial \eta}\left(-\frac{z}{x^2}\right)\right\}.$$

I.e. $\qquad x\frac{\partial u}{\partial x} = nx^n F - x^{n-1}\left\{y\frac{\partial F}{\partial \xi} + z\frac{\partial F}{\partial \eta}\right\}.$

Also $\qquad \frac{\partial u}{\partial y} = x^n\left\{\frac{\partial F}{\partial \xi}\frac{\partial \xi}{\partial y} + \frac{\partial F}{\partial \eta}\frac{\partial \eta}{\partial y}\right\} = x^n\frac{\partial F}{\partial \xi}\left(\frac{1}{x}\right).$

I.e. $\qquad y\frac{\partial u}{\partial y} = x^{n-1} y\frac{\partial F}{\partial \xi}.$

Similarly,

$$z\frac{\partial u}{\partial z} = x^{n-1} z\frac{\partial F}{\partial \eta},$$

and hence

$$x\frac{\partial u}{\partial x} + y\frac{\partial u}{\partial y} + z\frac{\partial u}{\partial z} = nx^n F = nu.$$

This result can be expressed symbolically in the form

$$\left(x\frac{\partial}{\partial x} + y\frac{\partial}{\partial y} + z\frac{\partial}{\partial z}\right)u = nu.$$

Ex. 15. *If* $u = x^3 + y^3 + z^3 - 3xyz$, *evaluate* $x\frac{\partial u}{\partial x} + y\frac{\partial u}{\partial y} + z\frac{\partial u}{\partial z}.$

As u is homogeneous of degree 3 in $x, y, z,$

$$x\frac{\partial u}{\partial x} + y\frac{\partial u}{\partial y} + z\frac{\partial u}{\partial z} = 3u.$$

Ex. 16. *If* $u = \tan^{-1}\dfrac{x^3 + y^3}{x - y}$, *prove that* $x\dfrac{\partial u}{\partial x} + y\dfrac{\partial u}{\partial y} = \sin 2u$.

We have

$$\tan u = \frac{x^3 + y^3}{x - y}, \text{ a homogeneous function of degree 2 in } x, y.$$

∴ writing $\tan u = z$,

$$x\frac{\partial z}{\partial x} + y\frac{\partial z}{\partial y} = 2z.$$

But $\dfrac{\partial z}{\partial x} = \sec^2 u\dfrac{\partial u}{\partial x}$ and $\dfrac{\partial z}{\partial y} = \sec^2 u\dfrac{\partial u}{\partial y}.$

$$\therefore \sec^2 u\left(x\frac{\partial u}{\partial x} + y\frac{\partial u}{\partial y}\right) = 2z = 2\tan u.$$

I.e. $x\dfrac{\partial u}{\partial x} + y\dfrac{\partial u}{\partial y} = 2\sin u\cos u = \sin 2u.$

EXAMPLES 16c

1. In triangle ABC, show that $dA + dB + dC = 0$.

2. If $z^2 = x^2 + y^2$, show that $z\,dz = x\,dx + y\,dy$.

3. Given that $u = x^p y^q z^r$, prove that $\dfrac{du}{u} = p\dfrac{dx}{x} + q\dfrac{dy}{y} + r\dfrac{dz}{z}$.

4. If $x = r\cos\theta$, $y = r\sin\theta$, express dx, dy in terms of dr, $d\theta$ and deduce that: (i) $dx^2 + dy^2 = dr^2 + r^2\,d\theta^2$; (ii) $x\,dy - y\,dx = r^2\,d\theta$.

5. The volume of a circular cylinder radius r, height h is V. Express dV in terms of dr, dh.

6. The area of an ellipse of semi-axes a, b is A; prove that $\dfrac{dA}{A} = \dfrac{da}{a} + \dfrac{db}{b}$.

7. If $u = e^{\frac{1}{2}(x^2 + y^2 + z^2)}$, show that $\dfrac{du}{u} = x\,dx + y\,dy + z\,dz$.

8. Express Δ, the area of triangle ABC, as a function of a, B, C and deduce that $\dfrac{d\Delta}{\Delta} = 2\dfrac{da}{a} + \dfrac{c\,dB}{a\sin B} + \dfrac{b\,dC}{a\sin C}.$

9. With the usual notation for a triangle ABC prove that

$$a\,da = (b - c\cos A)db + (c - b\cos A)dc + bc\sin A\,dA.$$

Deduce that $da = \cos C\,db + \cos B\,dc + c\sin B\,dA.$

10. Find $\dfrac{dy}{dx}$ in the following cases:

(i) $x^4 + y^4 - 4x^2y^2 = 0$;   (ii) $x^3y + y^3x = 1$;   (iii) $\sin xy = x$;

(iv) $x^2 + y^2 = e^{x/y}$;   (v) $x^2 - 2xy + 2y^2 - 3x + 2y - 1 = 0$.

11. If $x^5 + y^5 = a^5$, show that $\dfrac{d^2y}{dx^2} = -\dfrac{4a^5x^3}{y^9}$.

12. Show that the equation of the tangent to the curve $f(x, y)=0$ at the point (x_1, y_1) is $(x - x_1)\dfrac{\partial f}{\partial x}+(y - y_1)\dfrac{\partial f}{\partial y}=0$, the values of the partial derivatives being those for the point (x_1, y_1).

13. Find the equation of the tangent at the point $(1, 1)$ to the curve $x^2 y + xy^2 = 2$.

14. For the curve $y^3 = x^2(2a - x)$, find the points at which: (i) the tangent is parallel to the x-axis; (ii) the tangent is parallel to the y-axis.

15. If in a triangle ABC, a, b are constant, show that

$$a \cos B \, dB = b \cos A \, dA$$

and deduce that $c \, dA = - a \cos B \, dC$.

16. If $f(x, y, z)=$ constant, prove that $f_x \, dx + f_y \, dy + f_z \, dz = 0$.

17. Perform the following differentiations if x, y are independent and z is a function of x, y:

(i) $\dfrac{\partial}{\partial x}(x \sin xy)$;

(ii) $\dfrac{\partial}{\partial y}\left(y\,\dfrac{\partial z}{\partial y}\right)$;

(iii) $\dfrac{\partial}{\partial x}\left(\dfrac{\cos x}{y}\,\dfrac{\partial z}{\partial x}\right)$;

(iv) $\left(x\,\dfrac{\partial}{\partial x}+y\,\dfrac{\partial}{\partial y}\right)\left(\dfrac{x}{y}\,\dfrac{\partial z}{\partial x}\right)$.

18. If $u=f(\xi, \eta)$, where $\xi=x+y$, $\eta=x - y$, write down expressions for $\dfrac{\partial u}{\partial x}$, $\dfrac{\partial u}{\partial y}$ and prove that $\dfrac{\partial u}{\partial \xi}=\dfrac{1}{2}\left(\dfrac{\partial u}{\partial x}+\dfrac{\partial u}{\partial y}\right)$; $\dfrac{\partial u}{\partial \eta}=\dfrac{1}{2}\left(\dfrac{\partial u}{\partial x}-\dfrac{\partial u}{\partial y}\right)$.

19. Find $\dfrac{dy}{dz}$ in terms of y and z from the equations $3 \sin x + \sin y = 2$, $3 \cos x + \cos z = 2$.

20. If $u=\phi(x, y)$, where $f(x, y)=0$, show that

$$\frac{du}{dx}=\frac{1}{\dfrac{\partial f}{\partial y}}\begin{vmatrix}\dfrac{\partial \phi}{\partial x} & \dfrac{\partial \phi}{\partial y}\\[2mm]\dfrac{\partial f}{\partial x} & \dfrac{\partial f}{\partial y}\end{vmatrix}.$$

21. If $u=f(p, q, r)$, where $p=x^2 - y^2$, $q=y^2 - z^2$, $r=z^2 - x^2$, prove that

$$\frac{1}{x}\frac{\partial u}{\partial x}+\frac{1}{y}\frac{\partial u}{\partial y}+\frac{1}{z}\frac{\partial u}{\partial z}=0.$$

22. Find the value of $x\dfrac{\partial u}{\partial x}+y\dfrac{\partial u}{\partial y}+z\dfrac{\partial u}{\partial z}$ in each of the following cases:

(i) $x^2 + y^2 + z^2 = u$; (ii) $x^2 + y^2 + z^2 = u^2$; (iii) $x^2 + y^2 + z^2 = e^u$.

23. If $V=f(u, v)$, where $u=x^2 + y^2$, $v=2xy$, show that

$$x\frac{\partial V}{\partial x}-y\frac{\partial V}{\partial y}=2(u^2 - v^2)^{\frac{1}{2}}\frac{\partial V}{\partial u}.$$

24. If V is a function of r, θ, simplify:

(i) $\cos \theta\,\dfrac{\partial}{\partial r}\left(\cos \theta\,\dfrac{\partial V}{\partial r}-\dfrac{\sin \theta}{r}\dfrac{\partial V}{\partial \theta}\right)$; (ii) $\dfrac{\sin \theta}{r}\dfrac{\partial}{\partial \theta}\left(\cos \theta\,\dfrac{\partial V}{\partial r}-\dfrac{\sin \theta}{r}\dfrac{\partial V}{\partial \theta}\right)$.

25. Show that the function $u = (x - y)(\log x - \log y)$ is homogeneous of degree one and by finding the value of $x\,\dfrac{\partial u}{\partial x} + y\,\dfrac{\partial u}{\partial y}$ verify Euler's theorem.

26. If $\xi = x + y$, $\eta = \sqrt{(xy)}$ and z is a function of x and y, prove that

$$x\,\frac{\partial z}{\partial x} + y\,\frac{\partial z}{\partial y} = \xi\,\frac{\partial z}{\partial \xi} + \eta\,\frac{\partial z}{\partial \eta}.$$

27. If $P\,dx + Q\,dy$ is the differential of some function u of x and y, prove that $\dfrac{\partial P}{\partial y} = \dfrac{\partial Q}{\partial x}$; hence solve the equations:

(i) $0 = (3x^2 y^2 + 2xy^3)dx + (2x^3 y + 3x^2 y^2)dy$;

(ii) $0 = \sin y + x \cos y\,\dfrac{dy}{dx}$.

28. If u is a function of x, y, where $x = r \cos \theta$, $y = r \sin \theta$, establish the results $\dfrac{\partial u}{\partial x} = \left(\cos \theta\,\dfrac{\partial}{\partial r} - \dfrac{\sin \theta}{r}\,\dfrac{\partial}{\partial \theta} \right)u$, $\dfrac{\partial u}{\partial y} = \left(\sin \theta\,\dfrac{\partial}{\partial r} + \dfrac{\cos \theta}{r}\,\dfrac{\partial}{\partial \theta} \right)u$.

By writing $\dfrac{\partial^2 u}{\partial x^2}$ in the form $\left(\cos \theta\,\dfrac{\partial}{\partial r} - \dfrac{\sin \theta}{r}\,\dfrac{\partial}{\partial \theta} \right)\left(\dfrac{\partial u}{\partial x} \right)$, express it in terms of r, θ and by similarly expressing $\dfrac{\partial^2 u}{\partial y^2}$ prove the result

$$\frac{\partial^2 u}{\partial x^2} + \frac{\partial^2 u}{\partial y^2} = \frac{\partial^2 u}{\partial r^2} + \frac{1}{r}\,\frac{\partial u}{\partial r} + \frac{1}{r^2}\,\frac{\partial^2 u}{\partial \theta^2}.$$

MISCELLANEOUS EXAMPLES

1. If $u = \sin^{-1}(x + y)$, prove that $\dfrac{\partial u}{\partial x} = \dfrac{\partial u}{\partial y}$.

2. If $u = xy/(x + y)$ verify:

(i) $x\,\dfrac{\partial u}{\partial x} + y\,\dfrac{\partial u}{\partial y} = u$; (ii) $x^2\,\dfrac{\partial^2 u}{\partial x^2} + 2xy\,\dfrac{\partial^2 u}{\partial x\,\partial y} + y^2\,\dfrac{\partial^2 u}{\partial y^2} = 0$.

3. If $z = f\left(\dfrac{y}{x}\right)$, prove that $x\,\dfrac{\partial z}{\partial x} + y\,\dfrac{\partial z}{\partial y} = 0$.

4. Verify that $u = f(x) + g(y)$, where f, g are arbitrary functions, is a solution of the equation $\dfrac{\partial^2 u}{\partial x\,\partial y} = 0$.

5. If $u = ax^2 + by^2 + cz^2 + 2fyz + 2gzx + 2hxy$ and $\dfrac{\partial^2 u}{\partial x^2} + \dfrac{\partial^2 u}{\partial y^2} + \dfrac{\partial^2 u}{\partial z^2} = 0$, prove that $a + b + c = 0$.

6. Find the value of $\dfrac{\partial}{\partial x}(xe^y + ye^x)$ when $x = 0$, $y = 1$.

7. If $u = a(x - y) + 2b(x + y) + abz + c$, where a, b, c are constants, show that $\left(\dfrac{\partial u}{\partial x} \right)^2 - \left(\dfrac{\partial u}{\partial y} \right)^2 = 8\,\dfrac{\partial u}{\partial z}$.

8. Given that $u = \phi(y + ax) + \psi(y - ax)$, prove that $\dfrac{\partial^2 u}{\partial x^2} = a^2\,\dfrac{\partial^2 u}{\partial y^2}$.

9. If $e^x + e^y = 2xy$, find the value of $\dfrac{dy}{dx}$.

10. If $u = \dfrac{xy}{2x+z}$, verify that $\dfrac{\partial^3 u}{\partial y\,\partial z^2} = \dfrac{\partial^3 u}{\partial z^2\,\partial y}$.

11. If $u = \sin^{-1}\dfrac{x^2 - y^2}{x^2 + y^2}$, show that $x\dfrac{\partial u}{\partial x} + y\dfrac{\partial u}{\partial y} = 0$.

12. V is a function of r and h given by the formula $V = \pi r^2 h$. Prove that

$$\text{(i)} \ r\frac{\partial V}{\partial r} + 2h\frac{\partial V}{\partial h} = 4V; \quad \text{(ii)} \ \frac{dV}{V} = 2\frac{dr}{r} + \frac{dh}{h}.$$

13. Find $\dfrac{\partial y}{\partial x}$, $\dfrac{\partial y}{\partial z}$ if $x^4 + y^4 + z^4 = 1$.

14. If $ax^2 + 2hxy + by^2 + 2gx + 2fy + c = 0$, prove that: (i) $\dfrac{dy}{dx} = -\dfrac{ax + hy + g}{hx + by + f}$;

(ii) $\dfrac{d^2y}{dx^2} = \dfrac{abc + 2fgh - af^2 - bg^2 - ch^2}{(hx + by + f)^3}$.

15. Find the radius of curvature of the curve $x^2y = x^2 + y^2$ at the point (x, y).

16. If $u = \sin^{-1}\dfrac{x+y}{\sqrt{x} + \sqrt{y}}$, prove that $x\dfrac{\partial u}{\partial x} + y\dfrac{\partial u}{\partial y} = \tfrac{1}{2}\tan u$.

17. Verify the result $\dfrac{\partial^2 u}{\partial x\,\partial y} = \dfrac{\partial^2 u}{\partial y\,\partial x}$ when: (i) $u = \log\{x\tan^{-1}(x^2 + y^2)\}$;
(ii) $u = x^y$.

18. Prove that the equation $\dfrac{\partial^2 \phi}{\partial r^2} + \dfrac{1}{r}\dfrac{\partial \phi}{\partial r} + \dfrac{1}{r^2}\dfrac{\partial^2 \phi}{\partial \theta^2} = 0$ is satisfied by $\phi = (Ar^n + Br^{-n})\cos n\theta$.

19. If $u = f(x, y, z)$, where $x = qr/p$, $y = rp/q$, $z = pq/r$, prove that

$$p\frac{\partial u}{\partial p} + q\frac{\partial u}{\partial q} + r\frac{\partial u}{\partial r} = x\frac{\partial u}{\partial x} + y\frac{\partial u}{\partial y} + z\frac{\partial u}{\partial z}.$$

20. Find an expression for $\dfrac{dy}{dx}$ if $y\log\cos x = x\log\sin y$.

21. If $x^2 + y^2 = z^2$, show that $\dfrac{\partial z}{\partial x} = \dfrac{x}{z}$, $\dfrac{\partial z}{\partial y} = \dfrac{y}{z}$ and deduce the result $\dfrac{\partial^2 z}{\partial x^2} + \dfrac{\partial^2 z}{\partial y^2} = \dfrac{1}{z}$.

22. The area of a triangle ABC is calculated from values of a, B, C. If there is a small error $\varepsilon°$ in the value of B and the other measurements are accurate, prove that the resulting error in the area is approximately $\pi c^2 \varepsilon / 360$.

23. If $r = \sqrt{(x^2 + y^2 + z^2)}$, prove that $\dfrac{\partial^2}{\partial x^2}\left(\dfrac{1}{r}\right) + \dfrac{\partial^2}{\partial y^2}\left(\dfrac{1}{r}\right) + \dfrac{\partial^2}{\partial z^2}\left(\dfrac{1}{r}\right) = 0$.

24. Find $\dfrac{dy}{dx}$ and $\dfrac{d^2y}{dx^2}$ if $x^5 + y^5 - 5a^3xy = 0$.

25. If $f(x, y) = 0$ and $g(x, z) = 0$, prove that $\dfrac{dy}{dz} = \dfrac{f_x g_z}{f_y g_x}$.

26. If $z = x^2 \tan^{-1} \dfrac{y}{x} - y^2 \tan^{-1} \dfrac{x}{y}$, show that $\dfrac{\partial^2 z}{\partial x \, \partial y} = \dfrac{x^2 - y^2}{x^2 + y^2}$.

27. Prove that, if the sides a, b, c of a triangle ABC receive equal small increments x, the increments in the angles A, B, C are given by $\delta A \simeq \dfrac{xa}{\Delta}(1 - \cos B - \cos C)$ and similar expressions, where Δ is the area of the triangle.

28. If $\left(\dfrac{x}{a}\right)^3 + \left(\dfrac{y}{b}\right)^3 + \left(\dfrac{z}{c}\right)^3 = 1$, find the values of $\dfrac{\partial z}{\partial x}$ and $\dfrac{\partial^2 x}{\partial y \, \partial z}$.

29. If z is a function of x and y, where $x = \xi\eta$, $y = 1/\eta$ and if $2xy \dfrac{\partial z}{\partial x} + 2(1 - y^2)\dfrac{\partial z}{\partial y} + x^2 yz = 0$, prove that $2\xi\eta \dfrac{\partial z}{\partial \xi} + 2(1 - \eta^2)\dfrac{\partial z}{\partial \eta} + \xi^2 \eta z = 0$.

30. Given that $x = u + e^{-v}\cos u$, $y = v + e^{-v}\sin u$, where u, v are independent variables, prove that $\dfrac{\partial u}{\partial x}$ is not equal to $1 \Big/ \dfrac{\partial x}{\partial u}$. Prove also that $\dfrac{\partial u}{\partial x} = \dfrac{\partial v}{\partial y}$.

31. The length of the hypotenuse of a right-angled triangle is calculated from the lengths of the other two sides; the latter are measured as 8 and 15 cm with a possible error of 0·1 cm in each. Find the maximum possible error in the calculated length of the hypotenuse.

32. If $\sin^2 x + \sin^2 y = 2 \cos x \cos y$, show that $\dfrac{dy}{dx} = -\sin x \operatorname{cosec} y$.

33. The radius R of the circumcircle of a triangle ABC is constant and keeping the vertices B, C fixed, the angle B is increased by a small amount ε minutes. Show that the resulting percentage increase in the area of the triangle is approximately $\pi R(c^2 - b^2)\varepsilon/54abc$.

34. If $u = f(ax^2 + 2hxy + by^2)$, $v = g(ax^2 + 2hxy + by^2)$, prove that
$$\frac{\partial}{\partial y}\left(u \frac{\partial v}{\partial x}\right) = \frac{\partial}{\partial x}\left(u \frac{\partial v}{\partial y}\right).$$

35. Show that the function $V = \dfrac{1}{r}$, where $r^2 = x^2 + y^2 + z^2$, is a solution of the equation $\dfrac{\partial^2 V}{\partial x^2} + \dfrac{\partial^2 V}{\partial y^2} + \dfrac{\partial^2 V}{\partial z^2} = 0$. If $z = r \cos \theta$, show that $V = \dfrac{1}{r^2}\cos \theta$ is also a solution.

36. If z is an arbitrary function of $(x + ay)$, prove that $\dfrac{\partial z}{\partial y} = a \dfrac{\partial z}{\partial x}$.

37. If $z = f(x + iy) + F(x - iy)$, where $i = \sqrt{-1}$, prove that $\dfrac{\partial^2 z}{\partial x^2} + \dfrac{\partial^2 z}{\partial y^2} = 0$.

38. If $V = (1 - 2xy + y^2)^{-\frac{1}{2}}$, prove that:

(i) $x \dfrac{\partial V}{\partial x} - y \dfrac{\partial V}{\partial y} = y^2 V^3$;   (ii) $\dfrac{\partial}{\partial x}\left\{(1 - x^2)\dfrac{\partial V}{\partial x}\right\} + \dfrac{\partial}{\partial y}\left\{y^2 \dfrac{\partial V}{\partial y}\right\} = 0$.

39. The vertex A of a triangle ABC is displaced a small distance parallel to BC while B, C remain fixed. With the usual notation, prove the approximate results:

$$\text{(i) } \cos C \, \delta b + \cos B \, \delta c \simeq c \sin B \, \delta B + b \sin C \, \delta C;$$
$$\text{(ii) } c \, \delta b + b \, \delta c + bc \cot A \, \delta A = 0.$$

40. If $f(x, y) = 0$, prove that $\left(\dfrac{dx}{dy}\right)^2 \dfrac{d^2 y}{dx^2} + \dfrac{dy}{dx} \dfrac{d^2 x}{dy^2} = 0.$

41. Express the area Δ of a triangle ABC as a function of a, b, c and prove that $d\Delta = R(\cos A \, da + \cos B \, db + \cos C \, dc)$, where R is the circumradius.

42. If the function $g(u, v)$ is transformed by the substitutions $ur \cos \theta = 1$, $\tan \theta = v$ into the function $f(r, \theta)$ prove:

$$\text{(i) } r \frac{\partial f}{\partial r} = -u \frac{\partial g}{\partial u}; \qquad \text{(ii) } \frac{\partial f}{\partial \theta} = uv \frac{\partial g}{\partial u} + (1 + v^2) \frac{\partial g}{\partial v}.$$

43. If $V = \phi(x, y)$, where $x = r \cosh \theta$, $y = r \sinh \theta$, prove that

$$\frac{\partial^2 V}{\partial x^2} - \frac{\partial^2 V}{\partial y^2} = \frac{\partial^2 V}{\partial r^2} + \frac{1}{r} \frac{\partial V}{\partial r} - \frac{1}{r^2} \frac{\partial^2 V}{\partial \theta^2}.$$

44. The variables x, y in $f(x, y)$ are changed to ξ, η by the substitutions $x = \frac{1}{2}(\xi^2 - \eta^2)$, $y = \xi\eta$. Prove that:

$$\text{(i) } \xi \frac{\partial f}{\partial \xi} + \eta \frac{\partial f}{\partial \eta} = 2\left(x \frac{\partial f}{\partial x} + y \frac{\partial f}{\partial y} \right);$$

$$\text{(ii) } \frac{\partial f}{\partial x} = \frac{1}{\xi^2 + \eta^2}\left(\xi \frac{\partial f}{\partial \xi} - \eta \frac{\partial f}{\partial \eta} \right);$$

$$\text{(iii) } \frac{\partial^2 f}{\partial \xi^2} + \frac{\partial^2 f}{\partial \eta^2} = (\xi^2 + \eta^2)\left(\frac{\partial^2 f}{\partial x^2} + \frac{\partial^2 f}{\partial y^2} \right).$$

45. If u is a homogeneous function of degree n in x, y, prove that

$$x^2 \frac{\partial^2 u}{\partial x^2} + 2xy \frac{\partial^2 u}{\partial x \, \partial y} + y^2 \frac{\partial^2 u}{\partial y^2} = n(n-1)u.$$

REVISION PAPERS

PAPER A (1)

1. The circumcentre and orthocentre of a triangle ABC are O, H respectively. Prove that if AH meets BC at D and the circumcircle again at P, then $HD = DP$.

Show how to construct a triangle given the circumcentre, the orthocentre and the straight line containing one side. (O.C.)

2. Determine the ranges of values of p for which the equation $(x-1)(x-4) = px$ has real roots.

If p is small, prove that the roots of the equation are approximately $1 - \frac{1}{3}p + \frac{4}{27}p^2$ and $4 + \frac{4}{3}p - \frac{4}{27}p^2$. (L.)

3. (i) Find the values of k for which the quadratic equations $x^2 + kx - 6k = 0$, $x^2 - 2x - k = 0$ have a common root.

(ii) Solve the equation $\begin{vmatrix} 2x & 7 & 1 \\ 7 & 2x & 1 \\ 2 & 7 & x^2 \end{vmatrix} = 0$. (N.)

4. A circle S passes through the point $(2, 0)$ and cuts the circle $x^2 + y^2 = 1$ at the ends of a diameter of that circle. Find the equation of the locus of the centre of S.

Also find the equation of S if it cuts the circle $x^2 + y^2 - 4y - 5 = 0$ at right angles. (L.)

5. Solve the equations:

(i) $\sqrt{(3x+4)} - \sqrt{(x+2)} = 2$; (ii) $\log_4 x + \log_x 4 = 2 \cdot 5$. (L.)

6. From a variable point on the parabola $y^2 = 4ax$ two straight lines of gradients ± 1 are drawn to meet the parabola again at P, Q. The tangents at P, Q meet at R. Prove that the locus of R is a parabola whose vertex is the point $(-4a, 0)$.

7. (a) The sum of the first n terms of an arithmetic series is the same as the sum of the first p terms where $n \neq p$. Prove that the sum of the first $(n+p)$ terms is zero.

(b) The nth term of a series whose first term is unity is
$$r^{n-1}(1 + r + r^2 + \ldots + r^{n-1}).$$
If $|r| \neq 1$, prove that the sum of the first n terms is
$$\frac{(1-r^n)(1-r^{n+1})}{(1-r)(1-r^2)}. \tag{N.}$$

8. Expand $y = e^{\sin x}$ in a series of ascending powers of x as far as the term in x^5 and find the value of y, correct to three significant figures, when $x = 0 \cdot 3$.

337

9. Evaluate: (i) $\int \dfrac{dx}{2-x-x^2}$, $x<1$;   (ii) $\int_0^{\frac{1}{2}\sqrt{3}} \dfrac{dx}{(1-x)(1-x^2)^{\frac{1}{2}}}$;

(iii) $\int x^3 (\log x)^2\, dx$.

10. By writing the following polar equations in Cartesian coordinates, identify the curves represented by them giving a rough sketch in each case:

(i) $r(1+\cos\theta)=2a$;   (ii) $r=2a\cos\theta$;   (iii) $r^2\sin 2\theta=2c^2$.   (L.)

11. A pulley wheel is made by cutting a groove, whose cross-section is a semicircle radius r, round a right circular cylinder of height $2r$ and radius $R(R>r)$.   Show that the total surface area of the pulley is $2\pi(R^2+\pi Rr-2r^2)$ and that its volume is $\frac{1}{3}\pi(6R^2r-3\pi Rr^2+4r^3)$.

12. Prove that the lines joining the mid-points of opposite edges of a tetrahedron meet at a point G and are bisected there.

Prove that the lines joining the vertices of the tetrahedron to the centroids of the opposite faces also meet at G.

PAPER A (2)

1. The tangent at P to the circumcircle of a triangle ABP meets AB produced at O.   Prove that: (i) $OA \cdot OB = OP^2$; (ii) $OA:OB=PA^2:PB^2$.

Hence, or otherwise, prove that if P is a variable point in a plane containing two fixed points A and B, and if the ratio $PA:PB$ has a constant value k, greater than unity, then the locus of P is a circle of radius $kAB/(k^2-1)$.   (L.)

2. A triangle ABC is inscribed in a circle radius R.   The internal bisectors of the angles A, B and C meet the circle again at A_1, B_1 and C_1 respectively. Prove that the lengths of the sides of the triangle $A_1B_1C_1$ are $2R\cos\frac{1}{2}A$, $2R\cos\frac{1}{2}B$, $2R\cos\frac{1}{2}C$.

3. (a) Solve the simultaneous equations $xy+x+3=0$, $x^2y^2+x^2-5=0$.

(b) Prove that there are two values of k for which the equation $(x+a)(x+b)+k(x^2-c)=0$ has equal roots.   (Assume a, b and c are non-zero.)

Show that these values of k are real and different only when c does not lie between a^2 and b^2.   (N.)

4. Prove that the equation of the pair of straight lines through the origin perpendicular to the pair $ax^2+2hxy+by^2=0$ is $bx^2-2hxy+ay^2=0$.

Deduce the equation of the pair of straight lines through the point (x', y') which are perpendicular to the pair $ax^2+2hxy+by^2=0$ and that of the circle through the four points of intersection of these two pairs.   (C.)

5. Two complex numbers z_1, z_2 are represented by points on an Argand diagram.   Show how to construct geometrically the points which represent z_1+z_2 and z_1-z_2.   Find geometrically, or otherwise, the following loci on the Argand diagram:

(i) $|z+3i|^2-|z-3i|^2=12$;   (ii) $|z+ik|^2+|z-ik|^2=10k^2$;
(iii) $am\{(z-2)/(z+2)\}=\frac{1}{3}\pi$.

6. The four points of the parabola $x = at^2$, $y = 2at$ with parameters t_1, t_2, t_3, t_4 lie on a circle. Prove that $t_1 + t_2 + t_3 + t_4 = 0$.

Prove that the parabola $y^2 = 16x$ and the circle $x^2 + y^2 - 40x - 16y - 48 = 0$ meet at the point P (36, 24) and one other point Q. Prove further that PQ is a diameter of the circle and a normal at Q to the parabola.

7. State the sum of the first n terms of the geometrical progression whose first term is a and whose common ratio is r when $r \neq 1$.

Show that $\sum_{r=1}^{r=n} (x^{2r-1} + 1/x^{2r-1}) = (x^{4n} - 1)/x^{2n-1} (x^2 - 1)$ if $x \neq 0$ or ± 1.

Hence, or otherwise, prove that

$$\cosh u + \cosh 3u + \ldots + \cosh (2n-1)u = \sinh 2nu/2 \sinh u,$$

when $u \neq 0$. (N.)

8. (i) Expand $2x/(1-x)(1+x^2)$, where $|x| < 1$, in ascending powers of x and find the coefficients of x^n when n is in the forms $4m$, $4m+1$, $4m+2$, $4m+3$ respectively.

(ii) Prove that the coefficient of x^n in the expansion of $\log (1 + x + x^2)$ is $-2/n$ or $1/n$, stating the condition under which each occur. (L.)

9. (i) Integrate: (a) $\int \sin^2 x \cos^3 x \, dx$; (b) $\int \sin 2x \cos 3x \, dx$.

(ii) Prove that $\int_0^{\frac{1}{2}\pi} \dfrac{2 \cos x + 11 \sin x}{3 \cos x + 4 \sin x} \, dx = \pi + \log \frac{3}{4}$. (L.)

10. By putting $y = tx$, obtain a parametric representation of the curve $x^3 + y^3 = 3axy$. Sketch the curve and obtain the radii of curvature of the two branches at the origin. (O.C.)

11. Find the equation of the plane passing through the line $x = \frac{1}{2}(y-3) = \frac{1}{3}(z-5)$ and perpendicular to the plane $2x + 7y - 3z = 1$.

12. The variables r, θ, x, y are connected by the equations $r = \sqrt{(x^2 + y^2)}$, $\theta = \tan^{-1} (y/x)$. Determine the partial differential coefficients $\dfrac{\partial r}{\partial x}$, $\dfrac{\partial r}{\partial y}$, $\dfrac{\partial \theta}{\partial x}$, $\dfrac{\partial \theta}{\partial y}$ and verify that $\dfrac{\partial r}{\partial y} \Big/ \dfrac{\partial r}{\partial x} = -\dfrac{\partial \theta}{\partial x} \Big/ \dfrac{\partial \theta}{\partial y}$. (O.C.)

PAPER A (3)

1. In a triangle ABC, D is the mid-point of CA and E is the point on BC such that $2BE = EC$. The lines AE, BD meet at F; show that $AF = 3FE$ and $BF = FD$.

The lines CF, AB meet at P; show that EP is parallel to CA. (O.C.)

2. (a) If $x+2$ and $x-4$ are factors of the quartic $2x^4 - 5x^3 + ax^2 + bx + 8$, find the values of a and b. Determine the other linear factors of the quartic.

(b) If a and b are real, prove that the roots of the quadratic equation $(3a-b)x^2 + (b-a)x - 2a = 0$ are real. (N.)

3. Verify that the expression $a^2+b^2+c^2-2bc-2ca-2ab$ is equal to $(a+b-c)^2-4ab$.

Hence, or otherwise, prove that the expression is equal to

$$(\alpha+\beta+\gamma)(\alpha-\beta-\gamma)(\alpha-\beta+\gamma)(\alpha+\beta-\gamma),$$

where $\alpha=\sqrt{a}$, $\beta=\sqrt{b}$, $\gamma=\sqrt{c}$.

Hence, or otherwise, find one solution of each of the following equations:

(i) $\sqrt{(x-6)}+\sqrt{(x-1)}=\sqrt{(3x-5)}$;
(ii) $\sqrt{(6-x)}-\sqrt{(1-x)}=\sqrt{(5-3x)}$. (O.C.)

4. (i) Show that $x+y+z$ is a factor of the determinant

$$\begin{vmatrix} y+z & -y & 2z \\ -x & z+x & -z \\ 2x & 2y & x+y \end{vmatrix}$$

and evaluate the determinant as a product of linear factors.

(ii) Solve completely the equation

$$\begin{vmatrix} x & 2 & x-4 \\ 2x-2 & 3x-2 & 4 \\ 2x+3 & 3x & 5 \end{vmatrix}=0.$$ (L.)

5. Prove that the y-axis is the radical axis of the circles $x^2+y^2-4x-9=0$, $x^2+y^2+6x-9=0$. Find the equation of the smallest circle through the common points A and B of these two circles.

Find also the equations of the circles through A and B which have radius 5.

Show that any circle which cuts orthogonally all circles through A and B has its centre on the y-axis. If such a circle also cuts orthogonally the circle $x^2+y^2-2x-4y-25=0$, find its equation. (N.)

6. (i) Show that, if the roots of the equation $x^3-5x^2+qx-8=0$ are in geometric progression, then $q=10$.

(ii) If α, β, γ are the roots of the equation $x^3-x^2+4x+7=0$, find the equation whose roots are $\beta+\gamma$, $\gamma+\alpha$, $\alpha+\beta$. (C.)

7. A given line $lx+my=1$ meets the hyperbola $x^2/a^2-y^2/b^2=1$ at A, B and its asymptotes at C, D. Prove that AB and CD have the same mid-point M and that M lies on the line $mx/a^2+ly/b^2=0$.

If the given line passes through the fixed point (α, β), prove that the locus of M is $(x^2-\alpha x)/a^2-(y^2-\beta y)/b^2=0$. (O.C.)

8. (a) If $3u_{n+1}=2u_n-1$ for all positive integral values of n and $u_1=1$, prove by induction that $u_n=3(\frac{2}{3})^n-1$. Find the sum of the first n terms of the series whose nth term is u_n.

(b) If $|x|<1$, prove that the sum to infinity of the series

$$1+5x+9x^2+ \ldots +(4n+1)x^n+ \ldots$$

is $(1+3x)/(1-x)^2$. (N.)

9. Integrate with respect to x: (i) $\dfrac{x-1}{x(x-2)}$; (ii) $\dfrac{1}{x^2}\log(1+x^2)$.

Evaluate $\displaystyle\int_0^{\frac{1}{4}\pi} \dfrac{dx}{a^2\cos^2 x+b^2\sin^2 x}$.

10. If p is the perpendicular from the pole O to the tangent to a curve at a point P whose distance from O is r, prove that the radius of curvature at P is $r\dfrac{dr}{dp}$. If C is the centre of curvature at P for the curve given by $r^3 = 2ap^2$, prove that $PC = \tfrac{2}{3}\sqrt{(2ar)}$ and $OC = \tfrac{1}{3}\sqrt{(8ar - 3r^2)}$.

11. $ABCD$ is a rectangle and O is a point on the normal at C to the plane of the rectangle; $AB = a$, $AD = b$ and $CO = h$. P is a point on AO and the line through P in the plane AOB which is perpendicular to AO meets AB at M.

If $AP = x$, show that $PM = x\sqrt{(b^2 + h^2)}/a$, $AM = x\sqrt{(a^2 + b^2 + h^2)}/a$.

Prove that the cosine of the acute angle between the planes OAB and OAD is $ab/\sqrt{\{(a^2 + h^2)(b^2 + h^2)\}}$. (L.)

12. Show that the spheres

$$x^2 + y^2 + z^2 = 25, \quad x^2 + y^2 + z^2 - 18x - 24y - 40z + 225 = 0$$

touch each other and find the coordinates of the common point.

PAPER A (4)

1. In the acute-angled triangle ABC the perpendicular from A to BC cuts the incircle at P and Q; the centre of the incircle is I and its radius r. Prove that $AI = r \operatorname{cosec} \tfrac{1}{2}A$; the perpendicular distance of I from PQ is the positive value of $r \operatorname{cosec} \tfrac{1}{2}A \sin \tfrac{1}{2}(C - B)$; and the length PQ is

$$2r \operatorname{cosec} \tfrac{1}{2}A \sqrt{(\cos B \cos C)}. \qquad \text{(O.C.)}$$

2. (i) The expression $ax^3 + bx^2 + cx + d$ has the values 7, 2, 1, 10 respectively when x is equal to 1, 2, 3, 4. Evaluate a, b, c and d.

(ii) Given that $x = 2$ is one solution of the equation

$$84x^3 - 157x^2 - kx + 78 = 0,$$

find the value of k and obtain the other solutions. (O.C.)

3. If the equation $ax^2 + 2hxy + by^2 = 0$ represents the pair of lines $y = m_1 x$, $y = m_2 x$, show that $m_1 + m_2 = -2h/b$, $m_1 m_2 = a/b$.

Find the equation of the pair of lines obtained by rotating the lines $x^2 + 2kxy + y^2 = 0$ in the positive sense through the acute angle whose tangent is 2, expressing the coefficients in terms of k. (N.)

4. A, B, C, D are the points in the Argand diagram representing the complex numbers α, β, γ, δ. If $(\alpha - \beta)/(\gamma - \delta)$ is purely imaginary, prove that AB, CD are perpendicular.

Show also that, if A, B, C are the vertices of an isosceles triangle right-angled at B, then $\alpha^2 + 2\beta^2 + \gamma^2 = 2\beta(\alpha + \gamma)$.

5. Prove that, if α is a repeated root of the polynomial equation $f(x) = 0$, then α is a root of the equation $f'(x) = 0$.

Given that the equation $4x^4 + x^2 + 3x + 1 = 0$ has a repeated root, find its value. (C.)

6. (i) Show that
$$x(x+1)(2x+1) \equiv Ax(x+1)(x+2)(x+3) + B(x-2)(x-1)x(x+1)$$
for certain constant values of A and B and find these values.
Hence, or otherwise, sum to n terms the series
$$1.2.3 + 2.3.5 + 3.4.7 + \ldots$$

(ii) Prove that the sum of n terms of the series
$$\frac{2.1}{2.3} + \frac{2^2.2}{3.4} + \frac{2^3.3}{4.5} + \ldots$$
is $2^{n+1}/(n+2) - 1$.   (O.C.)

7. State Taylor's theorem for the expansion of $f(a+h)$ in a series of ascending powers of h. Prove that the first four terms in the Taylor expansion of $\tan^{-1}(1+h)$ are $\frac{1}{4}\pi + \frac{1}{2}h - \frac{1}{4}h^2 + \frac{1}{12}h^3$.

8. Prove that: (i) $\displaystyle\int_0^{\frac{1}{2}\pi} \frac{\cos x}{\sqrt{(4 - \sin^2 x)}} \, dx = \frac{1}{6}\pi$;   (ii) $\displaystyle\int_0^1 \frac{x}{1+x^4} dx = \frac{1}{8}\pi$;

(iii) $\displaystyle\int_1^4 \frac{\log x}{\sqrt{x}} \, dx = 8 \log 2 - 4$.   (N.)

9. If $n > 0$, prove that $\displaystyle\int_0^1 x^n(1-x)^{\frac{1}{2}} \, dx = \frac{2n}{2n+3} \int_0^1 x^{n-1}(1-x)^{\frac{1}{2}} \, dx$.

Hence evaluate $\displaystyle\int_0^1 x^5(1-x)^{\frac{1}{2}} \, dx$.

10. A straight line $y = mx - c$ crosses the axis OX at A. Find the equation of the line in polar coordinates using O as pole and OX as initial line.

If $P(r, \theta)$ is a point on the line where $0 < \theta < \frac{1}{2}\pi$, find the volume formed by the revolution of the triangle OPA about the axis OX in terms of m, c, θ.

11. The sides of a triangle a, b, c are of lengths 5, 6, 7 cm respectively. If the percentage errors made in the measurements of the sides were $+0.2$, $+0.4$, $+0.6$ respectively, use logarithmic differentiation to find the percentage error in the area of the triangle.

12. Find the equation of the plane through the points $(1, 0, 0)$, $(0, 3, 4)$ and parallel to the straight line joining the points $(0, 2, 0)$, $(0, 0, 3)$. Also find the perpendicular distance between the plane and the straight line.
                                                                    (L.)

PAPER A (5)

1. If P is any point on the circumcircle of a triangle ABC, prove that L, M, N the feet of the perpendiculars from P to BC, CA, AB respectively are collinear—the pedal line of P.

If Q is any other point on the circumcircle prove that the pedal lines of P and Q intersect at an angle equal to angle PCQ.

2. (i) Use the substitution $x = t - 2$ to solve the equation
$$x^4 + 8x^3 + 16x^2 - 36 = 0,$$
giving only the values of the real solutions.

(ii) If the equations $x^2 + x + p = 0$, $qx^2 - x + 1 = 0$ have a common root, prove that $(pq - 1)^2 + (p+1)(q+1) = 0$.

3. Prove that, if x is real and a, b are unequal, the expression $(x^2 + ax + c)/(x^2 + bx + c)$ can take any value when $c \leqslant 0$.

Sketch the graph of $y = (x^2 + 5x - 6)/(x^2 - x - 6)$.   (C.)

4. Show that
$$\begin{vmatrix} t_1^2 & 2t_1 & 1 \\ t_2^2 & 2t_2 & 1 \\ t_1 t_2 & t_1 + t_2 & 1 \end{vmatrix} = (t_2 - t_1)^3.$$

The tangents at the points Q, R on the parabola $y^2 = 4ax$ meet at P. If S is the mid-point of QR and P moves in such a way that the area of the triangle PQR is constant, show that the distance between P and S is constant.   (N.)

5. The equations of two circles S_1, S_2 are
$$x^2 + y^2 - 6x - 3 = 0, \qquad x^2 + y^2 + 8x + 11 = 0.$$
Show that the coaxal system to which S_1 and S_2 belong has real limiting points and find the coordinates of these points.

Obtain the equation of the circle through the point $(0, 1)$ orthogonal to S_1 and S_2.   (N.)

6. (i) Find the coefficients of x^5 and x^8 in the expansion of $(1 + x + 2x^2)^5$.

(ii) Prove that
$$\frac{(2n+1)(2n+3)}{(n+1)(n+2)} - \frac{(2n-1)(2n+1)}{n(n+1)} = \frac{2(2n+1)}{n(n+1)(n+2)}.$$

Find the sum of the first n terms of the series
$$\frac{3}{1 \cdot 2 \cdot 3} + \frac{5}{2 \cdot 3 \cdot 4} + \frac{7}{3 \cdot 4 \cdot 5} + \cdots$$ (O.C.)

7. Find the first differential coefficient of y with respect to x if $y = \sin^{-1} x$. Use this result to expand $\sin^{-1} x$ as far as the term in x^{11} and hence show that the value of π to five significant figures is $3 \cdot 1416$.

8. (i) Evaluate the integrals $\int x \tan^{-1} x^2 \, dx; \quad \int \dfrac{dx}{x\sqrt{(1 - x^2)}}$.

(ii) Prove that if m, n are integers, $\displaystyle\int_0^{2\pi} \cos mx \cos nx \, dx = 0$ if $m \neq n$,
$$= \pi \text{ if } m = n.$$

9. (i) If $I(z) = \displaystyle\int_1^z \frac{(x-1)^p(2-x)^p}{x^{p+1}} \, dx$, $p > 0$, by writing $x = 2/y$, prove that
$$2I(\sqrt{2}) = I(2).$$

(ii) Without attempting to evaluate them, determine whether the following integrals are positive, negative, or zero:
$$\int_0^1 x^3(1-x)^3 \, dx; \quad \int_0^\pi \sin^2 x \cos^3 x \, dx; \quad \int_0^\pi e^{-x} \sin x \, dx. \quad \text{(O.C.)}$$

10. Find the volume of the solid formed by rotating the circle $x^2 + y^2 - 4y + 3 = 0$ about the x-axis.

11. G is the centroid of a triangle whose vertices are the points in which the coordinate axes meet the plane $lx + my + nz = p$, where $l^2 + m^2 + n^2 = 1$. The perpendicular at G to this plane meets the coordinate planes in A, B, C. Prove that $1/GA + 1/GB + 1/GC = 3/p$.   (L.)

z

12. If V is defined by the relationships

$$V = \frac{1}{r}, \quad r^2 = (x-a)^2 + (y-b)^2, \quad \text{where } a, b \text{ are constants,}$$

prove that:

(i) $(x-a)\dfrac{\partial V}{\partial x} + (y-b)\dfrac{\partial V}{\partial y} + V = 0$; (ii) $\dfrac{\partial}{\partial x}\left(\dfrac{\partial V}{\partial x}\right) + \dfrac{\partial}{\partial y}\left(\dfrac{\partial V}{\partial y}\right) = V^3$;

(iii) $\dfrac{\partial}{\partial x}\left(\dfrac{\partial V}{\partial y}\right) = \dfrac{\partial}{\partial y}\left(\dfrac{\partial V}{\partial x}\right)$. (O.C.)

PAPER A (6)

1. If H is the orthocentre of triangle ABC and the altitude AD is produced to meet the circumcircle at P, prove that $HD = DP$.

If the diameter of the circumcircle through A meets the circle again at Q, prove that HQ bisects BC. (C.)

2. Writing u_n for $x^{2n} + x^n + 1$, where n is a positive integer, express $u_{n+3} - x^6 u_n$ as a product of two factors one of which is $x^3 - 1$.

Deduce that, if $x^2 + x + 1$ is a factor of u_n, then it is also a factor of u_{n+3} and prove that $x^2 + x + 1$ is a factor of u_{100}. (O.C.)

3. Show that if $y = (x^2 - x + a)/(x-1)^2$, then for all real values of x,

$$y \geqslant 1 - 1/4a \text{ if } a > 0; \quad y \leqslant 1 - 1/4a \text{ if } a < 0.$$

Sketch the graph of the function when $a = -1$. (L.)

4. Find the condition that the circle $x^2 + y^2 + 2g_1 x + 2f_1 y + c_1 = 0$ should cut the circle $x^2 + y^2 + 2gx + 2fy + c = 0$ at the ends of a diameter of the latter circle.

Find the locus of the centre of a circle which cuts the circles $x^2 + y^2 = 25$, $x^2 + y^2 - 2x - 4y - 11 = 0$ at the ends of diameters of the latter circles.

5. (i) If z_1, z_2 are complex numbers such that $|z_1| = |z_2|$, prove that $(z_1 + z_2)/(z_1 - z_2)$ is purely imaginary.

(ii) Represent the roots of the equation $z^3 + 8 = 0$ in an Argand diagram.

(iii) Find the value of $\dfrac{(1-i)^2(\sqrt{3}+i)}{1 - i\sqrt{3}}$. (O.C.)

6. Prove that there are just two values of the constant a for which the three equations $3x - 2y = 8$, $2x - ay = 2a + 1$, $(a-2)x + y = 4 - a$ have a common solution and find these values. Solve the equations for each of these values of a. (N.)

7. A rectangular hyperbola is given parametrically by the equations $x = ct$, $y = c/t$. If the four points of the curve with parameters t_1, t_2, t_3, t_4 lie on a circle, show that $t_1 t_2 t_3 t_4 = 1$ and prove the converse result.

A variable circle passes through the fixed points A, B of a rectangular hyperbola and meets the hyperbola again at P, Q. Show that the direction of PQ is fixed. (O.C.)

8. (i) If S_n is the sum of n terms of a G.P., common ratio r, prove that

$$(r-1)\frac{dS_n}{dr} = (n-1)S_n - nS_{n-1}.$$

(ii) Find the first three terms in the expansion of $\log(1 + \tan x)$ in ascending powers of x.

9. (i) Find $\int e^x \sin 2x \, dx$.

(ii) Prove that $\displaystyle\int_0^{\sqrt{2}} \frac{x^2 \, dx}{\sqrt{(x^2+2)}} = \sqrt{2} - \log_e(1+\sqrt{2})$. (C.)

10. If $u_n = \displaystyle\int_0^1 x^n \cos \pi x \, dx$, where $n > 1$, show that

$$\pi^2 u_n + n(n-1)u_{n-2} + n = 0,$$

and hence evaluate $\displaystyle\int_0^1 x^4 \cos \pi x \, dx$.

11. Sketch the curve $r = a(1 - \cos\theta)$ and prove that ϕ, the angle between the radius vector and the tangent, is equal to $\frac{1}{2}\theta$. If any line through the pole cuts the curve at points P and Q prove: (i) the tangents at P, Q are perpendicular; (ii) the mid-point of PQ lies on a circle.

12. A minor arc of a circle, radius a, revolves about its chord which subtends an angle 2α at the centre of the circle. Prove that the volume generated is $2\pi a^3 (\sin\alpha - \frac{1}{3}\sin^3\alpha - \alpha\cos\alpha)$ and find its surface area.

PAPER A (7)

1. If O is the circumcentre and H the orthocentre of a triangle ABC, prove the following results:

(i) the radius of the circle BCH is R, the radius of the circumcircle of triangle ABC;

(ii) $AH = 2R \cos A$;

(iii) the area of triangle $OAH = \frac{1}{2}R^2(\sin 2B \sim \sin 2C)$.

2. (i) It is required to express $x^2 + 7y^2 + 20z^2 + 8yz - 2zx + 4xy$ in the form

$$A(x + py + qz)^2 + B(y + rz)^2 + Cz^2,$$

where A, B, C, p, q, r are constants. Determine the values of these constants and deduce that the given expression is never negative for real values of x, y, z.

(ii) Show that, if a, b, p, q are real numbers, so also are the roots of the equation,

$$\frac{a^2}{x-p} + \frac{b^2}{x-q} = 1.$$

3. Prove that

$$\begin{vmatrix} a & a^2 & a^4 \\ b & b^2 & b^4 \\ c & c^2 & c^4 \end{vmatrix} = kabc(a-b)(b-c)(c-a)(a+b+c),$$

where k is a numerical constant and find the value of k.

Factorise $\begin{vmatrix} a & a^3 & a^4 \\ b & b^3 & b^4 \\ c & c^3 & c^4 \end{vmatrix}$. (C.)

4. Show that the area of the triangle with vertices $(0, 0)$, (x_1, y_1), (x_2, y_2) is $\pm\frac{1}{2}(x_1y_2 - x_2y_1)$.

If O is the origin and if the line $lx + my = 1$ meets the line pair $ax^2 + 2hxy + by^2 = 0$ at P and Q, prove that the area of the triangle OPQ is

$$\pm\frac{\sqrt{(h^2 - ab)}}{am^2 - 2hlm + bl^2}.$$

5. Prove that the equation of a circle is of the form

$$x^2 + y^2 + 2gx + 2fy + c = 0.$$

Two circles intersect at the points A and B. The x-axis is taken along the common chord; the length of AB is $2h$ and the mid-point of AB is the origin O. Prove that the equations of the circles are

$$x^2 + y^2 - 2k_1y = h^2, \quad x^2 + y^2 - 2k_2y = h^2.$$

Find the condition for the circles to cut at right angles. (O.C.)

6. Obtain expressions for $\cos 7\theta$ and $\sin 7\theta$ in terms of $\cos\theta$ and $\sin\theta$ by equating the values of $(\cos\theta + i\sin\theta)^7$ given by the binomial theorem and by de Moivre's theorem.

Hence express $\tan 7\theta$ in terms of $\tan\theta$.

Prove that $\tan^2 \pi/7 + \tan^2 2\pi/7 + \tan^2 3\pi/7 = 21$.

7. Prove that the equation of the normal to the ellipse $x^2/a^2 + y^2/b^2 = 1$ at the point $(a\cos\theta, b\sin\theta)$ is $ax\sin\theta - by\cos\theta = (a^2 - b^2)\sin\theta\cos\theta$.

Show that when $b\sqrt{2} > a > b > 0$ all normals meet the minor axis at points within the ellipse. If $a > b\sqrt{2}$, find the gradients of the two normals apart from the y-axis that pass through the point $(0, -b)$. If these normals are at right angles, find the eccentricity of the ellipse. (N.)

8. (i) If a_n denotes the nth term of the series which begins

$$1 + \frac{2^2}{1 \cdot (1 + 2 \cdot 2^2)} + \frac{3^2}{1 \cdot (1 + 2 \cdot 2^2)(1 + 2 \cdot 3^2)} + \cdots,$$

prove that the sum to n terms is $\frac{1}{2}(3 - a_n/n^2)$.

(ii) Prove by induction that if n is a positive integer, then $2 \cdot 4^{2n+1} + 3^{3n+1}$ is divisible by 11. (O.C.)

9. Prove that

(i) $\displaystyle\sum_{n=1}^{\infty} (-1)^{n-1} 2^{2n-1} \frac{x^{2n}}{(2n)!} = \sin^2 x; \quad \sum_{n=1}^{\infty} (-1)^n \frac{3 + 3^{2n}}{4} \frac{x^{2n}}{(2n)!} = \cos^3 x.$

10. A curve is given by the equations

$$x = a(2\cos t - \cos 2t), \quad y = a(2\sin t - \sin 2t),$$

where t is a parameter. Prove that the equation of the tangent at the point parameter t is

$$x \sin(3t/2) - y \cos(3t/2) = 3a \sin(t/2).$$

Show that the distance from the origin at which this tangent meets the line $y = x \tan t$ is independent of t.

11. (a) Prove that

(i) $\int_0^{\frac{1}{4}\pi} \dfrac{\cos x - \sin x}{\cos x + \sin x}\,dx = \frac{1}{2}\log 2;$ (ii) $\int_0^1 \dfrac{5x^2 - 1}{3x^4 + 10x^2 + 3}\,dx = 0.$

(b) If $0 < \alpha < \pi$, show that

$$\int_\alpha^{\pi-\alpha} \frac{x}{\sin x}\,dx = \int_\alpha^{-\alpha} \frac{\pi - x}{\sin x}\,dx$$

and deduce that $\displaystyle\int_{\pi/3}^{2\pi/3} \frac{x}{\sin x}\,dx = \frac{1}{2}\pi \log 3.$ (N.)

12. Find the centre and radius of the sphere

$$x^2 + y^2 + z^2 - 2x - 4y - 6z - 2 = 0.$$

Show that the intersection of this sphere and the plane $x + 2y + 2z - 20 = 0$ is a circle centre the point $(2, 4, 5)$ and find the radius of this circle.   (L.)

PAPER A (8)

1. Prove the theorem of Menelaus that, if a line meets the sides BC, CA, AB of a triangle in L, M, N, then

$$\frac{BL}{LC} \cdot \frac{CM}{MA} \cdot \frac{AN}{NB} = -1.$$

The mid-points of BC, CA, AB are D, E, F; a line meets EF, FD, DE in P, Q, R respectively and AP, BQ, CR meet BC, CA, AB in L, M, N. Prove that L, M, N are collinear.   (O.C.)

2. (i) By writing $y = x + \dfrac{1}{x}$, solve the equation

$$2x^4 - 9x^3 + 14x^2 - 9x + 2 = 0.$$

(ii) Factorise $b^2c + c^2a + a^2b - bc^2 - ca^2 - ab^2.$

3. If a, b, c are unequal and

$$\begin{vmatrix} 1 & bc + ax & a^2 \\ 1 & ca + bx & b^2 \\ 1 & ab + cx & c^2 \end{vmatrix} = 0,$$

prove that $x = a + b + c.$

4. Prove that the equation of the pair of straight lines joining the origin to the points of intersection of the circle $x^2 + y^2 + 2gx + 2fy = 0$ and the line $px + qy = r$ is

$$(2pg + r)x^2 + 2(pf + qg)xy + (2qf + r)y^2 = 0.$$

Hence obtain the equation of the line joining the two points of intersection, other than the origin, of the circle $x^2 + y^2 + 2x + 2y = 0$ and the line-pair $x^2 - 4xy + 2y^2 = 0.$ (C.)

5. Prove that, when n is an integer, $(\cos\theta + i\sin\theta)^n = \cos n\theta + i\sin n\theta.$

By writing $2\cos\theta = z + z^{-1}$, $2i\sin\theta = z - z^{-1}$, where $z = \cos\theta + i\sin\theta$, show that

$$2^6 \sin^5\theta \cos^2\theta = \sin 7\theta - 3\sin 5\theta + \sin 3\theta + 5\sin\theta.$$ (L.)

6. The roots of the equation $ax^3 - bx^2 + cx - d = 0$ are α, β, γ. Prove that the equation whose roots are $\beta^{-1} + \gamma^{-1}$, $\gamma^{-1} + \alpha^{-1}$, $\alpha^{-1} + \beta^{-1}$ is

$$d^2 y^3 - 2cd y^2 + (c^2 + bd)y + ad - bc = 0.$$

If $\dfrac{1}{\alpha} + \dfrac{1}{\gamma} = \dfrac{2}{\beta}$, prove that $2c^3 - 9bcd + 27ad^2 = 0$. (C.)

7. Prove that the equation of the normal to the parabola $y^2 = 4ax$ at the point $(at^2, 2at)$ is $y + tx = 2at + at^3$.

Hence prove that, if the normals at the points $(at_1^2, 2at_1)$, $(at_2^2, 2at_2)$, $(at_3^2, 2at_3)$ are concurrent, then $t_1 + t_2 + t_3 = 0$.

P, Q are variable points on the parabola such that PQ is parallel to the fixed line $x + ky = 0$. The normals to the curve at P, Q meet at R. Prove that the locus of R is the normal to the parabola at a fixed point and find the coordinates of this point. (O.C.)

8. Sum to n terms each of the series:

(i) $1^2 . 2 + 2^2 . 3 + 3^2 . 4 + 4^2 . 5 + \ldots$;

(ii) $1 + 3x + 5x^2 + 7x^3 + \ldots$

9. Prove that

(i) $\displaystyle\int_0^{\frac{1}{3}} \frac{(x+1)\,dx}{\sqrt{(4 - 9x^2)}} = \frac{1}{18}(\pi + 4 - 2\sqrt{3})$; (ii) $\displaystyle\int_1^e x^2 \log_e x \, dx = \frac{1}{9}(2e^3 + 1)$.

Evaluate $\displaystyle\int_0^{\frac{1}{2}\pi} \frac{dx}{2 + \cos x}$. (N.)

10. If $a > 0$, prove that

(i) $\displaystyle\int_1^a \frac{\log x}{\sqrt{x}}\,dx = 4 - 2(2 - \log a)\sqrt{a}$; $\displaystyle\int_1^a \frac{(\log x)^2}{x}\,dx = \frac{1}{3}(\log a)^3$.

Show that $(\log x)/\sqrt{x}$ has a maximum value when $x = e^2$.

The curve $y = (\log x)/\sqrt{x}$ meets the x-axis at A, and B is the foot of the maximum ordinate PB. Show that the distance from the x-axis of the centroid of the area bounded by AB, BP and the arc AP is $\frac{1}{3}$. (N.)

11. Prove that the pedal equation of the curve $r^2 = a^2 \cos 2\theta$ is $r^3 = a^2 p$.

Prove that the area of one loop of this curve is $\frac{1}{2}a^2$ and that the area of the surface formed by the rotation of this loop about the initial line is $(2 - \sqrt{2})\pi a^2$.

12. Find the equations of the straight line through the point $(-6, -4, -6)$ which cuts each of the straight lines $\frac{1}{2}x = y = \frac{1}{3}z$, $-x - 2 = \frac{1}{2}(y - 1) = -z - 1$ and the coordinates of the points in which it meets them.

PAPER A (9)

1. Prove that, if P, Q, R are points on the sides BC, CA, AB respectively of a triangle ABC and if $BP . CQ . AR = PC . QA . RB$, then AP, BQ and CR are concurrent.

AP, BQ, CR are medians of a triangle ABC. P' is the point on BC such that $\angle BAP' = \angle CAP$ and $\angle CAP' = \angle BAP$; Q', R' are points on CA, AB similarly defined. Prove that AP' BQ', CR' are concurrent. (C.)

2. (i) If the expression $ax^2 + 2bx + c$ can be written in the form $A(x - x_1)^2 + B(x - x_2)^2$, where A, B are independent of x, prove that $ax_1x_2 + b(x_1 + x_2) + c = 0$.

(ii) Find a and b if $x^2 + x + 1$ is a factor of

$$2x^6 - x^5 + ax^4 + x^3 + bx^2 - 4x - 3.$$

3. (a) Find the values of k for which the lines

$$2x + ky + 4 = 0, \quad 4x - y - 2k = 0, \quad 3x + y - 1 = 0$$

are concurrent.

(b) Show that

$$\begin{vmatrix} 1+a, & a+a^2, & a^2+1 \\ 1+b, & b+b^2, & b^2+1 \\ 1+c, & c+c^2, & c^2+1 \end{vmatrix} = k(b-c)(c-a)(a-b),$$

and find the value of the numerical constant k. (N.)

4. A system of coaxal circles is defined by one of the limiting points $(-1, 2)$ and the circle $x^2 + y^2 + 18x + 4y - 35 = 0$. Find the coordinates of the second limiting point.

Find also the equation of the other circle of the system which has the same radius as the given circle. (C.)

5. The roots of the equation $x^3 = qx + r$ are α, β, γ. Prove that:

(i) $\sum \alpha^2 = 2q$; (ii) $\sum \alpha^3 = 3r$;

(iii) $\alpha^5 = q\alpha^3 + r\alpha^2$; (iv) $6\sum \alpha^5 = 5\left(\sum \alpha^3\right)\left(\sum \alpha^2\right)$. (O.C).

6. Find the equation of the chord joining the points with parameters θ and ϕ on the ellipse $x^2/a^2 + y^2/b^2 = 1$.

If this chord is a tangent to the hyperbola $x^2/a^2 - y^2/b^2 = 1$, find the equation of the locus of the mid-point of the chord. (L.)

7. Find the sums of the first n terms of the series:

(i) $1^2 + 3^2 + 5^2 + \ldots + (2n - 1)^2$;

(ii) $1.2.3.4 + 2.3.4.5 + 3.4.5.6 + \ldots$

$$+ n(n+1)(n+2)(n+3);$$

(iii) $\sin \theta + \sin 3\theta + \sin 5\theta + \ldots + \sin (2n - 1)\theta$.

8. Prove that if $y = x - (1 - x^2)^{\frac{1}{2}} \sin^{-1} x$, then $(1 - x^2) \dfrac{dy}{dx} = x(x - y)$.

Use this result to evaluate $\dfrac{dy}{dx}, \dfrac{d^2y}{dx^2}, \dfrac{d^3y}{dx^3}$ at $x = 0$.

By means of Maclaurin's theorem show that, when x is small, $x - (1 - x^2)^{\frac{1}{2}} \sin^{-1} x$ is approximately equal to $\frac{1}{3}x^3$. (O.C.)

9. (a) Prove that $\displaystyle\int_0^1 \dfrac{(3x + 7)\, dx}{(x + 1)(x + 2)(x + 3)} = \log_e 2$.

(b) If $\quad A = \displaystyle\int_{-1}^1 \dfrac{x^2\, dx}{e^x + 1}, \qquad B = \displaystyle\int_{-1}^1 \dfrac{x^2 e^x\, dx}{e^x + 1}$,

show by putting $x = -u$ in A, that $A = B$.

Evaluate $A + B$ and deduce that $A = \frac{1}{3}$. (N.)

10. For the polar curve $r = f(\theta)$, prove that $\tan\phi = r\dfrac{d\theta}{dr}$, where ϕ is the angle between the radius vector and the tangent and obtain results for $\sin\phi$ and $\cos\phi$.

If P, P' are neighbouring points on a plane curve and PQ, $P'Q$ are drawn perpendicular to OP, OP', where O is the pole, show that, as $P' \to P$, the angle $POQ \to \frac{1}{2}\pi - \phi$ and the length $PQ \to \dfrac{dr}{d\theta}$.

11. Show that the equations of any line cutting both the lines $y - mx = 0 = z - c$, $y + mx = 0 = z + c$ can be expressed in the form

$$(mx + \lambda c)/\mu = -(y - \mu c)/\lambda = z.$$

12. A function z of two independent variables x and y is defined by the relationship

$$z = x + y + x\sqrt{(x + y)}.$$

If $V = \dfrac{\partial z}{\partial x} - \dfrac{\partial z}{\partial y}$, prove that $\dfrac{\partial V}{\partial x} = \dfrac{\partial V}{\partial y}$.

Express V as a function of x and z and prove that when V is expressed in terms of x and z:

(i) $x\dfrac{\partial V}{\partial z} - 2\dfrac{\partial V}{\partial x} = 1$; (ii) $\dfrac{\partial}{\partial x}\left(\dfrac{\partial V}{\partial x}\right) + z\dfrac{\partial}{\partial z}\left(\dfrac{\partial V}{\partial z}\right) = 0.$ (O.C.)

PAPER A (10)

1. Prove that, in any triangle ABC:

(i) $a\sin\frac{1}{2}B\sin\frac{1}{2}C = r\cos\frac{1}{2}A$; (ii) $\Delta = r^2\cot\frac{1}{2}A\cot\frac{1}{2}B\cot\frac{1}{2}C$,

where r is the radius of the incircle and Δ the area of the triangle.

In a triangle $r = 10$ cm, $A = 80°$, $B = 60°$. Calculate to three significant figures the length of the side a and the area of the triangle. (O.C.)

2. (i) If $a > 0$ and $b^2 < 4ac$, prove that $ax^2 + bx + c > 0$ for all real values of x.

(ii) Prove that $2x^2 + 4xy + 5y^2 + 3x + 6y + 4 > 0$ for all real values of x and y. (C.)

3. The line and circle whose equations are $x + h = 0$ and $x^2 + y^2 = a^2$ are denoted by L and S respectively. Prove that, if $h \neq 0$, the locus of a point whose distance from L is equal to the length of a tangent to S is a parabola. Prove also that if L does not meet S, then the parabola does not meet L or S; and that if L meets S at A and B, then the parabola touches S at A and B. (O.C.)

4. The complex number $z = x + iy$ is represented by $P(x, y)$ in the Argand diagram. If $(z - 1)/(z - i)$ is of the form iq, where q is real, prove that P must lie on the circle, centre $(\frac{1}{2}, \frac{1}{2})$, radius $1/\sqrt{2}$.

5. The cubic equation $x^3 + qx + r = 0$ has two roots each equal to α, express q and r in terms of α and prove that $4q^3 + 27r^2 = 0$.

Solve the equation $27x^3 - 36x - 16 = 0$.

6. By induction, or otherwise, prove the following results:

(i) $1^2 \cdot 2^2 + 2^2 \cdot 3^2 + 3^2 \cdot 4^2 + \ldots n$ terms
$$= \tfrac{1}{15}n(n+1)(n+2)(3n^2 + 6n + 1);$$

(ii) $\dfrac{1}{1 \cdot 3}2 + \dfrac{4}{2 \cdot 4}2^2 + \dfrac{7}{3 \cdot 5}2^3 + \ldots n$ terms $= \dfrac{3n+4}{(n+1)(n+2)}2^{n+1} - 4.$

7. P is the point $(a, 2a)$ on the parabola $y^2 = 4ax$. Find the equation of the normal to the parabola at P and verify that it passes through the point $(5a, -2a)$.

Prove that every chord of the parabola, other than this normal, which passes through $(5a, -2a)$ subtends a right angle at P. (L.)

8. (i) If $y = e^{\sin^2 x}$, prove that $\dfrac{dy}{dx} = y \sin 2x$; $\dfrac{d^2y}{dx^2} = \tfrac{1}{2}y(1 + 4 \cos 2x - \cos 4x)$.

Obtain the expansion of y by Maclaurin's theorem as far as the term in x^4.

(ii) By integrating term by term the expansion of $(1 + x^2)^{-1}$, $|x| < 1$, find the sum of the infinite series:
$$1 - \tfrac{1}{3} + \tfrac{1}{5} - \tfrac{1}{7} + \tfrac{1}{9} - \ldots$$

9. Integrate with respect to x, $\dfrac{x}{\sqrt{(2 + 2x - x^2)}}$.

Find the values of:

(i) $\displaystyle\int_0^\pi x^2 \sin x \, dx$; (ii) $\displaystyle\int_0^{\frac{1}{2}\pi} \dfrac{dx}{2 - \cos x}$.

10. If a, b, c are constants such that $b^2 \neq 4ac$, determine constants P, Q, R such that
$$\frac{d}{dx}\left(\frac{Px + Q}{ax^2 + bx + c}\right) = \frac{1}{(ax^2 + bx + c)^2} - \frac{R}{ax^2 + bx + c}.$$

Evaluate the integrals
$$\int_0^1 \frac{dx}{(x^2 + 4x + 1)^2} \quad \text{and} \quad \int_0^1 \frac{dx}{(x^2 + 4x + 4)^2}. \tag{N.}$$

11. Find the equations of the planes through the line $3x = 2y = 3z$ which make angles of $30°$ with the plane $z = 0$. If the axis of z is vertical, show that the lines of greatest slope in these planes make angles of $\tan^{-1}\tfrac{1}{4}$ with the given line.

12. In a tetrahedron $PQRS$, the edges PQ, RS are perpendicular to the faces PRS, PQS respectively; L is the mid-point of PS and M the mid-point of QR.

Prove that: (i) $PQ^2 + RS^2 = QR^2 - PS^2$; (ii) $PM = SM = \tfrac{1}{2}QR$;
(iii) $4LM^2 = PQ^2 + RS^2$. (O.C.)

PAPER A (11)

1. Prove that the feet of the perpendiculars from a point P on the circumcircle of a triangle to the sides of the triangle lie on a straight line— the Simson line of P.

If AD, BE, CF are the altitudes of triangle ABC and AD produced meets the circumcircle at Q, prove that the Simson line of Q is parallel to EF. (C.)

2. (i) Show that the equation $\sqrt{(x^2+2)} - \sqrt{(x^2+2x+5)} = 1$ has no solution if it is assumed that the square roots are positive.

(ii) Show that, if $x^3 + 3px + q = 0$ and $x = y - p/y$, then y^3 satisfies a certain quadratic equation. By solving this quadratic equation in the case $p = q = 2$, obtain one root of the equation

$$x^3 + 6x + 2 = 0. \qquad \text{(O.C.)}$$

3. (i) Evaluate　　　　　　　(ii) Solve for x the equation

$$\begin{vmatrix} 1 & -1 & -1 \\ -1 & 1 & -1 \\ -1 & -1 & 1 \end{vmatrix};$$

$$\begin{vmatrix} x+n & n+1 & n+2 & n+3 \\ n & x+n+1 & n+2 & n+3 \\ n & n+1 & x+n+2 & n+3 \\ n & n+1 & n+2 & x+n+3 \end{vmatrix} = 0.$$
　　　　　　　　　　　　　　　　　　　　　　　　　　　　　(C.)

4. The line $x \cos \alpha + y \sin \alpha = p$ meets the circle $x^2 + y^2 = a^2$ at the points P, Q. Prove that the equation of the circle S of which PQ is a diameter is

$$x^2 + y^2 - a^2 = 2p(x \cos \alpha + y \sin \alpha - p).$$

The line PQ varies in such a manner that S is always orthogonal to the fixed circle $x^2 + y^2 + 2fy + a^2 = 0$. Prove that the equation of the locus of the centre of S is $x^2 + y^2 + fy = 0$. 　　　　　(N.)

5. Mark on an Argand diagram a point P to represent a certain complex number z and put, in the same diagram, points Q, R to represent $z - 2$ and $1/z$ respectively.

Determine the locus of Q and R when P moves such that: (i) its modulus remains constant; (ii) its amplitude remains constant; (iii) its real part remains constant. 　　　　　(C.)

6. The coordinates of the mid-point of the line joining the points $(au^2, 2au)$, $(av^2, 2av)$ are (X, Y). Express $u + v$ and uv in terms of X and Y.

A variable chord of the parabola $y^2 = 4ax$ passes through the fixed point $(b, 0)$. Prove that the locus of the mid-point of the chord is a parabola and find the coordinates of its vertex and focus.

7. (i) Write down the nth term of the series

$$1 \cdot 2 + 2 \cdot 5 + 3 \cdot 8 + 4 \cdot 11 + \ldots$$

and prove that the sum of the first n terms is $n^2(n+1)$.

(ii) Numbers $A_1, A_2, A_3, \ldots$ are defined as follows:

$$A_1 = 2; \quad A_{n+1} = 2(A_1 + A_2 + \ldots + A_n), \text{ for } n = 1, 2, \ldots$$

Find A_2, A_3 and A_4 and prove that the numbers $A_2, A_3, A_4, \ldots$ form a G.P.
Find the sum of n terms of the series $A_1 + A_2 + A_3 + \ldots$
　　　　　　　　　　　　　　　　　　　　　　　　　　　　　(O.C.)

8. If $y = e^{2x} \sin 2x$, prove the results

$$\frac{dy}{dx} = 2\sqrt{2}\, e^{2x} \sin (2x + \tfrac{1}{4}\pi); \qquad \frac{d^n y}{dx^n} = (2\sqrt{2})^n e^{2x} \sin (2x + \tfrac{1}{4}n\pi).$$

Deduce that, if x^5 and higher powers are neglected in the Maclaurin expansion of y, then

$$y = 2x + 4x^2 + \tfrac{8}{3}x^3. \qquad \text{(O.C.)}$$

9. Integrate with respect to x: (a) $\dfrac{e^x}{1+e^x}$; (b) $\dfrac{\cos x}{1+\cos x}$.

Sketch the curve $y = \sec^{-1} x$ for $-\frac{1}{2}\pi < y < \frac{1}{2}\pi$ and show that the area bounded by this portion of the curve and the ordinate $x = 2$ is

$$\tfrac{4}{3}\pi - 2 \log (2 + \sqrt{3}). \tag{C.}$$

10. By using the method of integration by parts, show that, if n is a positive integer greater than 2,

$$\int_0^\infty \frac{\sinh^2 u}{\cosh^n u}\, du = \frac{1}{n-1} \int_0^\infty \frac{du}{\cosh^{n-2} u}.$$

Deduce that

$$\int_0^\infty \frac{du}{\cosh^n u} = \frac{n-2}{n-1} \int_0^\infty \frac{du}{\cosh^{n-2} u} \text{ and evaluate } \int_0^\infty \frac{du}{\cosh^5 u}. \tag{L.}$$

11. The normal to the curve $r^2 = a^2 \cos 2\theta$ at a point P meets the initial line at G. Prove that if r is the distance of P from the pole,

$$PG = a^2 r/(a^2 + 2r^2).$$

12. Find the coordinates of the centre of the circle which passes through the points $(-1, 0, 0)$, $(0, 2, 0)$, $(0, 0, 3)$.

PAPER A (12)

1. The inscribed circle of a triangle ABC touches BC, CA, AB at P, Q, R respectively. Express the angle RPQ in terms of the angles of the triangle ABC.

Prove that, if A is the area of triangle ABC, the area of triangle PQR is $4\Delta^3/abc(a+b+c)$. (N.)

2. (a) If $x + y = 4a$ and $x^3 + y^3 = 40a^3$, find the value of $x^2 + y^2$ and show that $x^4 + y^4 = 136a^4$.

(b) Solve the equation

$$\begin{vmatrix} x & 2a & a \\ a & x+a & a \\ 2a & 2a & x-a \end{vmatrix} = 0. \tag{N.}$$

3. Solve, if possible, the simultaneous equations,

$$2x - 5y + 8z = 1, \quad 3x + 2y - 6z = 12, \quad 7x - 8y + 10z = \lambda;$$

in the cases: (i) $\lambda = 14$; (ii) $\lambda = 12$.

Show that in one case the number of solutions is infinite and in this case give a general solution in which x, y, z are expressed in terms of a single parameter. (C.)

4. Prove that the equation $x^2 + 2hxy - y^2 = 0$ represents a pair of perpendicular lines through the origin O.

If A, B are the points in which these lines are cut by the line

$$x \cos \alpha + y \sin \alpha = p,$$

prove that the radius of the circumcircle of the triangle OAB is

$$p\sqrt{(1 + h^2)}/(\cos 2\alpha + h \sin 2\alpha). \tag{N.}$$

5. (i) If $2 < |z-1+2i| < 3$, show that the point representing the number z in the Argand diagram lies in a certain region of the plane and indicate this region.

(ii) The equation $x^3 + px^2 + qx + 6 = 0$, where p, q are real, has $1+i$ as one root. Find p and q and solve the equation completely. (C.)

6. Express $\dfrac{x^2 + 3x + 1}{x^2(x+1)^2}$ in partial fractions.

Prove that $\displaystyle\sum_{r=1}^{n} \frac{r^2 + 3r + 1}{r^2(r+1)^2} = \frac{n(2n+3)}{(n+1)^2}.$ (C.)

7. If $S=0$, $S'=0$ are the equations of two circles and k is a constant, what does the equation $S + kS' = 0$ represent?

A circle S and points O, A are given; a variable circle S' passes through O and is such that the radical axis of S and S' passes through A. Prove that the centre of S' lies on a fixed line perpendicular to OA. How are S, O, A related if this fixed line passes through the centre of S? (O.C.)

8. Interpret the equation $S + kLM = 0$, where $S = 0$ is the equation of a conic and $L = 0$, $M = 0$ are the equations of two lines while k is a constant.

The line $px + qy = 1$ meets the conic $ax^2 + 2hxy + by^2 + 2gx + 2fy + c = 0$ at A and B and from the origin O lines OA, OB are drawn to meet the conic again at C and D. Find the equation of the line pair OA, OB, and hence show that the equation of CD is

$$c(px + qy + 1) + 2(gx + fy) = 0. \quad \text{(O.C.)}$$

9. (i) Evaluate $\displaystyle\int_0^{\pi} \frac{d\theta}{5 - 4\cos\theta}.$

(ii) Prove that (i) $\displaystyle\int_0^3 \frac{dx}{(x+1)\sqrt{(2x^2 + 2x + 1)}} = \log_e 2;$

(ii) $\displaystyle\int_0^{\infty} e^{-x} \cos x \cos 3x \, dx = \frac{11}{85}.$ (L.)

10. Sketch the curve $r = a\cos^3 \frac{1}{3}\theta$ and show that its total length is $\frac{3}{2}\pi a$.

11. In a tetrahedron $ABCD$, AB is perpendicular to CD and AC is perpendicular to BD. Prove that AD is perpendicular to BC.

Through the orthocentre H of a triangle ABC is drawn the line HD perpendicular to the plane ABC. Prove that $ABCH$ is a tetrahedron in which each edge is perpendicular to the opposite edge.

12. (i) If $u = \dfrac{3xy - 2yz - zx}{x^2 + y^2}$, prove that $x\dfrac{\partial u}{\partial x} + y\dfrac{\partial u}{\partial y} + z\dfrac{\partial u}{\partial z} = 0.$

(ii) If $x^2 + 2y^2 - 3xyz = 0$ and $f(x, y, z) = x^4 y^3 z$, find the values of $\dfrac{\partial f}{\partial x}$ for $x = y = z = 1$ when the independent variables are: (a) x and y; (b) x and z.

PAPER S (1)

1. Given the incentre I of a triangle ABC and the excentres I_1, I_2 opposite A, B respectively, show how to construct the triangle ABC.

Show that: (i) $AI \cdot AI_1 = AB \cdot AC$; (ii) $AI_1 \cdot II_1 + BI_2 \cdot II_2 = I_1 I_2^2$. (N.)

2. (i) Find the range of values of λ for which

$$4\lambda x^2 + 4(\lambda + 1)x + 3\lambda + 3$$

is of invariable sign for real values of x.

(ii) Prove that for positive integral values of n,

$$1 + nx + \frac{n(n-1)}{2!} x(x-1) + \frac{n(n-1)(n-2)}{3!} x(x-1)^2 + \ldots$$
$$+ x(x-1)^{n-1} = 1 + x + x^2 + \ldots + x^n. \quad \text{(L.)}$$

3. (i) When a polynomial is divided either by $ax - b$ or $bx - a$, where $a \neq b$, the remainders are equal and the quotients are $Q_1(x)$ and $Q_2(x)$ respectively. Show that $ax - b$ is a factor of $Q_2(x)$ and that $x - 1$ is a factor of $Q_1(x) + Q_2(x)$.

(ii) Show that

$$\begin{vmatrix} 1 & a & a^2 \\ \cos x & \cos 2x & \cos 3x \\ \sin x & \sin 2x & \sin 3x \end{vmatrix} = (1 - 2a \cos x + a^2) \sin x.$$

$\qquad\qquad\qquad\qquad\qquad\qquad\qquad\qquad\qquad\qquad$ (N.)

4. The line $lx + my + n = 0$ divides the circle $x^2 + y^2 + 2gx + 2fy + c = 0$ into two arcs, one of which is three times as long as the other, prove that $2(lg + mf - n)^2 = (l^2 + m^2)(f^2 + g^2 - c)$.

5. State the general solution of the equation $\cos \theta = \cos \alpha$, where α is given, and obtain the general solution of the equation $\cos 4\theta = \sin 3\theta$ in the form $\theta = (4k + 1)\pi/14$, where k is an integer.

Express this equation as an equation in $\sin \theta$ and prove that

$$8 \sin \pi/14 \sin 3\pi/14 \sin 5\pi/14 = 1. \quad \text{(L.)}$$

6. Find the equation of the normal to the parabola $y^2 = 4ax$ at the point $(at^2, 2at)$.

The parameters of the points P, Q are t_1, t_2 respectively. Show that, if PQ passes through the point $(-2a, 0)$, then $t_1 t_2 = 2$ and the normals at P and Q meet at a point R on the parabola.

If O is the origin, show that the circumcircle of triangle PQR passes through O. (C.)

7. Write down the nth term of the series $\dfrac{1}{2 \cdot 4} + \dfrac{1 \cdot 3}{2 \cdot 4 \cdot 6} + \dfrac{1 \cdot 3 \cdot 5}{2 \cdot 4 \cdot 6 \cdot 8} + \ldots$

Prove that the sum of the first n terms is $\dfrac{1}{2} - \dfrac{1 \cdot 3 \cdot 5 \ldots (2n+1)}{2 \cdot 4 \cdot 6 \ldots (2n+2)}$. (L.)

8. Prove that, when $a > 0$,

(i) $\log_e (a + x) = \log_e a + \log_e (1 + x/a)$; (ii) $a^x = e^{x \log_e a}$.

Prove that the expansion of $a^x - 1 - x \log_e(a + x)$ as a power series in x, begins with a term in x^2 and find the coefficient of this term. (O.C.)

9. (i) Integrate $1/(x^2 - 6x + a)$, distinguishing between the cases when a is less than, equal to or greater than 9.

(ii) Use the substitution $x = \cos^2 \theta + 2 \sin^2 \theta$ to evaluate

$$\int_1^2 [(x-1)(2-x)]^{\frac{3}{2}} \, dx.$$

10. If the normal at any point P of a curve cuts the x-axis in G and if the length of the radius of curvature at P is twice PG, prove that $\dfrac{2p}{1+p^2}\dfrac{dp}{dy}=\dfrac{1}{y}$, where $p=\dfrac{dy}{dx}$.

Hence show that $p=(cy-1)^{\frac{1}{2}}$, where c is a constant and show further that the curve is a parabola with axis parallel to the y-axis. (N.)

11. Two planes make angles α, β with a horizontal plane and meet this plane in two perpendicular straight lines.

 (i) If θ is the inclination of the line of intersection of the two planes to the horizontal, prove that $\cot^2\theta=\cot^2\alpha+\cot^2\beta$.
 (ii) If ϕ is the angle between the normals to the two planes, prove that $\cos\phi=\cos\alpha\cos\beta$. (N.)

12. A sphere of radius R passes through the origin. Show that the ends of the diameter parallel to the x-axis lie on one of the spheres $x^2+y^2+z^2\pm2Rx=0$. (L.)

PAPER S (2)

1. From a point P on the circumcircle of a triangle ABC perpendiculars PL, PM are drawn to the sides AB, BC. The perpendicular from A to BC meets the circumcircle again at K and AK, LM meet at X. Show that the points P, M, K, X are concyclic.

2. Show that polynomials P, Q of the second degree can be found such that
$$\frac{1}{(x-1)^3(x+1)^3}\equiv\frac{P}{(x-1)^3}+\frac{Q}{(x+1)^3}.$$

Hence show that, if $f(x)=(x+1)^3P-(x-1)^3Q$, then $f(x)+1$ is divisible by $(x+1)^3$ and $f(x)-1$ is divisible by $(x-1)^3$.

Evaluate the coefficients in the polynomial $f(x)$. (O.C.)

3. Prove that
$$\begin{vmatrix}(b+c-a-d)^4, & (b+c-a-d)^2, & 1\\(c+a-b-d)^4, & (c+a-b-d)^2, & 1\\(a+b-c-d)^4, & (a+b-c-d)^2, & 1\end{vmatrix}=64(b-c)(c-a)(a-b)(a-d)(b-d)(c-d).$$
(C.)

4. A variable straight line intersects the line pair $ax^2+2hxy+by^2=0$ in P and Q; R is the mid-point of PQ. If PQ is of constant length $2l$, show that the equation of the locus of R is $(ax+hy)^2+(hx+by)^2=l^2(h^2-ab)$. (N.)

5. If P_1, P_2 are points in the complex plane representing the complex numbers z_1, z_2, give a geometrical construction for the point representing z_1-z_2.

The point representing the complex number z moves so that
$$\left|\frac{z-3-4i}{z-6-7i}\right|=\tfrac{1}{2}.$$

Prove that its locus is a circle. Find the radius of this circle and the complex number represented by its centre.

6. (*a*) Express $\dfrac{2k}{(2k-1)(2k+1)(2k+3)}$ as the sum of partial fractions and

prove the result

$$\sum_{k=1}^{k=n} \frac{2k}{(2k-1)(2k+1)(2k+3)} = \frac{n(n+1)}{(2n+1)(2n+3)}.$$

(*b*) Find the coefficient of x^3 in the expansion of $\dfrac{1}{(x-2)(2x+1)^2}$ in a

series of ascending powers of x. State the range of values of x for which
the expansion is valid. (N.)

7. Two points P_1, P_2 on the hyperbola whose parametric representation
is $x=t$, $y=t^{-1}$, have parameters t_1, t_2. The circle on P_1P_2 as diameter cuts
the hyperbola again at P_3, P_4; find the parameters of these points. Show
that the chord P_3P_4 is bisected by the origin and that one of the angles
subtended by it at the circumference of the circle is $2 \tan^{-1} \sqrt{(-t_1/t_2)}$. (N.)

8. State Leibnitz's theorem for the nth derivative of a product uv, where
u, v are functions of x.

If $y = \sin(m \sin^{-1} x)$, prove that

$$(1-x^2)y_{n+2} - (2n+1)xy_{n+1} + (m^2-n^2)y_n = 0$$

for $n \geqslant 0$, where y_n denotes $\dfrac{d^n y}{dx^n}$ for $n>0$ and $y_0=y$.

By use of Maclaurin's theorem, prove that, when $m=7$,

$$y = 7x - 56x^3 + 112x^5 - 64x^7 \ldots \tag{C.}$$

9. Evaluate: (i) $\displaystyle\int_0^1 \frac{x^2\,dx}{(1+x^2)^{\frac{3}{2}}}$; (ii) $\displaystyle\int_0^{\frac{1}{4}\pi} \tan^4 x\,dx$; (iii) $\displaystyle\int_1^2 \frac{dx}{x(x^3+1)}$. (N.)

10. Find the Cartesian equation of the curve $x=3t^2$, $y=t(3-t^2)$ and
sketch the curve.
Determine the equations of the two tangents to the curve at the point
$(9, 0)$ and show that the area of the loop of the curve is $72\sqrt{3}/5$.

11. (i) Show that the sphere

$$(x-a-p)(x-a)+(y-b-q)(y-b)+(z-c-r)(z-c)=R^2$$

meets the sphere $(x-a)^2+(y-b)^2+(z-c)^2 = R^2$ along a great circle
of the second sphere.

(ii) Find the equation of the sphere of minimum radius which belongs
to the system
$$S_1 + \lambda S_2 = 0,$$
where $\qquad S_1 \equiv x^2+y^2+z^2+2x-2y+4z+2;$
$$S_2 \equiv x^2+y^2+z^2+4x+2y-4z. \tag{L.}$$

12. Variables u, v are defined by the equations
$$u = x \sin x \cosh y - y \cos x \sinh y,$$
$$v = y \sin x \cosh y + x \cos x \sinh y.$$

Write down the values of $\dfrac{\partial u}{\partial x}, \dfrac{\partial v}{\partial y}, \dfrac{\partial u}{\partial y}, \dfrac{\partial v}{\partial x}$.

Prove that: (i) $2\dfrac{\partial}{\partial x}(uv) = \dfrac{\partial}{\partial y}(v^2-u^2)$; (ii) $\dfrac{\partial^2 u}{\partial x^2}+\dfrac{\partial^2 u}{\partial y^2} = \dfrac{\partial^2 v}{\partial x^2}+\dfrac{\partial^2 v}{\partial y^2}=0.$ (O.C.)

PAPER S (3)

1. If D is any point on the side BC of the triangle ABC, prove that the distance between the circumcentres of the triangles ADB, ADC is $\frac{1}{2}BC$ cosec $\angle ADB$.

2. If a, b, c are unequal numbers and $a^2 - bc = b^2 - ca = k$, prove that: (i) $a^2 + b^2 + c^2 = 2k$, (ii) $a^3 + b^3 + c^3 = 3abc$.

3. (a) Discuss the values of a and b for which the pair of equations in x, y,

$$5x + (3a + b)y = 6a + 2, \quad 2x + (a + b)y = a + 5b,$$

have: (i) an infinite number of solutions; (ii) no finite solution; (iii) one solution.

(b) If $f(z) \equiv Az^4 + Bz^3 + Cz^2$, find values of the constants A, B, C such that

$$f\{x(x + 1)\} - f\{x(x - 1)\} \equiv x^7.$$

Deduce the sum of the series $1^7 + 2^7 + 3^7 + \ldots + n^7$.   (L.)

4. Prove that if α is a root of the equation $x^3 - 3x + 1 = 0$, then a second root is $\alpha^2 - 2$. What is the value of the third root?

5. Prove that the value of the determinant

$$\begin{vmatrix} x & a & b & c \\ a & x & c & b \\ b & c & x & a \\ c & b & a & x \end{vmatrix}$$

is unaltered when any two of the letters a, b, c are reversed in sign. Prove also that $x + a + b + c$ is a factor and determine all the linear factors.   (C.)

6. A point moves such that the sum of the squares of its distances from two fixed points is constant. Show that it describes a circle.

S_1, S_2 are two fixed circles. A variable circle S cuts S_1 orthogonally and meets S_2 in points which are the ends of a diameter of S. Show that the locus of the centre of S is a circle.

7. Find the equation of the chord of the parabola $y^2 = 4ax$ which is bisected at the point (h, k).

Find the locus of the mid-points of chords of this parabola which touch the curve $(2ma - ly)^2 = 8la(xl - 1)$.   (L.)

8. Prove that:

(i) $\displaystyle\sum_{r=1}^{n} \frac{2r + 1}{r(r + 1)(r + 2)} = \frac{n(5n + 7)}{4(n + 1)(n + 2)}$;

(ii) $\displaystyle\sum_{r=0}^{n} {}_nC_r \cos(\alpha + 2r\theta) = (2 \cos \theta)^n \cos(\alpha + n\theta)$.

9. Evaluate: (i) $\displaystyle\int_{0}^{\frac{1}{2}\pi} \frac{\tan \theta \, d\theta}{1 + \tan \theta}$; (ii) $\displaystyle\int x \sin^{-1}x \, dx$; (iii) $\displaystyle\int \sin^6 \theta \cos^3 \theta \, d\theta$.

10. If $u_n = \displaystyle\int_{0}^{2} \frac{x^n \, dx}{x^3 + 1}$, evaluate $u_0 + u_1$, $u_0 - u_1 + u_2$ and u_2.

Hence obtain the values of u_0 and u_1.

Show also that if n is a positive integer, $u_{n+2} = \dfrac{2^n}{n} - u_{n-1}$ and deduce the values of u_3, u_4 and u_5.   (N.)

11. If $b^2r^2 \cos^2 \theta + a^2r^2 \sin^2 \theta = a^2b^2$, obtain the indefinite integral $\frac{1}{2}\int r^2\, d\theta$ in the form $\frac{1}{2}ab \tan^{-1} (a \tan \theta/b)$.

Two equal ellipses of eccentricity e have the same centre O and can be obtained each from the other by rotation through $90°$ about O. If the area common to the two ellipses is one-half the area of either, prove that $e^2 = 2(\sqrt{2} - 1)$.

12. Three concurrent edges of a cube are OA, OB, OC. A plane equally inclined to these edges intersects them, produced if necessary, in the points X, Y, Z and cuts the cube in a section of area S. If $OA = OB = OC = a$; $OX = OY = OZ = x$, show that

$$S = \tfrac{1}{2}\sqrt{3}x^2,\ 0 < x < a; \quad S = \tfrac{1}{2}\sqrt{3}(6ax - 2x^2 - 3a^2),\ a < x < 2a;$$
$$S = \tfrac{1}{2}\sqrt{3}(3a - x)^2,\ 2a < x < 3a. \quad \text{(N.)}$$

PAPER S (4)

1. In a triangle ABC, I is the incentre and O the circumcentre. With the usual notation, show that: (i) $AI = 4R \sin \frac{1}{2}B \sin \frac{1}{2}C$; (ii) $\angle IAO = \pm\frac{1}{2}(B - C)$.

Deduce the result, $16\, IO^2 = (a + b - 2c)^2 \sec^2 \frac{1}{2}C + (a - b)^2 \csc^2 \frac{1}{2}C$.

2. Prove that if $f(x)$ is a polynomial in x and a is a number such that $f(a) = 0$, then $x - a$ is a factor of $f(x)$.

Hence show that if $f(x)$ has degree $n > 0$, then the equation $f(x) = 0$ has at most n distinct roots; and that $f(x)$ cannot assume the same value for more than n values of x. (L.)

3. Prove that the line $ax + by + c = 0$ forms with the two lines

$$(ax + by)^2 = 3(ay - bx)^2$$

an equilateral triangle.

Find the equation of the bisectors of the angles between the lines represented by the latter equation. (C.)

4. (i) Find the equation whose roots are the cubes of the roots of $x^3 + a(x^2 + x + 1) = 0$.

(ii) Find the values of a such that there is a pair of roots of the given equation whose product is the square of the third root.

5. If $w = u + iv$, $z = x + iy$ are complex numbers connected by the relationship $w(z + 1) = z - 1$, find the loci described in the Argand diagram by the point representing w when the point representing z describes: (i) the line $x = 0$; (ii) the circle $|z + 1| = 1$.

6. If $|x| < 1$, find the coefficient of x^n in the expansion in ascending powers of x of $(a + bx + cx^2)/(1 - x)^3$. Determine a, b and c so that this expansion reduces to $\sum\limits_{n=1}^{\infty} n^2 x^n$ and show that $\sum\limits_{n=1}^{\infty} n^2/2^n = 6$. (N.)

7. The centre of each circle belonging to a family of circles is on the line $y = mx + c\,(c \neq 0)$ and the length of the tangent from the origin to each circle of the family is l. Find the equation of the family of circles.

Show that the polars of the origin with respect to these circles are concurrent. (L.)

A A

8. Find the equation of the tangent to the curve $xy = 1$ at the point $(t, 1/t)$ and the equation of the normal to the curve $27y^2 = 4x^3$ at the point $(3u^2, 2u^3)$. Show that just one tangent to the first curve, other than an asymptote, is also a normal of the second. (L.)

9. Evaluate the integrals:

(i) $\int \dfrac{\log x\, dx}{(1+x)^2}$; (ii) $\int_1^2 (x-1)(2-x)^{\frac{1}{2}}\, dx$; (iii) $\int_0^{\frac{1}{2}\pi} \dfrac{d\theta}{\sin^2\theta + 4\cos^2\theta}$.

10. Sketch the curve $x = a\cos^3 t$, $y = a\sin^3 t$ $(0 \leqslant t \leqslant 2\pi)$.
Calculate: (i) the area enclosed by the curve; (ii) the volume of the solid of revolution obtained when this area is rotated about the axis of x. (N.)

11. A plane cuts a sphere of radius R in a circle of radius r. A second plane at right angles to the first also cuts the sphere in a circle of radius r. The line of intersection of the two planes meets the sphere in the points A, B. Prove that if $4r^2 = 3R^2$, then the sphere described on AB as diameter passes through the centre of the original sphere.

12. If f is a function of u where $u = (x^2 + y^2)\tan^{-1} y/x$, prove that

$$x\,\frac{\partial f}{\partial y} - y\,\frac{\partial f}{\partial x} = (x^2 + y^2)\frac{df}{du}.$$

PAPER S (5)

1. Prove that the circle through the mid-points of the sides of a triangle passes through the feet of the perpendiculars drawn from the vertices to the opposite sides.
AD, BE, CF are the altitudes of a triangle ABC and M is the mid-point of AB. The circle on MD as diameter cuts DE in H and DF in K. Prove that HK is perpendicular to AB. (L.)

2. (a) Find the range of values of x for which $|(x-3)/(x+1)| < 2$.
(b) If x, y, z are positive, show that
$$2(x^3 + y^3) \geqslant (x^2 + y^2)(x + y)$$
and $\qquad 3(x^3 + y^3 + z^3) \geqslant (x^2 + y^2 + z^2)(x + y + z)$. (N.)

3. Solve the equations $x - y + z = 1$, $2x - y + 3z = 4$, $4x - 3y + (5 - a)z = 6$, when: (i) $a \neq 0$; (ii) $a = 0$.

4. If α, β, γ are the roots of the equation $x^3 + px + q = 0$, find the equation whose roots are $\alpha^2 + \beta\gamma$, $\beta^2 + \gamma\alpha$, $\gamma^2 + \alpha\beta$.

5. Show that the circles represented by the equation $x^2 + y^2 + 2\lambda x + c = 0$, where λ is a parameter and c is a positive constant, form a coaxal system with real limiting points.
If $c > 1$, find the equation of the ellipse with foci at the limiting points of the system and with eccentricity $1/\sqrt{c}$. A diameter of this ellipse touches the circle with parameter λ_1, and the conjugate diameter touches the circle with parameter λ_2; prove that $(\lambda_1^2 - c)(\lambda_2^2 - c) = (c - 1)^2$. (L.)

6. Sketch roughly the curves $S_1 \equiv 4(x-1)^2 + y^2 - 4 = 0$, $S_2 \equiv y^2 - 4ax = 0$, $0 < a < 2$, marking clearly their points of intersection.

What curves are represented by the equation $S_1 + \lambda S_2 = 0$, where λ is a real parameter?

Find the rectangular hyperbola of this system and sketch it in the cases $0 < a < \frac{2}{5}$ and $\frac{2}{5} < a < 2$. (L.)

7. If $(1+x)^n = c_0 + c_1 x + c_2 x^2 + \ldots + c_n x^n$, show that

$$c_r^2 > c_{r+1} c_{r-1} \quad (0 < r \leqslant n-1).$$

If for some r, $c_r^2 = 2c_{r+1} c_{r-1}$, show that $n = 5$.

8. (a) Evaluate $\displaystyle\int_0^1 \sqrt{(2x - x^2)} \, dx$.

(b) If $y = (x+1)^a (x-1)^b$, where a, b are constants, prove that

$$\frac{d^n y}{dx^n} = (x+1)^{a-n} (x-1)^{b-n} f_n(x), \tag{N.}$$

where $f_n(x)$ is a polynomial in x of degree not greater than n.

9. If $C_n = \displaystyle\int_0^x t^n \cos t \, dt$, $S_n = \displaystyle\int_0^x t^n \sin t \, dt$, where n is a positive integer, prove that: (i) $C_n + nS_{n-1} = x^n \sin x$; (ii) $S_n - nC_{n-1} = -x^n \cos x$.

Show that $\displaystyle\int_0^\pi x^4 \sin x \, dx = \pi^4 - 12\pi^2 + 48$.

10. Prove the formula $\tan \phi = r \, d\theta / dr$.

Show that for the curve $r^2 = a^2 \sin 2\theta$ we have $\phi = 2\theta$, and sketch the curve. Two points P and Q on the loop of the curve in the first quadrant are such that the tangent at P is parallel to OQ and the tangent at Q parallel to OP. Show that the area of the triangle OPQ is $\frac{1}{4}a^2$ and that the chord PQ divides the area of the loop in the ratio $(1 + 2\sqrt{2}) : 1$.

11. The ends of a straight line lie on two fixed planes which are at right angles to one another, and the straight line subtends a right angle at each of two given points. Show that the locus of the mid-point of the straight line is a plane.

12. (i) If $x^3 + y^3 = 3xy$, find $\dfrac{d^2 y}{dx^2}$.

(ii) If $(x/a)^n + (y/b)^n + (z/c)^n = 1$, find $\dfrac{\partial z}{\partial x}$.

PAPER S (6)

1. (i) If H is the orthocentre of the triangle ABC, show that

$$HA^2 + BC^2 = HB^2 + CA^2 = HC^2 + AB^2.$$

(ii) If P is a point in the plane of a triangle ABC such that $PA^2 + BC^2 = PB^2 + CA^2$, prove that CP is perpendicular to AB. (L.)

2. Find the range of values of c for which the function $(x^2 - 1)/\{(x-3)(x+c)\}$ assumes all real values for real values of x.

Find the possible values of the function if $c = 3$.   (L.)

3. If $x + y + z = 0$ and none of the numbers x, y, z is zero, and if

$$a = \frac{y}{z} + \frac{z}{y}, \quad b = \frac{z}{x} + \frac{x}{z}, \quad c = \frac{x}{y} + \frac{y}{x},$$

prove that: (i) $a + b + c = -3$;   (ii) $abc = a^2 + b^2 + c^2 - 4 = 5 - 2(bc + ca + ab)$.
                                                                                       (N.)

4. Prove that

$$\begin{vmatrix} 1, & x, & x^2, & x^3 + yxt \\ 1, & y, & y^2, & y^3 + ztx \\ 1, & z, & z^2, & z^3 + txy \\ 1, & t, & t^2, & t^3 + xyz \end{vmatrix} = 0.$$
                                                                                       (C.)

5. If the line $x + 2y = 5$ meets the lines $x^2 + 3xy + y^2 = 0$ in L, M, find the equation of the circle on LM as diameter. If the equation of this circle is written $S = 0$, and it meets the lines $x^2 + 3xy + y^2 = 0$ again in P and Q, find, by considering the equation $S + \lambda(x^2 + 3xy + y^2) = 0$, or otherwise, the equation of PQ.

6. Find the three roots of the equation $8x^3 = (2 - x)^3$, expressing each in the form $a + ib$.

7. Show that, in general, a circle cuts a parabola in four points. If these points are A, B, C, D, show that the lines AB, CD are equally inclined to the axis of the parabola.

Deduce that if a circle touches a parabola at P and cuts it at Q, R and if U, V are points on the circle such that QU and RV are parallel to the axis of the parabola, then UV is parallel to the tangent at P.   (L.)

8. Show that the sum of the first n terms of the series

$$\cos a + \cos (a + 2b) + \cos (a + 4b) + \ldots$$

is $\cos [a + (n - 1)b] \sin nb \operatorname{cosec} b$.

Hence, or otherwise, find the sum of the first n terms of the series

$$\cos^2 \theta \cos \theta + \cos^2 2\theta \cos 3\theta + \cos^2 3\theta \cos 5\theta + \ldots$$

9. If $y = x^2 \sin x$, prove by induction that

$$\frac{d^{2n}y}{dx^{2n}} = (-1)^n \{x^2 \sin x - 4xn \cos x - 2n(2n - 1) \sin x\}.$$

Deduce the $2n$th derivative of $x^2 \sin 2x$.   (L.)

10. Prove that $\displaystyle\int_0^\pi \frac{1 - a \cos \theta}{1 - 2a \cos \theta + a^2} \, d\theta = \pi$ or 0 according as $|a| <$ or > 1.
                                                                                       (N.)

11. The groove in a rope pulley has a parabolic cross-section with the axis of the parabola perpendicular to that of the pulley. The outside diameter of the pulley is 24 cm, the depth of the groove 2 cm and the width of the groove at the outer diameter 3 cm. Determine the volume of metal removed to form the groove leaving your answer as a multiple of π.

12. In a tetrahedron $ABCD$ the lengths AB, AC, AD are equal and the angles CAD, DAB, BAC are right angles. The foot of the perpendicular from A to the plane BCD is P. Prove that the distance of P from each of the lines AB, AC, AD is the same and equal to two-thirds of the distance of A from each of the lines CD, DB, BC.

PAPER S (7)

1. If I_1, I_2, I_3 are the excentres of a triangle ABC, prove that:

    (i) $I_1I_2 = c \operatorname{cosec} \frac{1}{2}C$;

    (ii) $I_2I_3 : I_3I_1 : I_1I_2 = \cos \frac{1}{2}A : \cos \frac{1}{2}B : \cos \frac{1}{2}C$;

    (iii) the radius of the circle $I_1I_2I_3 = 2R$.   (L.)

2. Solve the equations:

    (i) $(x^2 + 1)(y^2 + 1) = 250$, $x + y = 5$;

    (ii) $x^6 - 3x^5 - 2x^4 + 7x^3 + 2x^2 - 3x = 1$.

3. (i) If v and w are real numbers, prove that $v^2 + w^2 \geqslant \frac{1}{2}(v + w)^2$.

    (ii) If u, v, w are positive numbers satisfying the relationships

$$u + v + w = 3, \quad u^2 + v^2 + w^2 = 6,$$

show that $\qquad u \leqslant 1 + \sqrt{2}$.

4. Prove that abc is a factor of

$$\begin{vmatrix} (b+c)^2 & a^2 & a^2 \\ b^2 & (c+a)^2 & b^2 \\ c^2 & c^2 & (a+b)^2 \end{vmatrix},$$

and show that the value of the determinant is $2abc(a + b + c)^3$.

5. By means of De Moivre's theorem, express $\sin 8\theta / \sin \theta \cos \theta$ as a polynomial in X, where $X = 4 \sin^2 \theta$.

Hence, or otherwise, solve the equation $x^6 - 6x^4 + 10x^2 - 4 = 0$.

6. (a) Find the equations of the two circles which pass through the point (2, 1) and touch both the coordinate axes. What is the other point of intersection of the circles?

    (b) Find the radii of the two circles which touch the x-axis and pass through both the points (1, 3) and (2, 4).   (N.)

7. The point (h, k) lies on the curve $x^2 - y^2 = a^2$. Show that the chord of the curve $xy = c^2$ which is bisected by the point (h, k) is normal to the curve $x^2 - y^2 = a^2$.

8. If $x > 1$, prove that

$$x^2 - 1 > 2x \log_e x > 4(x - 1) - 2 \log_e x. \qquad \text{(C.)}$$

9. Prove that $\displaystyle\int_0^\pi f(\theta)\, d\theta = \int_0^\pi f(\pi - \theta)\, d\theta.$

Evaluate: (i) $\displaystyle\int_0^\pi (\cos \theta + \cos^3 \theta + \cos^5 \theta)\, d\theta$;   (ii) $\displaystyle\int_0^\pi \frac{\theta}{1 + \sin \theta}\, d\theta.$ (L.)

10. If $I_{m,\,n} = \int_0^\pi x^m \sin^n x\ dx$, prove that

$$n^2 I_{m,\,n} = n(n-1)I_{m,\,n-2} - m(m-1)I_{m-2,\,n}.$$

Calculate $I_{4,\,2}$. (O.C.)

11. A circular disc has radius a and O is a point on its circumference; at any point P of the disc the surface density is μOP. Find: (i) the mass; (ii) the position of the centre of gravity of the disc.

12. AB is the shortest distance between two skew lines AC, BD and the distances AC, BD are equal. Prove that the line joining the mid-points of AB and CD cuts both these lines at right angles.

PAPER S (8)

1. The altitudes of the triangle ABC meet the circumcircle again in L, M, N. Prove that the triangle formed by the Simson lines of L, M, N with respect to the triangle ABC has its sides parallel and equal to those of triangle LMN.

2. (i) If the roots of $ax^2 + bx + c = 0$ $(a>0)$ are α and β, show that for sufficiently small values of x

$$\log_e (a - bx + cx^2) = \log_e a - \sum_{n=1}^\infty \frac{(-x)^n}{n}(\alpha^n + \beta^n).$$

(ii) Find the sum of all the products, two at a time, of the odd numbers in the first $2n$ natural numbers, no product to consist of repeated numbers. (L.)

3. If $x+y+z=0$, $(a-b)x+ay+(a+b)z=0$, $(a-b)^2x+a^2y+(a+b)^2z=0$ and x, y, z are not all zero, prove that $b=0$.

4. (i) Show that the equation of the tangents from the origin to the circle $x^2+y^2+2gx+2fy+c=0$ is $(gx+fy)^2=c(x^2+y^2)$.

(ii) Prove that the radical axes of a given circle with each circle of a coaxal system are concurrent.

5. (i) Find the square roots of $16+30i$.

(ii) If $z=x+iy$ and the point (x, y) represented by the complex number z moves round a circle with centre the origin and radius 1, what is the locus of the point which represents $2+iz$?

6. Express $x^2+y^2+z^2$ and $x^3+y^3+z^3$ in terms of $x+y+z$, $yz+zx+xy$ and xyz.

Hence solve the equations $x+y+z=2$, $x^2+y^2+z^2=26$, $x^3+y^3+z^3=38$. (O.C.)

7. Show that, if the normals at P_1, P_2, P_3 to the parabola $y^2=4ax$ meet at a point, then G the centroid of the triangle $P_1P_2P_3$ is on the axis of the parabola.

Show further that, if P_1P_2 passes through the focus, the abscissa of P_3 is equal to $\frac{3}{2}OG - a$, where O is the origin. (N.)

8. If r is a positive integer and $S_r = 1^r + 2^r + \ldots + n^r$, show, by considering the expression $(1 + x)^{r+1} - x^{r+1}$, or otherwise, that

$$\frac{(n+1)^{r+1} - (n+1)}{(r+1)!} = \frac{S_1}{r! \, 1!} + \frac{S_2}{(r-1)! \, 2!} + \cdots + \frac{S_r}{1! \, r!}.$$

9. If $y = (1 + x^2)^{\frac{1}{2}} \log_e \{(x + \sqrt{(1 + x^2)}\}$, prove that $(1 + x^2)\dfrac{dy}{dx} = xy + 1 + x^2$.

Assuming y can be expanded in the form $\displaystyle\sum_{0}^{\infty} a_n x^n$, show that

$$a_0 = a_2 = a_4 = \ldots = a_{2n} = 0.$$

Find the values of a_1 and a_3 and show that, if $n > 1$,

$$a_{2n+1} = (-1)^{n-1} \frac{2 \cdot 4 \cdot 6 \ldots 2n-2}{3 \cdot 5 \cdot 7 \ldots 2n-1} \cdot \frac{1}{2n+1}. \tag{L.}$$

10. (i) Express $\dfrac{3x^4 + 12x + 8}{(x+1)^5}$ in partial fractions.

(ii) Evaluate $\displaystyle\int_0^2 \frac{x(x+1)}{(x-4)(x^2+4)} \, dx$.

11. The coordinates (x, y) of a point on a closed curve are expressed in terms of a parameter t. Show that the area enclosed by the curve is given by the integral $\frac{1}{2}\displaystyle\int\left(x \frac{dy}{dt} - y \frac{dx}{dt}\right) dt$ taken between suitable limits.
Prove that the area of the curve $x = \cos t - 3 \sin t$, $y = 2 \cos t + \sin t$ is 7π.

12. The functions u, v are defined in terms of the variables x, y by the equations $x = u + v + uv$, $y = u^2 + v^2$.
Prove that $\dfrac{\partial u}{\partial x} = \dfrac{v}{(v-u)(v+u+1)}$ and obtain expressions for $\dfrac{\partial u}{\partial y}, \dfrac{\partial v}{\partial x}, \dfrac{\partial v}{\partial y}$.

Show also that $\dfrac{\partial u}{\partial x}\dfrac{\partial v}{\partial y} - \dfrac{\partial v}{\partial x}\dfrac{\partial u}{\partial y} = \dfrac{1}{2(v-u)(v+u+1)}.$ (O.C.)

PAPER S (9)

1. AD, BE, CF are the medians of a triangle ABC and FE is produced to H so that $FE = EH$. Prove that $DH = BE$, that $AH = FC$ and that E is the centroid of triangle ADH.

Hence, or otherwise, show that the area of a triangle whose sides are equal to the medians of triangle ABC is three-quarters of the area of the latter triangle.

2. The bisectors of the angles A, B, C of a triangle ABC meet the opposite sides in X, Y, Z respectively. Prove that the ratio of the area of triangle XYZ to the area of triangle ABC is $2abc : (b+c)(c+a)(a+b)$, where a, b, c are the lengths of the sides of the triangle ABC.

3. (i) Find a quartic polynomial in x, with integral coefficients, which vanishes when $x = \sqrt{2} + \sqrt{3}$. For what other values of x does the polynomial vanish?

(ii) The remainder on dividing a cubic polynomial in x by $x^2 + 1$ is $x + 1$, and the remainder on dividing the cubic by $x + 2$ is 4. The sum of the coefficients of x, x^2, x^3 is 10. Find the polynomial. (L.)

4. Prove that

$$\begin{vmatrix} x & a & a & a \\ b & y & b & b \\ c & c & z & c \\ d & d & d & t \end{vmatrix} = (x-a)(y-b)(z-c)(t-d)\left\{1 + \frac{a}{x-a} + \frac{b}{y-b} + \frac{c}{z-c} + \frac{d}{t-d}\right\}.$$ (C.)

5. A circle of given radius moves so that the radical axis of the moving circle and a fixed circle always passes through a fixed point. Show that the locus of the centre of the moving circle is a circle with centre at the fixed point.

6. Show that, if n is not a multiple of 3, $x^{2n} + 1 + (x-1)^{2n}$ is divisible by $x^2 - x + 1$.

7. A rectangular hyperbola is cut by a circle in four points. Prove that the sum of the squares of the distances of these four points from the centre of the hyperbola is equal to the square of the diameter of the circle. (L.)

8. Evaluate: (i) $\int \frac{\sin^2 x}{1 + \cos^2 x}\, dx$; (ii) $\int_0^a \frac{x^{\frac{3}{2}}}{(a-x)^{\frac{1}{2}}}\, dx$.

9. Sketch the curve $r^2 = a^2 \cos 2\theta$ and find the area of a loop.

Show that ψ, the angle between the tangent to the curve and the initial line or axis of x, is given by $\psi = 3\theta + \frac{1}{2}\pi$ and determine the values of θ for which the tangent is parallel to the initial line. Verify these values by using the Cartesian equation of the curve.

10. If ρ is the radius of curvature at the point P of the ellipse $x^2/a^2 + y^2/b^2 = 1$ $(a > b)$, prove that $\rho = (b^2/a) \sec^3 \phi$, where ϕ is half the angle between the lines joining P to the foci of the ellipse. (N.)

11. Find the condition that the sphere $x^2 + y^2 + z^2 + 2ux + 2vy + 2wz + d = 0$ may touch the plane $lx + my + nz = p$.

Find the equations of the two spheres which pass through the points in which the plane $x + y + z = 1$ cuts the axes and also touches the plane $2x + y + 2z = 3$. (L.)

12. The area of a triangle ABC is calculated from the measured values a, b of the sides BC, CA and the measured value $90°$ of the angle C. It is found that the calculated area is too small by a small error z and that the true lengths of the sides are $a - x$, $b - y$, where x and y are small. Show that the error in the angle C is approximately $\dfrac{180}{\pi}\sqrt{\left(\dfrac{2z + ay + bx}{\frac{1}{2}ab}\right)}$ degrees.

PAPER S (10)

1. Prove that, if P be any point on the circumcircle of a triangle ABC and PQ be drawn parallel to BC to meet the circumcircle again in Q, then QA is perpendicular to the Simson line of P with respect to the circle.

2. P is a fixed point within a circle, centre O; AB is any chord parallel to OP. Prove that $AP^2 + BP^2 =$ constant.

3. If $f(x)$ is a polynomial in x and α is a root of $f(x) = 0$ and of $f'(x) = 0$, show that α is a multiple root of $f(x) = 0$.

Hence, or otherwise, solve the equation $4x^4 - 12x^3 + x^2 + 12x + 4 = 0$.

4. Find a formula for the area of a triangle with vertices $(0, 0)$, (x_1, y_1), (x_2, y_2).

The sides BC, CA, AB of a triangle are divided in the same ratio $k : 1$ by points P, Q, R. Show that the triangles ABC, PQR have the same centroid and that their areas are connected by the result

$$\triangle PQR : \triangle ABC = (k^2 - k + 1) : (k + 1)^2.$$

5. P represents the complex number $z = x + iy$ in the Argand diagram. Illustrate the positions of the points P_1, P_2 which represent $\dfrac{1}{z}$ and $-\dfrac{1}{z}$, where $\bar{z} = x - iy$.

Show that for all real values of t, $|z - it| + |1/z - it| \geqslant PP_2$.

6. Find the sums to n terms of the series:

(i) $\dfrac{1}{x} + \dfrac{2}{x^2} + \dfrac{3}{x^3} + \ldots + \dfrac{n}{x^n}$;

(ii) $a \cos 0 - a^2 \cos 2\theta + a^3 \cos 3\theta + \ldots + (-1)^{n-1} a^n \cos n\theta$;

(iii) $\dfrac{1}{1 \cdot 2 \cdot 3} + \dfrac{1}{2 \cdot 3 \cdot 4} + \dfrac{1}{3 \cdot 4 \cdot 5} + \ldots + \dfrac{1}{n(n+1)(n+2)}$.

7. Prove that $\lim\limits_{x \to 0} \dfrac{\cos (\sin x) + \sin (1 - \cos x) - 1}{x^4} = \frac{1}{6}$.

8. Prove that the equation of the chord of the ellipse $x^2/a^2 + y^2/b^2 = 1$ whose mid-point is (h, k) is $(x - h)h/a^2 + (y - k)k/b^2 = 0$.

A variable chord PQ of the ellipse passes through the fixed point K (α, β), inside the ellipse. Find the locus of the centroid of the triangle OPQ, where O is the centre of the ellipse. (C.)

9. Prove that $\displaystyle\int_0^a f(x)\, dx = \int_0^a f(a - x)\, dx$, and hence show that if $(a - x) = f(x)$, then $\displaystyle\int_0^a x\, f(x)\, dx = \frac{1}{2}a \int_0^a f(x)\, dx$.

Prove also that $\displaystyle\int_0^a F(x)\, dx = a\, F(a) - \int_0^a x\, F'(x)\, dx$ and deduce that, if $F'(a - x) = F'(x)$, then $\displaystyle\int_0^a F(x)\, dx = \frac{1}{2}a\{F(a) + F(0)\}$. (O.C.)

10. Show that the area of a loop of the curve $x = a \sin 2t$, $y = a \sin t$ is $\frac{4}{3}a^2$.

11. OA, OB, OC are three mutually perpendicular straight lines; AD is the perpendicular from A to BC and OE is the perpendicular from O to AD. Prove that OE is perpendicular to the plane ABC.

12. If the function $f(u, v)$ becomes $F(x, y)$ when $u = x^2 + y^2$, $v = y/x$, prove that $x \dfrac{\partial F}{\partial x} + y \dfrac{\partial F}{\partial y} = 2u \dfrac{\partial f}{\partial u}$. Hence prove that, if $x \dfrac{\partial F}{\partial x} + y \dfrac{\partial F}{\partial y} = 0$, then $F(x, y)$ is a function of y/x only.

By putting ϕ equal to $x^n \psi$, prove that if $x \dfrac{\partial \phi}{\partial x} + y \dfrac{\partial \phi}{\partial y} = n\phi$, then ϕ is a homogeneous function of x and y of degree n. (O.C.)

PAPER S (11)

1. Two triangles are determined by the given values of a, b, A. If O_1, O_2 are the circumcentres of these two triangles and H_1, H_2 are their orthocentres, prove that $H_1 H_2 = 2O_1 O_2 \cos A$.

2. If A is a point not on the line BC, show that the equation of the circle on AP as diameter, where P is the point dividing BC in the ratio $k : 1$, is $S_3 + kS_2 = 0$, where $S_3 = 0$, $S_2 = 0$ are the equations of the circles on AB, AC as diameters in the forms in which the coefficient of x^2 and y^2 is unity. Hence show that, if a transversal cuts the sides BC, CA, AB of a triangle at P, Q, R, then the circles on AP, BQ, CR as diameters have two points in common.

3. If the sides of a parallelogram are parallel to the lines $ax^2 + 2hxy + by^2 = 0$ and one diagonal is parallel to $lx + my = 0$, show that the other is parallel to $(hl - am)x + (bl - hm)y = 0$.

4. Given that $3(ax + by + cz) = (a + b + c)(x + y + z)$,
and $3(al + bm + cn) = (a + b + c)(l + m + n)$,
prove that $a = b = c$ or $x(m - n) + y(n - l) + z(l - m) = 0$. (N.)

5. (i) If the equations $x^3 + ax + b = 0$, $x^3 + cx + d = 0$ have a common root, show that $(b - d)^3 = (ad - bc)(a - c)^2$.
(ii) If the equations $x^4 + px^2 + qx + t = 0$, $x^4 + rx^2 + sx + t = 0$ have a double root in common and $t \neq 0$, show that $p = r$ and $q = s$. (C.)

6. The complex numbers $z = x + iy$ and $w = u + iv$ are connected by the equation $wz = z^2 + 1$. Prove that if, in the Argand diagram, z lies on the straight line $y = kx$, $k \neq 0$, then w lies on a certain hyperbola and that the branch of the hyperbola on which w lies depends only on the sign of the real part of z.

7. A sequence of numbers $a_0, a_1, a_2, \ldots$ is such that $a_{n+1} - a_n = br^n$ $(r \neq 1)$. Show that a_n can be expressed in the form $p + qr^n$, where p and q are independent of n, and find the values of p, q in terms of a_0, b and r.
Verify that the numbers 1, 4, 10, 22 begin a sequence of the above type. Obtain a formula for the nth term of this sequence and find the sum of the first n terms of the sequence. (N.)

8. By considerations of area, or otherwise, show that if $f(x)$ increases strictly with x, then $f(n - 1) < \displaystyle\int_{n-1}^{n} f(x)\, dx < f(n)$.
(i) Using the case $f(x) = \log x$, show that if $n > 1$, $(n - 1)! < n^n e^{1-n} < n!$;
(ii) show that if $n > 1$, $0 < 1 + \dfrac{1}{2} + \dfrac{1}{3} + \ \ldots \ + \dfrac{1}{n} - \log n < 1$.

9. Prove that if $y = \log_e \cos x$, then $\dfrac{d^3y}{dx^3} + 2\dfrac{d^2y}{dx^2}\dfrac{dy}{dx} = 0$.

Hence obtain the Maclaurin expansion of $\log_e \cos x$ as far as the term in x^4. Deduce the approximate relationship $\log_e 2 = \frac{1}{16}\pi^2(1 - \pi^2/96)$. (O.C.)

10. Prove that $\displaystyle\int_0^a f(x)\,dx = \int_0^{\frac{1}{2}a} \{f(x) + f(a - x)\}\,dx$.

If $0 < \alpha < \pi/2$, prove that $\displaystyle\int_0^\pi \dfrac{x \sin x\,dx}{\sqrt{(1 + \tan^2 \alpha \sin^2 x)}} = \dfrac{\pi\alpha}{\tan \alpha}$. (C.)

11. A function of z, $F(z)$, is written as a function of x and y by means of the substitution $z = x + iy$. Given that $F(z) \equiv F(x + iy) \equiv u(x, y) + iv(x, y)$, where $u(x, y)$ and $v(x, y)$ are both real, prove that

$$\dfrac{\partial u}{\partial x} = \dfrac{\partial v}{\partial y} \quad \text{and} \quad \dfrac{\partial u}{\partial y} = -\dfrac{\partial v}{\partial x}.$$

Find $u(x, y)$ and $v(x, y)$ when $F(z) = e^z$ and verify the given relations between the partial derivatives of u and v. (O.C.)

12. AB is the common perpendicular of two skew lines AP, BQ. If H is the mid-point of AB and M the mid-point of PQ, prove that HM is perpendicular to AB.

PAPER S (12)

1. H is the orthocentre and O the circumcentre of a triangle ABC. AO meets the circumcircle again in P. Prove that: (i) HP passes through the mid-point of BC; (ii) the triangles ABC, AHP have the same centroid.

2. Find the maximum and minimum values of the function $x + 2y$ when x, y are subjected to the restrictions

$$5x + 2y - 17 \geqslant 0, \quad 4x - 3y - 9 \leqslant 0, \quad x + 5y - 31 \leqslant 0.$$ (L.)

3. The equation $x^4 - px^3 + rx + s = 0$ has two pairs of equal roots. Prove that $8r = p^3$, $64s = p^4$, and that the distinct roots are $p(1 \pm \sqrt{3})/4$. (C.)

4. Use De Moivre's theorem to prove that the roots of the equation $x^n = (x - 1)^n$, where n is a positive integer, are

$$\tfrac{1}{2}\{1 + i \cot (r\pi/n)\}, \quad r = 0, 1, 2, \ldots (n - 1).$$

5. Find the equation of the circumcircle of the triangle whose sides are the line $lx + my + n = 0$ and the line-pair $ax^2 + 2hxy + by^2 = 0$. Interpret the result geometrically when $am^2 - 2hlm + bm^2 = 0$.

6. Prove that four normals can be drawn to a rectangular hyperbola from a general point P in its plane. If the feet of these normals are the points A, B, C, D, prove that: (i) each of the points A, B, C, D is the orthocentre of the triangle formed by the other three; (ii) the circle through B, C, D meets the hyperbola again at the opposite end A' of the diameter of the hyperbola through A.

7. If $S=0$ is the equation of a conic and $u=0$ is the equation of a straight line, what locus does the equation $S+ku^2=0$ represent?

The line $x+y=1$ cuts the conic $5x^2-6xy+y^2+3=0$ at the points P, Q. Obtain the equation of the rectangular hyperbola which touches the given conic at P and Q. Show also that this hyperbola passes through the origin. (N.)

8. (a) Express in partial fractions with real irreducible denominators

$$6x/(x^6-1).$$

(b) Find the sum of the first n terms of the series

$$1+2^2x+3^2x^2+4^2x^3+ \ . \ . \ .$$

If $|x|<1$, find also the sum to infinity of the series. (N.)

9. Prove that if $a>0$,

$$\int_0^1 \sin(\pi x^a)\,dx + a\pi \int_0^1 x^a \cos(\pi x^a)\,dx = 0;$$

$$\int_0^1 \cos(\pi x^a)\,dx - a\pi \int_0^1 x^a \sin(\pi x^a)\,dx = -1;$$

$$\int_0^1 (1+a+a^2\pi^2 x^{2a}) \sin(\pi x^a)\,dx = a\pi. \qquad \text{(L.)}$$

10. Sketch the curve with polar equation $r=1+\cos 2\theta$.

Prove that the length of the curve corresponding to $0\leqslant\theta\leqslant 2\pi$ is

$$8+\frac{4}{\sqrt{3}} \log(2+\sqrt{3}).$$

11. A surface is formed by rotating an arc of a parabola about a line in its plane perpendicular to its axis. The height of the resulting barrel-shaped body is h and the radius of either end is a and of the middle b. Show that the volume of the body is $\frac{1}{15}\pi h(3a^2+4ab+8b^2)$.

12. (i) Prove that, if $u=x^n f(Y, Z)$ where $Y=y/x$, $Z=z/x$, then

$$x\frac{\partial u}{\partial x}+y\frac{\partial u}{\partial y}+z\frac{\partial u}{\partial z}=nu.$$

Find the values of $x\dfrac{\partial u}{\partial x}+y\dfrac{\partial u}{\partial y}+z\dfrac{\partial u}{\partial z}$ when:

(i) $u=\log(x^2+y^2+z^2)$;

(ii) $u=(x^2+y^2+z^2) \tan^{-1}\left(\dfrac{y^2+z^2}{x^2}\right).$

(ii) Show that $V=Ar^n \cos(n\theta-\alpha)$ satisfies the equation

$$\frac{\partial^2 V}{\partial x^2}+\frac{\partial^2 V}{\partial y^2}=0, \text{ when } x=r\cos\theta, \ y=r\sin\theta. \qquad \text{(L.)}$$

ANSWERS

EXAMPLES 1a (Page 3)

1. 12·26 cm.   **2.** 3·464 cm.   **3.** (i) $(\frac{4}{3}, 1)$;   (ii) $(\frac{1}{3}a, \frac{1}{3}b)$;   (iii) $(\frac{2}{3}x, \frac{2}{3}y)$.
4. 9·695 cm.   **9.** Yes.   **10.** (1, 0).   **12.** 4·485 cm.   **16.** 45° 14′.

EXAMPLES 1b (Page 9)

2. 1·70 cm.   **11.** 3·25 cm.

EXAMPLES 1d (Page 18)

3. $BL : CL = 6 : 1$.   **4.** 3 : 10.
9. $AO : OD = 5 : 9$; $CO : OF = 11 : 3$.   **14.** 25 : 9.

MISCELLANEOUS EXAMPLES (Page 24)

22. $AQ : QB = 1 : 4$.   **40.** The centroid of the triangle ABC.

EXAMPLES 2a (Page 29)

1. $x^4 + 10x^3 + 35x^2 + 50x + 24$.   **2.** $a^2 + b^2 + 4c^2 - 4bc + 4ca - 2ab$.
4. (i) $5(a - b + c)(b - a - c)$;   (ii) $(3y - x)(7x^2 + 3xy + 3y^2)$;
   (iii) $(a^2 - \sqrt{3}ab + b^2)(a^2 + \sqrt{3}ab + b^2)$;   (iv) $(2a + b)(4a^2 - 2ab + b^2 - 2)$.
5. $32 - 80x + 80x^2 - 40x^3 + 10x^4 - x^5$.
6. $-2[a^2 + b^2 + c^2 - 2bc - 2ca - 2ab]$.
7. $x^3 - y^3 + 8z^3 + 3x^2(2z - y) + 3y^2(x + 2z) + 12z^2(x - y) - 12xyz$.
8. (i) $24\sqrt{2}$;   (ii) $24\sqrt{2}$.
10. (i) $\sqrt{3} + \sqrt{2}$;   (ii) $\frac{1}{4}(\sqrt{2} + \sqrt{6} - 2)$;   (iii) $\frac{1}{2}(3^{\frac{2}{3}} + 3^{\frac{1}{3}} + 1)$.
11. (i) $3(a^2 + b^2 + c^2) - 2(bc + ca + ab)$;   (ii) $2(a^2 + b^2 + c^2)$.
12. $(x^2 - 2x + 3)(x^2 + 2x + 3)$.
13. $(2x - y)(x + y)$; $(2x - y - 1)(x + y + 5)$.   **14.** $178\sqrt{3}$.
15. (i) $(x - 1)(x - 2)$;   (ii) $(2a + 3b)(a - b)$.   **17.** $(a + b)/(a^2 + ab + b^2)$.
18. (i) $(x - 3)^2$;   (ii) $(a + 3 - b/a)(a^2 + 9 + b^2/a^2 - 3a + b + 3b/a)$;
   (iii) $(x^2 - \sqrt{2}x + 2)(x^2 + \sqrt{2}x + 2)$.
20. $-[x^2 + y^2 + z^2 + (a + b)(x + y + z) + 3ab]/(y - z)(z - x)(x - y)$.
21. (i) 4;   (ii) 18.   **22.** $(x^2 - 3x + 4)(x^2 + x - 1)$.
24. (i) 0;   (ii) -1.   **26.** $\frac{3}{2}n(n + 1)$.
27. (i) $(a^2 - \sqrt{3}ab + 3b^2)(a^2 + \sqrt{3}ab + 3b^2)$;
   (ii) $(2a^2 + 2ab + b^2)(a^2 - ab + b^2)$.
28. $\dfrac{\sqrt{2} - x}{2\sqrt{2}(x^2 - \sqrt{2}x + 1)} + \dfrac{\sqrt{2} + x}{2\sqrt{2}(x^2 + \sqrt{2}x + 1)}$.   **30.** $x^4 + 1$.
31. $[a + b - c - 2\sqrt{(ab)}][a + b - c + 2\sqrt{(ab)}]$.   **33.** 13.

EXAMPLES 2b   (Page 34)

1. -720.   **2.** $2x^2 - x + 3$.   **3.** $(x-2)(x+2)(x^2 - 3x - 2)$.

4. $a = 3$.   **5.** $a^4 + a^3 b + a^2 b^2 + ab^3 + b^4$.

6. $a = 3$.   **7.** $x - 2$.

8. (i) $(x+1)(x-2)(2x-3)$;   (ii) $-(b-c)(c-a)(a-b)$.

9. $a = 3$, $b = -25$; $(x+2)(x-3)(x^2 + 4x + 1)$.

10. (i) $2x - y$;   (ii) $x - 3$.   **12.** $c = \tfrac{1}{2}$, -4.

13. (i) $(x+2)(x+4)(2x-1)$;   (ii) $(x-1)^2(x^2 + 2x + 3)$;
(iii) $(a+2b)(2a^2 + ab + b^2)$.

14. $x^2 - x + 3$.   **15.** $x^2 - x - 1$.

16. (i) $-(b-c)(c-a)(a-b)$;   (ii) $(b-c)(c-a)(a-b)$;
(iii) $(b-c)(c-a)(a-b)(a+b+c)$.

17. $a = 5$, $b = -7$, $c = 2$.   **19.** $(x-1)(x^2 + x + 1)(x^6 + x^3 + 1)$.

20. (i) 0;   (ii) $(a+b+c)(bc+ca+ab)$;
$$5(b-c)(c-a)(a-b)(a^2 + b^2 + c^2 - bc - ca - ab).$$

21. $x^2 + 1$.   **23.** $a = -1$, $b = -4$; $(x^2 + 2x - 1)(x^4 - x^3 + 2x^2 - 2)$.

24. (i) $3abc(b+c)(c+a)(a+b)$;   (ii) $80abc(a^2 + b^2 + c^2)$.

25. $(2x-1)^2(x^2 + x + 3)$.   **26.** $(y-z)(z-x)(x-y)(x+y+z)$.

EXAMPLES 2c   (Page 36)

3. p/q.   **5.** $x = 2$, $y = -\tfrac{2}{3}$, $z = \tfrac{2}{3}$.   **6.** $\tfrac{8}{11}$.

7. $x = \tfrac{2}{3}a$, $y = \tfrac{2}{3}b$, $z = \tfrac{2}{3}c$.

8. $z = xy/(x-y)$.

11. (i) $x = 9$, $y = 15$, $z = 20$;   (ii) $x = \tfrac{1}{5}$, $y = \tfrac{3}{5}$, $z = \tfrac{2}{5}$; $x = -\tfrac{1}{5}$, $y = -\tfrac{3}{5}$, $z = -\tfrac{2}{5}$.

12. $\tfrac{86}{85}$.   **15.** $x = a$, $y = b$, $z = c$.

EXAMPLES 2d   (Page 41)

2. (i) $-4 < x < \tfrac{3}{2}$;   (ii) $-\tfrac{4}{3} > x > 5$.   **4.** $\lambda = 16$.   **5.** $8\tfrac{1}{4}$.

6. -12.   **9.** Positive.   **10.** (i) $1 \geqslant x \geqslant 3$;   (ii) $1 - 1/\sqrt{2} \geqslant y \geqslant 1 + 1/\sqrt{2}$.

11. Min. $\tfrac{1}{3}$, Max. 3.   **13.** $x = 3$, $y = 2$.   **15.** $\tfrac{1}{3} \leqslant \text{function} \leqslant 3$.

16. $0 \leqslant \lambda < 1$.   **20.** Values > 0 and < 4.   **22.** $\lambda \geqslant 6$.

EXAMPLES 2e   (Page 44)

1. $\dfrac{1}{2(x+1)} - \dfrac{4}{x+2} + \dfrac{9}{2(x+3)}$.   **2.** $-\dfrac{2}{x} + \dfrac{1}{x-1} + \dfrac{2}{2x-1}$.

3. $\dfrac{1}{9(x+1)} - \dfrac{2}{3(x+1)^2} + \dfrac{4-x}{9(x^2+2)}$.

4. $-\dfrac{1}{6(x+1)} + \dfrac{1}{x+2} - \dfrac{3}{2(x+3)} + \dfrac{2}{3(x+4)}$.

5. $\dfrac{1}{3(x+2)^3} - \dfrac{2}{9(x+2)^2} - \dfrac{2}{27(x+2)} - \dfrac{2}{27(x-1)}.$

6. $\dfrac{2}{x^4} - \dfrac{1}{x^3} + \dfrac{1}{x^2} - \dfrac{1}{x} + \dfrac{1}{x+1}.$ **7.** $\dfrac{2}{3(x-1)} - \dfrac{2(x-1)}{3(x^2+x+1)}.$

8. $x+4+\dfrac{10}{x-1} + \dfrac{10}{(x-1)^2} + \dfrac{5}{(x-1)^3} + \dfrac{1}{(x-1)^4}.$ **9.** $\dfrac{x}{x^2-x+1} - \dfrac{x+1}{x^2+x+1}.$

10. $-\dfrac{1}{2(x-1)} - \dfrac{3}{2(x-3)} - \dfrac{15}{2(x-5)} + \dfrac{35}{2(x-7)}.$

11. $\dfrac{1}{(x+2)^2} - \dfrac{6}{(x+2)^3} + \dfrac{12}{(x+2)^4} - \dfrac{8}{(x+2)^5}.$ **12.** $\dfrac{x-1}{x^2+1}.$

13. $\dfrac{6}{(x-2)^5} - \dfrac{3}{(x-2)^4} + \dfrac{3}{2(x-2)^3} - \dfrac{3}{4(x-2)^2} + \dfrac{3}{8(x-2)} - \dfrac{3}{8x}.$

14. $\dfrac{1}{3(x-1)^4} + \dfrac{7}{9(x-1)^3} + \dfrac{10}{27(x-1)^2} - \dfrac{14}{81(x-1)} + \dfrac{14x-16}{81(x^2+2)}.$

15. $\dfrac{1}{3(x+1)} - \dfrac{1}{3(x+1)^2} - \dfrac{x-3}{x^2-x+1}.$

16. $-\dfrac{2}{x^6} + \dfrac{1}{x^5} + \dfrac{2}{x^4} - \dfrac{1}{x^3} - \dfrac{2}{x^2} + \dfrac{1}{x} + \dfrac{2-x}{x^2+1}.$ **17.** $\dfrac{x+1}{(x^2+1)^2} + \dfrac{2x-1}{x^2+1}.$

19. $\dfrac{1}{6(x-1)} - \dfrac{1}{6(x+1)} - \dfrac{x-1}{x^2+x+1} + \dfrac{x+1}{x^2-x+1}.$

EXAMPLES 2f (Page 47)

1. $x=4.$ **2.** $x=10.$ **3.** $x=-1,\ \pm 3.$

4. $x=-2, \frac{1}{2}, 3.$ **5.** $x=4.$ **6.** $x=-1,\ -1,\ \frac{1}{2}(3\pm\sqrt 5).$

7. $x=\pm 1, \frac{1}{2}(-3\pm\sqrt 5).$ **8.** $x=-2.$

9. $x=0, 9.$ **10.** $x=-1,\ -1, -1, \frac{1}{2}, 2.$

11. $x=-1$; other roots complex. **12.** $x=0, 4$; other roots complex.

13. $x=-4,\ -2, 2, 3.$ **14.** $x=-1,\ -2.$

15. $x=-2, 3, \frac{1}{4}(1\pm\sqrt{33}).$

16. (i) $x=a+b+c,\ b+c-a;$ (ii) $x=3, y=-1;\ x=-1, y=3;$ other roots complex.

17. (i) $x=15;$ (ii) $x=\pm\sqrt{\frac{45}{32}}.$ **18.** $x=0, 1.$ **19.** $x=-2,\ -2, 3\pm\sqrt 5.$

20. $a=12, b=16;\ x=-3,\ -2,\ -1, 2;$ other roots complex.

21. $x=5, y=7, z=4;\ x=-1, y=-3, z=0.$

MISCELLANEOUS EXAMPLES   (Page 48)

1. $3\sum a^2 - 2\sum bc$.   **2.** (i) $2(a-1)(a^2+4a+7)$;   (ii) $(x+y-z)(x-y+2z)$.

3. $(x^2+xy+y^2)/(x^2-xy+y^2)$.

5. (i) Positive for $x<\frac{3}{2}$ and $x>5$, negative for $\frac{3}{2}<x<5$;
    (ii) $3\geqslant$ Expression $\geqslant\frac{1}{3}$.

7. (i) $\dfrac{39}{85(3x-1)} - \dfrac{1}{45(x-2)} - \dfrac{40}{153(2x+5)}$;

    (ii) $\dfrac{1}{2(x+1)^4} - \dfrac{3}{2(x+1)^3} + \dfrac{5}{4(x+1)^2} - \dfrac{1}{4(x^2+1)}$.

8. (i) $(y-z)(z-x)(x-y)(x+y+z)$;   (ii) $(y-z)(z-x)(x-y)(yz+zx+xy)$.

9. $X^2-2,\; X^3-3X,\; X^4-4X^2+2$.

10. (i) $x=\frac{1}{3},\; 3,\; \frac{1}{3}(-1\pm i\,2\sqrt{2})$;
    (ii) $x=2,\,y=3;\;\; x=-2,\,y=-3;\;\; x=3\;y=4;\;\; x=-3,\,y=-4$.

11. (i) negative.   **12.** $a^2+b^2+c^2=2ca$.

13. $x=-1,\; 2\pm\sqrt{2},\; \frac{1}{2}(1\pm\sqrt{5})$.

14. (i) $2-\sqrt{3}$;   (ii) $\dfrac{4+3\sqrt{3}-\sqrt{5}+2\sqrt{15}}{22}$;

    (iii) $\dfrac{(1+\sqrt{x}+\sqrt{y})(1+x-y-2\sqrt{x})}{(1+x-y)^2-4x}$.

15. $x=3,\; y=2$.

16. (i) $(2a^2-ab+b^2)(2a^2+ab+b^2)$;   (ii) $a=-4,\; b=14$.

17. $\dfrac{1}{3(x-1)^3} + \dfrac{8}{9(x-1)^2} + \dfrac{19}{27(x-1)} + \dfrac{8}{27(x+2)}$;
    $\frac{1}{27}[(-1)^n/2^{n-2} - \frac{1}{2}(9n^2-21n+8)]$.

19. (i) $x=-2,\; \frac{1}{2}(3\pm\sqrt{5})$;   (ii) $x=1-\frac{1}{7}\sqrt{7}$.   **21.** $\lambda\geqslant1$.

22. $x=z-y$.   **24.** $\dfrac{1}{2-x} + \displaystyle\sum_1^n \dfrac{1}{(x-1)^r}$.   **25.** $\lambda=3,\; -7$.

26. (i) $x=10$;   (ii) no real solutions.

27. $(a-b)(b-c)(c-a)[3(a^2+b^2+c^2)-(bc+ca+ab)]$.

30. (i) $4\sqrt{3}$;   (ii) $(a+b)^2+b^2$.

32. (i) $(a+b)(b+c)(c+a)$;   (ii) $(2x^2-17x+36)(2x^2-23x+36)$.

33. $x=-1,\; 2,\; 1\pm\sqrt{5}$.   **34.** $x=0\cdot9397,\; -0\cdot1737,\; -0\cdot7660$.

35. $a+c=0$;   (i) $x=a\pm\sqrt{(a^2+b)}$.

36. $-3\leqslant y\leqslant-2,\; 2\leqslant y\leqslant3$.   **39.** (ii) $\lambda=6,\; -\frac{9}{2}$.

42. $a=0,\,b=0;\;\; a=-1,\,b=-1;\;\; a=\frac{300}{19},\,b=\frac{10}{19}$.

43. $6x^5-15x^4+10x^3$.   **44.** x^2-x+1.

EXAMPLES 3a (Page 53)

1. 10. **2.** -2. **3.** 36. **4.** 6. **5.** 0.

6. -8. **7.** 3. **8.** 8. **9.** 0. **10.** -8.

11. 4. **12.** 0. **13.** $b^2 - a^2$. **14.** $-5xy$. **15.** $a^2 + b^2$.

16. $-6xy$. **17.** $-ab(a + b)$. **18.** $1 + yz + zx + xy$. **19.** $a^6 - a^4 - a^3 + a$.

20. 0. **21.** $(x - 1)^3$. **22.** $(a^2 - b^2)^2$. **23.** $(b - a)^3$.

EXAMPLES 3b (Page 58)

1. 23. **2.** 418. **3.** 204. **4.** 267. **5.** 7760.

6. 176. **7.** 0. **8.** 1. **9.** 0. **10.** 0.

11. 0. **12.** 0. **13.** $-6xy$. **14.** $(a - b)^2(b^2 - a^2)$.

15. $-3b(a^2 - b^2)(a - 2b)$. **16.** $-(a^3 - 1)^2$. **17.** $2xyz(x - y)(y - z)(z - x)$.

18. 0. **19.** $-x^3 + 17x^2 - 43x + 27$. **20.** $3a^4$.

21. $-(a^4 - 1)^3$. **22.** 0. **25.** $x = \pm 2$.

27. (i) $4abc$; (ii) 0. **28.** $36x + 96$; $x = -\frac{8}{3}$.

EXAMPLES 3c (Page 63)

1. $ab(b - a)$. **2.** $20xy$. **3.** $(a - b)(a + b)$.

4. $(a - b)(a + b)^2[1 - 2a - 2b]$. **5.** $18xyz$. **6.** $280abc$.

7. $y^2(y - x)(y + x)$. **8.** $(a - b)(b - c)(c - a)$. **9.** $8xyzt$.

10. $-66xyzt$. **11.** $-2(1 + c)(b - c)(b + c)$.

12. (i) -2; (ii) -2. **13.** $x(x + 1)(x - 1)(4 - x)$.

14. $bc + ca + ab - (a^2 + b^2 + c^2)$.

15. $bc - f^2$, $ca - g^2$, $ab - h^2$, $gh - af$, $hf - bg$, $fg - ch$.

17. (i) $x = 1, 1, 4$; (ii) $x = 3, -4 \pm \sqrt{21}$; (iii) $x = 1, 8 \pm \sqrt{37}$.

19. (i) $4abc$; (ii) $2(x - y)/x^3y^4$. **20.** (i) Δ; (ii) 3Δ.

21. $3z(y - x)$. **22.** $-(a - b)(a - c)(a - d)(b - c)(b - d)(c - d)$.

EXAMPLES 3d (Page 70)

1. $x = -1, y = 1$. **2.** $x = 1, y = 1$. **3.** $x = -1, y = 3$.

4. Equations inconsistent. **5.** $x = 3, y = -5$.

6. Equations not independent. **7.** $x = 7, y = -2$.

8. Equations inconsistent. **9.** $x = 4, y = 2$.

10. Equations inconsistent. **11.** $x = 1, y = 1, z = 2$.

12. $x = 3, y = 7, z = -4$. **13.** $x = 3, y = -2, z = 2$.

14. $x = y = z = 1$. **15.** Equations inconsistent.

16. $x = 0, y = -1, z = 4$. **17.** Equations not independent.

B B

18. Equations inconsistent.   **19.** $x = \frac{79}{49}$, $y = \frac{24}{49}$, $z = \frac{17}{49}$.

20. Equations not independent.   **21.** Equations not independent.

22. (i) $(\frac{22}{5}, -\frac{4}{5})$;   (ii) $(-\frac{4}{31}, \frac{15}{31})$;   (iii) $(-\frac{16}{23}, \frac{11}{23})$.

23. (i) $2 : 11 : 7$;   (ii) $-7 : 5 : 11$;   (iii) $3 : 19 : 26$.

24. (i) $\lambda = -1$;   (ii) no values.

25. (i) $\mu = 1$;   (ii) $\mu = 1$;   (iii) $\mu = \frac{1}{4}(-5 \pm \sqrt{89})$.   **26.** 3.

27. (i) (a) $\lambda = -1$, (b) $\lambda = 3$;   (ii) (a) $\lambda = -2, \frac{1}{2}$, (b) none;
(iii) (a) $\lambda = -8, 2$, (b) none.

28. $x = \dfrac{(k-b)(k-c)}{(a-b)(a-c)}$, $y = \dfrac{(k-c)(k-a)}{(b-c)(b-a)}$, $z = \dfrac{(k-a)(k-b)}{(c-a)(c-b)}$.

29. $x = \dfrac{\mu - 3}{\lambda - 4}$, $y = \dfrac{3\lambda - 5\mu + 3}{2(\lambda - 4)}$, $z = \dfrac{7\lambda - 11\mu + 5}{10(\lambda - 4)}$;   (i) $\lambda = 4, \mu \neq 3$;
(ii) $\lambda = 4, \mu = 3$.

31. $x = \dfrac{3a - b - 2ab + 26}{3(13 + 5a)(3 - a)}$, $y = \dfrac{3b - 5a}{(13 + 5a)(3 - a)}$, $z = \dfrac{65 + 2b - 5ab}{3(13 + 5a)(3 - a)}$;
(i) inconsistent;   (ii) not independent.

32. Equation (iv); $4y - z + 3 = 0$.

33. If $\lambda \neq 1$, $x = -\dfrac{(\lambda + 1)}{\lambda + 2}$, $y = \dfrac{1}{\lambda + 2}$, $z = \dfrac{(\lambda + 1)^2}{\lambda + 2}$;   (i) equations not independent,   (ii) inconsistent.

34. (i) $x = -1$, $y = 0$, $z = 3$, $t = -2$;   (ii) $x = 3 = y$, $z = -5$, $t = -1$.

35. $\lambda = 3, \frac{1}{2}(-13 \pm \sqrt{265})$.   **36.** $a = -\frac{3}{5}$, $b = \frac{27}{10}$, $c = -\frac{9}{10}$, $d = -\frac{6}{5}$.

EXAMPLES 3e   (Page 75)

2.   (i) $\lambda = -8$; $1 : 2$;   (ii) $\lambda = \pm 4$; $1 : \pm 2$;
(iii) $\lambda = 2, -1$; $1 : -1$, $1 : 2$;   (iv) $\lambda = 0$, ± 2; $1 : \pm 2$.

3. (i) $p^2 + q^2 = 0$;   (ii) $3l - 2m = 0$;   (iii) $ab = 0$;   (iv) $(a - 1)(b + 1) = 0$.

5. (i) $1 : 1 : -1$;   (ii) $6 : -13 : -17$;   (iii) $nr - mq : r - q : n - m$.

6.   (i) $-a + 4b + 7c = 0$;   (ii) $m^2 - lm + nl = 0$;
(iii) $(y_1 z_2 - y_2 z_1) - (x_1 z_2 - x_2 z_1) + (x_1 y_2 - x_2 y_1) = 0$.

8. $\lambda = 3, -1$; $x = -\frac{3}{2}$, $y = \frac{7}{2}$; $x = \frac{1}{2}$, $y = -\frac{1}{2}$.

9. $abc + 2fgh - af^2 - bg^2 - ch^2 = 0$.

10. (i) $\lambda = 3$;   (ii) $\lambda = 2, \frac{9}{2}$;   (iii) $\lambda = 1, 4$.

11. $x : y : z = 1 : 2 : -3$; $a : b : c = 1 : 1 : 1$.

12. (i) $1 + 2abc - bc - ca - ab = 0$;   (ii) $1 + qr + rp + pq = 0$.

14. $\begin{vmatrix} a_1 & b_1 & c_1 \\ a_2 & b_2 & c_2 \\ 1 & -t & t^2 \end{vmatrix} = 0.$

MISCELLANEOUS EXAMPLES (Page 77)

1. $x = \frac{5}{4}$, $y = \frac{19}{2}$, $z = -\frac{5}{3}$.

4. (i) $(a-b)(b-c)(c-a)$;   (ii) $(a-b)(b-c)(c-a)(a+b+c)$.

5. $x = \lambda(\lambda+1)/(\lambda-1)$, $y = \lambda(\lambda-2)/(\lambda-1)$, $z = \lambda/(\lambda-1)$; $\lambda = 1$, inconsistent.

6. (i) $x = \frac{6}{7}$, -2; $x = a, b$.   **7.** $1 + bc + ca + ab = 0$.

8. $x(x-1)(x+11)$; $x = 0, 1, -11$.

9. $x = -a+b+c$, $y = a-b+c$, $z = a+b-c$.

11. (i) $1/3^3 4^3 5^2$;   (ii) $2(a+b+c)^3$.   **12.** -2.

15. Equation (ii); constant term -1.   **18.** $1+a+b+c$.   **19.** $x = \pm 1$.

21. (i) $x = -3$, $y = 3/(1-k)$, $z = (1-4k)/(1-k)$;   (ii) not independent;
(iii) inconsistent.

22. $-(a-b)(b-c)(c-a)(a+b+c)^2$.

24. (i) $x = 3$, $3 \pm \sqrt{6}$; (ii) $x = 0$, -1.   **26.** $\pm(af - be + cd)$.

28. $-2abc(a+b+c)[(a-b)^2 + (b-c)^2 + (c-a)^2]$.

29. $\lambda = 3$; $1:1:-2$; $\lambda = 5$; $3:1:-4$; $\lambda = -8$; $6:2:5$.

31. $a = 1$, ω, ω^2, where $\omega^3 = 1$.

32. $-2x^4 y^2 + y^6 - x^4 - 10x^2 y^2 + 2y^4 - 8x^2 - 16y^2 - 4$.

33. (i) $(a+b+c+d)(a-b+c-d)\{(a-c)^2 + (b-d)^2\}$;
(ii) $-(x-a)(x-b)(x-c)(a-b)(b-c)(c-a)(x+a+b+c)$.

34. $\lambda = \pm 1, 2$.

37. $x = \dfrac{d(b-c)}{(a-b)^2 + (b-c)^2 + (c-a)^2}$, $y = \dfrac{d(c-a)}{(a-b)^2 + (b-c)^2 + (c-a)^2}$,
$z = \dfrac{d(a-b)}{(a-b)^2 + (b-c)^2 + (c-a)^2}$.

EXAMPLES 4a   (Page 83)

1. (i) $x + 4y = 19$;   (ii) $4x + 5y = 8$;   (iii) $x + y + 4 = 0$;   (iv) $x + y = a + b$.

3. (i) $(-\frac{8}{7}, \frac{5}{7})$;   (ii) $(\frac{4}{7}, \frac{9}{7})$;   (iii) $(-19, 14)$;   (iv) $(-\frac{39}{34}, -\frac{7}{34})$.

5. (i) $\frac{1}{2}$;   (ii) 11;   (iii) 3;   (iv) $17\frac{1}{2}$;   (v) 5;   (vi) $\frac{1}{2}(t^2 + t)$.

6. $2x - y(t_1 + t_2) + 2at_1 t_2 = 0$.   **7.** $(at_1 t_2, \overline{at_1 + t_2})$.

8. (i) $\lambda = \frac{37}{9}$;   (ii) $\lambda = 4$;   (iii) $\lambda = 2$.   **9.** $x + yt_1 t_2 = c(t_1 + t_2)$.

11. $x(t_1^2 + t_1 t_2 + t_2^2) - y(t_1 + t_2) = t_1^2 t_2^2$.   **14.** $\frac{81}{40}$.   **15.** $20\frac{1}{2}$.

EXAMPLES 4b (Page 87)

1. (i) $x^2 - y^2 = 0$;   (ii) $2x^2 - xy - 6y^2 = 0$;
   (iii) $x^2 - y^2 + 3x - y + 2 = 0$;   (iv) $6x^2 + xy - 2y^2 - 7x + 7y - 5 = 0$.

2. (i) $2x + y = 0 = x - y$;   (ii) $x + y + 2 = 0 = x - y + 2$;
   (iii) $x - 1 = 0 = x - y + 2$;   (iv) $3x + y - 2 = 0 = x - 2y + 1$;
   (v) $x + 1 = 0 = y - 3$;   (vi) $2x - 3 = 0 = x + y - 1$.

3. (i), (ii), (iv), (vi).   4. $(-2, -1)$.   6. $h = 1$.

7. (i) $\lambda = 3$;   (ii) $\lambda = 1$;   (iii) $\lambda = -3$;
   (iv) $\lambda = 2$;   (v) all values;   (vi) $\lambda = \pm 4, -2$.

9. $(2, -3), (-2, 1)$.

10. (i) $3x^2 + 8xy + 3y^2 = 0$;   (ii) $7x^2 - 32xy + 24y^2 = 0$;
    (iii) $xy - 2y^2 = 0$;   (iv) $2x^2 - 2xy - y^2 = 0$;
    (v) $9x^2 - 14xy + 6y^2 = 0$;   (vi) $13x^2 - 60xy + 13y^2 = 0$.

11. $xy - 12y^2 = 0$.   12. $h = 0$.   13. $2\sqrt{5}$.

15. $x^2 - 4xy + 4y^2 + x - 2y - 12 = 0$, $4x^2 + 12xy + 9y^2 - 10x - 15y - 6 = 0$,
    $3x^2 + 16xy + 5y^2 - 11x - 13y + 6 = 0$.

16. $42x^2 - 13xy - 42y^2 - 56x + 122y - 56 = 0$,
    $2x^2 + 3xy - 2y^2 + 10x - 15y - 28 = 0$,
    $10x^2 - 21xy - 10y^2 - 76x + 132y + 112 = 0$.

17. $6x + 6y + 1 = 0$; $61x^2 + 114xy + 55y^2 = 0$.   19. $x^2 + y^2 - 2y = 0$.

20. $x^2 + y^2 + (x - 2y)(lx + my) = 0$; $x + 2y = 1$.   21. $(-\frac{1}{2}, -\frac{1}{2})$.

22. $\lambda = 0, \frac{15}{2}, -\frac{5}{2}$.

EXAMPLES 4c (Page 91)

1. (i) $\tan^{-1} 2\sqrt{6}$; (ii) $\tan^{-1} 2\sqrt{21}$; (iii) $\tan^{-1} \frac{1}{7}$; (iv) $\tan^{-1} 5$; (v) $\tan^{-1} \frac{3}{5}$.

2. (i), (iii), (v).

3. (i) $x^2 - xy - y^2 = 0$; (ii) $11x^2 + 6xy - 11y^2 = 0$; $11x^2 - 26xy - 11y^2 = 0$.

4. $\lambda = \pm 3$.   6. $\dfrac{4}{\sqrt{5}}$.   8. $x^2 - xy - 2y^2 + 9y - 9 = 0$.

9. $a = 1, b = 2$.   10. $\frac{3}{2}$.   11. $\frac{1}{2}$.

12. $x^2 + xy - 2y^2 - 7x + 10y - 8 = 0$.   13. $7x^2 + 8xy + y^2 = 0$.

14. $a^2l^2 + b^2m^2 = 1$; line is a tangent.   16. $2x^2 - xy - 3y^2 = 0$.

18. $11x^2 - 6xy - 11y^2 - 60x + 40y + 70 = 0$.

19. $c(l^2 + m^2) + 2(gl + fm + 1) = 0$.

22. $\dfrac{2}{a}\sqrt{\left(\dfrac{g^2 - a^2c}{a^2 + b^2}\right)}$.   26. (i) $(1, 2)$; (ii) $(-1, 0)$.

28. $2gx + 2fy + c = 0$, $f(ax + hy) = g(hx + by)$.

EXAMPLES 4d (Page 95)

1. (i) $7x^2 - 24xy + 14y^2 + 16x + 12y - 50 = 0$;   (ii) $x^2 - 8y^2 + 6x + 9 = 0$;
(iii) $7x^2 + 8xy + y^2 - 2x + 4y - 5 = 0$;   (iv) $17x^2 - 20xy - 4y^2 = 0$;
(v) $5x^2 - 4y^2 + 8y - 4 = 0$;   (vi) $8x^2 - 48xy - 47y^2 + 80x - 2y + 81 = 0$;
(vii) $3x^2 - 10xy + 3y^2 - 22x - 6y - 45 = 0$.

2. $x = 0$, $y = 0$; $x + y - 2 = 0$.

3. $3x^2 - 10xy + 3y^2 + 28x - 4y - 20 = 0$; $\tan^{-1} \frac{4}{3}$.

5. (i) $5x + 2y - 2 = 0$;   (ii) $x - 2y + 4 = 0$;   (iii) $6x + 8y + 3 = 0$;
(iv) $y + 1 = 0$;   (v) $x + 2y + 6 = 0$;   (vi) $5x + 4y - 7 = 0$.

6. $(9, 1)$, $(4, 0)$.   **8.** $x - y - 4 = 0$.   **12.** $g^2 + f^2 = h^2 + k^2 + 2gh + 2fk + 2c$.

13. $(-4, 4)$.   **14.** (i) $x - y = 1$;   (ii) $x^2 + y^2 - x + y + 1 = 0$.

16. $(0, 0)$, $x^2 - 3y^2 = 0$.   **17.** $(\frac{2}{3}, 0)$, $9x^2 - 16y^2 - 12x + 4 = 0$.

18. $x = 0$, $7x - 24y = 0$.

MISCELLANEOUS EXAMPLES (Page 97)

1. $a = 5$.   **3.** (i) $(0, 0)$;   (ii) $\frac{3}{2}$.   **4.** $y = x + 1 \pm 2\sqrt{2}$.   **5.** $(-1, 1)$.

6. $abc + 2fgh - af^2 - bg^2 - ch^2 = 0$; $\{(hf - bg)/(ab - h^2), (gh - af)/(ab - h^2)\}$.

7. $\lambda = 4$, $\frac{1}{2}$.   **8.** $3x^2 + 4xy = 0$; $\tan^{-1} \frac{4}{3}$.

9. $\{\frac{1}{2}(x_1 + x_2 + y_2 - y_1), \frac{1}{2}(y_1 + y_2 + x_1 - x_2)\}$,
                $\{\frac{1}{2}(x_1 + x_2 + y_1 - y_2), \frac{1}{2}(y_1 + y_2 + x_2 - x_1)\}$.

10. $2x^2 + 3xy - 2y^2 + 5x + 10y = 0$.   **13.** $a = 2$; $c = -3$.   **14.** $(1, -2)$.

15. $3\frac{1}{2}$.   **17.** $x^2 + 12xy + 6y^2 + 18x - 12y - 39 = 0$; $\tan^{-1} \frac{2}{7}\sqrt{30}$.

19. $x + 3y + 12 = 0$; $(-3, -3)$, $(0, -4)$.   **20.** $60°$.   **21.** $\lambda = \mu = -\frac{5}{6}$.

24. $(-1, 2)$.   **30.** $bx^2 - 2hxy + ay^2 = 0$; $\left(\frac{1}{2}\frac{hf - bg}{ab - h^2}, \frac{1}{2}\frac{gh - af}{ab - h^2}\right)$.

34. $x^2 + y^2 - 3x = 0$.   **40.** $7(x^2 + y^2) + 31x - 5y + 12 = 0$.

EXAMPLES 5a (Page 103)

2. (i) 21, outside;   (ii) -3, inside;   (iii) $\frac{1}{2}$, outside.

4. (i) $4x + y - 10 = 0$;   (ii) $4x - 5 = 0$;   (iii) $7x - 9y + 14 = 0$.

5. Perpendicular bisector of AB.   **6.** $3x + 2y - 5 = 0$.

8. $4x + 3y - 6 = 0$.   **9.** $(-\frac{77}{36}, \frac{17}{18})$.

16. $c = -4$.   **18.** $2\alpha'(\alpha - \alpha') + 2\beta'(\beta - \beta') + c' - c = 0$.

EXAMPLES 5b (Page 111)

1. (i) $x^2 + y^2 - 1 + \lambda(x^2 + y^2 - 2x) = 0$, $x^2 + y^2 - 1 + \mu(2x - 1) = 0$;

(ii) $x^2 + y^2 - 2y + \lambda(x^2 + y^2 - 3x - y + 1) = 0$,
$x^2 + y^2 - 2y + \mu(3x - y - 1) = 0$;

(iii) $2(x^2 + y^2) - x - 2 + \lambda(x^2 + y^2 - 4y - 2) = 0$,
$2(x^2 + y^2) - x - 2 + \mu(x - 8y - 2) = 0$;

(iv) $x^2 + y^2 - 5x + 2y - 3 + \lambda(3x^2 + 3y^2 - 2y - 6) = 0$,
$x^2 + y^2 - 5x + 2y - 3 + \mu(15x - 8y + 3) = 0$.

2. $3x^2 + 3y^2 + 6x - 2y - 21 = 0$.   **3.** $S + \mu L = 0$ in each case.

4. $x^2 + y^2 - 4x + 3 = 0$, $x^2 + y^2 + 8x + 15 = 0$.   **7.** $2x - y - 1 = 0$.

8. (i) $(\pm 2, 0)$;   (ii) $(0, \pm 3)$;   (iii) $(0, 0), (4, 0)$;

(iv) $(1, 0), (-1, 0)$;   (v) $(0, 0), (2, 2)$;   (vi) $(3, 0), (-3, 0)$.

9. $(-\frac{11}{5}, \frac{2}{5})$.   **10.** $8x - 2y - 7 = 0$; $(-1, 1), (3, 0)$.

11. (i) $(x - 2)^2 + (y - 1)^2 + \lambda(x^2 + y^2) = 0$;

(ii) $x^2 + (y + 4)^2 + \lambda(x^2 + y^2) = 0$;

(iii) $(x - 1)^2 + (y - 1)^2 + \lambda\{(x - 2)^2 + (y + 1)^2\} = 0$;

(iv) $(x - 2)^2 + (y + 3)^2 + \lambda\{(x - 4)^2 + y^2\} = 0$.

13. $10x + 4y - 13 = 0$; $13(x^2 + y^2) + 102x - 6y = 0$.

16. $(-1, 1), (0, -1)$; $x^2 + y^2 - 2x + 6y = 0$.

17. $13(x^2 + y^2) - 28x + 16y - 43 = 0$.   **18.** $x^2 + y^2 + 2x - 2y = 0$.

24. (i) $(\frac{1}{5}, \frac{8}{5})$;   (ii) $x^2 + y^2 + 2x - 4y + 1 = 0$, $5(x^2 + y^2) - 32x - 6y + 33 = 0$.

EXAMPLES 5c (Page 115)

2. (i) $60°$;   (ii) $\cos^{-1} \frac{1}{4}\sqrt{6}$.   **3.** $3x + 4y - 17 = 0$.   **4.** $a = 4$.

5. $x^2 + y^2 + 8x + 2y - 8 = 0$.   **7.** $x^2 + y^2 - 2ax - 2by + r^2 = 0$.

9. $9x^2 + 9y^2 + 29x - 15y = 0$.   **10.** $x^2 + y^2 - 2y - 3 = 0$.

11. $x^2 + y^2 - x - 3y + \mu(x - 3y + 4) = 0$ with alternative forms.

12. $x^2 + y^2 - 3x - 5y + 1 = 0$.   **14.** $x^2 + y^2 + 2gx + 2fy + r^2 = 0$.

16. $2\sqrt{\{(g_1^2 + f_1^2 - c_1)(g_2^2 + f_2^2 - c_2)\}} = 2g_1 g_2 + 2f_1 f_2 - c_1 - c_2$.

18. $x^2 + y^2 - 5x + 2y + 1 = 0$.

19. $x^2 + y^2 + \mu y - 1 = 0$; $9x^2 + 9y^2 + 26y - 9 = 0$, $x^2 + y^2 - 6y - 1 = 0$.

EXAMPLES 5d (Page 119)

1. (i) $3x^2 + 3y^2 - 20x + 12 = 0$; (ii) $x^2 + y^2 - 5x + 4 = 0$;
(iii) $5x^2 + 5y^2 - 52x + 20 = 0$; (iv) $x = 0$.

2. $(\frac{5}{3}, 0)$, $\frac{4}{3}$; $(\frac{17}{16}, 0)$, $\frac{15}{8}$; $(-\frac{5}{3}, 0)$, $\frac{4}{3}$; $(-\frac{17}{16}, 0)$, $\frac{15}{8}$. **6.** $3\frac{3}{4}$ cm.

7. $x^2 + y^2 - 3ax + a^2 = 0$. **8.** $8x^2 + 8y^2 + 93x - 25y + 107 = 0$.

11. (i) $5x^2 + 5y^2 - 34x - 7 = 0$; (ii) $5x^2 + 5y^2 - 2x - 7 = 0$; $(0, \pm\sqrt{\frac{7}{5}})$.

18. The circle $(a - b)(x^2 + y^2) - 2abx = 0$.

MISCELLANEOUS EXAMPLES (Page 120)

1. $x^2 + y^2 - 6y = 0$, $x^2 + y^2 + 24y = 0$. **2.** $x^2 + y^2 \pm ax \pm bx = 0$.

3. $(-3, -2)$, $(1, 2)$. **4.** $x + 2y - 1 = 0$.

6. $2x^2 + 2y^2 + 2x + 6y + 1 = 0$. **7.** 30; $x^2 + y^2 - 6x - 4y - 17 = 0$.

9. $4x + 3y + 1 = 0$; $(-\frac{4}{25}, -\frac{3}{25})$. **10.** $(3, 0)$, $(7, 0)$.

11. $x^2 + y^2 + 4x + 4 = 0$, $x^2 + y^2 - 6x + 4 = 0$.

13. $x - y = 0$; $\sqrt{\{\frac{1}{2}(a+b)^2 - 4c\}}$. **15.** $(\mp a, 0)$.

16. $x^2 + y^2 - 8x - 10y + 31 = 0$. **17.** $(\mp 3, 0)$; $x^2 + y^2 \pm 8x + 9 = 0$.

21. $(-1, 0)$, $(2, 4)$; $3x^2 + 3y^2 + 12x + 8y - 16 = 0$.

22. (i) $x^2 + y^2 + 10x + 10y = 0$; (ii) $2x^2 + 2y^2 + 14x + 12y + 5 = 0$.

29. The circle $x^2 + y^2 = a^2 + b^2$.

EXAMPLES 6a (Page 127)

2. (i) 5, $\tan^{-1}\frac{4}{3}$; (ii) 4, $\frac{\pi}{2}$; (iii) 3, 0; (iv) 13, $\tan^{-1} - \frac{12}{5}$;
(v) 2, $-\frac{2\pi}{3}$; (vi) $\sqrt{(2 + 2\sin\theta)}$, $\tan^{-1}\{\cos\theta/1 + \sin\theta\}$.

3. (i) $x = \pm 2i$; (ii) $x = -4 \pm 3i$; (iii) $x = \cos\theta \pm i\sin\theta$.

4. $x = 1$, $\frac{1}{2}(-1 \pm i\sqrt{3})$. **5.** $x = -2$, $1 \pm i\sqrt{3}$.

6. (i) $x = \frac{7}{2}$, $y = \frac{3}{2}$; (ii) $x = -\frac{1}{3}$, $y = \frac{1}{3}$.

8. (i) Circle, centre $(0, 0)$ radius 4; (ii) circle, centre $(1, 0)$ radius 2;
(iii) circle, centre $(-2, 0)$ radius 2; (iv) circle, centre $(0, 0)$ radius 2.

9. (i) Circle, centre $(1, 1)$ radius 3; (ii) circle, centre $(-1, -1)$ radius 3;
(iii) straight line, $x = 1$; (iv) straight line, $y + 1 = \sqrt{3}(x + 1)$.

11. Max. 10, min. 4. **12.** (i) 4; (ii) $2(1 + \sqrt{2})$.

18. (i) $2 + i$; (ii) $1 + \frac{4}{3}i$. **19.** $2 + i$. **20.** $\cos\theta + i\sin\theta$ with $\theta = \frac{1}{3}\pi$, π, $\frac{5}{3}\pi$.

EXAMPLES 6b   (Page 130)

1. (i) $-2-6i$;   (ii) 2;   (iii) $-5-12i$;   (iv) $-2-2i$;
(v) $\frac{1}{2}(3-i)$;   (vi) $\frac{1}{25}(-6+17i)$;   (vii) $\frac{1}{10}(-9-13i)$;   (viii) $-\frac{1}{4}(1+i)$.

2.   (i) $\cos 2\theta + i \sin 2\theta$;   (ii) $4(\cos 4\theta + i \sin 4\theta)$;
(iii) $\cos \theta + i \sin \theta$;   (iv) $\cos 3\theta - i \sin 3\theta$;
(v) $\cos 2\theta + i \sin 2\theta$;   (vi) $\cos 6\theta - i \sin 6\theta$;
(vii) -1;   (viii) -1.

3. $x^2 - 2x \cos \frac{1}{3}\pi + 1$ or $x^2 - x + 1$.   **4.** $x^2 - 2x \cos \frac{1}{5}\pi + 1$.

5. (i) $x = \frac{2}{29}$, $y = -\frac{5}{29}$;   (ii) $x = -4$, $y = 0$;   (iii) $x = 16$, $y = 30$.

6. (i) $\cos \theta - i \sin \theta$;   (ii) $2 \cos \theta$;   (iii) $2i \sin \theta$.

8. (i) $-i\, 16\sqrt{3}$;
(ii) $1 + 3 \cos \theta + 3 \cos 2\theta + \cos 3\theta + i(3 \sin \theta + 3 \sin 2\theta + \sin 3\theta)$.

9. $2 + i$, $-2 - i$.   **10.** $\frac{3}{2}z$.   **13.** $(z_1 - z_2)/(z_1 - z_3)$ imaginary.

EXAMPLES 6c   (Page 135)

1. (i) $\sqrt{2}$;   (ii) $\sqrt{13}$;   (iii) $\sqrt{13}$; acute-angled.

2. Positive, positive, negative.   **3.** When z_1, z_2, z_3 are collinear.

4. Max. $\sqrt{5} + 1$, min. $\sqrt{5} - 1$; $\tan^{-1} 2$.   **7.** $u = x^2 - y^2$, $v = 2xy$.

9. The lines are parallel.

10. (i) Max. 3, min. 1;   (ii) max. 4, min. 2.

14. Circle, $x^2 + y^2 + 6x + 5 = 0$.

17. $(0, -2)$, 2;   (i) $0 \leqslant |z| \leqslant 4$;   (ii) $-\pi \leqslant am\ z \leqslant 0$.   **18.** $2x + y = 5$.

EXAMPLES 6d   (Page 138)

1.   (i) $\cos \pi + i \sin \pi\ (= -1)$;   (ii) $\cos \frac{1}{2}\pi + i \sin \frac{1}{2}\pi\ (= i)$;
(iii) $\cos \frac{1}{4}\pi - i \sin \frac{1}{4}\pi$;   (iv) $e(\cos \frac{1}{2}\pi + i \sin \frac{1}{2}\pi)\ (= ie)$;
(v) $\cos \theta - i \sin \theta$;   (vi) $\cos \omega t + i \sin \omega t$;
(vii) $e^x(\cos \sqrt{2}x + i \sin \sqrt{2}x)$;   (viii) $\cos \theta$.

2. (i) e^0;   (ii) $e^{\frac{1}{3}i\pi}$;   (iii) $e^{4i\theta}$;   (iv) $e^{-i\theta}$;   (v) $e^{i(\frac{1}{2}\pi - \theta)}$;
(vi) $5e^{-i\phi}$, where ϕ is the acute value of $\tan^{-1} \frac{3}{4}$.

3. (i) $R(e^{2ix})$;   (ii) $R(e^{5ix})$;   (iii) $R(e^{i\overline{A+B}})$;   (iv) $R(e^{i\overline{A-B}})$;   (v) $R(e^{x(a+ib)})$.

7. $\cos 3\theta = 4 \cos^3 \theta - 3 \cos \theta$; $\sin 3\theta = 3 \sin \theta - 4 \sin^3 \theta$.

9. $2e^{ax} \cos bx$.

10. (i) $\frac{1}{2}(e^{2i\theta} + e^{-2i\theta})$;   (ii) $\frac{1}{2i}(e^{3i\theta} - e^{-3i\theta})$;   (iii) $\frac{1}{i}\left\{\dfrac{e^{i\theta} - e^{-i\theta}}{e^{i\theta} + e^{i\theta}}\right\}$.

11. (i) $\frac{1}{2}e^x(\cos x + \sin x)$;   (ii) $\frac{1}{5}e^x(\sin 2x - 2 \cos 2x)$;
(iii) $\frac{1}{17}e^{2x}(8 \cos \frac{1}{2}x + 2 \sin \frac{1}{2}x)$;   (iv) $-\frac{1}{13}e^{-x}(4 \sin \frac{3}{2}x + 6 \cos \frac{3}{2}x)$.

12. (i) $y = e^{-\frac{1}{2}x}\left\{C \cos \frac{\sqrt{3}}{2}x + S \sin \frac{\sqrt{3}}{2}x\right\}$;

(ii) $y = e^{\frac{1}{2}x}\left\{C \cos \frac{\sqrt{7}}{2}x + S \sin \frac{\sqrt{7}}{2}x\right\}$;

(iii) $y = e^{-\frac{3}{4}x}\left\{C \cos \frac{\sqrt{7}}{4}x + S \sin \frac{\sqrt{7}}{4}x\right\}$;

(iv) $y = C \cos mt + S \sin mt$;

(v) $S = e^{-kt}\{C \cos \lambda t + S \sin \lambda t\}$, $\lambda = \sqrt{(\mu - k^2)}$.

13. $1 + (1 + i)x + ix^2 + \frac{1}{3}(i-1)x^3 - \frac{1}{6}x^4$; $\quad 1 + x - \frac{1}{3}x^3 - \frac{1}{6}x^4$. **14.** $2x - 2x^2 - \frac{1}{3}x^3$.

15. $(2 + 11i)e^{x(2+i)}$; $\quad e^{2x}(2 \cos x - 11 \sin x)$, $e^{2x}(11 \cos x + 2 \sin x)$. **16.** 161.

MISCELLANEOUS EXAMPLES (Page 139)

1. $\frac{1}{2}\{1 - i \tan \frac{1}{2}\theta\}$. **2.** 128. **4.** Circle $|z| = 1$ anticlockwise.

5. $(1, 1)$, 2; (i) circle centre $(3, 1)$, radius 2; (ii) circle centre $(-\frac{1}{2}, \frac{1}{2})$, radius 1.

7. (i) $2 \cos x$; (ii) $2e^x \cos \sqrt{2}x$; (iii) $2i \sin \omega t$.

9. (i) $x^2 + y^2 = 4$;   (ii) $(x-3)^2 + y^2 = 16$;

(iii) $y = \sqrt{3}x$;   (iv) $(x-2)^2 + (y-1)^2 = 1$;

(v) $y = x - 1$;   (vi) $3x^2 + 3y^2 - 16x + 16 = 0$;

(vii) $x^2 + y^2 = 1$.

11. $\cos \theta = \frac{1}{2}(e^{i\theta} + e^{-i\theta})$, $\sin \theta = \frac{1}{2i}(e^{i\theta} - e^{-i\theta})$.

13. (i) Circle centre A, radius OB; (ii) straight line AB.

14. (i) $\sqrt{5} + 1$; (ii) $\sqrt{5} - 1$.

15. (i) $2\sqrt{2}$, $\frac{7}{12}\pi$; (ii) 2, $-\frac{1}{2}\pi$; (iii) 4, π; (iv) $\frac{1}{8}\sqrt{2}$, $\frac{3}{4}\pi$; (v) 8, π.

17. $\frac{a}{a^2 + b^2}\{(-1)^{\frac{1}{2}b} - 1\}$; $\frac{b}{a^2 + b^2}\{1 - (-1)^{\frac{1}{2}b}\}$. **19.** $-2 + 2i$, $\frac{3}{2} + \frac{9}{2}i$.

21. (i) e^u; (ii) e^u; (iii) 1.

22. (i) $2 \cos \theta$, θ; (ii) $-2 \cos \theta$, $\theta - \pi$; (iii) $2 \cos \theta$, θ; (iv) $2 \cos \theta$, $\theta - 2\pi$.

27. $\frac{1}{2i}\left\{\frac{(1+i)^n - (1-i)^n}{n!}\right\}$. **31.** $\cot \frac{1}{2}\theta$, $\frac{1}{2}\pi$.

33. 1, $\frac{2}{3}\pi$; 1, $-\frac{2}{3}\pi$. **34.** Inside the circle $x^2 + y^2 = 1$.

36. w moves along the imaginary axis from the origin to $+\infty$ and returns to the origin from $-\infty$.

37. -4.

41. (i) $1 + i \cot \theta$; $\frac{1}{2(1 - \cos \theta)}\{1 - \cos \theta + \cos \overline{n-1}\,\theta - \cos n\theta$
$+ i(\sin \theta + \sin \overline{n-1}\,\theta - \sin n\theta\lambda)\}$.

EXAMPLES 7a (Page 145)

3. 5. **4.** $x = \pm 2\sqrt{5}, \frac{7}{3}.$ **5.** $x = \pm\sqrt{2}, -\frac{9}{7}.$ **7.** $x = 2 + i, \frac{11}{2}.$

8. $x = \pm 2i, \frac{1}{2}(1 \pm \sqrt{5}).$ **10.** $x = \pm 1/\sqrt{2}, \frac{1}{2}(5 \pm \sqrt{17}).$

11. $x = 1 \pm \sqrt{3}, \pm i.$ **12.** 3.

13. $x = \pm 2i, 1, -\frac{3}{2}.$ **16.** $x = 1, \pm i, 2 \pm i\sqrt{3}.$

17. -2 and -1, 0 and 1, 3 and 4.

18. $(x^2 - 6x + 2)(x^2 - 4x - 2);\ x = 3 \pm \sqrt{7}, 2 \pm \sqrt{6}.$

EXAMPLES 7b (Page 150)

1. $a + b + 1 = 0.$ **2.** $x = -\frac{1}{2}, -\frac{1}{2}, \frac{2}{3}.$ **3.** $k = -9, 6.$

4. $k = \frac{176}{27}, x = \frac{4}{3}, \frac{4}{3}, -\frac{11}{3};\ k = -12, x = -2, -2, 3.$

5. $2p^2 - 3pq + 2q^2 = 0.$ **6.** $x = -2, -2, -2, \frac{2}{3}.$

7. $(10a + b)^2 = (20h - 3b)(2h + 3a).$ **8.** $x = -\frac{2}{3}, -\frac{2}{3}, \frac{4}{3}.$

9. $(4b - 7)^2 + (2a + 15)(7a + 30b) = 0.$

10. $(ab' - a'b)^2 = 4(ah' - a'h)(hb' - h'b).$

11. $x = -2, -2, \frac{1}{2}(1 \pm i\sqrt{11}).$

12. $(bc - ca + b)^2 + (b^2 + c^2)(ab - b^2 + c) = 0.$ **13.** $x = -2, -2, -2, \frac{1}{2}.$

15. $27a^4 = 256b.$ **16.** $\lambda = -5.$ **17.** $x = \frac{1}{2}, \frac{1}{2}, \pm\sqrt{3}.$

18. $(q - s)^3 = (r - p)^2(ps - qr).$

EXAMPLES 7c (Page 153)

1. (i) 6; (ii) -3; (iii) 3. **2.** $x = -2, 3, 6.$

4. $x = -4, \pm\frac{1}{2}\sqrt{19}.$ **5.** (i) 36; (ii) 393.

6. $x = -\frac{5}{3}, \frac{3}{4}, \frac{3}{2}.$ **7.** (i) 6; (ii) $\frac{1}{2}.$

8. 10. **9.** $x^3 - 14x^2 - 7x - 1 = 0.$

10. $x = \frac{2}{3}, 1, \frac{5}{4}.$ **11.** $x = -\frac{7}{2}, -\frac{3}{2}, \frac{1}{2}.$

12. (i) $\frac{15}{2}$; (ii) $-\frac{5}{2}.$ **14.** $x = -5, -\frac{3}{2}, \frac{1}{2}, 1.$

15. (i) $x, y, z = -2, 1, 2$; (ii) $x, y, z = -4, 2, 3$; (iii) $x, y, z = -2, -1, 1.$

16. $x = -1, -\frac{1}{2}, 1 \pm \sqrt{2}.$ **17.** $5pq.$ **20.** $(1, -2).$

21. $a, b, c = -3, -1, 2.$ **22.** $a^3b.$

23. (i) $x^3 + px - q = 0$; (ii) $x^3 + 4px^2 + 5p^2x + 2p^3 + q^2 = 0.$

25. $x = -2, -\frac{1}{2}, 1, \frac{5}{2}.$

EXAMPLES 7d   (Page 157)

1. $y^3 + 3y^2 - 1 = 0$.

2. (i) $y^3 - 4y^2 - 8 = 0$;   (ii) $y^3 + 2y^2 + 1 = 0$;   (iii) $y^3 + 2y - 1 = 0$.

3. $3y^4 - y^2 + 2y - 1 = 0$.   **4.** $y^3 - 6y^2 + 18y - 22 = 0$.

5. $y^4 + 3y^3 + 4y^2 + 3y + 1 = 0$.   **6.** 19.

7. $y^3 - 3y + 3 = 0$; -3.   **8.** $y^3 + 3y^2 - 9 = 0$.

9. $y^4 - 13y^2 + 36 = 0$; $x = -4, -3, 1, 2$.

10. $y^3 + 3y^2(2b - 1) + 3y(3b^2 + 6b - 2c + 1) - (c + 1)^2 = 0$.

11. $h = 2$; $y^3 - 3y + 2 = 0$.   **12.** $a = \frac{1}{2}$, $b = -\frac{3}{2}$; $y^3 - 7y + 6 = 0$.

13. $by^4 + 4by^3 + 6by^2 + y(a + 4b) + a + b + 1 = 0$.

14. $y^3 + 6y^2 + 5y + 4 = 0$.   **15.** $y^3 + 5y^2 + 9y + 4 = 0$; 7.   **16.** c.

17. $by^3 - 3by^2 + b(ab + 3)y + b(b^2 - ab - 1) = 0$.

19. $\alpha(2 - \alpha)$; $y^3 - 8y^2 + 26y - 15 = 0$.

MISCELLANEOUS EXAMPLES   (Page 158)

2. $x = -\frac{5}{2}$, $3 \pm 2\sqrt{5}$.   **3.** $x = -\frac{2}{3}$, 3, 3.

4. $+, -, +, -, +$.   **5.** $x = a, a, a(-1 \pm i\sqrt{2})$.

6. $a = -2, 10$.   **7.** $x = \frac{1}{3}$, $1 \pm 2i$.

9. $x^2 - acx + a^2d + c^2b - 4bd = 0$.   **10.** (i) $-\frac{3}{4}$; (ii) $\frac{19}{8}$; (iii) $\frac{33}{16}$.

11. $4p^3 + 27q = 0$.   **12.** $x = -\frac{4}{3}$, $\pm\frac{3}{2}$.

13. $x = -\frac{3}{2}$, $\frac{1}{3}(5 \pm \sqrt{13})$.   **15.** $y^3 + 4py - 8q = 0$.

16. $(c_2^2 + c_1b_2 - c_2b_1)(b_2^2 + b_1 - c_2) = (b_2c_2 + c_1)^2$.   **17.** $x, y, z = -4, -1, 5$.

18. 0 and 1.   **19.** $x = -2, -2, \pm i$.   **20.** $\lambda = 1$, $\frac{1}{2}(7 \pm \sqrt{5})$.

21. 1.   **22.** $x = -\frac{5}{3}, \frac{3}{4}, \frac{3}{2}$.   **23.** $27a^3 + 3b$, $243a^5 + 45a^2b$.

24. (i) $x, y, z = -2, 1, 3$;   (ii) $x = 5, y = 6, z = 7$; $x = 5, y = 7, z = 6$.

25. $[(b^2 + c^2 - a^2)(a^2 - c^2) + b^2c^2][ab(b^2 + c^2 - a^2) + b^2c^2] + b^2[c(a^2 - c^2) - abc]^2 = 0$.

26. $a = 33, b = 30$.   **27.** $x = -2, -2, \pm\sqrt{2}$.

28. $x = -1, 1, 2$; $-13 < a < -8$.   **29.** $x = 1$, $\pm i\sqrt{2}$, $\frac{1}{2}(-1 \pm \sqrt{5})$.

31. $x, y, z = -1, 1, \pm 2$.   **32.** $x = \pm\frac{5}{3}$, $\frac{1}{5}(3 \pm i\sqrt{6})$.

33. $6t^3 - 3bt - 2c = 0$; $b^3 = 6c^2$.   **34.** $y^3 + 6py^2 + 9p^2y + 4p^3 + 27q^2 = 0$.

35. $x = -\frac{5}{3}, -\frac{2}{3}, \frac{1}{3}, \frac{4}{3}$.

36. (i) $2a^3 - 9ab + 27c = 0$; (ii) $a^3c = b^3$; $\lambda^3(2a^3 - 9ab + 27c)$
$+ \lambda^2(a^4 - 3a^2b + 27ac - 9b^2) + \lambda(a^3b + 9a^2c - 6ab^2) + a^3c - b^3 = 0$.

38. $a = 6, b = 7$.   **40.** $(\beta - \gamma)(\gamma - \alpha)(\alpha - \beta)$; $-(4a^3 + 27b^2)$.

EXAMPLES 8a   (Page 164)

1. $x = 1$.   **2.** $3x + 16y = 4$.   **3.** $x + 2y + 2 = 0$.   **4.** $y = x - 2$.

5. $4x + 20y = 3$.   **6.** $9x + y + 1 = 0$.   **8.** $\beta y = 2a(x - a)$.   **9.** $(-1, 2)$.

10. $(\frac{9}{2}, 4)$.   **11.** $(-6, -2)$.   **12.** $(6, 4)$.   **13.** $(3, 1)$.

14. $(4, 2)$.   **15.** $(-\frac{12}{7}, \frac{4}{7})$.   **16.** $x^2 + 4y^2 - x - 4y = 0$.   **22.** $(-8, -2)$.

EXAMPLES 8b   (Page 168)

1. $t^4 = 1$; $t = \pm 1$.   **2.** $(0, \pm 1)$, $(\pm \frac{4}{3}\sqrt{2}, \frac{1}{3})$.   **3.** $y + tx = 2t + t^3$; $\sqrt{2}$.

5. $y - x + 6 = 0$.   **7.** $y - x + 3 = 0$; $y - 2x + 12 = 0$; $y + 3x - 33 = 0$.

8. $2at(t^2 - 1)x + 2bt(t^2 + 1)y = (a^2 + b^2)(t^4 - 1)$.   **14.** $x = a$.

15. $(at^2, 2at)$; $t = -2, -1, 3$.   **22.** $2a^2$.

EXAMPLES 8c   (Page 171)

2. $t^4 - 2t^3 + t^2 + 2t + 1 = 0$;   (i) 2,   (ii) 1,   (iii) -2,   (iv) 1.

3. $b^2t^4 + 2t^2(3b^2 - 2a^2) + b^2 = 0$.   **4.** $(c/t_1t_2t_3, \ ct_1t_2t_3)$.

EXAMPLES 8d   (Page 176)

1. Ellipse;   (ii) line pair;   (iii) rect. hyperbola;   (iv) rect. hyperbola;   (v) parabola;   (vi) rect. hyperbola;   (vii) ellipse;   (viii) parabola.

2. (i) $\lambda = 3$;   (ii) $\lambda = \pm \frac{3}{2}\sqrt{2}$.   **4.** $x^2 - 4xy + 2y^2 + 1 = 0$; a hyperbola.

5. $3x^2 + 2y^2 - 12x + 2y = 0$.

6. Conics passing through the common points of: (i) the circle $x^2 + y^2 = 1$ and the rect. hyperbola $xy = 1$; (iv) the ellipse $x^2/4 + y^2/2 = 1$ and the circle $x^2 + y^2 = 3$; (iii) the parabola $y^2 = 8x$ and the line pair $(x + y - 1)(2y - x) = 0$; (iv) the rect. hyperbola $x^2 - y^2 = 1$ and the ellipse $x^2/8 + y^2/2 = 1$; (v) the line pair $(x - y + 1)(x + y - 1) = 0$ and the coordinate axes; (vi) the ellipses $4x^2 + 9y^2 = 36$, $9x^2 + 4y^2 = 36$.

7. $x^2 - y^2 - 4x + 7 = 0$.

8. $(a_2 - a_1)[a_1(b_2 - y) - a_2(b_1 - x)] = [(b_1 - b_2) - (x - y)]^2$.

9. $x(3x + 2y - 9) + \lambda y(x - y + 2) = 0$ with alternative forms; $3x^2 + 9xy - 7y^2 - 9x + 14y = 0$.

10. $3x^2 - 2xy - 2y^2 - 3x + 8y - 6 = 0$; a hyperbola.

12. $2x^2 + 5xy + 2y^2 - 8x - 8y - 4 = 0$; a hyperbola.   **14.** $3x^2 - 3y^2 = 8$.

15. $\lambda = \pm 2$.   **16.** (i) $\lambda = -15$;   (ii) $\lambda = 1$;   (iii) $\lambda = 0, -3, -8$.

17. $(a^2 + b^2)x^2 + 2a^2xy + 2a^2y^2 - 2a^2b(x + y) = 0$.

18. Conics through the common points of: (i) the line pairs $(x+y-1)(2x-y+3)=0$, $(x-1)(y-2)=0$; (ii) the circle $x^2+y^2=4$ and the chords $x-y=0$, $x+y+1=0$; (iii) conics touching the rect. hyperbola $xy=1$ at the ends of the chord $x+y=2$; (iv) conics touching the lines $x-y=0$, $x+y=0$ at their points of intersection with the line $x=2$.

19. $6x^2 - 5xy + 16y^2 - 19x + 8y = 0$.

20. $x^2 + y^2 - 2a^2 + \lambda(x+y-2a)(x+y-a) = 0$; $2xy - 3a(x+y) + 4a^2 = 0$.

22. At the ends of the chord $x + 2y + 3a = 0$; the points $(a, -2a)$, $(9a, -6a)$.

24. $(\pm\sqrt{(a^2-b^2)}, 0)$.

MISCELLANEOUS EXAMPLES   (Page 178)

1. $4x - 9y + 13 = 0$.   **2.** $(-1, 2)$.   **3.** $2xy - 3x - 2y = 0$.

5. $(x^2+y^2)^2 = 9(x^2-y^2)$.   **6.** $(a^2-b^2)xy + b^3x + a^3y = 0$.

11. $(-a\,\overline{t^2+2}, -2a/t)$; $xy^2 + 2ay^2 + 4a^3 = 0$.   **12.** $x - y - 3 = 0$, $x + y + 1 = 0$.

15. $4(a^2x^2 - b^2y^2) = (a^2+b^2)^2$.   **17.** $b^2x(h-x) - a^2y(k-y) = 0$.

18. $\beta(y-\beta) = 2a(x-\alpha)$.   **22.** $b^2x^2 + a^2y^2 - a^2by = 0$.

33. $xy + bx - ay - ab = 0$.   **34.** $2x^2 + 2xy + 3y^2 - 10x - 15y + 18 = 0$.

37. Conics touching the lines $2x - y + 1 = 0$, $x + 2y - 1 = 0$ at their points of intersection with the axis $x = 0$; $\lambda = 0$, $\lambda = -\frac{25}{8}$.

38. $y^2 - 4ax + \lambda(y\,\overline{t_1+t_2} - 2x - 2at_1t_2)(y\,\overline{t_3+t_4} - 2x - 2at_3t_4) = 0$.

39. $(l^2+m^2)(ax^2 + 2hxy + by^2) - (a+b)(lx + my - 1)^2 = 0$.

EXAMPLES 9a   (Page 183)

1. (i) $\cos 5\theta + i \sin 5\theta$;   (ii) 1;   (iii) $\cos 3\theta - i \sin 3\theta$;
(iv) $\cos 4\theta + i \sin 4\theta$;   (v) $\cos 8\theta - i \sin 8\theta$;   (vi) $\cos 5\theta + i \sin 5\theta$;
(vii) $-\sin 6\theta - i \cos 6\theta$.

2. (i) $-8i$;   (ii) $8(1+i)$;   (iii) $-128(1+i\sqrt{3})$;
(iv) $-\frac{1}{32}(1+\sqrt{3})$;   (v) $-2^{10}\,i\sqrt{3}$;   (vi) $-\dfrac{i\sqrt{3}}{2^{10}}$.

3. $\frac{125}{8}(\cos 6\theta + i \sin 6\theta)$, where $\theta = \tan^{-1} 3$.

4. (i) $\cos \theta - i \sin \theta$;   (ii) $2 \cos \theta$;   (iii) $2 \cos 2\theta$;   (iv) $2i \sin 3\theta$;
(v) $2 \cos 5\theta$;   (vi) $2 \cos 4\theta + 2 \cos 2\theta + 1$;   (vii) $\sin 5\theta/\sin \theta$.

6. $2^{n+1} \cos \frac{1}{3}n\pi$.   **7.** $5^{\frac{1}{2}n}(\cos n\theta + i \sin n\theta)$, where $\theta = \tan^{-1} \frac{1}{2}$.

8. (i) $\pm(\cos\theta + i\sin\theta)$; (ii) $\pm 2(\cos\frac{1}{2}\theta + i\sin\frac{1}{2}\theta)$;

(iii) $\pm(\cos 2\theta - i\sin 2\theta)$; (iv) $\pm[\cos(\frac{1}{4}\pi - \theta) + i\sin(\frac{1}{4}\pi - \theta)]$;

(v) $\pm\dfrac{1}{\sqrt{2}}(1 + i)$; (vi) $\pm\sqrt{2}(1 + i)$;

(vii) $\pm 2^{\frac{1}{4}}(\cos\frac{1}{8}\pi + i\sin\frac{1}{8}\pi)$; (viii) $\pm(\sqrt{3} + i)$; (ix) $\pm\dfrac{1}{\sqrt{2}}(1 - i)$.

9. (i) $\cos\frac{1}{3}(2r\pi + 3\theta) + i\sin\frac{1}{3}(2r\pi + 3\theta)$, $r = 0, 1, 2$;

(ii) $\cos\frac{1}{3}(2r\pi + 6\theta) + i\sin\frac{1}{3}(2r\pi + 6\theta)$, $r = 0, 1, 2$;

(iii) $2\{\cos\frac{1}{3}(2r\pi + \theta) + i\sin\frac{1}{3}(2r\pi + \theta)\}$, $r = 0, 1, 2$;

(iv) $\cos\frac{1}{3}(2r\pi + \theta - \frac{1}{2}\pi) + i\sin\frac{1}{3}(2r\pi + \theta - \frac{1}{2}\pi)$, $r = 0, 1, 2$;

(v) i, $-\frac{1}{2}(\sqrt{3} \pm i)$; (vi) -1, $\frac{1}{2}(1 \pm i\sqrt{3})$; (vii) $-2i$, $i \pm \sqrt{3}$;

(viii) $2^{\frac{1}{6}}\{\cos\frac{1}{3}(2r\pi - \frac{1}{4}\pi) + i\sin\frac{1}{3}(2r\pi - \frac{1}{4}\pi)\}$, $r = 0, 1, 2$.

10. (i) ± 1, $\pm i$; (ii) $-i$, $\frac{1}{2}(i \pm \sqrt{3})$;

(iii) $\pm 2i$; (iv) $\pm\dfrac{1}{\sqrt{2}}(-1 + i)$, $\pm\dfrac{1}{\sqrt{2}}(1 + i)$;

(v) 2, $2(\cos\frac{2}{5}\pi \pm i\sin\frac{2}{5}\pi)$, $2(\cos\frac{4}{5}\pi + i\sin\frac{4}{5}\pi)$;

(vi) -1, $\cos\frac{1}{5}\pi \pm i\sin\frac{1}{5}\pi$, $\cos\frac{3}{5}\pi \pm i\sin\frac{3}{5}\pi$;

(vii) $2^{\frac{1}{6}}\{\cos\frac{1}{3}(2r + \frac{1}{4})\pi + i\sin\frac{1}{3}(2r + \frac{1}{4})\pi\}$, $r = 0, 1, 2$;

(viii) $2^{\frac{2}{3}}\{\cos\frac{2}{3}(2r + \frac{1}{6})\pi + i\sin\frac{2}{3}(2r + \frac{1}{6})\pi\}$, $r = 0, 1, 2$.

12. (i) $\pm 2^{-\frac{1}{4}}(\cos\frac{1}{8}\pi - i\sin\frac{1}{8}\pi)$; (ii) $-i$, $\frac{1}{2}(i \pm \sqrt{3})$. **13.** 1.

14. (i) $\pm(\cos\frac{1}{8}\pi - i\sin\frac{1}{8}\pi)$, $\pm(\cos\frac{3}{8}\pi + i\sin\frac{3}{8}\pi)$;

(ii) $2^{-\frac{1}{6}}\{\cos\frac{1}{3}(2r + \frac{1}{4})\pi + i\sin\frac{1}{3}(2r + \frac{1}{4})\pi\}$, $r = 0, 1, 2$.

15. (i) -2; (ii) -1; (iii) 1. **16.** (i) $\pm i\sqrt{3}$; (ii) ± 2; (iii) 2.

17. (i) $x = -1$, $\frac{1}{2}(1 \pm i\sqrt{3})$; (ii) $\pm 2(\cos\frac{1}{8}\pi - i\sin\frac{1}{8}\pi)$, $\pm 2(\cos\frac{3}{8}\pi + i\sin\frac{3}{8}\pi)$.

EXAMPLES 9b (Page 189)

1. (i) $x = \pm 1$, $\pm i$;

(ii) $x = -1$, $\cos\frac{1}{7}\pi \pm i\sin\frac{1}{7}\pi$, $\cos\frac{3}{7}\pi \pm i\sin\frac{3}{7}\pi$, $\cos\frac{5}{7}\pi \pm i\sin\frac{5}{7}\pi$;

(iii) $x = -\frac{3}{2}$, $\frac{3}{4}(1 \pm i\sqrt{3})$; (iv) $x = 3$, $\pm i\sqrt{3}$;

(v) $x = \pm\dfrac{1}{\sqrt{2}}(1 + i)$, $\pm\dfrac{1}{\sqrt{2}}(1 - i)$, -1, $\frac{1}{2}(1 \pm i\sqrt{3})$.

2. (i) $(x + 1)(x^2 - x + 1)$; (ii) $(x^2 + \sqrt{2}x + 1)(x^2 - \sqrt{2}x + 1)$;

(iii) $(x - 1)(x^2 - 2x\cos 2\pi/5 + 1)(x^2 - 2x\cos 4\pi/5 + 1)$;

(iv) $(x^2 + 1)(x^2 - 2x\cos\pi/6 + 1)(x^2 - 2x\cos 5\pi/6 + 1)$;

(v) $(2x + 1)(4x^2 - 4x\cos\pi/5 + 1)(4x^2 - 4x\cos 3\pi/5 + 1)$;

(vi) $(x + 1)(x^2 - x + 1)(x^2 + x + 1)$.

3. $z = \pm 2$, $1 \pm i\sqrt{3}$, $-1 \pm i\sqrt{3}$. **4.** $x = \pm\frac{1}{2}(1 \pm i\sqrt{3})$.

5. (i) $x = 3$, $\frac{1}{7}i\sqrt{3}(2 - i\sqrt{3})$, $-\frac{1}{7}i\sqrt{3}(2 + i\sqrt{3})$; (ii) $x = 0$, $\pm i$.

6. (i) $(x^2 - 2x \cos \frac{2}{9}\pi + 1)(x^2 - 2x \cos \frac{8}{9}\pi + 1)(x^2 - 2x \cos \frac{14}{9}\pi + 1)$;

(ii) $\{x^2 - 2x \cos \theta + 1\}\{x^2 - 2x \cos (\theta + \frac{2}{3}\pi) + 1\}\{x^2 - 2x \cos (\theta + \frac{4}{3}\pi) + 1\}$.

7. $x = \pm 1$, $\cos \dfrac{\pi}{4} \pm i \sin \dfrac{\pi}{4}$, $\cos \dfrac{3\pi}{4} \pm i \sin \dfrac{3\pi}{4}$; $\pm i$.

9. (i) $\dfrac{1}{2i}\left(\dfrac{1}{x-i} - \dfrac{1}{x+i}\right)$;

(ii) $\dfrac{1}{2i \sin \theta}\left\{\dfrac{1}{x - (\cos \theta + i \sin \theta)} - \dfrac{1}{x - (\cos \theta - i \sin \theta)}\right\}$;

(iii) $\dfrac{1}{2\sqrt{3}}\left\{\dfrac{x + \sqrt{3}}{x^2 + \sqrt{3}x + 1} - \dfrac{x - \sqrt{3}}{x^2 - \sqrt{3}x + 1}\right\}$.

10. $x = -\frac{1}{2}$, $-\frac{1}{2}(1 \pm i\sqrt{3})$, $-\frac{1}{6}(3 \pm i\sqrt{3})$.

11. (i) $(x^2 + x + 1)(x^2 - x + 1)(x^2 - x\sqrt{3} + 1)(x^2 + x\sqrt{3} + 1)$;

(ii) $(x^2 - 2x \cos \frac{1}{9}\pi + 1)(x^2 - 2x \cos \frac{2}{9}\pi + 1)(x^2 - 2x \cos \frac{7}{9}\pi + 1)$
$\qquad (x^2 - 2x \cos \frac{8}{9}\pi + 1)(x^2 - 2x \cos \frac{13}{9}\pi + 1)(x^2 - 2x \cos \frac{14}{9}\pi + 1)$.

13. (i) $x = \frac{1}{2}i$, $i\{1 - \cos \frac{1}{5}\pi \pm i \sin \frac{1}{5}\pi\}/2(1 - \cos \frac{1}{5}\pi)$,

$\qquad i\{1 - \cos \frac{3}{5}\pi \pm i \sin \frac{3}{5}\pi\}/2(1 - \cos \frac{3}{5}\pi)$;

(ii) $z = 2$, $2i$, $2(1 + i)$, 0.

16. $PP_r{}^2 = r^2 + x^2 - 2rx \cos (r - 1)2\pi/n$.

EXAMPLES 9c (Page 193)

1. (i) $2 \cos 2\theta$; (ii) $2i \sin \theta$; (iii) $2 \cos 6\theta$; (iv) $2i \sin 4\theta$;

(v) $2 \cos 2\theta + 4 \cos \theta$; (vi) $2 \cos 3\theta + 1 + 2i \sin \theta$;

(vii) $5 + 4 \cos \theta$; (viii) $1 + \sin^2 \theta + \sin 2\theta$.

2. (i) $z^4 + 1/z^4$; (ii) $z^5 - 1/z^5$; (iii) $\frac{1}{2}(z^7 + 1/z^7)$;

(iv) $\frac{1}{4}(z + 1/z)^2$; (v) $\frac{1}{16}(z - 1/z)^4$; (vi) $\frac{1}{256}(z^2 - 1/z^2)^4$.

3. (i) $\frac{1}{4}(\cos 3\theta + 3 \cos \theta)$; (ii) $\frac{1}{8}(\cos 4\theta - 4 \cos 2\theta + 3)$;

(iii) $\frac{1}{16}(\sin 5\theta - 5 \sin 3\theta + 10 \sin \theta)$;

(iv) $\frac{1}{64}(\cos 7\theta + 7 \cos 5\theta + 21 \cos 3\theta + 35 \cos \theta)$;

(v) $-\frac{1}{8}(\sin 4\theta - 2 \sin 2\theta)$;

(vi) $-\frac{1}{64}(\sin 7\theta + \sin 5\theta - 3 \sin 3\theta - 3 \sin \theta)$.

5. (i) $8 \cos^4 \theta - 8 \cos^2 \theta + 1$; (ii) $8 \cos^3 \theta - 4 \cos \theta$;

(iii) $32 \cos^6 \theta - 48 \cos^4 \theta + 18 \cos^2 \theta - 1$;

(iv) $32 \cos^5 \theta - 32 \cos^3 \theta + 6 \cos \theta$.

6. (i) $3 \sin \theta - 4 \sin^3 \theta$; (ii) $8 \sin^4 \theta - 8 \sin^2 \theta + 1$;

(iii) $16 \sin^5 \theta - 20 \sin^3 \theta + 5 \sin \theta$; (iv) $16 \sin^4 \theta - 12 \sin^2 \theta + 1$.

7. (i) $(3 \tan \theta - \tan^3 \theta)/(1 - 3 \tan^2 \theta)$;

(ii) $(4 \tan \theta - 4 \tan^3 \theta)/(1 - 6 \tan^2 \theta + \tan^4 \theta)$;

(iii) $(7 \tan \theta - 35 \tan^3 \theta + 21 \tan^5 \theta - \tan^7 \theta)/(1 - 21 \tan^2 \theta$
$\qquad\qquad\qquad\qquad\qquad\qquad\qquad\qquad + 35 \tan^4 \theta - 7 \tan^6 \theta)$.

8. $\pm\sqrt{3}$. **11.** (i) $\frac{5}{32}\pi$; (ii) $\frac{3}{256}\pi$.

15.   (i) $\frac{1}{2}(1 - i \tan \theta)$;   (ii) $(1 + \cos^2 \theta - i \sin \theta \cos \theta)/2(1 + \cos^2 \theta)$;

    (iii) $8 \cos^3 \theta$;

    (iv) $\{ - (1 + \cos \theta + 2 \cos 3\theta + \cos 4\theta - \cos 5\theta) + i(3 \sin \theta - 2 \sin 3\theta$
$$- \sin 4\theta + \sin 5\theta)\}/(5 - 4 \cos \theta);$$

    (v) $(1 - x \cos \theta - ix \sin \theta)/(1 - 2x \cos \theta + x^2)$;

    (vi) $2^n \cos^n \frac{1}{2}\theta(\cos \frac{1}{2}n\theta + i \sin \frac{1}{2}n\theta)$;

    (vii) $\{1 - \cos^2 \theta - \cos^n \theta \cos n\theta + \cos^{n+1} \theta \cos \overline{n - 1}\,\theta$
$$+ i(\sin \theta \cos \theta - \cos^n \theta \sin n\theta + \cos^{n+1} \theta \sin \overline{n - 1}\,\theta)\}/\sin^2 \theta;$$

    (viii) $\{1 - x \cos \theta - x^n \cos n\theta + x^{n+1} \cos \overline{n - 1}\,\theta + i(x \sin \theta - x^n \sin n\theta$
$$+ x^{n+1} \sin \overline{n - 1}\,\theta)\}/(1 - 2x \cos \theta + x^2).$$

18. (i) 21;   (ii) 24.

MISCELLANEOUS EXAMPLES   (Page 194)

1. -256.   **2.** $-i$, $\pm(\cos \frac{1}{10}\pi - i \sin \frac{1}{10}\pi)$, $\pm(\cos \frac{3}{10}\pi + i \sin \frac{3}{10}\pi)$.

3. $\frac{1}{2}(1 - i \tan \frac{1}{2}\theta)$.

4. (i) $(x + 1)(x^2 - 2x \cos \pi/7 + 1)(x^2 - 2x \cos 3\pi/7 + 1)(x^2 - 2x \cos 5\pi/7 + 1)$;

    (ii) $(x^2 - 2x \cos \frac{1}{18}\pi + 1)(x^2 - 2x \cos \frac{13}{18}\pi + 1)(x^2 - 2x \cos \frac{25}{18}\pi + 1)$.

5. $\frac{1}{3} \tan^{-1} \frac{3}{4}$, $\frac{2}{3}\pi + \frac{1}{3} \tan^{-1} \frac{3}{4}$, $-\frac{2}{3}\pi + \frac{1}{3} \tan^{-1} \frac{3}{4}$.

7. $\cos 8\theta = 128 \cos^8 \theta - 256 \cos^6 \theta + 160 \cos^4 \theta - 32 \cos^2 \theta + 1$;

    $\sin 8\theta = \cos \theta(- 128 \sin^7 \theta + 192 \sin^5 \theta - 80 \sin^3 \theta + 8 \sin \theta)$.

8. $1\cdot18 + 0\cdot43i$, $-0\cdot97 + 0\cdot81i$, $-0\cdot22 - 1\cdot24i$.

9. $\dfrac{1}{2i}\left(\dfrac{1}{x - i} - \dfrac{1}{x + i}\right)$; $24(5x^4 - 10x^2 + 1)/(x^2 + 1)^5$.

11. $x = \pm\sqrt{2}(\cos \frac{1}{12}\pi \pm i \sin \frac{1}{12}\pi)$, $\pm\sqrt{2}(\cos \frac{7}{12}\pi \pm i \sin \frac{7}{12}\pi)$.

13. $\frac{5}{3} \tan^{-1} \frac{4}{3}$, $-\frac{2}{3}\pi + \frac{5}{3} \tan^{-1} \frac{4}{3}$, $-\frac{4}{3}\pi + \frac{5}{3} \tan^{-1} \frac{4}{3}$.   **15.** $\pm\dfrac{\sqrt{\cot \frac{1}{2}\theta}}{\sqrt{2}}(1 + i)$.

16. $\pm(1\cdot44 - 0\cdot17i)$, $\pm(0\cdot17 + 1\cdot44i)$.

17. $\pm(\cos \frac{1}{18}\pi \pm i \sin \frac{1}{18}\pi)$, $\pm(\cos \frac{5}{18}\pi + i \sin \frac{5}{18}\pi)$, $\pm(\cos \frac{7}{18}\pi + i \sin \frac{7}{18}\pi)$,
$$\pm(\cos \tfrac{11}{18}\pi + i \sin \tfrac{11}{18}\pi), \pm(\cos \tfrac{13}{18}\pi + i \sin \tfrac{13}{18}\pi).$$

19. $\dfrac{1}{2ai \sin \theta}\left[\dfrac{1}{x - a(\cos \theta + i \sin \theta)} - \dfrac{1}{x - a(\cos \theta - i \sin \theta)}\right]$;
$$\sin (n + 1)\theta/a^{n+2} \sin \theta.$$

20. $\pm2^{\frac{1}{4}}(\cos \frac{1}{24}\pi - i \sin \frac{1}{24}\pi)$, $\pm2^{\frac{1}{4}}(\cos \frac{11}{24}\pi + i \sin \frac{11}{24}\pi)$.

22. 1.   **25.** $\theta = \frac{1}{16}(4r + 1)\pi$.

26. $(x^2 - 2x \cos \frac{2}{21}\pi + 1)(x^2 - 2x \cos \frac{8}{21}\pi + 1)(x^2 - 2x \cos \frac{2}{3}\pi + 1)$
$$(x^2 - 2x \cos \tfrac{20}{21}\pi + 1)(x^2 - 2x \cos \tfrac{26}{21}\pi + 1)$$
$$(x^2 - 2x \cos \tfrac{32}{21}\pi + 1)(x^2 - 2x \cos \tfrac{38}{21}\pi + 1).$$

27. 1, $\cos \frac{2}{7}\pi \pm i \sin \frac{2}{7}\pi$, $\cos \frac{4}{7}\pi \pm i \sin \frac{4}{7}\pi$, $\cos \frac{6}{7}\pi \pm i \sin \frac{6}{7}\pi$.

30. $(\cot^7 \theta - 21 \cot^5 \theta + 35 \cot^3 \theta - 7 \cot \theta)/(7 \cot^6 \theta - 35 \cot^4 \theta + 21 \cot^2 \theta - 1)$.

31. $z = \frac{1}{2}\left(\cot \dfrac{r\pi}{n} - i\right)$, $r = 0, 1, \ldots (n - 1)$.

32. Circle centre $(- 1, 0)$, radius 2.

EXAMPLES 10a (Page 199)

1. $r(r+1)$; $\frac{1}{3}n(n+1)(n+2)$.

2. $(r+2)(r+3)$; $\frac{1}{3}[(n+2)(n+3)(n+4)-24]$.

3. $(3r-1)(3r+2)$; $\frac{1}{9}[(3n-1)(3n+2)(3n+5)+10]$.

4. $(5r-4)(5r+1)$; $\frac{1}{15}[(5n-4)(5n+1)(5n+6)+24]$. **5.** $\dfrac{1}{r(r+1)}$; $\dfrac{n}{n+1}$.

6. $\dfrac{1}{(2r+1)(2r+3)}$; $\dfrac{n}{3(2n+3)}$.

7. $r(r+1)(r+2)$; $\frac{1}{4}n(n+1)(n+2)(n+3)$.

8. $(3r-2)(3r+1)(3r+4)$; $\frac{1}{12}[(3n-2)(3n+1)(3n+4)(3n+7)+56]$.

9. $\dfrac{1}{r(r+1)(r+2)}$; $\dfrac{1}{2}\left[\dfrac{1}{2}-\dfrac{1}{(n+1)(n+2)}\right]$.

10. $\dfrac{1}{(2r+1)(2r+3)(2r+5)}$; $\dfrac{1}{4}\left[\dfrac{1}{15}-\dfrac{1}{(2n+3)(2n+5)}\right]$.

11. $(r+1)(r+2)(r+3)(r+4)$; $\frac{1}{5}[(n+1)(n+2)(n+3)(n+4)(n+5)-120]$.

12. $\dfrac{1}{(2r-1)(2r+1)(2r+3)(2r+5)}$; $\dfrac{1}{6}\left[\dfrac{1}{15}-\dfrac{1}{(2n+1)(2n+3)(2n+5)}\right]$.

13. (i) $\frac{1}{2}n(n^3+2n^2+1)$; (ii) $\frac{1}{12}n(n+1)(3n^2+11n+4)$;
(iii) $\frac{1}{2}n(n^3+8n^2+17n-2)$.

14. (i) $n(n+1)^2$; (ii) $\frac{1}{12}n(n+1)(3n^2+19n+8)$. **15.** $\dfrac{n^2+2n}{(n+1)^2}$.

16. (i) $\frac{1}{3}n(4n^2-1)$; (ii) $\frac{1}{3}n(2n+1)(6n^2+31n+37)$;
(iii) $\frac{1}{3}n(2n+1)(12n^2+10n+1)$.

17. (i) $\dfrac{1}{(r+2)(r+3)}-\dfrac{1}{(r+1)(r+2)(r+3)}$; $\dfrac{n(n+1)}{4(n+2)(n+3)}$;

(ii) $\dfrac{1}{(r+2)(r+3)}+\dfrac{1}{(r+1)(r+2)(r+3)}$; $\dfrac{n(5n+13)}{12(n+2)(n+3)}$;

(iii) $\dfrac{1}{r+3}-\dfrac{1}{(r+2)(r+3)}-\dfrac{1}{(r+1)(r+2)(r+3)}$.

18. $\frac{1}{20}n(n+1)(n+2)(n+3)(8n+7)$.

19. (i) $\dfrac{3n^2+5n}{8(n+1)(n+2)}$; (ii) $\dfrac{17n^3+66n^2+61n}{72(n+1)(n+2)(n+3)}$;
(iii) $\dfrac{11n^3+48n^2+49n}{36(n+1)(n+2)(n+3)}$.

20. $6r-1$; $9n^2+2n$.

22. (i) $\frac{1}{3}n(48n^3+80n^2-6n-47)$; (ii) $\dfrac{5n^3+30n^2+37n}{36(n+1)(n+2)(n+3)}$.

23. (i) $\dfrac{3n^2+5n}{4(n+1)(n+2)}$; (ii) $\dfrac{3n^2+n}{4(n+1)(n+2)}$; (iii) $\dfrac{68n^3+132n^2+61n}{36(n+1)(2n+1)(2n+3)}$.

EXAMPLES 10b (Page 203)

1. $\sin r\theta$; $\dfrac{\sin \frac{1}{2}n\theta \sin \frac{1}{2}(n+1)\theta}{\sin \frac{1}{2}\theta}$. **2.** $\cos r\theta$; $\dfrac{\sin \frac{1}{2}n\theta \cos \frac{1}{2}(n+1)\theta}{\sin \frac{1}{2}\theta}$.

3. $\sin \frac{1}{2}(r+1)\theta$; $\dfrac{\sin \frac{1}{4}n\theta \sin \frac{1}{4}(n+3)\theta}{\sin \frac{1}{4}\theta}$. **4.** $\cos 2r\theta$; $\dfrac{\sin n\theta \cos (n+1)\theta}{\sin \theta}$.

5. $\sin (\theta + \frac{1}{2}\overline{r-1}\,\pi)$; $\sqrt{2}\sin \frac{1}{4}n\pi \sin (\theta + \frac{1}{4}\overline{n-1}\,\pi)$.

6. $\cos (\theta + \frac{2}{3}\overline{r-1}\,\pi)$; $\dfrac{2}{\sqrt{3}}\sin \frac{1}{3}n\pi \cos (\theta + \frac{1}{3}\overline{n-1}\,\pi)$.

7. $2^{r-1}\cos \overline{r-1}\,\theta$; $(1 - 2\cos \theta - 2^n \cos n\theta + 2^{n+1}\cos \overline{n-1}\,\theta)/(5 - 4\cos \theta)$.

8. $(\frac{1}{2})^{r-1}\sin \overline{r-1}\,\theta$; $(5 + 2\sin \theta - 4\cos \theta - 2^{-n+2}\sin n\theta + 2^{-n+1}\sin \overline{n-1}\,\theta)/$
$$(5 - 4\cos \theta).$$

9. $(-1)^{r-1}x^{r-1}\cos (r-1)\theta$; $\{1 + x\cos \theta + (-1)^{n+1}x^n \cos n\theta$
$$+ (-1)^{n+1}x^{n+1}\cos \overline{n-1}\,\theta\}/(1 + 2x\cos \theta + x^2).$$

10. $(-1)^{r-1}\cos (2r-1)\theta$; $\{1 + \cos \theta + (-1)^{n+1}(\cos n\theta + \cos \overline{n+1}\,\theta)\}/$
$$2(1 + \cos \theta).$$

11. (i) $\frac{1}{2}n - \dfrac{\sin \frac{1}{2}n\alpha \cos \frac{1}{2}(n+1)\alpha}{2\sin \frac{1}{2}\alpha}$; (ii) $\dfrac{\sin \frac{1}{2}n\alpha \sin \frac{1}{2}(n+1)\alpha}{2\sin \frac{1}{2}\alpha}$.

12. $\dfrac{1}{2^{n-1}}\cot \dfrac{1}{2^{n-1}}x - 2\cot 2x$. **13.** $\cot \frac{1}{2}x - \cot nx$.

14. $\cos^{n+1}\theta \sin n\theta/\sin \theta$. **15.** $(\cot \theta - \cot \overline{n+1}\,\theta)/\sin \theta$.

17. $\sqrt{2}\sin \frac{1}{4}n\pi[\sin (\theta + \frac{1}{4}\overline{n-1}\,\pi) - \sin (\theta + \frac{1}{4}n\pi)]$.

18. $\dfrac{1}{\tan x}(\tan \overline{n+1}\,x - \tan x) - n$. **19.** $(2\cos \frac{1}{2}\beta)^n \cos (\alpha + \frac{1}{2}n\beta)$.

20. (i) $\dfrac{\sinh \frac{1}{2}nx \sinh \frac{1}{2}\overline{n+1}\,x}{\sinh \frac{1}{2}x}$; (ii) $\dfrac{\sinh \frac{1}{2}nx \cosh \frac{1}{2}\overline{n+1}\,x}{\sinh \frac{1}{2}x}$.

22. $\tan^{-1}n + \tan^{-1}\overline{n+1} - 1$.

EXAMPLES 10c (Page 207)

1. $\dfrac{1 - na^n}{1 - a} + \dfrac{a(1 - a^{n-1})}{(1-a)^2}$. **2.** $\frac{1}{4}[1 + (-1)^{n-1}(2n+1)]$.

3. $\frac{3}{2}[3 - 2n(\frac{1}{3})^n - (\frac{1}{3})^{n-1}]$. **4.** $2\{3 - (n+1)(\frac{1}{2})^n - (\frac{1}{2})^{n-1}\}$.

5. $\dfrac{1 - (-1)^n n \cos^n \theta}{1 + \cos \theta} - \dfrac{\cos \theta(1 + (-1)^n \cos^{n-1}\theta)}{(1 + \cos \theta)^2}$.

6. $\dfrac{1 - (2n-1)(-1)^n x^n}{1 + x} - \dfrac{2x(1 - (-1)^{n-1}x^{n-1})}{(1+x)^2}$.

7. $2\{a - (a + \overline{n-1}d)(\frac{1}{2})^n + d(1 - (\frac{1}{2})^{n-1})\}$.

8. $\frac{1}{4}\{7(1 - 3^n) + 2n3^{n+1}\}$. **9.** $\frac{1}{8}[7 - (-1)^n(2n^2 + 7)]$.

10. $\dfrac{1}{1-x}[2 - \frac{1}{2}(n^2 - n + 2)x^n] + \dfrac{x(1 - x^{n-1})}{(1-x)^3} - \dfrac{\overline{n-1}\,x^n}{(1-x)^2}$.

11. (i) $\dfrac{1-(2n-1)x^n}{1-x}+\dfrac{2x(1-x^{n-1})}{(1-x)^2}$;

(ii) $\dfrac{1-\frac{1}{2}n(n+1)x^n}{1-x}+\dfrac{x(2-nx^{n-1})}{(1-x)^2}+\dfrac{x^2(1-x^{n-2})}{(1-x)^3}$.

14. (i) $(1+x)^n+nx(1+x)^{n-1}$;

(ii) $(1+x)^n+3nx(1+x)^{n-1}+n(n-1)x^2(1+x)^{n-2}$.

16. (i) $\dfrac{1-(n+1)x^n}{1-x}+\dfrac{x(1-x^n)}{(1-x)^2}$;

(ii) $\dfrac{1-(n+1)^2x^n}{1-x}+\dfrac{3x-(2n+3)x^{n+1}}{(1-x)^2}+\dfrac{2x^2(1-x^n)}{(1-x)^3}$.

17. $\frac{1}{2}(3^n+1)$. **20.** (i) $n[2^{n-1}+(n-1)2^{n-2}]$; (ii) $n[2^n+(n-1)2^{n-2}]$.

22. $(-1)^{\frac{1}{2}n}{}_nC_{n/2}$.

MISCELLANEOUS EXAMPLES (Page 212)

1. (i) $\frac{1}{4}n(27n^3-18n^2-9n+4)$; (ii) $\frac{1}{2}n(n^3+4n^2+4n-1)$;

(iii) $\frac{1}{12}n(n+1)(3n^2+19n+26)$.

3. $n(n+2)(n+3)$.

4. (i) $n(2n^3+8n^2+7n-2)$; (ii) $\frac{1}{4}n(n+1)(n^2+9n+20)$. **6.** $-8n^2$.

7. (i) $\dfrac{1}{2}\left[\dfrac{3}{2}-\dfrac{2n+3}{(n+1)(n+2)}\right]$; (ii) $\dfrac{n(n+2)}{(n+1)^2}$.

9. (i) $\frac{1}{12}n(n+1)(3n^2+11n+10)$; (ii) $\dfrac{n}{3n+1}$.

11. $\left\{4-2\cos\theta-\dfrac{1}{2^{n-2}}\cos n\theta+\dfrac{1}{2^{n-1}}\cos\overline{n-1}\,\theta\right\}/(5-4\cos\theta)$.

12. $\frac{1}{6}n(n+1)(2n^2+2n-1)$. **13.** $\frac{1}{24}(n-1)n(n+1)(3n+2)$.

14. (i) $\dfrac{1-(3n-2)x^n}{1-x}+\dfrac{3x(1-x^{n-1})}{(1-x)^2}$; (ii) $\frac{5}{8}+3^n(\frac{1}{4}n^2+\frac{1}{2}n-\frac{5}{8})$.

16. $\frac{1}{6}n(n+1)(4n+11)+6(2^n-1)$.

17. (i) $\dfrac{1}{2}\left[\dfrac{1}{2}-\dfrac{1}{(n+1)(n+2)}\right]$; (ii) $\dfrac{1}{3}\left[\dfrac{1}{6}-\dfrac{1}{(n+1)(n+2)(n+3)}\right]$.

18. 107, 745. **22.** $\dfrac{1}{4}\left[\dfrac{1}{2n+1}+\dfrac{1}{2n+3}\right]$; $\dfrac{1}{4}\left[\dfrac{1}{3}+(-1)^{n+1}\dfrac{1}{2n+3}\right]$.

23. (i) $\frac{1}{3}n(7n^2-1)$; (ii) $\dfrac{1}{2n}$. **24.** $\frac{1}{2}n(n+1)^2(n+2)$.

29. (i) $\frac{1}{4}n(n+1)(n+4)(n+5)$; (ii) $\dfrac{2n^2+2n+1}{n(n+1)(n+2)}-\dfrac{1}{4}$.

32. (i) $\dfrac{2n^2+2n+1}{n(n+1)(n+2)}-\dfrac{1}{4}$; (ii) $\frac{1}{6}n(n+1)(n+2)$. **33.** (i) $(ab)^{\frac{1}{2}n}$.

34. $\dfrac{1}{4}\left[3\cos\theta+(-1)^{n-1}\dfrac{1}{3^{n-1}}\cos(3^n\theta)\right]$. **39.** $\frac{1}{3}n(n+1)(n+2)-\dfrac{n}{n+1}$.

40. (i) $\dfrac{1}{1-a}\left[\dfrac{1}{1+x}-\dfrac{a^n}{1+a^nx}\right]$; (ii) $\dfrac{1-\frac{1}{2}n(n+1)x^n}{1-x}+\dfrac{2x-nx^n}{(1-x)^2}+\dfrac{x^2(1-x^{n-2})}{(1-x)^3}$.

EXAMPLES 11a (Page 218)

13. $1 - \frac{1}{2}x + \frac{1}{12}x^2 - \frac{1}{720}x^4 \ldots$

16. $x - \frac{1}{3}x^3 + \frac{2}{15}x^5 \ldots$

17. $1 - 2x^2 + \frac{5}{3}x^4 - \frac{34}{45}x^6 \ldots$

18. $5x - \frac{70}{3}x^3 + \frac{110}{3}x^5 \ldots$

19. $1 - x + x^2 - \frac{5}{6}x^3 + \frac{2}{3}x^4; \quad 1 + x + x^2 + \frac{5}{6}x^3 + \frac{2}{3}x^4 \ldots; \quad 1 + x^2 + \frac{2}{3}x^4 \ldots$

20. $\log 2 - x + \frac{1}{4}x^2 - \frac{1}{6}x^3 + \frac{7}{96}x^4 \ldots$
    21. 2.   **22.** 0.   **23.** $-\frac{1}{2}$.

EXAMPLES 11b (Page 221)

12. $\frac{1}{4}\pi + x - \frac{1}{3}x^3$.
    13. $-\frac{1}{6}$.

14. (i) 0·0009995; (ii) 0·50025; (iii) 0·7953 rad.

17. (i) 2; (ii) -1; (iii) 3; (iv) 1.
    18. $-\frac{1}{3}$.

EXAMPLES 11c (Page 222)

1. $\cos x = 1 - \frac{x^2}{2!} + \frac{x^4}{4!} - \ldots; \quad \sin x = x - \frac{x^3}{3!} + \frac{x^5}{5!} - \ldots$

2. $\cosh x = 1 + \frac{x^2}{2!} + \frac{x^4}{4!} + \ldots; \quad \sinh x = x + \frac{x^3}{3!} + \frac{x^5}{5!} + \ldots$

3. (i) $1 - 2x + 3x^2 - 4x^3 + \ldots;$ (ii) $x - \frac{1}{2}x^2 + \frac{1}{3}x^3 - \frac{1}{4}x^4 + \ldots$

4. $\sin^{-1} x = x + \frac{1}{6}x^3 + \frac{3}{40}x^5 + \ldots; \quad \cos^{-1} x = \frac{1}{2}\pi - x - \frac{1}{6}x^3 - \frac{3}{40}x^5 - \ldots$

6. $x - \frac{1}{6}x^3 + \frac{3}{40}x^5 \ldots$
    7. $2x - \frac{2}{3}x^3 + \frac{2}{5}x^5 - \frac{2}{7}x^7 + \ldots$

8. (i) $\frac{1}{4}\pi + x - \frac{1}{3}x^3 + \ldots;$ (ii) $2x + \frac{1}{3}x^3 + \frac{3}{20}x^5 \ldots;$
(iii) $2x + \frac{1}{3}x^3 + \frac{3}{20}x^5 \ldots$

9. 3·1416.

10. (i) $(1 - x)^{-2};$ (ii) $1 - \log(1 - x);$ (iii) $2x + (1 - x)\log(1 - x).$

EXAMPLES 11d (Page 226)

1. $1 + nx + \frac{n(n-1)}{2!}x^2 \ldots$
    2. $1 + x + \frac{1}{2}x^2 - \frac{1}{6}x^3 \ldots$

3. $1 - \frac{m^2 x^2}{2!} + \frac{m^4 x^4}{4!} - \ldots$
    4. $1 + mx + \frac{m^2 x^2}{2!} + \frac{m^3 x^3}{3!} + \ldots$

5. $1 + x \log 2 + \frac{(x \log 2)^2}{2!} + \frac{(x \log 2)^3}{3!} + \ldots$

6. $x - \frac{1}{2}x^2 + \frac{1}{3}x^3 - \frac{1}{4}x^4 + \ldots$
    7. $x + \frac{1}{6}x^3 + \frac{3}{40}x^5 \ldots$

8. $mx + \frac{(mx)^3}{3!} + \frac{(mx)^5}{5!} + \ldots$
    9. $1 + \frac{(mx)^2}{2!} + \frac{(mx)^4}{4!} + \ldots$

10. $2x - \frac{2}{3}x^3 + \frac{2}{5}x^5 - \frac{2}{7}x^7 + \ldots$
    11. $x - \frac{1}{6}x^3 + \frac{3}{40}x^5 \ldots$

12. $x - \frac{4}{3}x^3 + \frac{23}{15}x^5 \ldots$
    13. $a_0 = a_1 = a_3 = 0, \; a_2 = 1, \; a_4 = \frac{1}{3}$.

19. $y = k(1 + x + \frac{1}{2}x^2 + \frac{5}{18}x^3 + \frac{25}{144}x^4 \ldots).$

MISCELLANEOUS EXAMPLES (Page 227)

1. $-x + \frac{1}{2}x^2 + \frac{2}{3}x^3 + \frac{1}{4}x^4$.
2. $(-1)^r/e^2 \cdot r!$.
3. $(-1)^{\frac{3}{2}r}(3 + 3^{3r})/4 \cdot (3r)!$.
4. $\frac{1}{2}x^2 - \frac{1}{6}x^4 + \frac{3}{16}x^6$.
5. 1.
7. $1 + x^2 + \frac{1}{3}x^4 + \frac{1}{120}x^6$.
9. $1 + 2x + 2x^2 + \frac{2}{3}x^3 - \frac{2}{3}x^4 - \frac{2}{3}x^5$.
11. $1 + x + \frac{1}{2}x^2 + \frac{1}{2}x^3$.
12. $\cos\theta$, $\frac{1}{2}(\cos 2\theta + \cos^2\theta)$, $\frac{1}{4}(\cos 3\theta + \cos^3\theta)$.
13. $\log 2 + x + \frac{1}{4}x^2 + \frac{1}{6}x^3 + \frac{7}{96}x^4$.
14. 3·14159.
15. 2.
16. $-\frac{1}{2}x^2 - \frac{1}{12}x^4 - \frac{1}{48}x^6$.
18. $x - \frac{1}{2}x^2 + \frac{1}{6}x^3 - \frac{1}{12}x^4 + \frac{1}{24}x^5$; 0·106.
21. (i) $\frac{1}{2}$; (ii) 1; (iii) 1; (iv) 0.
23. $x + \frac{1}{6}x^3 + \frac{3}{40}x^5$.
25. $\frac{1}{4}\pi + \frac{1}{2}ax + \frac{1}{4}(2b - a^2)x^2 + \frac{1}{12}(a^3 - 6ab)x^3 \ldots$
26. $e^{(1+x)\log(1+x)}$.
27. $a = 0$, $b = 1$, $c = 4$, $d = 1$.
28. $y_1 = 1$, $y_2 = 3$.
29. -2.
30. $x - x^2 + \frac{1}{3}x^4$.
33. (i) $\dfrac{\log\frac{4}{3}}{\log 2}$; (ii) -2.
35. $x - \frac{1}{180}x^5$.

EXAMPLES 12a (Page 231)

1. $-\frac{2}{3}\sqrt{(1 - x^3)} + c$.
2. $\frac{1}{2}e^{x^2} + c$.
3. $\frac{1}{2}(\log x)^2 + c$.
4. $\frac{1}{2}\log\sin 2x + c$.
5. $\log(\sin x - \cos x) + c$.
6. $\frac{1}{2}(\sinh^{-1} x)^2 + c$.
7. $\frac{1}{3}(x^2 + 1)^{\frac{3}{2}} + c$.
8. $\frac{1}{3}(x^2 - 2x + 2)^{\frac{3}{2}} + c$.
9. $\dfrac{1}{n+2}(x^2 + a^2)^{\frac{1}{2}n+1} + c$.
10. $2\sin\sqrt{x} + c$.
11. $-(x^2 + 2x + 2)e^{-x} + c$.
12. $x\tan^{-1} x - \frac{1}{2}\log(x^2 + 1) + c$.
13. $x\sinh^{-1} x - (1 + x^2)^{\frac{1}{2}} + c$.
14. $\frac{1}{4}(2x^2 - 1)\sin^{-1} x + \frac{1}{4}x(1 - x^2)^{\frac{1}{2}} + c$.
15. $\frac{1}{4}x^4\tan^{-1} x - \frac{1}{4}[\frac{1}{3}x^3 - x + \tan^{-1} x] + c$.
16. $x\cos^{-1}\dfrac{1}{x} - \cosh^{-1} x + c$.
17. $2\tan^{-1} x - \dfrac{1}{x}\log(x^2 + 1) + c$.
18. $\frac{1}{2}(\sinh x\sin x - \cosh x\cos x) + c$.
19. $x\log^2 x - 2x\log x + 2x + c$.
20. $e^x - \dfrac{xe^x}{1 + x} + c$.
21. $2 - \sqrt{3}$.
22. $\frac{2}{3}(\sqrt{2} - 1)$.
23. $\log\frac{1}{2}(3 + 2\sqrt{2})$.
24. $\frac{1}{27}(5e^3 - 2)$.
25. $\dfrac{1}{\sqrt{2}}\tan^{-1}\dfrac{1}{\sqrt{2}}$.
26. $\frac{1}{2}\pi - \log 2$.
27. 2.
28. $\frac{1}{2}\pi - \log 2$.
30. (i) $\frac{1}{2}\sin 2\theta\log(1 + \tan\theta) - \frac{1}{2}\theta + \frac{1}{2}\log(\cos\theta + \tan\theta) + c$; (ii) $e^x\tan\frac{1}{2}x + c$.

EXAMPLES 12b (Page 236)

1. $\frac{1}{2}\log\dfrac{x^2 - 1}{x^2} + c$.
2. $\frac{1}{4}\log\dfrac{x + 1}{x - 1} - \dfrac{1}{2(x - 1)} + c$.
3. $\dfrac{1}{b^2 - a^2}\left\{\dfrac{1}{a}\tan^{-1}\dfrac{x}{a} - \dfrac{1}{b}\tan^{-1}\dfrac{x}{b}\right\}$.
4. $x + \frac{9}{2}\log(x - 3) - \frac{1}{2}\log(x - 1) + c$.
5. $\frac{1}{4}\log(x^2 + 1) - \frac{1}{2}\log(1 - x) - \frac{1}{2}\tan^{-1} x + c$.

6. $\frac{1}{4}\log\frac{x+1}{x-1} - \frac{x}{2(x^2-1)} + c.$

7. $\frac{1}{3}\log(x-1) - \frac{1}{6}\log(x^2+x+1) + \frac{1}{\sqrt{3}}\tan^{-1}\frac{2x+1}{\sqrt{3}} + c.$

8. $\frac{1}{2}\log(x+1) - \frac{1}{4}\log(x^2+1) + \frac{1}{2}\tan^{-1}x + c.$

9. $\frac{4}{15}\log(x-3) - \frac{1}{10}\log(x+2) - \frac{1}{6}\log x + c.$ **10.** $\frac{1}{3}x^3 - x + \tan^{-1}x + c.$

11. $\sqrt{3}\tan^{-1}\frac{2x-1}{\sqrt{3}} - \frac{1}{\sqrt{3}}\tan^{-1}\frac{2x+1}{\sqrt{3}} + c.$ **12.** $\frac{1}{\sqrt{2}}\tan^{-1}\frac{x\sqrt{2}}{1-x^2} + c.$

13. $\frac{1}{20}\log\frac{x-1}{x+1} - \frac{1}{30}\tan^{-1}\frac{1}{3}x + c.$ **14.** $\log x - \frac{1}{2}\log(x^2+1) + \frac{1}{2(x^2+1)} + c.$

15. $\tan^{-1}\frac{x}{1-x^2} + c.$ **16.** $\frac{1}{16}\tan^{-1}\frac{1}{2}x + \frac{x}{8(x^2+4)} + c.$

17. $\log\frac{\sqrt{(x+2)}-1}{\sqrt{(x+2)}+1} + c.$

18. $\log(x+\sqrt{(1-x)}) - \frac{1}{\sqrt{5}}\log\frac{\sqrt{5}-1+2\sqrt{(1-x)}}{\sqrt{5}+1-2\sqrt{(1-x)}} + c.$

19. $\sqrt{(x^2+x)} - \frac{1}{2}\cosh^{-1}(2x+1) + c.$ **20.** $\sin^{-1}(x-2) + c.$

21. $\sqrt{(x^2+2x+2)} - \sinh^{-1}(x+1) + c.$

22. $\frac{1}{2}x(x^2+x)^{\frac{1}{2}} + \frac{1}{4}(x^2+x)^{\frac{1}{2}} - \frac{1}{8}\cosh^{-1}(2x+1) + c.$

23. $2\sqrt{(x+2)} + \frac{2}{\sqrt{3}}\log\frac{\sqrt{(x+2)}-\sqrt{3}}{\sqrt{(x+2)}+\sqrt{3}} + c.$

24. $-\frac{1}{2}\sinh^{-1}x + \frac{1}{2}x\sqrt{(1+x^2)} + c.$ **25.** $-\sinh^{-1}\left(\frac{1}{x}\right) + c.$

26. $\frac{1}{2\sqrt{2}}\log\frac{x+\sqrt{(2x+2)}+2}{x-\sqrt{(2x+2)}+2} - \frac{1}{\sqrt{2}}\tan^{-1}\frac{\sqrt{2}(x+1)}{x} + c.$

27. $\frac{1}{\sqrt{3}}\sinh^{-1}\frac{3+x}{\sqrt{2x}} + c.$ **28.** $-\frac{1}{\sqrt{2}}\sinh^{-1}\sqrt{\frac{x^2+1}{x^2-1}} + c.$

29. $\frac{1}{\sqrt{(a^2-b^2)}}\tan^{-1}\sqrt{\frac{x^2+b^2}{a^2-b^2}} + c.$

30. $\cosh^{-1}x + \sin^{-1}\frac{1}{x} + c.$

31. $\sqrt{\frac{1+x}{1-x}} - \cosh^{-1}\left(\frac{1}{x}\right) + c.$ **32.** $-x/\sqrt{(x^2-1)} + c.$

33. (i) $-\frac{1}{2}\log 2$;   (ii) $\log\frac{4}{3}.$

34. (i) $\cosh^{-1}\frac{2x-(a+b)}{b-a} + c$;   (ii) $\sin^{-1}\frac{2x-(a+b)}{b-a} + c.$

35. $\frac{3}{2}\pi + 3\log 2 - \frac{409}{70}.$

37. (i) $\sqrt{8} - \sqrt{3} + \cosh^{-1}3 - \cosh^{-1}2$;   (ii) $\frac{1}{8}\pi(b-a)^2.$

38. $\frac{1}{2}\sinh^{-1}x + \frac{1}{2}x(1+x^2)^{\frac{1}{2}} - \frac{1}{2}x^2 + c.$

40. (i) $\frac{2}{3}\left(1 - \frac{1}{2\sqrt{2}}\right)$;   (ii) $\sinh^{-1}1.$

EXAMPLES 12c (Page 243)

1. $\sin x - \frac{2}{3}\sin^3 x + \frac{1}{5}\sin^5 x + c.$ **2.** $\frac{1}{5}\cos^5 x - \frac{1}{3}\cos^3 x + c.$

3. $-\frac{1}{8}\cos 4x - \frac{1}{4}\cos 2x + c.$ **4.** $\tan x - x + c.$

5. $\frac{1}{4}\sin x \cos^3 x + \frac{3}{8}\sin x \cos x + \frac{3}{8}x + c.$

6. $-\frac{1}{6}\cos x \sin^5 x - \frac{5}{24}\cos x \sin^3 x - \frac{5}{16}\cos x \sin x + \frac{5}{16}x + c.$

7. $\frac{1}{4}\tan^4 x + c.$ **8.** $-\frac{1}{2}\cos^4 x + c.$ **9.** $\tan x - \cot x + c.$

10. $\frac{1}{4}\tan^4 x - \frac{1}{2}\tan^2 x + \log \sec x + c.$ **11.** $-\frac{1}{2}\cot^2 x - \log \sin x + c.$

12. $-\frac{1}{6}\sin^3 x \cos^3 x - \frac{1}{8}\sin x \cos^3 x + \frac{1}{16}\sin x \cos x + \frac{1}{16}x + c.$

13. $\frac{1}{3}\tan^3 x + \tan x + c.$

14. $\frac{1}{4}\tan x \sec^3 x + \frac{3}{8}\tan x \sec x + \frac{3}{8}\log(\sec x + \tan x) + c.$

15. $-\frac{1}{8}\cos 2x - \frac{1}{16}\cos 4x + \frac{1}{24}\cos 6x + c.$ **16.** $\sec x + \log \sec x + c.$

17. $\frac{2}{3}\tan^{-1}(\frac{1}{3}\tan \frac{1}{2}x) + c.$

18. $2x + \log(2\cos x + \sin x + 3) + c.$

19. $x - \dfrac{1}{\sqrt{2}}\tan^{-1}\left(\dfrac{1}{\sqrt{2}}\tan x\right) + c.$

20. $\dfrac{1}{a\sqrt{(a^2 - b^2)}}\tan^{-1}\left(\dfrac{a}{\sqrt{(a^2 - b^2)}}\tan x\right) + c.$

21. $\dfrac{1}{(a^2 + b^2)^{\frac{1}{2}}}\log \tan \frac{1}{2}\left(x + \tan^{-1}\dfrac{a}{b}\right) + c.$

22. $\dfrac{1}{a^2 + b^2}\{ax + b\log(a\cos x + b\sin x)\} + c.$

23. $-\dfrac{1}{a^2 + b^2}\cot\left(x + \tan^{-1}\dfrac{b}{a}\right) + c.$

24. $-\log(\operatorname{cosec} x + \cot x) + \dfrac{2}{1 + \tan \frac{1}{2}x} + c.$ **25.** $\sinh x + \frac{1}{3}\sinh^3 x + c.$

26. $\dfrac{1}{2}\left\{\dfrac{1}{m+n}\sinh(m+n)x + \dfrac{1}{m-n}\sinh(m-n)x\right\} + c.$

27. $\frac{1}{2}\tanh x \operatorname{sech} x + \tan^{-1}(e^x) + c.$ **28.** $\frac{1}{7}\cosh^7 x - \frac{1}{5}\cosh^5 x + c.$

29. $\dfrac{2}{\sqrt{(a^2 - b^2)}}\tan^{-1}\left(\sqrt{\dfrac{a+b}{a-b}} \cdot e^x\right) + c.$

30. $(x - \alpha)\cos \alpha + \sin \alpha \log \sin(x - \alpha) + c.$ **31.** $\frac{1}{3}\log\dfrac{\sin x(1 + \cos x)}{(1 + 2\cos x)^2} + c.$

32. $\tan x + 2\cot x - \frac{1}{3}\cot^3 x + c.$ **33.** $\frac{1}{16}(3\sqrt{2} - 4).$

34. $\frac{5}{32}\pi.$ **35.** $\frac{3}{2} - \log 2.$ **36.** $\frac{1}{4}\pi(a+b).$

37. $\frac{1}{4}\log 3.$ **38.** $\dfrac{\pi}{3\sqrt{3}}.$ **39.** $-\dfrac{1}{\sqrt{(b^2 - a^2)}}\log\dfrac{\sqrt{(b+a)} - \sqrt{(b-a)}}{\sqrt{(b+a)} + \sqrt{(b-a)}}.$

40. $\sqrt{2}\tan^{-1}\dfrac{1}{\sqrt{2}} - \frac{1}{4}\pi.$

41. $\dfrac{1}{(1 - e^2)^{\frac{3}{2}}}(\phi - e\sin \phi) = \dfrac{1}{(1 - e^2)^{\frac{3}{2}}}2\tan^{-1}\sqrt{\left(\dfrac{1 - e}{1 + e}\right)}\tan \frac{1}{2}\theta - \dfrac{e}{1 - e^2}\dfrac{\sin \theta}{1 + e\cos \theta}.$

43. (i) $\frac{1}{2}\pi - \log 2;$ (ii) $\pi;$ (iii) $\dfrac{1}{8} + \dfrac{7\sqrt{2}}{16}\tan^{-1}\dfrac{1}{\sqrt{2}}.$

EXAMPLES 12d (Page 247)

1. $\frac{1}{40}(3e^{\pi} - 13)$. **3.** $\frac{63}{512}\pi$. **9.** $\frac{1}{2}e - 1$. **10.** $\frac{4}{3}(1 - \sqrt{2})$.

11. $2(n-1)I_n = \dfrac{x}{(x^2+1)^{n-1}} + (2n-3)I_{n-1}$; $I_3 = \frac{1}{4} + \frac{3}{32}\pi$. **12.** $\frac{32}{315}$.

14. (i) $nI_n = \cosh x \sinh^{n-1} x - (n-1)I_{n-2}$;
(ii) $(n-1)I_n = (n-1)I_{n-2} - \tanh^{n-1} x$.

17. $(2n+1)I_n = 2nI_{n-1} - x^{2n}(1 - x^2)^{\frac{1}{2}}$.

19. $I_n = -\dfrac{(n-2)x \cos x + \sin x}{(n-1)(n-2)\sin^{n-1} x} + \dfrac{n-2}{n-1} I_{n-2}$.

EXAMPLES 12e (Page 252)

3. (i) π; (ii) $\frac{1}{4}\pi^2$. **8.** (i) $\frac{2}{3}\pi$; (ii) 0.

13. (i) π^2; (ii) $\frac{1}{16}\pi^2$. **17.** (i) $\dfrac{\pi}{\sqrt{2}} \tan^{-1} \dfrac{1}{\sqrt{2}}$.

EXAMPLES 12f (Page 256)

1. (i) $\frac{1}{2}$; (ii) 1. **2.** (i) $\frac{1}{8}\pi$; (ii) $\frac{3}{8}\pi$; (iii) $\frac{1}{2}\pi$.

3. (i) $\frac{1}{2}$; (ii) $\frac{1}{2}$. **5.** 1. **7.** (i) $\frac{1}{2}\pi$; (ii) $\cosh^{-1} 2$.

8. 10. **9.** (i) $\pi\sqrt{2} - \sqrt{2}\tan^{-1}(1/\sqrt{2})$; (ii) $\pi\sqrt{2}$.

10. (i) $\frac{1}{2}\pi$; (ii) π. **11.** $\frac{3}{8}$. **12.** (i) π; (ii) π.

13. (i) $\frac{1}{2}$; (ii) 5; (iii) 1. **15.** 1. **16.** $\dfrac{2}{\sqrt{(a^2-b^2)}}\left\{\frac{1}{2}\pi - \tan^{-1}\sqrt{\dfrac{a+b}{a-b}}\right\}$.

17. $n!$. **18.** $\dfrac{\pi}{2}(a+b)$. **20.** (i) $1 + \frac{1}{2}\pi$; (ii) $\frac{1}{2}\pi$. **22.** $\frac{3}{16}\pi$.

MISCELLANEOUS EXAMPLES (Page 258)

1. (i) $\frac{1}{2}\log\dfrac{x-3}{x-1} + c$; (ii) $\cosh^{-1}(x-2) + c$;
(iii) $\sqrt{(x^2 - 4x + 3)} + 2\cosh^{-1}(x-2) + c$.

3. (i) $\frac{1}{2}\pi$; (ii) $\frac{1}{2}\sqrt{3}$. **4.** $\dfrac{1}{a^2+b^2}(a\cos bx \sinh ax + b\sin bx \cosh ax) + c$.

5. (i) $x + \frac{1}{5}\log(x^2+1) + \frac{8}{5}\log(x-2) - \frac{1}{5}\tan^{-1} x + c$;
(ii) $\frac{3}{7}(x+b)^{\frac{7}{3}} + \frac{3}{4}(a-b)(x+b)^{\frac{4}{3}} + c$; (iii) $-\dfrac{1}{x}\sqrt{(x^2+1)} + c$.

6. (i) $\frac{1}{2}(1 - \log 2)$; (ii) $\log\sqrt{3} - \frac{1}{2}$; (iii) $\frac{8}{15}$.

7. (i) $x\tan^{-1} x - \frac{1}{2}\log(1+x^2) + c$;
(ii) $x(\sinh^{-1} x)^2 + 2x - 2\sqrt{(x^2+1)}\sinh^{-1} x + c$.

8. (i) $\frac{1}{4}\pi$; (ii) $\frac{1}{2}\pi$. **9.** (i) $\sqrt{2}$; (ii) $2\sqrt{2} + \cosh^{-1} 3$.

10. (i) $\log\dfrac{e^x - 1}{e^x + 1} + c$; (ii) $\frac{1}{2}e^{\sin^{-1} x}\{x + (1-x^2)^{\frac{1}{2}}\} + c$; (iii) $-\frac{1}{2}(x^2+1)e^{-x^2} + c$.

13. (i) $\pi\dfrac{\sqrt{2}}{2}\tan^{-1}\sqrt{2}$;   (ii) $\frac{1}{2}\pi^2\left(1-\dfrac{1}{\sqrt{2}}\right)$;   (iii) $\dfrac{2}{\sqrt{3}}\pi^2$.

14. $I_n=\dfrac{2n+1}{2n+2}I_{n-1}+\dfrac{1}{n+1}2^{n-\frac{1}{2}}$; $\frac{67}{48}\sqrt{2}+\frac{5}{16}\log(1+\sqrt{2})$.

15. $\frac{1}{3}x^{\frac{3}{2}}\sqrt{(1+x^3)}+\frac{1}{3}\sinh^{-1}x^{\frac{3}{2}}+c$.   **17.** $\dfrac{\sqrt{2}}{4}\log(3+\sqrt{2})+\dfrac{1}{\sqrt{2}}\dfrac{\pi}{2}$.

18. (i) $\frac{1}{6}\pi$;   (ii) $\dfrac{1}{\sqrt{5}}[\sinh^{-1}3-\sinh^{-1}(\frac{1}{2})]$.   **19.** $\frac{16}{105}$.

23. (i) $\dfrac{2}{\sqrt{5}}\log\dfrac{\sqrt{5}+1}{\sqrt{5}-1}$;   (ii) $\frac{3}{8}\pi$.

24. (i) $2\sec\alpha\left[\tan^{-1}\dfrac{1+\sin\alpha}{\cos\alpha}-\alpha\right]$;   (ii) $\dfrac{\pi}{2\sqrt{10}}$.

26. (i) $\frac{1}{3}\pi-\frac{1}{3}\log 2-\frac{1}{6}$;   (ii) $\frac{1}{8}\pi$.

28. (i) $\frac{1}{4}\pi$;   (ii) $\dfrac{2\pi}{3\sqrt{3}}-\dfrac{1}{\sqrt{2}}\tan^{-1}2$.

29. $\dfrac{1}{\sqrt{(1-k^2)}}\sin^{-1}\left(\dfrac{t-k}{1-kt}\right)$.   **30.** 1.

31. (i) $2+\frac{3}{2}\cosh^{-1}\frac{5}{3}$;   (ii) $\log(2+\sqrt{3})-\frac{1}{2}\sqrt{3}$.

32. $\frac{1}{4}\pi\sec\frac{1}{2}\alpha$.   **36.** $\dfrac{1}{\sqrt{2}}(\sinh^{-1}\sqrt{3}-\sinh^{-1}1)$.

38. (i) $\theta\log\sec\theta$;   (ii) $\frac{1}{2}\pi(\pi-2)$.

39. (i) $\frac{3}{128}\pi(b-a)^4$;   (ii) $\dfrac{\pi}{2a}\log\dfrac{1+a}{1-a}$.

41. $(n-2)I_{n-2}=(n-1)I_n$; $I_1=\frac{1}{2}\pi$, $I_2=1$.   **42.** $\dfrac{\pi}{3\sqrt{3}}$.

EXAMPLES 13a   (Page 264)

1. $\phi=\frac{1}{2}\pi+\theta$; $p=r\cos\theta$.   **2.** $\phi=\theta$; $p=r\sin\theta$.

3. $\phi=\pi-\theta$, $p=r\sin\theta=a$.   **4.** $\phi=\alpha$; $p=r\sin\alpha$.

5. $\phi=\frac{1}{2}\theta$; $p=r\sin\frac{1}{2}\theta$.   **6.** $\phi=\pi-\frac{1}{2}\theta$; $p=r\sin\frac{1}{2}\theta=a\operatorname{cosec}\frac{1}{2}\theta$.

7. $\phi=2\theta$; $p=r\sin 2\theta=r^3/a^2$.

8. $\phi=\tan^{-1}\left(\dfrac{1+2\cos\theta}{2\sin\theta}\right)$; $p=r(1+2\cos\theta)/\sqrt{(5+4\cos\theta)}$.

9. $(\frac{1}{2},\frac{1}{6}\pi)$, $(\frac{1}{2},\frac{5}{6}\pi)$; $\frac{2}{3}\pi$.   **12.** $\left(\pm\dfrac{a}{2^{\frac{1}{4}}},\frac{1}{8}\pi\right)$.

14. $\frac{2}{3}\pi$.   **18.** $\left(\dfrac{8}{\sqrt{7}},\dfrac{5}{6}\pi-\tan^{-1}\dfrac{2}{\sqrt{3}}\right)$.

20. (i) $r=a\cos^2\frac{1}{2}\theta$;   (ii) $r^2=a^2\cos^3\frac{2}{3}\theta$;   (iii) $r\cos\theta+a=0$.

21. $r^2=a^2\cos^2\theta-b^2\sin^2\theta$.   **23.** $\frac{1}{2}\pi a$.   **24.** $8a$.

25. $\dfrac{a}{m}\sqrt{(1+m^2)}(e^{m\beta}-e^{m\alpha})$.   **27.** $8a$.   **29.** $s=\frac{1}{27}[(4+9\tan^2\theta)^{\frac{3}{2}}-8]$.

C C

EXAMPLES 13b (Page 267)

1. $[(\tfrac{1}{2}\pi)^2+4]^{\frac{3}{2}}/[(\tfrac{1}{2}\pi)^2+8]$. **2.** $\tfrac{1}{2}a$. **3.** $\tfrac{1}{5}a$.

4. $\tfrac{4}{3}a$. **5.** $\tfrac{5}{6}a\sqrt{5}$. **6.** $a\sqrt{2}$. **7.** $\dfrac{1}{6a}$.

8. $\dfrac{1}{2a^3}$ numerically. **9.** $\tfrac{1}{2}a$. **10.** b^2/a. **11.** $\tfrac{1}{3}a$.

12. $\tfrac{7}{2}a\sqrt{14}$. **14.** $p^2=ar$. **24.** $r^3=a^2p$.

EXAMPLES 13c (Page 273)

1. 6π. **3.** $\tfrac{1}{3}a^2t^3$. **4.** Area $=\pi r\sqrt{(h^2+r^2)}$; volume $=\tfrac{1}{3}\pi r^2h$.

6. Volume $=\tfrac{5}{4}\pi^2$; area $=5\pi^2$. **7.** $60\pi^2$ cm²; $\tfrac{55}{2}\pi^2$ cm³.

9. $\tfrac{288}{5}\pi$ cm³; $\tfrac{564}{5}\pi$ cm². **10.** $712\pi+162\pi^2$ cm².

13. Area $=\tfrac{8}{3}h\sqrt{(ah)}$; volume $=\tfrac{16}{5}\pi h^2\sqrt{(ah)}$; $\bar{x}=\tfrac{3}{5}h$.

14. $\tfrac{15}{128}\pi ab$. **16.** $\tfrac{8}{3}\pi a^3$. **17.** $\pi-\tfrac{8}{3}$.

18. Volume $=\tfrac{4}{3}\pi a^3\sin^3\alpha$; $\tfrac{1}{3}a(3\sin\alpha-3\alpha\cos\alpha-\sin^3\alpha)/(\alpha-\sin\alpha\cos\alpha)$.

19. $4ab\left(\tfrac{1}{2}\pi-\sin^{-1}\dfrac{a}{\sqrt{(a^2+b^2)}}\right)$. **21.** $\tfrac{1}{12}\pi^2a^3$.

MISCELLANEOUS EXAMPLES (Page 274)

4. $2\pi+\dfrac{3\sqrt{3}}{2},\ \pi-\dfrac{3\sqrt{3}}{2}$. **5.** $\tfrac{1}{2}\pi$. **7.** $\tfrac{256}{15}$ **10.** $2\pi^2abc$.

13. $\tfrac{1}{60}\pi(45\pi-8)$ cm³; $\tfrac{1}{5}\pi(15\pi-4)$ cm². **14.** $(2,\pi)$, $(-\tfrac{9}{8},\cos^{-1}\tfrac{1}{4})$.

15. $pr=a^2$. **17.** $\tfrac{1}{3}a^2(10\pi+9\sqrt{3})$. **18.** $\tfrac{6}{5}\sqrt{3}$. **21.** $\tfrac{5}{2}a^2$.

25. $\tfrac{4}{3}a$. **27.** $pa^m=r^{m+1}$. **28.** $\dfrac{2^{\frac{3}{2}}}{3^{\frac{3}{2}}}a$. **31.** $\tfrac{1}{4}\pi$.

EXAMPLES 14a (Page 279)

1. $(\pm1,0,0),\ (0,\pm1,0),\ (0,0,\pm1)$. **3.** $\sqrt{2};\ \sqrt{5};\ \sqrt{5};\ \sqrt{14};\ 5;\ 2$.

4. (i) $\sqrt{14}$; (ii) $2\sqrt{3}$; (iii) $\sqrt{22}$; (iv) $a\sqrt{6}$. **5.** $(1,\tfrac{4}{3},-\tfrac{2}{3})$.

7. $(\pm2,0,0)$. **8.** $2x^2+y^2=0,\ z=0$. **9.** $(\tfrac{4}{3},\tfrac{2}{3},\tfrac{5}{3})$.

10. $-2:3$. **11.** $x=2z$. **12.** $x+y+z=3$.

14. $G_1(\tfrac{1}{3},\tfrac{1}{3},\tfrac{1}{3})$; $G_2(\tfrac{1}{3},1,\tfrac{1}{3})$; $G_3(\tfrac{1}{3},\tfrac{1}{3},1)$; $G_4(1,\tfrac{1}{3},\tfrac{1}{3})$.

15. $[\tfrac{1}{2}(\alpha+\beta),\tfrac{1}{2}m(\alpha-\beta),0]$. **16.** $\left[\dfrac{\alpha+\lambda\beta}{1+\lambda},\ m\dfrac{(\alpha-\lambda\beta)}{1+\lambda},\ c\dfrac{(1-\lambda)}{1+\lambda}\right]$.

17. $x^2+y^2+z^2=4$; a sphere. **19.** $(2,1,0)$.

EXAMPLES 14b   (Page 283)

1. 1, 0, 0; 0, 1, 0; 0, 0, 1.   **3.** $n = \pm\frac{1}{2}$.

4. (i) $\dfrac{1}{\sqrt{3}}, \dfrac{1}{\sqrt{3}}, \dfrac{1}{\sqrt{3}}$;   (ii) $\dfrac{2}{\sqrt{29}}, \dfrac{3}{\sqrt{29}}, \dfrac{4}{\sqrt{29}}$;

(iii) $0, \dfrac{1}{\sqrt{2}}, -\dfrac{1}{\sqrt{2}}$;   (iv) $\dfrac{a}{r}, \dfrac{b}{r}, \dfrac{c}{r}$, where $r = \sqrt{(a^2 + b^2 + c^2)}$.

5. $\sqrt{\frac{7}{13}}$.   **6.** $\dfrac{2}{\sqrt{30}}, -\dfrac{5}{\sqrt{30}}, \dfrac{1}{\sqrt{30}}$.

7. (i) $\dfrac{2}{\sqrt{6}}, \dfrac{1}{\sqrt{6}}, \dfrac{1}{\sqrt{6}}$; (ii) $-\dfrac{1}{\sqrt{19}}, \dfrac{3}{\sqrt{19}}, \dfrac{3}{\sqrt{19}}$; (iii) $-\dfrac{1}{\sqrt{3}}, \dfrac{1}{\sqrt{3}}, -\dfrac{1}{\sqrt{3}}$;

(iv) $-\dfrac{1}{\sqrt{11}}, -\dfrac{3}{\sqrt{11}}, -\dfrac{1}{\sqrt{11}}$; (v) $\dfrac{1}{\sqrt{11}}, -\dfrac{1}{\sqrt{11}}, \dfrac{3}{\sqrt{11}}$.

8. $r = -\frac{1}{2}$.

9. $\dfrac{1}{\sqrt{3}}, \dfrac{1}{\sqrt{3}}, \dfrac{1}{\sqrt{3}}$; $-\dfrac{1}{\sqrt{3}}, \dfrac{1}{\sqrt{3}}, \dfrac{1}{\sqrt{3}}$; $\dfrac{1}{\sqrt{3}}, -\dfrac{1}{\sqrt{3}}, \dfrac{1}{\sqrt{3}}$; $\dfrac{1}{\sqrt{3}}, \dfrac{1}{\sqrt{3}}, -\dfrac{1}{\sqrt{3}}$.

10. $90°, 54° 44', 35° 16'$.   **11.** $60°$.

12. Plane $y = 0$, $l : 0 : n$; plane $x = 0$, $0 : m : n$.

13. $\dfrac{l}{\sqrt{(l^2 + m^2)}}, \dfrac{m}{\sqrt{(l^2 + m^2)}}, 0$.

14. $\cos^{-1}\left(\dfrac{1}{\sqrt{11}}\right) = 72° 27'$; $\dfrac{3\sqrt{10}}{2}$ sq. units.   **15.** $\cos^{-1}\left(\dfrac{1}{\sqrt{30}}\right) = 79° 29'$.

EXAMPLES 14c   (Page 288)

1. $(6, 0, 0)$; $(0, -3, 0)$; $(0, 0, 2)$.

3. (i) $3x - y - 2z = 0$; (ii) $2x - 2y + z = 2$; (iii) $2x - 3y - 10z + 3 = 0$.

4. $x - 2y - 2z = 3$.

5. (i) 2; 1, 0, 0;   (ii) 1; 0, 0, -1;   (iii) 2; $\frac{3}{5}, -\frac{4}{5}, 0$;

(iv) 2; $\frac{2}{3}, -\frac{1}{3}, \frac{2}{3}$;   (v) 1; $\dfrac{1}{\sqrt{3}}, -\dfrac{1}{\sqrt{3}}, \dfrac{1}{\sqrt{3}}$;

(vi) 0; $\dfrac{2}{\sqrt{38}}, \dfrac{5}{\sqrt{38}}, \dfrac{3}{\sqrt{38}}$;   (vii) $\dfrac{3}{\sqrt{110}}$; $-\dfrac{5}{\sqrt{110}}, \dfrac{7}{\sqrt{110}}, \dfrac{6}{\sqrt{110}}$.

6. $x - 2y + 2z = 0$; 3.

8. (i) $45°$; (ii) $\cos^{-1}\dfrac{1}{\sqrt{3}}$; (ii) $\cos^{-1}\frac{2}{5}$; (iv) $90°$.

9. $3x + 3y - 4z + 1 = 0$.

10. (i) 0; (ii) $\dfrac{2}{\sqrt{5}}$; (iii) $\dfrac{2}{\sqrt{14}}$; (iv) $\dfrac{20}{\sqrt{83}}$.   **12.** Opposite.

13. $12x - 19y - 5z + 12 = 0$.   **14.** $x - 2y + 2z = 9$.

16. $2x + 4y + 4z = 7$.　　　　　　**17.** $(-1, 0, 2)$.

18. (i) $3y - 2z = 0$;　(ii) $x \pm \sqrt{3}z = 0$.　　**19.** $-5x + 4y + z + 7 = 0$.

20. $11x + 8y - 7z + 26 = 0$.　　　　**21.** $x - y - z + 2 = 0$.

22. $x - 17y - 10z + 1 = 0$,　$19x + 7y - 10z - 11 = 0$.

23. (i) ABC, $z = 0$;　ABD, $12x - 9y + 2z = 0$;　ACD, $3x + 6y - 5z = 0$;

　　　BCD, $15x - 3y + 8z = 33$;

　　(ii) $\dfrac{33}{\sqrt{229}}$;　(iii) $\cos^{-1} \dfrac{223}{\sqrt{229}\sqrt{298}} = 31° \, 23'$.

24. $\dfrac{7}{\sqrt{44}}$.

EXAMPLES 14d　(Page 291)

1. $y = z = 0$;　$z = x = 0$;　$x = y = 0$.　　**2.** $x = y = z$.

3.　(i) $\dfrac{x}{1} = \dfrac{y}{2} = \dfrac{z}{2}$;　$\tfrac{1}{3}, \tfrac{2}{3}, \tfrac{2}{3}$;

　　(ii) $\dfrac{x-1}{6} = \dfrac{y}{3} = \dfrac{z}{2}$;　$\tfrac{6}{7}, \tfrac{3}{7}, \tfrac{2}{7}$;

　　(iii) $\dfrac{x+1}{2} = y + \tfrac{3}{2} = \dfrac{z+1}{-2}$;　$\tfrac{2}{3}, \tfrac{1}{3}, -\tfrac{2}{3}$;

　　(iv) $\dfrac{x - \tfrac{2}{3}}{4} = \dfrac{y-1}{-12} = \dfrac{z}{-3}$;　$\tfrac{4}{13}, -\tfrac{12}{13}, -\tfrac{3}{13}$.

4.　(i) $\dfrac{x-1}{2} = \dfrac{y}{2} = \dfrac{z+1}{1} = \dfrac{r}{3}$;　　(ii) $\dfrac{x}{1} = \dfrac{y-1}{-3} = \dfrac{z}{2} = \dfrac{r}{\sqrt{14}}$;

　　(iii) $\dfrac{x-1}{3} = \dfrac{y}{2} = \dfrac{z}{1} = \dfrac{r}{\sqrt{14}}$.

5. (i) $\dfrac{x}{2} = \dfrac{y}{1} = \dfrac{z}{3}$;　　(ii) $\dfrac{x-1}{1} = \dfrac{y+1}{1} = \dfrac{z}{3}$;　　(iii) $\dfrac{x-3}{2} = \dfrac{y+1}{-1} = \dfrac{z-2}{2}$.

6. $0, \dfrac{1}{\sqrt{2}}, \dfrac{1}{\sqrt{2}}$.　　　　　**7.** $x - \alpha = y - \beta = z - \gamma = \dfrac{r}{\sqrt{3}}$.

8. $(-\tfrac{1}{5}, \tfrac{3}{5}, -\tfrac{3}{5})$.　　　　**9.** $6x + y - 4z = 0$.

10. $x - 4y - 2z = 0$.　　　　**11.** $(\tfrac{4}{3}, -\tfrac{2}{3}, \tfrac{5}{3})$;　$\sqrt{5}$.

12. $90°$.　　　　**13.** $16x - 4y - 5z - 1 = 0$;　$x + 74y - 56z + 167 = 0$.

14. $\tfrac{2}{7}\sqrt{21}$.　　　　**15.** $\dfrac{x-1}{2} = \dfrac{y-1}{-1} = \dfrac{z-1}{-2} = \dfrac{r}{3}$.

16. $2x - 3y + 3z - 5 = 0$;　$9x + 8y + 2z - 1 = 0$,　$2x - 3y + 3z - 5 = 0$.

17. $(\tfrac{14}{9}, -\tfrac{1}{9}, \tfrac{8}{9})$.　　**18.** $2x - y + 2z - 6 = 0$,　$9x - 2y - 6z + 8 = 0$.

19. $(1\tfrac{2}{3}, 3\tfrac{1}{3}, -\tfrac{2}{3})$.　　**20.** $(1\tfrac{1}{3}, \tfrac{2}{3}, 0)$;　$(1, 0, 1)$;　$x - 1 = \tfrac{1}{2}y = \tfrac{1}{3}(1-z)$.

21. $\cos^{-1}(\tfrac{4}{21}) = 79° \, 1'$.

22. (i) $90° - \cos^{-1}\left(\dfrac{2}{\sqrt{14}}\right) = 32° \, 19'$;　(ii) $-\tfrac{1}{2}x = y = \tfrac{1}{3}z$;　(iii) $\dfrac{2\sqrt{6}}{3}$.

23. $\dfrac{x}{1} = \dfrac{y+1}{1} = \dfrac{z}{0}$;　$-\dfrac{1}{\sqrt{3}}, \dfrac{1}{\sqrt{3}}, \dfrac{1}{\sqrt{3}}$.

EXAMPLES 14e　(Page 297)

1. (i) $x = y$;　(ii) $9x - 5y + 3z - 13 = 0$;　(iii) $3x - 2y + z + 1 = 0$.

2. $(1, 3, 2)$.　　**3.** $5x + y - 9z + 10 = 0$;　$5x + y - 9z + 10 = 0$.

4. (i) $\dfrac{1}{\sqrt{2}}$;　(ii) $\dfrac{1}{\sqrt{10}}$;　(iii) $\dfrac{91}{\sqrt{3877}}$;　(iv) $\tfrac{2}{7}$.

5. (i) $(8, 3, 2), (-3, 8, 4)$;　$\dfrac{x-8}{11} = \dfrac{y-3}{-5} = \dfrac{z-2}{-2}$.

6. $\dfrac{x-2}{38} = \dfrac{y-1}{52} = \dfrac{z-3}{79}$.　　**7.** $\sqrt{3}y = x, \ z = -1$;　$\sqrt{3}y + x = 0, \ z = 1$.

10. $\dfrac{1}{\sqrt{5}}$.　　**11.** $4:9$.　　**12.** $7x + 4y - 6z + 13 = 0$;　$\dfrac{13}{\sqrt{101}}$.

13. $27 : 77 : 35$.　　**14.** $7x + 19y - 11z - 6 = 0$.　　**18.** $\sqrt{8}$ **m.**

MISCELLANEOUS EXAMPLES　(Page 300)

1. $\dfrac{2}{\sqrt{5}}$.　　**2.** $\tfrac{2}{7}, -\tfrac{6}{7}, \tfrac{3}{7}$; $(\tfrac{1}{5}, \tfrac{2}{5}, -\tfrac{6}{5})$.　　**3.** $2(x - y - z) + 3 = 0$.

4. Same side.　　**5.** $\cos^{-1} \tfrac{1}{14}$.　　　**6.** $\cos^{-1} \dfrac{39}{\sqrt{2299}} = 35° \, 35'$.

7. $2:3$.　　**8.** $90°, 45°, 45°$.　　**10.** $60°$.

11. $90° - \cos^{-1} \dfrac{11}{\sqrt{159}} = 60° \, 44'$.　　**12.** $15x + y - 7z + 2 = 0$.　　**13.** p.

14. (i) $3x + 2y - 2z = 0$;　(ii) $18x - 22y + 5z - 34 = 0$.

16. (i) $3x + 2y = 0$;　(ii) $4x + y - 4z - 1 = 0$;　$\cos^{-1} \dfrac{14}{\sqrt{429}}$.　　**17.** $\tfrac{19}{3}$.

18. $(\tfrac{15}{11}, \tfrac{16}{11}, -\tfrac{10}{11})$.　　**19.** $2x + 2y - 3z + 3 = 0$;　$(-3, 3, 1)$ or $(-\tfrac{1}{27}, \tfrac{25}{27}, \tfrac{43}{27})$.

21. $\cos^{-1} \dfrac{10}{\sqrt{418}}$;　$\dfrac{x}{14} = \dfrac{y}{-11} = \dfrac{z}{1}$.　　　**23.** $x - 2y + z = 0, \ x - y + 1 = 0$.

24. $(\tfrac{8}{5}, 0, \tfrac{4}{5})$.　　　**25.** $\dfrac{x-3}{7} = \dfrac{y-1}{5} = \dfrac{z}{1}$; $(\tfrac{43}{75}, -\tfrac{11}{15}, -\tfrac{26}{75})$.

27. $\dfrac{x-1}{0} = \dfrac{y-2}{-1} = \dfrac{z-3}{5}$.　　**28.** $9x - 2y - 5z + 4 = 0$;　$\dfrac{4}{\sqrt{165}}, \dfrac{-7}{\sqrt{165}}, \dfrac{10}{\sqrt{165}}$.

29. $\dfrac{\sqrt{5502}}{14}$.   **31.** $39x - 34y - 30z - 38a = 0,\ 33x - 74y - 48z + 33a = 0$.

32. $x - y + z + 1 = 0;\ 7x - 9y + 2z = 0;\ 4x - 6y - z - 3 = 0$.

33. $\cos^{-1}\dfrac{8}{\sqrt{213}} = 56° \ 46';\ 80 : -56 : 149$.   **35.** $\dfrac{4}{\sqrt{29}},\ \dfrac{3}{\sqrt{29}},\ \dfrac{2}{\sqrt{29}}$.

EXAMPLES 15a   (Page 305)

1.   (i) $x^2 + y^2 + z^2 = 1$;   (ii) $x^2 + y^2 + z^2 = 3$;
   (iii) $x^2 + y^2 + z^2 - 2x + 2z + 1 = 0$;   (iv) $x^2 + y^2 + z^2 + 2x - 2y - 4z - 3 = 0$;
   (v) $x^2 + y^2 + z^2 - 6x + 2y + 8z + 21 = 0$;
   (vi) $x^2 + y^2 + z^2 - 2ax - 2ay - 2az - a^2 = 0$.

2.   (i) $(0, 0, 0),\ \sqrt{3}$;   (ii) $(2, 0, 0),\ 2$;

   (iii) $(-1, 2, -3),\ 4$;   (iv) $(\tfrac{3}{2}, -1, -\tfrac{1}{2}),\ \dfrac{3\sqrt{2}}{2}$;

   (v) $(\tfrac{3}{2}, -\tfrac{1}{2}, \tfrac{5}{4}),\ \dfrac{\sqrt{57}}{4}$;   (vi) $\left(-\dfrac{b}{a}, \dfrac{c}{a}, 0\right),\ \dfrac{\sqrt{(b^2 + c^2 - ad)}}{a}$.

3. $x^2 + y^2 + z^2 - 2x - 2y - 2z + 2 = 0$.

4. $3(x^2 + y^2 + z^2) + 12x - 6y + 6z + z = 0$.   **6.** $\dfrac{x}{-1} = \dfrac{y}{4} = \dfrac{z}{-3};\ (-2, 8, -6)$.

7. $x^2 + y^2 + z^2 - 2x + 2y - 4z - 5 = 0$.

9. $\dfrac{x-1}{1} = \dfrac{y-2}{-8} = \dfrac{z+1}{4};\ (2, -6, 3)$.   **10.** $x = 0,\ 3y + 2z = 0$.

14.   (i) $3(x^2 + y^2 + z^2) - 5x - 5y - 5z + 2 = 0$;
   (ii) $4(x^2 + y^2 + z^2) - 5x + 30y - 25z = 0$;
   (iii) $2(x^2 + y^2 + z^2) - x + 18y - 23z - 26 = 0$.

15. $(\tfrac{5}{3}, \tfrac{5}{3}, \tfrac{13}{3});\ \tfrac{1}{3}\sqrt{219}$.   **16.** $x^2 + y^2 + z^2 - p(x + y + z) = 0$.

EXAMPLES 15b   (Page 309)

1. $x - y + z = 3$.   **2.** $x - 2y - 2z + 9 = 0$.   **3.** $6x - 3y - 2z = 49$.

4. $2y - z = 3$.   **5.** $5x - 4y - 4z + 17 = 0$.   **6.** $11y - 2z - 22 = 0$.

7. $2x - 3y + z + 14 = 0$.   **8.** $(\tfrac{2}{9}, \tfrac{2}{9}, -\tfrac{1}{9})$.   **9.** $p = -4,\ 14$.

10. $x + y + z + 2 \pm \sqrt{18} = 0$.   **11.** (i) $2\sqrt{3}$;   (ii) $\sqrt{10}$;   (iii) $\sqrt{13}$;   (iv) $3\sqrt{2}$.

12. Outside.   **13.** $4x + y - z = 0$.   **14.** $(5, -7, 3)$.

15. $2y \pm z = 0$.   **16.** $2x - y + 4z - 5 = 0;\ 4x - 2y - z - 16 = 0$.

EXAMPLES 15c (Page 313)

1. $3(x^2 + y^2 + z^2) - 4(x + y + z) - 8 = 0$.   **2.** $\frac{1}{2}\sqrt{17}$.   **3.** $(2, 3, \frac{7}{4})$.

4. $(-2, 0, 0)$.   **5.** $2x + y - 2z - 9 = 0$; $(\frac{7}{3}, \frac{5}{3}, -\frac{4}{3})$.

6. $x^2 + y^2 + z^2 - 4x - 2y + 6z + 1 = 0$.

7. $x^2 + y^2 + z^2 + 2x - 4y + 2z - 19 = 0$; $x^2 + y^2 + z^2 + 2x - 4y - 10z + 5 = 0$.

8. $8(x^2 + y^2 + z^2) - 31x + 10y - 30 = 0$.   **9.** $(\frac{1}{3}, \frac{2}{3}, -\frac{1}{3})$; $\dfrac{5\sqrt{3}}{3}$.

10. $x - 2y + 4 = 0$; $x^2 + y^2 + z^2 - x - 2y = 0$.

11. $x^2 + y^2 + z^2 - 4x + 2y - z + 5 = 0$; $x^2 + y^2 + z^2 - 4x - 2y + 3z + 5 = 0$.

12. $9(x^2 + y^2 + z^2) - 30x - 42y - 42z + 87 = 0$,
     $9(x^2 + y^2 + z^2) - 6x + 6y + 6z - 33 = 0$.

13. $3(x^2 + y^2 + z^2) + 16x + 8y - 8z + 16 = 0$.   **14.** $(\frac{135}{122}, \frac{50}{122}, \frac{208}{122})$.

15. $x^2 + y^2 + z^2 - 2x + 28y + 2z - 2 = 0$, $x^2 + y^2 + z^2 - 2x - 4y + 2z - 2 = 0$.

16. $(\frac{10}{3}, \frac{5}{3}, \frac{10}{3})$; 12.   **17.** $(\frac{203}{82}, \frac{1}{82}, \frac{199}{82})$.

18. $x^2 + y^2 + z^2 + 6x - 3y + 3z - 4 = 0$.

MISCELLANEOUS EXAMPLES (Page 314)

1. $2(x^2 + y^2 + z^2) - 13x + 12y + 12z - 14 = 0$.   **3.** $ux + vy + wz = 0$.

4. $x^2 + y^2 + z^2 + 6x - 2y + 4z - 4 = 0$; $(1, 0, -1)$.   **5.** $(2, 0, 0)$.

6. $\dfrac{x}{2} = \dfrac{y}{-2} = \dfrac{z}{-1}$; $(\frac{14}{3}, -\frac{14}{3}, -\frac{7}{3})$, $(-\frac{2}{3}, \frac{2}{3}, \frac{1}{3})$.

7. $x^2 + y^2 + z^2 - 16x - 6y - 4z - 73 = 0$.   **8.** $(-\frac{1}{3}, -\frac{2}{3}, \frac{4}{3})$.

10. $3(x^2 + y^2 + z^2) - 13x - 13y - 13z + 30 = 0$.   **11.** $\frac{41}{4}\pi, \frac{29}{4}\pi, 9\pi$.

12. $(-1, \frac{1}{2}, \frac{1}{2})$; $\sqrt{\frac{15}{2}}$.

13. $x^2 + y^2 + z^2 + 6z - 16 = 0$; $5(x^2 + y^2 + z^2) - 14x - 28y - 12z + 32 = 0$.

14. $x^2 + y^2 + z^2 - 10x \pm 8y \pm 8z + 16 = 0$.

15. $(\lambda^2 - 1)(x^2 + y^2 + z^2) - 2ax(\lambda^2 + 1) + a^2(\lambda^2 - 1) = 0$;
     centre $[a(\lambda^2 + 1)/(\lambda^2 - 1), 0, 0]$, radius $2a\lambda/(\lambda^2 - 1)$.

16. $x^2 + y^2 + z^2 - 2x - 2y - 2z + 2 = 0$.   **17.** $x^2 + y^2 + z^2 - 8x - 6y = 0$.

19. $x^2 + y^2 + z^2 - 2x + 2y - 3z = 0$, $3x - 3y + 2z - 6 = 0$; $(\frac{13}{22}, -\frac{13}{22}, \frac{27}{22})$.

20. $\frac{2}{3}\sqrt{14}$.   **21.** $4(x^2 + y^2 + z^2) + 10x - 25y - 2z = 0$.

22. $2(x^2 + y^2 + z^2) - 5x + 9y - 3z + 1 = 0$.   **23.** $(2, 4, 4)$, $(\frac{9}{7}, 4, \frac{64}{21})$.

24. $3(x^2 + y^2 + z^2) - 2x - 2y - 2z - 1 = 0$.

25. $(\frac{7}{9}, \frac{7}{9}, \frac{7}{9})$; radius $\frac{7}{9}$; $81(x^2 + y^2 + z^2) - 126(x + y + z) + 98 = 0$.

26. $x^2 + y^2 + z^2 - 10x + 4y - 6z - 11 = 0$; $\frac{12544}{265}\pi$.   **27.** $\frac{319}{102}\pi$.

29. $2x - y - 2z + 4 = 0$, $x - 2y - 2z + 7 = 0$; $\cos^{-1}\frac{8}{9}$.

31. $3(x^2 + y^2 + z^2) - 12x - 6y - 4z = 0$.

EXAMPLES 16a (Page 321)

1. $4x^3y,\ x^4.$

2. $\dfrac{1}{y},\ -\dfrac{x}{y^2}.$

3. $\sin y,\ x \cos y.$

4. $\dfrac{y^2}{x},\ 2y \log x.$

5. $3x^2y + y^3,\ x^3 + 3xy^2.$

6. $-y \sin xy,\ -x \sin xy.$

7. $2xy\, e^{x^2y},\ x^2\, e^{x^2y}.$

8. $\dfrac{y}{x^2+y^2},\ \dfrac{-x}{x^2+y^2}.$

9. $y \tan xy + xy^2 \sec^2 xy,\ x \tan xy + x^2y \sec^2 xy.$

10. $\dfrac{y^2}{(x+y)^2},\ \dfrac{x^2}{(x+y)^2}.$

11. $2nx(x^2+y^2)^{n-1},\ 2ny(x^2+y^2)^{n-1}.$

12. $yx^{y-1},\ x^y \log x.$ **13.** $4.$ **14.** $1/\sqrt{2}.$ **16.** $12,\ 4.$

17. (i) $24x^2y^2,\ 16x^3y,\ 16x^3y,\ 4x^4;$

(ii) $-2y \sin x^2y - 4x^2y^2 \cos x^2y,\ -2x \sin x^2y - 2x^3y \cos x^2y,$
$-2x \sin x^2y - 2x^3y \cos x^2y,\ -x^4 \cos x^2y;$

(iii) $\dfrac{2(y^2-x^2)}{(x^2+y^2)^2},\ \dfrac{-4xy}{(x^2+y^2)^2},\ \dfrac{-4xy}{(x^2+y^2)^2},\ \dfrac{2(x^2-y^2)}{(x^2+y^2)^2};$

(iv) $\sin^2 y\, e^{x \sin y}\ (1 + x \sin y),\ \cos y\, e^{x \sin y}\ (1 + x \sin y),$
$x\, e^{x \sin y}\ (x \cos^2 y - \sin y).$

20. $z + \sqrt{2}y = 3,\ x = 1.$ **21.** $-3.$

22. $\dfrac{\partial z}{\partial x} = -\dfrac{z}{x},\ \dfrac{\partial z}{\partial y} = -\dfrac{z}{y},\ \dfrac{\partial x}{\partial z} = -\dfrac{x}{z},\ \dfrac{\partial y}{\partial z} = -\dfrac{y}{z},\ \dfrac{\partial y}{\partial x} = -\dfrac{y}{x},\ \dfrac{\partial x}{\partial y} = -\dfrac{x}{y}.$

28. (i) $z = \lambda(y);$

(ii) $z = \lambda(x);$

(iii) $z = x^2 + \lambda(y);$

(iv) $z = -x \cos y + \lambda(x);$

(v) $z = x\lambda(y) + \mu(y);$

(vi) $z = -\sin x + x\lambda(y) + \mu(y);$

(vii) $z = \lambda(x) + \mu(y);$

(viii) $z = \tfrac{1}{2}x^2y^2 + \lambda(x) + \mu(y),$ where in all cases the functions $\lambda,\ \mu$ are arbitrary.

29. $\dfrac{\partial \theta}{\partial x} = -\dfrac{y}{x^2+y^2},\ \dfrac{\partial \theta}{\partial y} = \dfrac{x}{x^2+y^2}.$

EXAMPLES 16b (Page 324)

1. $3x^2h.$

2. $y^2h + 2xyk.$

3. $(yh - xk)/y^2.$

4. $h \sin y + kx \cos y.$

5. $2(xh + yk)/(x^2+y^2).$

6. $e^{x+y}(h+k).$

7. $n(x+y)^{n-1}(h+k).$

8. $(yh + xk)/(1 + x^2y^2).$

9. $31 \cdot 052.$

10. $\delta V \simeq \tfrac{1}{3}\pi r(2h\, \delta r + r\, \delta h).$

11. $\delta\Delta = \frac{1}{2}(c \sin A\ \delta b + b \sin A\ \delta c + bc \cos A\ \delta A)$; 5·0075 cm².

13. 0·8.   **14.** 3·5.   **15.** (i) 0·50025; (ii) 5·003; (iii) 9·9099.

16. $\frac{4\cdot1}{9}\pi$ cm³.   **18.** 4·21.   **20.** $\dfrac{kl^3}{bt^3}\left(\dfrac{3\delta l}{l} - \dfrac{\delta b}{b} - \dfrac{3\delta t}{t}\right).$

EXAMPLES 16c   (Page 331)

4. $dx = \cos\theta\ dr - r\sin\theta\ d\theta$; $dy = \sin\theta\ dr + r\cos\theta\ d\theta$.

5. $dV = \pi(2rh\ dr + r^2\ dh)$.

10. (i) $-\dfrac{x(x^2 - 2y^2)}{y(y^2 - 2x^2)}$;   (ii) $-\dfrac{y(3x^2 + y^2)}{x(x^2 + 3y^2)}$;   (iii) $\dfrac{1 - y\cos xy}{x\cos xy}$;

  (iv) $\dfrac{y(x^2 + y^2) - 2xy^2}{x(x^2 + y^2) + 2y^3}$;   (v) $\dfrac{2y - 2x + 3}{4y - 2x + 2}$.

13. $x + y = 2$.   **14.** (i) $(\frac{4}{3}a,\ \frac{1}{3}\sqrt[3]{32}\ .\ a)$;   (ii) $(0, 0)$.

17. (i) $\sin xy + xy\cos xy$;   (ii) $\dfrac{\partial z}{\partial y} + y\dfrac{\partial^2 z}{\partial y^2}$;

  (iii) $-\dfrac{\sin x}{y}\dfrac{\partial z}{\partial x} + \dfrac{\cos x}{y}\dfrac{\partial^2 z}{\partial x^2}$;   (iv) $\dfrac{x}{y}\dfrac{\partial z}{\partial x} + \dfrac{x^2}{y}\dfrac{\partial^2 z}{\partial x^2} - \dfrac{x}{y}\dfrac{\partial^2 z}{\partial y\partial x}$.

18. $\dfrac{\partial u}{\partial x} = \dfrac{\partial u}{\partial \xi} + \dfrac{\partial u}{\partial \eta}$; $\dfrac{\partial u}{\partial y} = \dfrac{\partial u}{\partial \xi} - \dfrac{\partial u}{\partial \eta}$.   **19.** $\dfrac{\sin z\ (2 - \cos z)}{\cos y\ (2 - \sin y)}$.

22. (i) $2u$;   (ii) u;   (iii) 2.

24. (i) $\cos\theta\left[\cos\theta\dfrac{\partial^2 V}{\partial r^2} + \dfrac{\sin\theta}{r^2}\dfrac{\partial V}{\partial\theta} - \dfrac{\sin\theta}{r}\dfrac{\partial^2 V}{\partial r\partial\theta}\right]$;

  (ii) $\dfrac{\sin\theta}{r}\left[-\sin\theta\dfrac{\partial V}{\partial r} + \cos\theta\dfrac{\partial^2 V}{\partial\theta\partial r} - \dfrac{\cos\theta}{r}\dfrac{\partial V}{\partial\theta} - \dfrac{\sin\theta}{r}\dfrac{\partial^2 V}{\partial\theta^2}\right].$

27. (i) $x^3 y^2 + x^2 y^3 = $ const.;   (ii) $x\sin y = $ const.

MISCELLANEOUS EXAMPLES   (Page 333)

6. $e + 1$.   **9.** $-\dfrac{e^x - 2y}{e^y - 2x}$.   **13.** $\dfrac{\partial y}{\partial x} = -\dfrac{x^3}{y^3}$; $\dfrac{\partial y}{\partial z} = -\dfrac{z^3}{y^3}$.

15. $\dfrac{[x^4 + 4x^2(y^2 - 3y + 1) + 4y^2]^{\frac{3}{2}}}{2(y - 1)(3x^4 - 4x^2 - 4y^2)}$.   **20.** $\dfrac{y\tan x + \log\sin y}{\log\cos x - x\cot y}$.

24. $\dfrac{dy}{dx} = -\dfrac{x^4 - a^3 y}{y^4 - a^3 x}$; $\dfrac{d^2 y}{dx^2} = -\dfrac{4x^8 y^3 - 2a^6 x^5 + 14a^3 x^4 y^4 - 4x^3 y^8 - 2a^9 xy - 2a^6 y^5}{(y^4 - a^3 x)^3}$.

28. $\dfrac{\partial z}{\partial x} = -\dfrac{c^3 x^2}{a^3 z^2}$; $\dfrac{\partial^2 x}{\partial y\partial z} = \dfrac{2a^3 z^2}{b^3 c^3 x^2}\left[\dfrac{b^3}{y} - \dfrac{a^3 y^2}{x^3}\right].$

30. $\dfrac{\partial u}{\partial x} = \dfrac{1 - e^{-v}\sin u}{1 - 2e^{-v}\sin u + e^{-2v}}$; $\dfrac{\partial x}{\partial u} = 1 - e^{-v}\sin u$.   **31.** 0·14 cm.

REVISION PAPERS (Page 337)

A.1. **2.** $-9 \geqslant p \geqslant -1$.   **3.** (i) $k = 0, 3, 8$;   (ii) $x = -3, -\frac{3}{2}, 1, \frac{7}{2}$.

4. $4x = 3$; $2(x^2 + y^2) - 3x + 6y - 2 = 0$.   **5.** (i) $x = 7$;   (ii) $x = 2, 16$.

8. $1 + x + \frac{1}{2}x^2 - \frac{1}{8}x^4 - \frac{1}{5}x^5$; $1 \cdot 34$.

9. (i) $\frac{1}{3} \log \dfrac{2 + x}{1 - x} + c$;   (ii) $1 + \sqrt{3}$;

(iii) $\frac{1}{32}x^4 [8(\log x)^2 - 4 \log x + 1]$.

10. (i) parabola;   (ii) circle;   (iii) rectangular hyperbola.

A.2. **3.** (a) $x = -1, y = 2$; $x = -2, y = \frac{1}{2}$.

4. $b(x - x')^2 - 2h(x - x')(y - y') + a(y - y')^2 = 0$;

$(x^2 + y^2)(a + b) + 2x(hy' - bx') + 2y(hx' - ay') + bx'^2 - 2hx'y' + ay'^2 = 0$.

5. (i) The straight line $y = 1$;   (ii) the circle, $x^2 + y^2 = 4k^2$;

(iii) segments of circles on chord $(-2, 0)$, $(2, 0)$ containing an angle of $\frac{1}{3}\pi$.

7. $a(1 - r^n)/(1 - r)$.   **8.** (i) $0, 2, 2, 0$;   (ii) $n = 3r, n \neq 3r$.

9. (i) (a) $\frac{1}{3} \sin^3 x - \frac{1}{5} \sin^5 x + c$;   (b) $\frac{1}{2}[\cos x - \frac{1}{5} \cos 5x] + c$.

10. $x = 3at/(1 + t^3)$, $y = 3at^2/(1 + t^3)$; $\rho = \dfrac{3a}{2}, \dfrac{3a}{2}$.

11. $9x - 3y - z + 14 = 0$.

12. $x/\sqrt{(x^2 + y^2)}$, $y/\sqrt{(x^2 + y^2)}$, $-y/(x^2 + y^2)$, $x/(x^2 + y^2)$.

A.3. **2.** (a) $a = -15, b = 10$; $x - 1, 2x + 1$.   **3.** (i) $x = 10$;   (ii) $x = \frac{2}{3}$.

4. (i) $3z(y - x)(x + y + z)$;   (ii) $x = -\frac{1}{2}, 5$.

5. $x^2 + y^2 = 9$; $x^2 + y^2 \pm 8x - 9 = 0$; $x^2 + y^2 + 8y + 9 = 0$.

6. (ii) $x^3 - 2x^2 + 5x - 11 = 0$.   **8.** (a) $6[1 - (\frac{2}{3})^n] - n$.

9. (i) $\frac{1}{2} \log\{x(x - 2)\} + c$;   (ii) $-\dfrac{1}{x} \log(1 + x^2) + 2 \tan^{-1} x + c$; $\dfrac{1}{ab} \tan^{-1} \dfrac{b}{a}$.

12. $(\frac{9}{5}, \frac{12}{5}, 4)$.

A.4. **2.** (i) $a = 1, b = -4, c = 0, d = 10$;   (ii) $k = 61$; $x = \frac{13}{21}, -\frac{3}{4}$.

3. $x^2(5 + 4k) - 6kxy + y^2(5 - 4k) = 0$.   **5.** $x = -\frac{1}{2}$.

6. (i) $A = \frac{1}{4}, B = -\frac{1}{4}$; $\frac{1}{2}n(n + 1)^2(n + 2)$.   **9.** $\frac{512}{9009}$.

10. $r(m \cos \theta - \sin \theta) = c$; $\dfrac{\pi c^3}{3m} \left[\dfrac{\tan^2 \theta}{(m - \tan \theta)^2} \right]$.   **11.** $0 \cdot 69$.

12. $17x + 3y + 2z = 17$; $11/\sqrt{302}$.

A.5. **2.** (i) $x = -2 \pm \sqrt{10}$.   **5.** $(-3, 0), (1, 0)$; $x^2 + y^2 + 2x + 2y - 3 = 0$.

6. (i) $161, 160$; $\dfrac{(2n + 1)(2n + 3)}{2(n + 1)(n + 2)} - \dfrac{3}{4}$.

7. $\dfrac{1}{\sqrt{(1 - x^2)}}$; $x + \dfrac{1^2 x^3}{3!} + \dfrac{1^2 \cdot 3^2 x^5}{5!} + \dfrac{1^2 \cdot 3^2 \cdot 5^2 x^7}{7!} + \dfrac{1^2 \cdot 3^2 \cdot 5^2 \cdot 7^2}{9!}x^9$

$+ \dfrac{1^2 \cdot 3^2 \cdot 5^2 \cdot 7^2 \cdot 9^2}{11!}x^{11}$.

8. (i) $\frac{1}{2}x^2 \tan^{-1} x^2 - \frac{1}{4} \log(1 + x^4) + c$, $\log \dfrac{x}{1 + \sqrt{(1 - x^2)}} + c$.

9. (ii) $+, 0, +$.   **10.** $4\pi^2$.

A.6.   **2.** $-(x^3-1)(x^{n+3}+x^3+1)$.

     4. $2g(g-g_1)+2f(f-f_1)=c-c_1$; $x+2y=2$.   **5.** (iii) 2.

     6. $a=\frac{11}{7}$, 3; $x=6$, $y=5$; $x=2$, $y=-1$.

     8. (ii) $x-\frac{1}{2}x^2+\frac{2}{3}x^3$.   **9.** (i) $\frac{1}{5}e^x(\sin 2x-2\cos 2x)$.

     10. $-\dfrac{4}{\pi^2}(\pi^2-6)$.   **12.** $4\pi a^2[\sin\alpha-\alpha\cos\alpha]$.

A.7.   **2.** (i) $A=1$, $B=3$, $C=7$, $p=2$, $q=-1$, $r=2$.

     3. (i) $k=1$;   (ii) $abc(b-c)(c-a)(a-b)(bc+ca+ab)$.

     5. $k_1k_2+h^2=0$.

     6. $\cos 7\theta=\cos^7\theta-21\cos^5\theta\sin^2\theta+35\cos^3\theta\sin^4\theta-7\cos\theta\sin^6\theta$;

        $\sin 7\theta=7\cos^6\theta\sin\theta-35\cos^4\theta\sin^3\theta+21\cos^2\theta\sin^5\theta-\sin^7\theta$;

        $\tan 7\theta=\dfrac{7\tan\theta-35\tan^3\theta+21\tan^5\theta-\tan^7\theta}{1-21\tan^2\theta+35\tan^4\theta-7\tan^6\theta}$.

     7. $\pm b^2/a\sqrt{(a^2-2b^2)}$; $2-\sqrt{2}$.   **12.** (1, 2, 3), 4; $\sqrt{7}$.

A.8.   **2.** (i) $x=\frac{1}{2}$, 1, 1, 2;   (ii) $-(b-c)(c-a)(a-b)$.

     4. $5x+3y+14=0$.   **7.** $(4ak^2, 4ak)$.

     8. (i) $\frac{1}{12}n(n+1)(3n^2+7n+2)$;   (ii) $\dfrac{1-(2n-1)x^n}{1-x}+\dfrac{2x(1-x^{n-1})}{(1-x)^2}$.

     9. $\dfrac{\pi}{3\sqrt{3}}$.   **12.** $\dfrac{x+6}{5}=\dfrac{y+4}{3}=\dfrac{z+6}{6}$;   (4, 2, 6), $(-1, -1, 0)$.

A.9.   **2.** (ii) $a=4$, $b=1$.   **3.** (a) $k=-\frac{5}{3}$, 3;   (b) $k=2$.

     4.   (3, 4); $x^2+y^2-22x-16y+65=0$.

     6. $\dfrac{x\cos\frac{1}{2}(\theta+\phi)}{a}+\dfrac{y\sin\frac{1}{2}(\theta+\phi)}{b}=\cos\frac{1}{2}(\theta-\phi)$; $\left(\dfrac{x^2}{a^2}+\dfrac{y^2}{b^2}\right)^2=\dfrac{x^2}{a^2}-\dfrac{y^2}{b^2}$.

     7. (i) $\frac{1}{3}n(4n^2-1)$;   (ii) $\frac{1}{5}n(n+1)(n+2)(n+3)(n+4)$;   (iii) $\sin^2 n\theta/\sin\theta$.

     8.   0, 0, 2.   **9.** (b) $\frac{2}{3}$.   **10.** $\sin\phi=r\dfrac{d\theta}{ds}$, $\cos\phi=\dfrac{dr}{ds}$.

     12. $2V=-x\pm\sqrt{(x^2+4z)}$.

A.10.   **1.**   44·8 cm;   567 cm².   **5.** $q=-3\alpha^2$, $r=2\alpha^3$; $x=-\frac{2}{3}$, $-\frac{2}{3}$, $\frac{4}{3}$.

     7. $x+y=3a$.   **8.** (i) $1+x^2+\frac{1}{6}x^4$;   (ii) $\frac{1}{4}\pi$.

     9. $\sqrt{(2+2x-x^2)}+\sin^{-1}\dfrac{x-1}{\sqrt{3}}$;   (i) π^2-4;   (ii) $\dfrac{2\pi}{3\sqrt{3}}$.

     10. $P=R=\dfrac{2a}{4ac-b^2}$, $Q=\dfrac{b}{4ac-b^2}$; $\dfrac{1}{4}-\dfrac{1}{12\sqrt{3}}\log(2+\sqrt{3})$; $\frac{19}{648}$.

     11. $(12+3\sqrt{3})x+(18-2\sqrt{3})y-39z=0$,

        $(12-3\sqrt{3})x+(18+2\sqrt{3})y-39z=0$.

A.11.   **2.** (ii) $t^2+qt-p^3=0$; $x=2^{\frac{1}{3}}-2^{\frac{2}{3}}$.   **3.** (i) -4;   (ii) $x=0$, $-(4n+6)$.

     6. $u+v=\dfrac{Y}{a}$, $uv=\frac{1}{2}\left(\dfrac{Y^2}{a^2}-\dfrac{2X}{a}\right)$; $(b, 0)$, $(b+\frac{1}{2}a, 0)$.

     7. (i) $n(3n-1)$;   (ii)   4, 12, 36; $2\cdot 3^{n-1}$.

     9. (a) $\log(1+e^x)+c$;   (b) $x-\tan\frac{1}{2}x+c$.   **10.** $\frac{3}{16}\pi$.

     12. $(-\frac{13}{98}, \frac{40}{49}, \frac{135}{98})$.

A.12. **1.** $\frac{1}{2}(B+C)$. **2.** (a) $12a^2$; (b) $x=-3a, a, 2a$.

3. (i) Infinite number of solutions; $x=\frac{62}{19}+14t$, $y=\frac{21}{19}+36t$, $z=19t$;
(ii) solutions infinite.

5. (i) Region between circles centre $(1,-2)$, radii 2 and 3;
(ii) $p=1, q=-4$; $x=-3, 1\pm i$.

6. $\dfrac{1}{x}+\dfrac{1}{x^2}-\dfrac{1}{x+1}-\dfrac{1}{(x+1)^2}$. **7.** Point O lies on S.

8. $ax^2+2hxy+by^2+2(gx+fy)(px+qy)+c(px+qy)^2=0$.

9. (i) $\frac{1}{3}\pi$. **12.** (ii) (a) $\frac{11}{3}$; (b) 7.

S.1. **2.** (i) $\lambda<-1, \lambda>\frac{1}{2}$. **5.** $8\sin^4\theta+4\sin^3\theta-8\sin^2\theta-3\sin\theta+1=0$.

6. $y+tx=2at+at^3$. **7.** $u_n=\dfrac{1.3.5\ldots(2n-1)}{2.4.6\ldots(2n+2)}$.

8. $\frac{1}{2}(\log_e a)^2-\dfrac{1}{a}$.

9. (i) $\dfrac{1}{2\sqrt{(9-a)}}\log\dfrac{x-\sqrt{(9-a)}}{x+\sqrt{(9-a)}}+c$; $-\dfrac{1}{x-3}+c$;

$\dfrac{1}{\sqrt{(a-9)}}\tan^{-1}\dfrac{x-3}{\sqrt{(a-9)}}+c$; (ii) $\dfrac{3\pi}{128}$.

S.2. **2.** $\frac{1}{8}(3x^5-10x^3+15x)$. **5.** $2\sqrt{2}, 2+3i$.

6. (a) $\dfrac{1}{8(2k-1)}+\dfrac{1}{4(2k+1)}-\dfrac{3}{8(2k+3)}$; (b) $\frac{215}{16}$, $-\frac{1}{2}<x<\frac{1}{2}$.

7. $\pm\sqrt{(-1/t_1 t_2)}$. **9.** (i) $\frac{1}{12}\sqrt{2}$; (ii) $\frac{1}{4}\pi-\frac{2}{3}$; (iii) $\frac{2}{3}\log\frac{4}{3}$.

10. $x(9-x)^2=27y^2$; $x-9=\pm\sqrt{3}y$.

11. (ii) $21(x^2+y^2+z^2)+58x-10y+20z+26=0$.

12. $\dfrac{\partial u}{\partial x}=\sin x\cosh y+x\cos x\cosh y+y\sin x\sinh y=\dfrac{\partial v}{\partial y}$;

$\dfrac{\partial u}{\partial y}=x\sin x\sinh y-\cos x\sinh y-y\cos x\cosh y=-\dfrac{\partial v}{\partial x}$.

S.3. **3.** (a) (i) $a=3, b=1$; (ii) $a=3b, b\neq1$; (iii) $a\neq3b$;
(b) $A=\frac{1}{8}, B=-\frac{1}{6}, C=\frac{1}{12}$;
$\frac{1}{24}n^2(n+1)^2[3n^4+6n^3-n^2-4n+2]$.

4. $2-\alpha-\alpha^2$.

5. $(x+a+b+c)(x+a-b-c)(x-a+b-c)(x-a-b+c)$.

7. $k(y-k)=2a(x-h)$; $lx+my=1$.

9. (i) $\frac{1}{4}\pi$; (ii) $\frac{1}{2}x^2\sin^{-1}x+\frac{1}{4}x\sqrt{(1-x^2)}-\frac{1}{4}\sin^{-1}x+c$;
(iii) $\frac{1}{7}\sin^7\theta-\frac{1}{9}\sin^9\theta+c$.

10. $\dfrac{\pi}{\sqrt{3}}$, $\log 3$, $\frac{2}{3}\log 3$; $u_0=\frac{1}{2}\left(\dfrac{\pi}{\sqrt{3}}+\frac{1}{3}\log 3\right)$, $u_1=\frac{1}{2}\left(\dfrac{\pi}{\sqrt{3}}-\frac{1}{3}\log 3\right)$;
$u_3=2-\frac{1}{2}\left(\dfrac{\pi}{\sqrt{3}}+\frac{1}{3}\log 3\right)$, $u_4=2-\frac{1}{2}\left(\dfrac{\pi}{\sqrt{3}}-\frac{1}{3}\log 3\right)$, $u_5=\frac{1}{3}(8-2\log 3)$.

S.4. **3.** $abx^2 - (a^2 - b^2)xy - aby^2 = 0.$

4. (i) $y^3 + y^2(a^3 - 3a^2 + 3a) - y(2a^3 - 3a^2) + a^3 = 0;$ (ii) $a = 0,\ 1.$

5. (i) The circle $u^2 + v^2 = 1;$ (ii) the circle $(u - 1)^2 + v^2 = 4.$

6. $\frac{1}{2}(n+1)(n+2)a + \frac{1}{2}n(n+1)b + \frac{1}{2}n(n-1)c;$ $a = 0,\ b = c = 1.$

7. $x^2 + y^2 - 2cy + l^2 + \lambda(my + x) = 0.$

8. $t^2 y + x = 2t;\quad uy + x = 3u^2 + 2u^4.$

9. (i) $-\dfrac{\log x}{1+x} + \log \dfrac{x}{1+x} + c;$ (ii) $\frac{4}{15};$ (iii) $\frac{1}{4}\pi.$

10. (i) $\frac{3}{8}\pi a^2;$ (ii) $\frac{32}{105}\pi a^3.$

S.5. **2.** (a) $x < -5,\ x > \frac{1}{3}.$

3. (i) $x = 3,\ y = 2,\ z = 0;$

(ii) infinite number of solutions, $x = 3 - 2t,\ y = 2 - t,\ z = t.$

4. $y^3 + py^2 - p^2 y - p^3 - 8q^2 = 0.$ **5.** $\dfrac{x^2}{c^2} + \dfrac{y^2}{c(c-1)} = 1.$

6. Conics touching S_1 and S_2 at the origin and passing through the other two points of intersection of S_1 and S_2;
$x^2 - y^2 + x(5a - 2) = 0.$

8. (a) $\frac{1}{4}\pi.$ **12.** (i) $-2xy/(y^2 - x)^3;$ (ii) $-c^n x^{n-1}/a^n z^{n-1}.$

S.6. **2.** $-1 \leqslant c \leqslant 1;$ all values except those between $\frac{1}{9}$ and 1.

5. $x^2 + y^2 - 20x + 5y - 50 = 0;\quad 6x + 3y + 10 = 0.$

6. $x = \frac{2}{3},\ \pm\dfrac{2i}{\sqrt{3}}.$

8. $\frac{1}{4}\cos(2n+1)\theta \sin 2n\theta \operatorname{cosec} 2\theta + \frac{1}{2}\cos n\theta \sin n\theta \operatorname{cosec} \theta + \frac{1}{4}n\cos\theta.$

9. $(-1)^n 2^{2(n-1)} [4x^2 \sin 2x - 8xn \cos 2x - 2n(2n-1)\sin 2x].$

11. $89\cdot6\pi$ cm^3.

S.7. **2.** (i) $x = 7,\ y = -2;\ x = -2,\ y = 7;\ x = \frac{1}{2}(5 \pm i\sqrt{39}),\ y = \frac{1}{2}(5 \mp i\sqrt{39});$

(ii) $x = \frac{1}{2}(1 \pm \sqrt{5}),\quad \frac{1}{2}\{1 + \sqrt{2} \pm \sqrt{(7 + 2\sqrt{2})}\},$
$$\frac{1}{2}\{1 - \sqrt{2} \pm \sqrt{(7 - 2\sqrt{2})}\}.$$

5. $8 - 20X + 12X^2 - 2X^3;\ x = \pm 2\sin\theta,$ when $\theta = \frac{1}{8}\pi,\ \frac{1}{4}\pi,\ \frac{3}{8}\pi.$

6. (a) $x^2 + y^2 - 2x - 2y + 1 = 0,\ x^2 + y^2 - 10x - 10y + 25 = 0;\ (1, 2);$
(b) $7 \pm 2\sqrt{6}.$

9. (i) 0;   (ii) 2.   **10.** $\frac{1}{10}\pi^5 - \frac{1}{2}\pi^3 + \frac{3}{4}\pi.$

11. (i) $\frac{32}{9}\mu a^3;$ (ii) $\frac{27}{64}\pi a$ from O on symmetrical radius.

S.8. **2.** (ii) $\frac{1}{6}n(n-1)(3n^2 - n - 1).$

5. (i) $\pm\sqrt{34}(\cos\frac{1}{2}\theta + i\sin\frac{1}{2}\theta),$ where $\tan\theta = \frac{15}{8};$
(ii) circle, centre $(2, 0)$, radius 1.

6. $x, y, z = 1, 4, -3.$ **9.** $a_1 = 1;\ a_3 = \frac{1}{3}.$

10. (i) $\dfrac{3}{x+1} - \dfrac{12}{(x+1)^2} + \dfrac{18}{(x+1)^3} - \dfrac{1}{(x+1)^5};$ (ii) $\frac{1}{8}\pi - \log 2.$

12. $-\dfrac{1+u}{2(v-u)(v+u+1)};\quad -\dfrac{u}{(v-u)(v+u+1)};\quad \dfrac{1+v}{2(v-u)(v+u+1)}.$

S.9. **3.** (i) $x^4 - 10x^2 + 1$; $x = \sqrt{2} - \sqrt{3}, \ -\sqrt{2} \pm \sqrt{3}$;

(ii) $2x^3 + 5x^2 + 3x + 6$.

8. (i) $-x + \sqrt{2} \tan^{-1}\left(\dfrac{1}{\sqrt{2}} \tan x\right) + c$; (ii) $\frac{3}{8}\pi a^2$.

9. $\frac{1}{2}a^2$; $\theta = \pm\frac{1}{6}\pi$.

11. $(lu + mv + nw + p)^2 = (l^2 + m^2 + n^2)(u^2 + v^2 + w^2 - d)$;

$x^2 + y^2 + z^2 - 1 = 0$, $x^2 + y^2 + z^2 + 12x + 12y + 12z - 13 = 0$.

S.10. **3.** $x = -\frac{1}{2}, \ -\frac{1}{2}, \ 2, \ 2$.   **4.** $\pm\frac{1}{2}(x_1 y_2 - x_2 y_1)$.

6. (i) $\dfrac{1 - nx^{-n}}{x - 1} + \dfrac{1 - x^{-n+1}}{(x-1)^2}$;

(ii) $\dfrac{a^2 + a\cos\theta + (-1)^{n+1} a^{n+1}[\cos\overline{n+1}\,\theta + a\cos n\theta]}{1 + 2a\cos\theta + a^2}$;

(iii) $\frac{1}{2}\left[\frac{1}{2} - \dfrac{1}{(n+1)(n+2)}\right]$.

8. $\dfrac{3x(2\alpha - 3x)}{a^2} + \dfrac{3y(2\beta - 3y)}{b^2} = 0$.

S.11. **7.** $p = a_0 + \dfrac{b}{1-r}$, $q = -\dfrac{b}{1-r}$; $u_n = 3 \cdot 2^{n-1} - 2$, $s_n = 3(2^n - 1) - 2n$.

9. $-\frac{1}{2}x^2 - \frac{1}{12}x^4 \ \ldots$ **11.** $e^x \cos y$, $e^x \sin y$.

S.12. **2.** Max. 16, min. 5.

5. $(am^2 - 2hlm + bl^2)(x^2 + y^2) - xn(la - lb + 2hm)$
$- yn(mb - ma + 2hl) = 0$.

7. System of conics touching $S = 0$ at the ends of the chord $u = 0$;

$x^2 - 6xy - y^2 + 3x + 3y = 0$.

8. (a) $\dfrac{1}{x+1} + \dfrac{1}{x-1} - \dfrac{x+1}{x^2 - x + 1} - \dfrac{x-1}{x^2 + x + 1}$;

(b) $\dfrac{1 - (n+1)^2 x^n}{1 - x} + \dfrac{3x - (2n+3)x^{n+1}}{(1-x)^2} + \dfrac{2x^2(1 - x^n)}{(1-x)^3}$;

$\dfrac{1}{1-x} + \dfrac{3x}{(1-x)^2} + \dfrac{2x^2}{(1-x)^3}$.

12. (i) 2;   (ii) $2u$.

INDEX

Amplitude of complex number, 124
Apollonius: circle of, 117; median theorem, 1
Arc length: polar curve, 263
Area of closed curve, 268; surface of revolution, 263; triangle, 82
Argand diagram, 123, 131

Binomial coefficients, 205; equations, 184; series, 205

Centroid, 1
Ceva's theorem, 14; converse, 15
Chord of contact: circle, 94; ellipse, 161; hyperbola, 161; parabola, 161
Circle: equations of, 310; equation of sphere through, 311
Circumcentre; circumcircle, 4
Coaxal circles: definition, 105; equation of, 106, 107; types of, 108
Cofactors, 61, 62
Collinear points, 81
Complex numbers, 123; amplitude of, 124; conjugate numbers, 123; exponential form of, 137; fundamental processes, 125, 128; geometrical representation, 123, 125, 126, 129; inequalities, 126; modulus of, 124
Complex variable, 136
Concurrent lines, 293
Concyclic points on a conic, 170
Conic: general equation of, 172; systems through four points, 173
Coplanar lines, 293
Curvature, radius of, 265

Definite integrals, properties of, 248
De Moivre's theorem, 181; applications to factors, 187; to multiple angles, 191; to powers of trigonometrical functions, 190; to roots, 182; to summation of series, 201
Determinants, 52; cofactors of, 61; factorisation of, 59; laws of, 54–56; minors, 61, 62
Difference method, 196
Differentials, 325
Direction-cosines, 280; ratios, 282

Equal fractions, 36
Equations: binomial, 184; cubic, 151; linear, 65, 73; miscellaneous, 45; of nth degree, 152; polynomial, 47, 142, 148; powers of roots of, 153; quartic, 152; reciprocal, 46; transformation of, 155; with a common root, 146, 147; with repeated roots, 149
Escribed circles, 10, 11
Excentres, 10
Expansions: algebraic and trigonometrical methods, 217; by differentiation and integration, 222; by formation of differential equation, 223; by Maclaurin's theorem, 220; by Taylor's theorem, 219

Factors: algebraic, 28; by use of De Moivre's theorem, 187; highest common, 34; of symmetrical expressions, 33
Finite series, 196; arithmetic type, 196; trigonometric, 200
Functions: homogeneous, 329; quadratic, 37; rational quadratic, 39

Highest common factor, 34
Homogeneous linear equations, 73; functions, 329

Identities, algebraic, 27
Incentre, 10
Inconsistent equations, 66, 68
Independent equations, 66, 68
Induction, 209
Infinite integrals, 253; series, 216
Inscribed circle, 10, 11
Integration: algebraic functions, 232; basic theorems, 230; by parts, 230; hyperbolic functions, 243; reduction formulae, 244; trigonometric functions, 237

Leibnitz's theorem, 224
Limiting points, 109, 110
Line-pair, 84; angles between, 89; bisectors of angles between, 91; through the origin, 86
Logarithmic function, 251

413